RAYMOND C. MOORE

Professor of Geology
University of Kansas

HISTORICAL GEOLOGY

Second Edition

McGRAW-HILL BOOK COMPANY, INC.

New York   Toronto   London

1958

PREFACE

The aim of this book is to give an account of the salient features of earth history in a manner suited to persons having no previous acquaintance with the subject. Except in the introductory chapters, which deal with general principles and with the origin of the earth, attention is directed primarily to the nature of physical conditions and the record of life during the geologic history of the continent of North America. Some notice is given to areas in Europe, because most major divisions of the rock succession were first recognized and defined there.

Many questions come to mind when we begin to think about the history of the land surface around us. How old is the earth? In what manner have its main surface features, continents and ocean basins, come into being? Why are mountain chains thousands of miles long, like the Appalachians and Rockies, distributed as belts roughly parallel to the eastern and western borders of North America, whereas the continental interior is mostly a vast lowland plain? What is the explanation of the occurrence of fossil marine shells in stratified rocks of many far-inland localities, as in Kansas, and at elevations of more than 10,000 feet above sea level, as in Colorado? Why are fossil remains of innumerable kinds of extinct animals and plants, of both sea and land, found to be arranged in an orderly sequence, the most primitive in lowermost rock layers and near-modern types in uppermost strata? All these and many other questions pertaining to geological history are answered with varying sureness on the basis of observations and deductions that belong within the province of this book. Historical geology brings knowledge of great cultural value, providing at least

some degree of comprehension of the immensity of geologic time. Also, it has much economic value, for when we know about the changing conditions associated with the origin of fuel deposits, many kinds of ores, and other earth materials useful to man, we are guided in finding and developing them. Special notice of the important economic resources of each main geologic division is given in this revised edition.

Features of *Introduction to Historical Geology* that seem worthy of special mention are (1) emphasis on clear explanation of principles, (2) graphic presentation of most significant data, and (3) avoidance of a multitude of unfamiliar technical terms in the text. In addition, because most students lack acquaintance with the distinguishing characters of many kinds of organisms that occur as fossils, information of this sort is organized in an Appendix readily available for reference.

In preparing the text, effort has been made to write straightforwardly in plain English, stating each pertinent observation or conclusion as simply and clearly as possible. Discussions of the historical significance of these facts are aimed at developing the reader's understanding of the reasons for each deduction. To think accurately and analyze soundly any set of observations are abilities far more valuable to a student than capacity for repeating something read or heard by him. Memory is useful as an adjunct of learning but not acceptable as substitute for real learning. Therefore, the relation between cause and effect is held in view constantly as data of the geologic record are examined. Questions at the end of chapters in the revised edition are designed to develop and test the student's ability to reach trustworthy conclusions. All parts of the text have been reviewed critically with the object of eliminating ambiguities and erroneous statements wherever found in the first edition, and in many places additions or changes have been introduced so as to bring the book thoroughly up to date. A few chapters have been rewritten entirely, some with appreciable enlargement aimed at securing better balance in the text as a whole; this pertains especially to the chapter on Precambrian and chapters treating Cenozoic history. The divisions named Tertiary and Quaternary are explained but, because these terms are considered to be distinctly outmoded, are replaced by the terms Paleogene and Neogene, as commonly used now in Europe.

Many illustrations accompanying the several chapters are new. They include photographs of typical rock exposures, topographic features, and characteristic fossils, but most important are numerous maps, sections, and block diagrams, which are designed to express in graphic form various subjects treated in the text. They should contribute materially to the ease and precision of full comprehension. The geologic maps showing distribution in middle North America of rocks belonging to each major division of the column are much larger in scale than corresponding maps in previously published textbooks on historical geology, for they utilize the maximum space provided by enlarged page size. These maps are unlike ordinary outcrop maps in that known and inferred subsurface distribution of the rock division is portrayed, thus providing a representation of total present-day occurrence. Necessarily, such maps are factual in aim, rather than interpretative restorations of original distribution, as in paleogeographic maps. As accurately as possible the maps record original distribution modified by total subsequent losses due to erosion and obliteration resulting from bathylithic intrusions. For comparison with occurrence of outcrops, the location of schools offering instruction in historical geology is plotted.

Another group of illustrations consists of charts showing time-stratigraphic units in important representative successions. More numerous sections are given than in the first edition, and lithologic characters are indicated graphically by symbols explained in the Appendix. The names of units are recorded for reference, but they are subordinate elements of the charts instead of seeming to have prime importance. Still another group of illustrations worthy of special mention are restorations of natural assemblages of plants and animals, for these aid greatly in obtaining a vivid concept of the appearance of long-extinct organisms. The fossils represent species that once were actually living things.

The brief descriptions that accompany the captions of most figures not only supplement discussion given in the text but independently serve to point out many important features belonging to the study of earth history. One who closely examines the illustrations and their explanations cannot fail to acquire a good deal of understanding of historical geology, even without reading the text. It is my judgment that all beginning students will find the few lines of description or comment added to the titles of figures decidedly helpful, because they call attention to significant items otherwise readily overlooked. Teachers recognize the value of such assistance, just as they appreciate the advantage of all sorts of visual instruction.

Many books on historical geology are burdened with a forbiddingly large vocabulary of technical words consisting chiefly of the scientific names of fossils and names of rock formations. The student is led to think, naturally enough, that acquisition of knowledge of historical geology consists mainly, if not essentially, of learning all these strange new terms. The task is to memorize, and some teachers do not help very much in developing a keen interest on the part of students in why's and wherefore's. If stress is put unduly on a catalogue of mere what's, the subject may seem dry and difficult indeed. It is dead, rather than alive with interest. Yet the names of fossils and of rock units are needed, especially by the student who goes on to more advanced work in geology. Accordingly, many such names are given in the illustrations used in this book, and without obtruding, they are available for such reference and attention as may be judged desirable by the student and teacher. They are not prerequisite to learning about geological history. A glossary of terms useful in study of earth history is given in Appendix C of the revised edition.

Besides persons mentioned as helping in preparation of the first edition of this book, especially C. W. Cooke, G. A. Cooper, R. W. Imlay, P. B. King, J. B. Knight, A. L. Loeblich, Jr., N. D. Newell, J. B. Reeside, Jr., L. W. Stephenson, and C. J. Stubblefield, I am indebted to numerous friends for aid of one sort or another in organizing this revised edition. Special thanks are due Erling Dorf, of Princeton University, for furnishing critical notes and suggestions; also to R. J. W. Douglas, Y. O. Fortier, J. M. Harrison, C. S. Lord, D. J. McLaren, and G. W. Sinclair, of the Geological Survey of Canada, for unpublished information on Precambrian and other rocks of Canada; to J. Tuzo Wilson, of the University of Toronto, for data on age of Precambrian rocks; and for assistance in supplying information concerning subsurface distribution of various rock divisions to N. W. Bass, O. E. Childs, A. J. Eardley, R. M. Jeffords, William McBee, E. D. McKee, J. G. Mitchell, M. R. Mudge, J. W. Skinner, W. L. Stokes, and Hunter Yarborough. Various illustrations consisting of photographs of rock outcrops, fossils, and restoration of extinct plant and animal groups are individually acknowledged, but it is appropriate to express special appreciation to Josef Augusta and his associate scientist-artist Z. Burian, of Praha, for permission to publish restorations made by them; to L. B. Kellum and I. G. Reimann, of the University of Michigan, for photographs of dioramas made at my request; and to J. C. Frye, of the Illinois Geological Survey, and Charles Deiss and J. B. Patton, of the Indiana Geological Survey, for photographs specially made for this book.

Raymond Cecil Moore

CONTENTS

Preface   v

1. Materials and Methods of Historical Geology   1
2. Evolution of Life   35
3. The Beginning of the Earth   46
4. Cryptozoic Eon   59
5. Paleozoic Era: Cambrian Period   107
6. Paleozoic Era: Ordovician Period   135
7. Paleozoic Era: Silurian Period   163
8. Paleozoic Era: Devonian Period   187
9. Paleozoic Era: Mississippian Period   211
10. Paleozoic Era: Pennsylvanian Period   231
11. Paleozoic Era: Permian Period   257
12. Nature and Evolution of Paleozoic Life   284
13. Mesozoic Era: Triassic Period   327
14. Mesozoic Era: Jurassic Period   347
15. Mesozoic Era: Cretaceous Period   366
16. Nature and Evolution of Mesozoic Life   394
17. Cenozoic Era: Paleogene Period   432
18. Cenozoic Era: Neogene Period   456
19. Cenozoic Era: Neogene Period (Pleistocene Epoch)   495
20. Nature and Evolution of Cenozoic Life   527
21. Geologic Record of Man   553

Appendix A. Characters of Organisms Represented among Fossils   567
Appendix B. Lithologic Symbols for Geologic Sections   623
Appendix C. Glossary   626

Index   639

1.

MATERIALS AND METHODS
OF HISTORICAL GEOLOGY

Records of earth history in walls of the Grand Canyon of Colorado River, Arizona.

N. W. Carkhuff, Courtesy of U.S. Geol. Survey

Historical geology is the branch of geologic science that relates to the past history of the earth. It depends on virtually all knowledge in the field of physical geology gained in study of minerals, rocks, geologic processes and structures, and it utilizes this knowledge in deducing the conditions and events of the earth's past. Among features belonging to study of earth history are the origin and development of the continents and oceans, the changing geography of seas and lands, the appearance and disappearance of great mountain systems, the occurrence of profound volcanic activity at different times and places, and great climatic changes. In addition, we find evidence of innumerable forms of prehistoric plants and animals, many of which represent types of life long vanished from the earth. The nature of this past life and its evolution during geologic time not only form an intrinsically interesting part of historical geology, but if these organic remains were not preserved in the rocks, many features of the earth record would not be decipherable. It is desirable to begin our study, then, by surveying the nature of historical geologic evidence and the methods by which this is to be interpreted.

As foundation, we accept the conclusion that nature's laws are unchanging. This means that we have no reason to doubt that the principles of physics and chemistry, the operation of gravity, and the essential nature of geologic processes are independent of time. They are unchanging. During past earth history rocks must have been formed and some of them subsequently broken down physically or chemically in the same manner as now; we may be sure that rains fell, water flowed downhill, winds blew, and waves beat against shores, just as we can see on the earth at the present time. This concept, which has come to be known by the formidable term of *uniformitarianism,* simply holds that the present is a key to the past. Our ability to analyze the rock record depends, first, on the completeness and accuracy of our understanding of these present-day laws and processes and, second, on the extent to which the rock record is available for study.

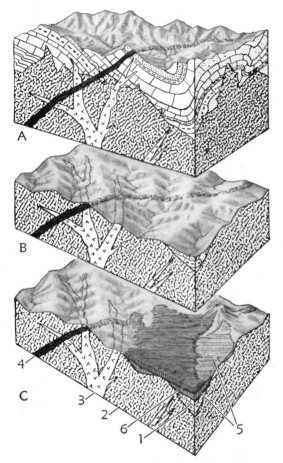

Fig. 1.1   Structural relations of igneous rock bodies indicating their relative age.——*A.* Folded sedimentary rocks are invaded by a large bathylithic mass of deep-seated plutonic rocks (granite), which is intersected by dikes, all igneous rocks being younger than the sedimentary strata.——*B.* Same area after prolonged erosion that has removed virtually all the original sedimentary-rock cover, thus exposing the igneous rocks widely.——*C.* Same area at a later time in its geologic history when extrusive igneous rocks (sheets of basaltic lava), divisible into an earlier and later series of flows, cover part of the region. Numbers denote relative age, from oldest (1) to youngest (6).

HISTORICAL MEANING OF ROCK CHARACTERS

Rocks comprise igneous, sedimentary, and metamorphic types. We know that igneous rocks originate as both intrusions and extrusions, that sedimentary rocks are formed by the breaking down and deposition of preexisting rock material, and that metamorphic rocks are produced mainly by heat and pressure affecting other rocks. Inasmuch as the origin and history of all these differ, each must be considered separately from the standpoint of historical geology.

Igneous Rocks

Texture, form, and distribution. The occurrence of outcrops of igneous rocks anywhere obviously constitutes evidence of volcanism in the past history of the region. The nature, extent, and geologic date of the volcanism may be learned from study of the texture, form, and distribution of the igneous rocks and especially from observation of their structural relations with associated rocks. Coarse, subequal-grained rocks, such as granite or diorite, represent deep-seated intrusions of bathylithic type. Such intrusions seem to be associated characteristically with crustal deformations that produce mountain building. Dikes, sills, and other intrusive igneous bodies may be identified by their form and relations to associated rocks, and they are commonly distinguished also by texture.

The location and nature of extrusive volcanism may be read from observation of characteristic features corresponding to those of modern lava flows, ash falls, or pyroclastic materials mingled with sediment. Such igneous bodies commonly are layered, and some of them show columnar jointing; cindery or scoriaceous texture at the top of a basaltic layer may serve to distinguish it as an individual lava flow. Pumice, tuff, and agglomerate denote explosive volcanic activity, and layers of volcanic ash or dust (commonly altered chemically to the clayey material called *bentonite*) denote wind action that served to transport the volcanic materials.

Structural relations. The geologic date of making igneous rocks can be determined with varying precision by observing structural relations with associated rocks. Intrusive igneous bodies are obviously younger than associated rocks that they intersect, but very often it is extremely difficult to tell how much younger. Extrusive igneous rocks are younger than the rocks that occur beneath them and older than the ones lying upon them. These age determinations are relative, and narrowness of geologic dating depends upon the accuracy with which the age of associated rocks is known (Fig. 1.1).

Sedimentary Rocks

Composition, texture, and distribution. Most of historical geology has to do with sedimentary rocks and their contained organic remains. This is accounted for by the fact that events of earth history are recorded mainly in terms of differing kinds of sedimentation, varying deformation of these sediments after they have been formed into rock layers, interruptions in rock building commonly accompanied by erosion, and evidence of evolution of life presented by fossils entombed in the sedimentary rocks.

Sedimentary rocks are divisible into clastic and nonclastic types. Clastic rocks, such as conglomerate, sandstone, arkose, and shale, are made up mainly of the broken fragments of preexisting rocks which denote mechanical disintegration of the source materials. The composition and degree of rounding of the clastic grains show the extent of sorting and reflect the effects of transportation. Applying knowledge of modern conditions of weather-

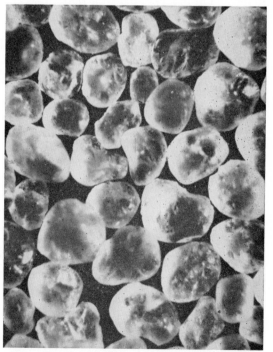

Fig. 1.2 Grains of St. Peter Sandstone. The rounded polished surfaces of quartz sand grains shown in this photomicrograph represent prolonged abrasion, probably by wind work mostly but also including wear from other transporting agents. The purity and good sorting of the grains are the effects of reworking many times.

ing, transportation, and sedimentation, study of the composition and texture of ancient sedimentary rocks permits deductions as to conditions under which they were formed. Thus, a very pure light-colored sandstone, 100 to 400 feet thick, that is widely distributed in the central and upper Mississippi Valley region, when examined with a lens or under the microscope, is seen to be composed of unusually well-sorted and rounded grains of quartz having frosted surfaces (Fig. 1.2). This deposit, known as the St. Peter Sandstone, evidently represents extensive sorting of the sedimentary materials in which all but the resistant quartz grains have been eliminated, and it shows prolonged transportation during which grains have been very well rounded and the surfaces frosted by impact of grain on grain. As shown by outcrops distributed through several states and by identifying the sandstone in innumerable well borings where younger strata overlie it, this deposit is known to be spread with essentially uniform characters over many ten-thousand square miles. What does this represent in terms of geologic

history? What was the source of the sand, and what were the agents of transportation and deposition? Conceivably, this sandstone indicates the former existence in the central United States of a Sahara-like desert where migrating sand dunes were spread by strong winds. On the other hand, perhaps the sand was laid down by water, being shifted by waves and currents of a shallow sea or spread as beach deposits at the margin of such a sea. Possibly work by wind, streams, and a shallow sea may all have had part in making the St. Peter Sandstone. Reliable conclusions must be based on a survey of all available evidence and proper interpretation of the meaning of each observation. Most of the bedding is parallel to the base and top of the deposit, which originally must have been nearly horizontal, and the evenness of the layers thus bespeaks deposition in an extensive water body. The sandstone contains almost no organic remains, but locally there are identifiable traces of shelled invertebrates. Also, the sand is found to grade laterally in places into calcareous marine beds. Hence, we conclude that, although the rounding and thorough sorting of grains indicate long transportation, probably by streams and winds, the sand was deposited in a shallow sea. Our deductions as to geologic history are essentially and mainly based on study of the composition, texture, and distribution of this deposit.

Similarly, other clastic deposits must be studied and the conditions of making them analyzed. Poorly sorted conglomerate, mixed with coarse to fine sand and silt, suggest a not-distant source of the deposits and imply topographic relief sufficient to permit rapid transportation of detritus (Figs. 1.3, 1.4). Such deposits compose many terrestrial formations formed in intermontane basins, in plains adjacent to highlands, or in shallow seas bordering precipitous coasts. Conversely, fine-grained clastic sediments, such as clay and shale, denote much greater sorting and longer transportation or sources in much lower lying lands.

Nonclastic sedimentary rocks comprise materials deposited by chemical precipitation or through the agency of organisms. Salt, gypsum,

Fig. 1.3 Ancient Precambrian conglomerate from southern Canada. In this rock, probably more than 2,000 million years old, the sandy matrix and igneous-rock pebbles and cobbles are about equally resistant to weathering. Timiskaming Sequence near Noranda, northwestern Quebec. (*M. E. Wilson, courtesy of Geol. Survey Canada.*)

anhydrite, and some deposits of limestone and dolostone (rock predominantly composed of carbonates with the mineral dolomite exceeding calcite plus aragonite) have been deposited by direct chemical precipitation from marine or inland waters made supersaturated by evaporation. Limestone is quantitatively much less important than shale and sandstone among sedimentary rocks of the world, but it is the chief nonclastic rock type. Kinds of limestone, classed on the basis of composition and texture, are almost without number, and each represents somewhat different conditions involved in making. Mainly, however, this represents the kind of lime-secreting organisms that have contributed to making the deposit and the extent to which original organic structures have been altered by action of sea- or lake-bottom scavengers and by compaction, recrystallization, and similar chemical-physical changes. The distribution of a limestone or other non-clastic sedimentary rock indicates at least partly the extent of the water body in which it was formed. Most such water-laid deposits are marine, but some were laid down in fresh water; the saline or fresh-water nature of the

Fig. 1.4 Coarse conglomerate composed of varied sorts of water-worn igneous and sedimentary rocks. The size, shape, and nature of the constituent boulders and pebbles, together with thickness, distribution, and relation of the conglomerate to associated strata, are important features in studying the origin of such a deposit. This is a stream-laid conglomerate of Paleogene age near Thistle, Utah. (*E. M. Spieker, courtesy of U.S. Geol. Survey.*)

depositional environment of the limestone commonly can be determined only from study of contained organisms in the deposit. Some dolostones comprise original calcareous de-

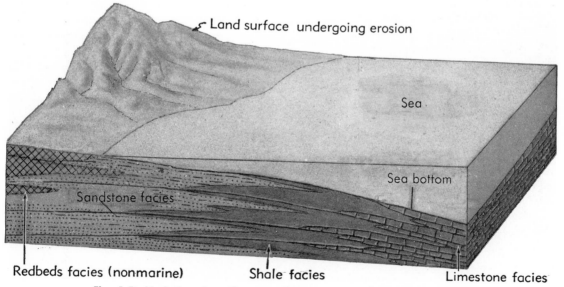

Land surface undergoing erosion

Sea

Sea bottom

Sandstone facies

Redbeds facies (nonmarine)   Shale facies   Limestone facies

Fig. 1.5 Variations in sedimentary facies. Types of sedimentary accumulations commonly differ according to the place and mode of their deposition. They may grade laterally one into another and interfinger as result of changing conditions. The deposits shaded most darkly represent offshore sediments.

posits rich in magnesium carbonate; these are termed *primary*. Others are formed by alteration of limestone in which magnesium carbonate replaces calcium carbonate; these are classed as *secondary*.

Lateral variation. A prevalent feature of sedimentary formations, which is to be expected from the nature of their making, is lateral variation. This gives rise to recognition of *facies* (Fig. 1.5). By this term is meant the composite assemblage of characters serving to differentiate various sedimentary environments. Thus, deposits of given age in a certain region may be distinguished as offshore, near-shore, coastal marshland, or terrestrial. Proof of age equivalence of these neighboring but differing kinds of deposits is found in the lateral transition of one to the other and interbedding or interfingering of one with another. Thus, parts of the western United States contain shale outcrops that represent offshore muds (Mancos Shale) containing marine organisms; these muds were laid down contemporaneously with near-shore and onshore beds (Mesaverde Sandstone) in which shallow water and beach deposits, coal-bearing marsh deposits, and stream-laid terrestrial deposits are respectively differentiated. Recognition of these sedimentary facies and their relations to one another aids importantly in understanding regional geography of the time and in interpreting geologic history.

The geologic date of sedimentary deposits is determined by study of their organic remains and by their relation to other deposits in vertical sequence, as discussed later in this chapter.

Stratification and features of bedding planes. Historical interpretation of sedimentary strata calls for attention to features shown by bedding. The thickness of individual sedimentary rock layers ranges from a fraction of a millimeter to many feet (Fig. 1.6). Very massive strata of uniform texture clearly mean relatively long persistence of uniform conditions of sedimentation. A bedding plane is introduced when these conditions are temporarily changed, as when a film of clay is spread

Fig. 1.6 Evenly stratified, thin-bedded sandstone. These layers of sand and silt in the Allegheny River Valley near Oil City, Pa., indicate very regular alternation of conditions affecting deposition in shallow water. The strata belong to the great coal-bearing succession of deposits called the Pennsylvanian System. (*R. M. Leggette, courtesy of U.S. Geol. Survey.*)

Fig. 1.7 Ripple-marked sandstone near Abingdon, Va. These markings plainly record wave movement in shallow water. They have been preserved by burial beneath layers of limemud subsequently hardened to limestone. Jonesboro Limestone, Lower Ordovician. (*Charles Butts, courtesy of U.S. Geol. Survey.*)

Fig. 1.8 Ancient rock surface showing mud cracks. The earthy limestone (Moccasin) of Middle Ordovician age in southwestern Virginia shown here reveals the effects of exposure and drying that produced mud cracks, which subsequently were filled with sediment of slightly different nature. (*R. C. Moore.*)

Fig. 1.9 Cross-bedded sandstone. This is part of very widespread, thick, wind-transported sand deposits of early Jurassic age at a weathered outcrop in southern Utah a few miles northeast of Kanab. Evenness of the inclined laminae indicates at least temporary local constancy of wind direction from west to east. (*R. C. Moore.*)

over an area of accumulating sand or of pure calcium carbonate. These bedding planes, which may be very smooth or wavy, reflect the temporary configuration of the surface of sedimentation, generally a sea bottom.

Ripple-marked bedding planes are of inter-

est because they indicate agitation of the accumulating sediments by waves or currents (Fig. 1.7); if the sediments are water-laid, this means that depth of water is sufficiently small to permit agitation of the bottom. Study of the pattern and profile of ripples permits differentiation of various types, such as oscillation ripples made by waves and current ripples produced by water currents or wind. This helps in interpreting conditions of ancient geography.

Some bedding planes show the characteristic polygonal pattern of mud cracks, which represent above-water desiccation of sediment, with subsequent filling of the cracks by other sediment (Fig. 1.8).

Cross-bedding, formed by inclined deposition of granular sediments on the lee slopes of bars and dunes, denotes current action, and study of the pattern of cross-bedding may permit determination of whether this structure was produced by winds, by currents in streams, or in shallow water along a shore line (Fig. 1.9).

Inasmuch as the original attitude of strata bearing mud cracks, ripple marks, and cross-bedding, as studied in physical geology, can be determined from study of these structures, they are useful in determining the top and bottom of a sequence of vertical or overturned beds, wherever found in such occurrence.

Organic remains. A characteristic feature of sedimentary rocks that is vitally important to historical geology is the common occurrence of fossilized remains of organisms (Fig. 1.10). Fossils are the remains or traces of animals or plants preserved in rocks (Latin *fossilis*, meaning "something dug out of the earth"). Before the time of modern science, men regarded shells, bones, or leaf imprints discovered in rocks as freaks of nature or the ineffective creative effort of some unknown plastic force

Fig. 1.10 Highly fossiliferous marine sandstone. The abundant, well-preserved shells, mostly snails, shown on the weathered surface of this silty sandstone indicate the abundance of life on a shallow sea bottom of Neogene (Miocene) time in the Chesapeake Bay region. The calcium carbonate shell substance has been preserved with virtually no change. The crowding and partial sorting of the shells suggest the effects of current action. (*Courtesy of U.S. Geol. Survey.*)

within the earth. A few men interpreted them as actual remains of life that existed before the flood of Noah, death and burial in sediments having resulted from the great flood, but it is hard to explain why fishes and other aquatic creatures would have been drowned.

Shortly before 1800, the discovery was made that fossils of a given bed or group of beds are characteristic of it and serve to distinguish it from other fossil-bearing rock layers. Furthermore, the sequence of natural assemblages of animals (faunas) and assemblages of plants (floras), as represented by fossils in rocks, is constant. The geologic distribution of these fossil assemblages in one region corresponds to that observed in others, and this provides the all-important foundation on which rock strata in different regions may be correlated and divisions that correspond in age may be recognized. If evidence derived from study of organic remains in the rocks were lacking, most of the record of earth history that is somewhat definitely and accurately known would be obscure or indecipherable and we would have virtually no tangible evidence bearing on the history and evolution of life on the earth.

Preservation of organic remains as a fossil commonly depends on two chief requisites: (1) that the organism be buried quickly in some protecting medium and (2) that it possess some sort of hard parts, such as a skeleton or shell. The death of an animal or plant normally is followed quickly by decay that destroys tissues and eventually obliterates all traces of the organism. If such decay is inhibited or prevented, as in embalming bodies

Fig. 1.11 Quarrying out a dinosaur skeleton. The specimen here partly exposed is unusual in that the bones lie in an undisturbed articulated position. The animal was lying on its side when buried in Cretaceous muds (Belly River Beds, Alberta, Can.). (*Courtesy of American Museum of Natural History.*)

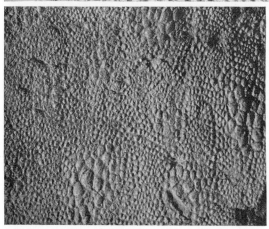

Fig. 1.12 Mummified remains of a duck-billed dinosaur. The remarkable specimen here shown indicates desiccation of the remains after the death of the animal, just as bones and skin may be preserved today in the dry desert air of parts of the southwestern United States. Eventually the bones of this dinosaur, with their covering of dried skin, were buried by drifting sand of Cretaceous age. The lower view shows the appearance of a part of the scaly skin. (*Courtesy of American Museum of Natural History.*)

to make mummies or by sealing them in a protective medium, organic structures—especially resistant parts such as shells, teeth, and bones—may be preserved (Fig. 1.11). Natural mummies may be made by the dry air of a desert or cave, and such remains later may be buried by sediment (Fig. 1.12). Woolly mammoths and rhinoceroses of the Ice Age have been found solidly frozen in ice of northern Siberia, so that even the flesh, internal organs, and undigested food in the stomach have been almost perfectly preserved. Insects showing every detail of structure and color have been found in amber, which is the fossilized resin of conifer trees.

The great majority of fossils have been made simply by covering by water in fine sediments. Although this does not ordinarily prevent bacterial decay of soft tissues, harder parts may be well preserved. Thus, chances of preservation of an organism as a fossil naturally are greatest in water bodies such as the sea, where hard parts are buried in muds and sands of the sea bottom. On land, the best opportunity for fossilization is found in lakes and swamps. Fresh-water deposits, such as the Green River Beds of Wyoming and the Florissant Beds of Colorado, contain beautifully preserved fishes, insects, fresh-water shells, and the leaves and twigs of land plants that were blown by winds or carried by streams to the area in which they are preserved.

Eruptions of volcanic ash, such as descended

Fig. 1.13 Fossil brachiopods preserved by silicification. After these marine shells were buried in Permian limestone of western Texas, their substance, which originally was calcium carbonate, was replaced by silica carried by percolating ground water. The shells were removed from the rock matrix by dissolving the limestone in dilute hydrochloric acid. The spiny projections of such brachiopods as *A–G* (productids) and the coral-shaped shells *H, I* (richtofeniids), which ordinarily break away in natural weathering, are here intact; also internal features of many fossils (as *J–M*) are found well preserved. Natural size or somewhat enlarged. (*Courtesy of G. A. Cooper, U.S. National Museum.*)

on the Roman cities of Pompeii and Herculaneum, may smother and bury numerous animals and plants. In this way the forests of standing trunks in Yellowstone Park have been formed and many fine fossil skeletons of mammals, as in the John Day Basin of Oregon, have been preserved.

The manner in which organic remains may be preserved in sediments varies widely. Some fossils consist of the hard parts of an animal or the woody tissues of a plant preserved unaltered in the sediment that buried them. Most fossils, however, have undergone change. Shells composed of calcium carbonate may be made more dense by infiltration of calcite deposited by ground water. Commonly, also, there has been replacement of the original hard parts by some other mineral in submicroscopic particles; such replacement by calcium carbonate is termed *calcification;* by silica, *silicification* (Fig. 1.13); and by iron pyrite, *pyritization.* This particle-by-particle replacement operates to preserve microscopic structures of the hard parts, even though chemical composition is changed. Slow decay under water of the tissue of plants (and less commonly of animals) may result in concentrations of carbon showing the form of the original organism; this is termed *carbonization* (Fig. 1.14).

After burial in sediment, the hard parts of an organism may be removed by solution so as to leave merely the *mold* of its form in the surrounding rock (Fig. 1.15). If the cavity is filled by some foreign mineral substance, just like metal poured into a foundry mold, the fossil is termed a *cast,* and such a cast retains no trace of original microscopic internal structure or shell substance.

Indirect evidence of the existence of organisms is found in the fossil tracks of land animals (Fig. 1.16), the trails or borings of worms and other invertebrates, and coprolites (fossil excrement). Gizzard stones of some ancient reptiles may be identified by their form, surface polish, and manner of occurrence, associated perhaps with actual skeletal remains. The stone implements or weapons of prehistoric man also are indirect fossils.

Fig. 1.14 Fossil fern showing preservation by carbonization. The form of these fern leaflets (*Neuropteris*, ×4) is clearly shown by the impression in the fine sediment that buried this plant, but in addition, the original tissue is represented by a thin film of carbon over the area of stem and leaflets. The specimen is from Early Pennsylvanian beds of Alabama. (*Charles Butts, courtesy of U.S. Geol. Survey.*)

The original form of organic remains is by no means always preserved in fossils. Compaction of sediments by the weight of overlying rocks is likely to produce a flattening of the contained fossils (Fig. 1.17). This is especially noteworthy in shale. Regional metamorphism is likely to distort or even obliterate fossils contained in sediments.

The terms *index fossil* and *guide fossil* are applied to kinds of fossils that are especially restricted in vertical range, widely distributed horizontally, fairly abundant, and sufficiently distinctive in character to permit ready identification. The only distinction between "index" and "guide" as here used is that the name of an index fossil is employed for designating strata containing it (for example, the trilobite *Elvinia* as name giver to the Elvinia Zone in Upper Cambrian rocks of the United States), whereas a guide fossil may be any that is useful for purposes of identifying and correlating the rock layers that contain it. Abundance makes such fossils more readily found, and if they are distinctive, they are less likely to be confused with a somewhat similar fossil. Usefulness as indicators of particular zones in which they occur is increased if they are very widespread geographically and is sharpened if they are restricted to a small thickness of beds vertically.

Structural relations. The age of any sedimentary deposit may be determined relatively by its structural position in respect to associated rocks. Thus, in a succession of undisturbed beds or only slightly warped strata, relative age is indicated by the order of se-

Fig. 1.15 Molds and casts of Mesozoic marine shells. The original shell substance has been removed by solution from the fine-grained sandstone that bears only the external and internal impressions to show the form of the shells. Replicas of the shells may be made by pouring or pressing a suitable substance into the mold so as to produce a cast. Two such artificially made casts are illustrated. Because the kinds of shells here represented are restricted vertically but widespread horizontally, they are valuable guide fossils. (*Courtesy of U.S. National Museum.*)

quence, the oldest beds occurring at the base and the youngest at the top. This *law of superposition* is a starting point in geologic chronology. By observing the fossil organic remains in a succession of beds, the order of sequence of faunas and floras is established, and once this is learned, the proper age position of isolated occurrences of fossils is indicated. A scale that shows the proper geologic sequence of all assemblages of organisms is built up.

Fig. 1.16 Fossil trail of a four-legged animal in sandstone of Permian age. The impressions on a bedding plane of the Coconino Sandstone in the Grand Canyon area of Arizona prove that the maker of the tracks, doubtless a reptile, had sharp-pointed toes. Even though no skeletal remains are found, different kinds of creatures may be identified by distinctive characters of their tracks. (*Courtesy of U.S. National Museum.*)

Fig. 1.17 A fossil fish from Cenozoic marine beds in the West Indies. The outline and various structural features of this fish (*Zebrasoma*) are well preserved, although flattened greatly by compaction of the sediment. The fish lies on a bedding plane, a carbonaceous residue differentiating the fossil from the surrounding rock. (*Courtesy of American Museum of Natural History.*)

Locally, where sedimentary rocks stand vertically or are overturned, relative age is indicated by fossils and also in many instances by physical evidence such as cross-bedding, ripple marks, and the attitude of joints and shear lines.

When the successions of sedimentary strata are studied throughout a region, special structural relations may be recognized, and these have direct bearing on interpretation of history. *Overlap* consists of the greater extent in some directions of successively younger beds than older ones, so that the more far-reaching or overlapping strata come to rest on older rocks than those they normally overlie (Fig. 1.18). Clearly, this defines an expanding area of sedimentation, as when a sea is slowly transgressing a land area, bringing successively younger marine strata directly into contact with what had been land. The opposite of

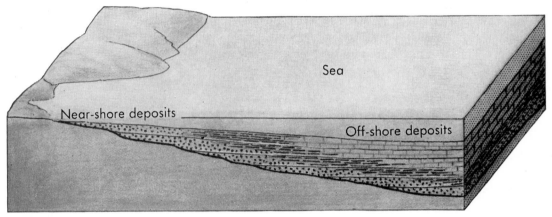

Fig. 1.18 Overlap of sedimentary formations. The diagram shows the characteristic structural relations of marine deposits belonging to an uninterrupted succession of beds laid down by a transgressing sea. Each rock layer overlaps in a landward direction the deposits occurring beneath them, so that progressively younger strata come to rest directly on older rocks in the marginal areas of their distribution. It is noteworthy, also, that different types of deposits shift in position as the sea advances on the land. Thus, near-shore deposits are everywhere in contact with older rocks, but they represent successively younger parts of the marine deposits.

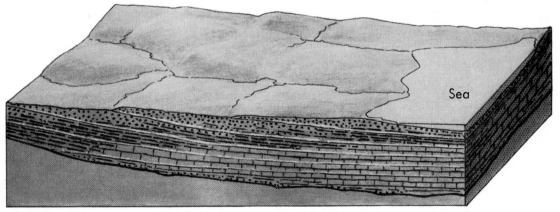

Fig. 1.19 Offlap of marine sedimentary formations. The reverse of overlap is offlap, which in marine deposits is produced by a regressing sea. Marginal marine deposits thus come to rest on strata that were laid down in an offshore position.

overlap is *offlap*, in which successively younger beds have more and more restricted distribution (Fig. 1.19). They indicate a retreating area of sedimentation, as when a sea regresses from the land. Study of these structural relations aids in recognizing movements of sea and land.

Sedimentary rock structures in many areas include *folds* and *faults,* especially in mountain belts. Obviously, every such fold and fault is geologically younger than the rocks that are deformed by the fold or fault. How much younger can be learned in those places where undisturbed strata abut or overlie the disturbed beds (Fig. 1.20). If oldest undisturbed rocks in such relations are only slightly younger than the latest formed sediments involved in deformation, the geologic date of the deformation may be somewhat narrowly defined. On the other hand, if the gap is large, there is no way to tell reliably whether deformation occurred shortly after deposition of the latest rocks involved in the disturbance or a very long time later but shortly before deposition of the oldest undisturbed beds. The age of mountain building in any area must be attacked in this way.

A structural relation of sedimentary rocks that is especially important in historical geology is that represented by unconformities (Fig. 1.21). These are discordances in rock successions that denote interruption in the continuity of rock-making processes. Unconformities are classifiable in two main categories on the basis of structural relations of the underlying and overlying rocks: (1) strata below and above the unconformity parallel, indicating lack of local crustal deformation associated with a break in continuity of sedimentation, and (2) rocks above the unconformity not parallel to those below, denoting something more than interrupted sedimentation with or without accompanying erosion.

In the first group of unconformities, the most obvious are recognized by unevenness of the contact between younger and older rocks, generally with an accompanying abrupt change in lithologic characters. The irregular

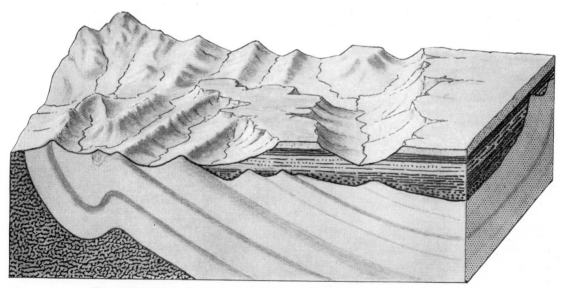

Fig. 1.20 Geologic dating of crustal deformation. The diagram, which represents part of the eastern border of the Rocky Mountains, shows two sequences of stratified rocks having discordant structure. The tilted and folded beds were truncated by erosion before deposition of the horizontal overlying series. Hard rocks of the folded series make hogbacks, and weak strata form monoclinal valleys. The deformed and eroded rocks were buried beneath younger deposits and then subsequently exhumed partly. The geologic date of the folding must be later than the youngest deformed stratum and older than the lowermost horizontal deposit.

Nonconformity

Fig. 1.21 Unconformity separating Precambrian and Paleozoic formations in the Grand Canyon region of Arizona. Rocks of the V-shaped inner gorge of the canyon are Precambrian igneous and metamorphic crystalline rocks. They are truncated evenly by the great unconformity (nonconformity) that forms the lower boundary of Paleozoic rocks in the area. The basal Paleozoic deposit, which is a cliff-making sandstone of Cambrian age, is seen at the summit of the inner gorge. The erosion surface buried by the sandstone is a remarkably even peneplain, which bespeaks very prolonged denudation in pre-Paleozoic time. (*R. C. Moore, courtesy of U.S. Geol. Survey.*)

contact signifies erosion of the older rocks sufficient to produce observable topographic relief. When deposition of sediment was resumed, depressions on the eroded surface were filled in first and higher parts later. This is a *disconformity* (Fig. 1.22). A very common but extremely obscure type of unconformity corresponds to disconformity in every way except that the contact between beds below and above the break is perfectly even or almost so and thus hardly distinguishable from an ordinary bedding plane; yet the actually existent break (with or without hint of accompanying removal of sediment formerly laid down) may be of very great duration, amounting to whole periods of geologic time. Such unconformities are named *para-*

conformities (Dunbar and Rodgers, 1957, p. 119) (Fig. 1.22). Paraconformities of minor time significance are called *diastems*, and in all probability these are extremely numerous.

Study of the second group of unconformities leads to distinction of one type in which stratified deposits lie on an eroded surface of massive crystalline rocks, either igneous or metamorphic. This is a *nonconformity* (Fig. 1.23). It is important in deciphering geologic history because invariably a nonconformity furnishes record of profound erosion that followed bathylithic igneous intrusions, regional metamorphism of rocks, or both, and these point to crustal disturbance preceding the erosion represented by the nonconformity. Another type of unconformity that corresponds to nonconformity in its general historical implications is called *angular unconformity* (Fig. 1.23). It is distinguished by the lack of parallelism between older and younger sets of stratified rocks, the younger resting on erosion-truncated edges of the older, which proves occurrence of crustal deformation prior to the erosion and subsequent deposition indicated by the angular unconformity. Obviously, both sets of strata may be affected by postunconformity disturbances.

Finally, we must observe that each of the described types of unconformities may pass laterally into any other type, because the succession of conditions existing·in one locality does not correspond necessarily to those in adjacent or distant areas (Figs. 1.22, 1.23). Also, the span of geologic time represented as "missing record" may differ appreciably from place to place along a physically continuous unconformity. Largely for this reason, a proposal to apply names to various unconformities has seemed to lack utility and with few exceptions (for example, "Eparchean Interval," mentioned in Chap. 4) has been avoided.

Metamorphic Rocks

Kind and distribution. Metamorphic rocks comprise meta-igneous types, derived by alteration of igneous rocks, and metasedimentary types, formed by alteration of preexisting sedi-

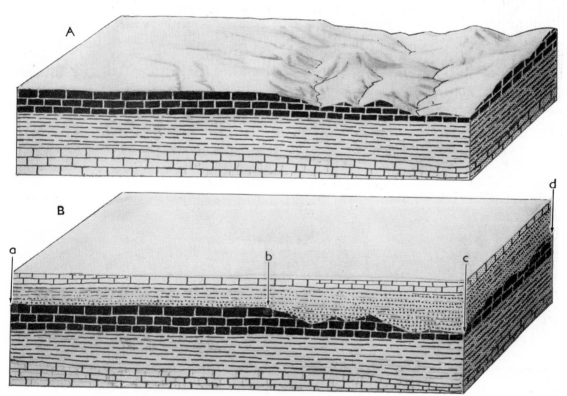

Fig. 1.22 Types of unconformities: disconformity and paraconformity. The upper block diagram (*A*) represents flat-lying limestone and shale deposits, the topmost unit having been exposed to weathering and erosion for a time of unknown duration. The land surface at the right shows distinct topographic unevenness, whereas that at the left is essentially flat and parallel to rock bedding planes. The lower diagram (*B*) shows the same region after younger deposits have been laid down over the formerly exposed limestone shown in black; the contact between older and younger rocks showing features seen from *a* to *b* is termed a paraconformity, and that showing irregularities such as seen from *b* to *c* and *d* is called a disconformity.

mentary formations. Identification of the nature of rock materials before metamorphism, wherever this is possible, contributes to correct reading of historical geologic features. Distribution of the metamorphic rocks also has significance. Tracts of metamorphosed rocks somewhat narrowly confined to borders of intrusive igneous rocks represent merely contact metamorphism, whereas very extensive

distribution denotes regional metamorphism, which typically affects deeper seated crustal zones and is associated with belts of mountain building. The geologic date when metamorphism of rocks in different areas occurred is indicated by structural relations comparable to those which indicate the time of disturbance of sedimentary rocks. Obliteration of organic remains in most metamorphic rocks

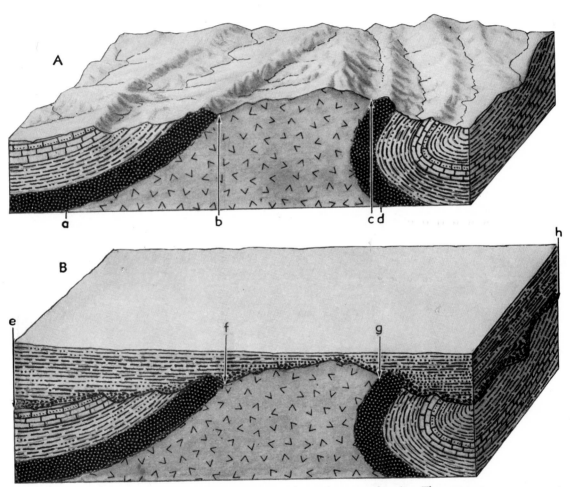

Fig. 1.23 Types of unconformities: nonconformity and angular unconformity. The upper diagram (*A*) shows a succession of stratified rocks that originally lay nearly flat, resting nonconformably on massive crystalline rocks; crustal deformation followed by erosion has produced conditions shown in *A*, the nonconformity at base of the sandstone (black) being represented from *a* to *b* and *c* to *d* but being destroyed by postuplift erosion between *b* and *c*. The lower diagram (*B*) shows flat-lying younger deposits resting unconformably on the older rocks of this region. The unconformity at the base of the younger rocks is classed as an angular unconformity from *e* to *f* and *g* to *h* but as a nonconformity between *f* and *g*. Note that the nonconformity *a* to *b* (= *f*) to *c* (= *g*) to *d* is physically continuous but very different from place to place in the geologic history indicated.

makes precise age determinations difficult or impossible.

NATURE AND OBJECTIVES OF CORRELATION

Correlation is determination of the close correspondence of two or more individually distinct things, such as outcrops of a given rock unit in different places or fossil specimens belonging to a single species or genus of animals or plants. Correlation also may apply to arrangement of events in geologic history so as to associate similar or dissimilar happenings of contemporaneous date, for this expresses equivalence in time. Thus, adjacent sedimentary deposits that reflect quite unlike origins may be identified as at least partly the same in geologic age if one grades laterally into the other or if sideward extensions of both are found locally interbedded. Furthermore, we may undertake to correlate effects with the causes that produced them, taking account of conditions and agencies recognizable from results of their former existence and operation. Historical geology depends essentially on these types of correlation, and therefore, clear understanding of main features of the subject is important to the student.

Kinds of Rock Equivalences

Two chief kinds of equivalence are discriminated in making geologic correlations. One consists of correspondence of rocks in mode of origin, for example, sedimentary deposits formed in identical or nearly identical environments in marine waters or on land. Collectively, rocks denoting similar conditions of origin are classifiable as *syntopogenic equivalents* (meaning formed in like places or manner). Comparison of rock bodies directed toward recognizing like conditions of origin lacks necessary implications as to geologic age, for almost every conceivable combination of rock-forming conditions has appeared again and again in different parts of the globe during geologic time.

A second, quite different type of equivalence constitutes identity or near-identity in geologic age. Such contemporaneous rocks may possess essentially identical characters in certain areas, but inevitably they are highly varied if a whole continent or the entire world is taken into account. Time-equivalent rocks are termed *synchronogenic* (meaning formed in the same part of geologic time).

Accordingly, the two main objectives of correlation are (1) discrimination of similar genetic units among rock bodies, with determination of their mode of origin as indicated by shape, dimensions, composition, structure, and relations to surrounding rocks, and (2) identification of the age equivalence of local rock bodies and geological conditions or events for the purpose of arranging them in proper time sequence. As applied to remains of life preserved in the rocks, correlation seeks to establish their natural affinities, spatial distribution, and placement in geologic time, thus providing a foundation for study of the evolution of plant and animal life.

Summarizing, correlation constitutes a piecing together of the physical and organic records observable in many parts of the world, with the aim of making a connected history of the earth. It is necessary to rely on correlation because no single area contains a complete record of the geologic past. Not only has contemporaneous sedimentation differed from place to place, reflecting unlike sorts of environments, but in various localities accumulation of sedimentary deposits can be demonstrated by correlation to belong to the same geologic time that elsewhere is represented by nondeposition, with or without accompanying erosion. Extensive volcanism in one district may correspond in age to absence of volcanic activity in others.

Discrimination and Correlation of Genetic Rock Units

An essential step toward reliable historical interpretation of the rock record is discrimination of unit bodies of rock as defined by their mode of origin. This applies to all kinds of rock masses—igneous, sedimentary, and metamorphic—and necessarily it takes account of the structural relations of each distinguished unit to neighboring bodies. No simple rules can be stated for defining the nature and magnitude of what should be classed as an individual rock body, because there is wide latitude in choosing the criteria adopted as the basis for distinctions. In any case, correlation of outcrops or of data obtained from subsurface exploration is required in order to define rock bodies and their relationships to one another. Consideration of a few examples will help toward clear understanding.

Sedimentary rock bodies. On hillsides and canyon walls in many square miles of northeastern Wyoming, outcrops of a light gray clay bed occur (Fig. 1.24, bed Z–Z). The clay has a distinctive property of swelling when wet, which, combined with microscopic characters, serves to identify it as altered volcanic ash called bentonite. The bed is a genetic unit formed by settling of fine ash over an inland shallow sea, existence of which is proved by marine fossils in shale below and above the bentonite. Each of the many individual outcrops of the bentonite must represent deposits precisely equivalent in origin and geologic age. The location of the volcano that produced the ash is unknown. Actually, sev-

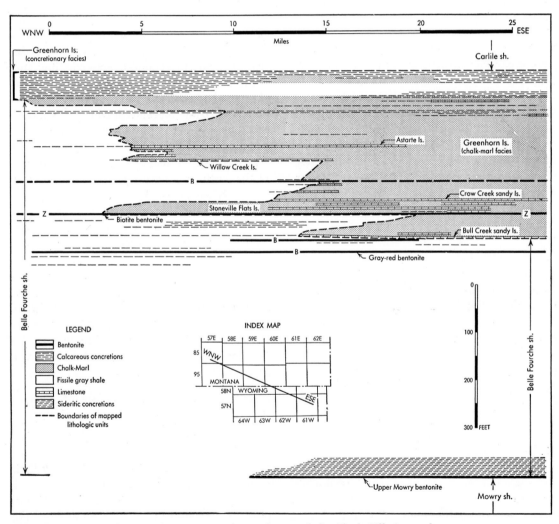

Fig. 1.24 Section of Upper Cretaceous rocks northwest of the Black Hills in northeastern Wyoming and adjacent parts of Montana. The chemically altered volcanic ash beds (bentonite), including the key bed Z–Z, are discussed in text.

eral beds of bentonite are found in the area, one occurring above another, separated by varying thicknesses of shale (Fig. 1.24). The individual bentonite layers can be recognized throughout their outcrop area by correlations depending on such evidence as (1) local continuity of certain beds established by mapping, (2) relative thickness of the bentonite beds and of the shale between bentonite layers, (3) occurrence of "key beds" distinguished by their fossil content or other characters, and (4) similarity of sequence of the rock strata.

Many widespread marine limestone deposits in North America, Europe, and other continents and some fresh-water lake deposits are genetic units having close similarity of origin and geologic age. Their discrimination is based on lithologic characters, fossil content, structural relations with associated rocks, continuity as determined by mapping, and position in sequence, but generally chief reliance in correlation is placed on fossil evidence.

Physical continuity and lithologic similarity of a sedimentary deposit as established by correlation, possibly extending hundreds of miles, may serve clearly to define a rock body that is classifiable as a genetic unit. This does not fix identity of geologic age applying to different parts of the unit, however. For example, sandstone deposits (Trinity) in Texas can be traced from south to north both along outcrops and in subsurface. Neither interruption nor significant change in lithologic characters is seen, yet associations with contiguous strata prove beyond question that the northern part of the sandstone is altogether much younger than the southern part (Fig. 1.25). The sandy deposits comprise the shore and near-shore sediment laid down by a shallow sea that advanced northward slowly during some millions of years of the Cretaceous Period. Despite difference of age of the sand from south to north, the whole deposit was formed in the same way and is a genetic unit.

Igneous rock bodies. The discrimination of igneous rock bodies for purposes of mapping and study of historical geology is guided by principles that are essentially like those applicable to sedimentary rocks. Differentiation and classification of the igneous rocks take account of composition, texture, general form of the rock mass, and structural relations to adjacent rocks, all of which have bearing on the mode of origin.

In the Connecticut River Valley near New Haven and farther north tilted sheetlike bodies of fine-grained dark-colored igneous rock are readily traceable along the outcrop for miles because they make prominent ridges. The igneous-rock sheets are parallel to similarly

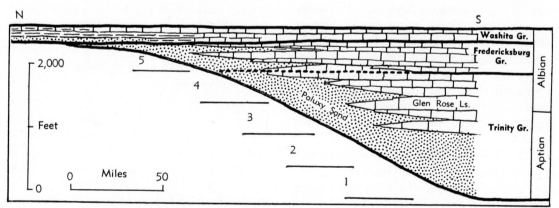

Fig. 1.25 Section of Lower Cretaceous deposits in western Texas. The basal sandstone (stippled pattern) is younger and younger proceeding northward, as indicated by arbitrarily marked time divisions 1 to 5 and by successive fossil zones in the limestone with which the sandstone interfingers. Aptian and Albian are two time-rock divisions of the European standard succession, and Trinity, Fredericksburg, and Washita Groups are units of Cretaceous classification in Texas. (*Data from W. S. Adkins, Texas Bureau of Economic Geology.*)

tilted red sandstone and shale beds below and above them, some of the sheets being identifiable as moderately thick sills and others as rock formed by cooling of ancient lava flows. A traverse across the geologic section along a line at right angles to the strike, that is, parallel to the dip, indicates the presence of several separate igneous layers, all having generally similar characters. This indicates periodic volcanic activity during the time of sedimentation when the red sandstone and shale strata, thousands of feet thick, were being accumulated. The relative age of the lava flows can be determined from their position in the rock succession, but the sills can be dated only as belonging to time later than that of making the sedimentary rocks inclosing them. The flows originally were flat-lying like the sedimentary strata below them and therefore all antedate the regional tilting of the rocks. Correlation of the similarities in lithology of the flows and sills strongly suggests identity of volcanic source and, accordingly, approximate sameness in geologic age. Considerable disturbance of the rocks by faulting is demonstrated by abrupt terminations of the igneous-rock ridges in aligned locations, the amount of offset along the faults being observed by matching the displaced rock bodies. Such correlation serves to identify some groups of parallel ridges as the topographic expression of a single set of igneous-rock sheets duplicated in outcrop by faulting parallel to the strike. The disturbance by faulting, like the regional tilting, was geologically subsequent to the igneous activity.

Unusual lithologic distinctions facilitate identification of several different Permian lava sheets in southern Norway near Oslo, making accurate correlation of outcrops comparatively easy. Each flow is found to contain large feldspar phenocrysts of rhombic form in cross section, the average size, shape, and spacing of phenocrysts in each sheet duplicating no other. Thus, the phenocrysts are like different kinds of fossils in successive sedimentary rock layers and can be used in the same way for correlation.

In many regions the discrimination of igneous rock masses, large and small, accompanied by observation of all their significant characters (including especially relations to associated sedimentary rocks), is essential for the study of historical geology, and everywhere correlation of one sort or another is involved in arriving at conclusions. Granitic rocks occurring through much of Canada, the Rocky Mountains, and Sierra Nevadas are examples. The enormous accumulation of basaltic rocks forming the Columbia Plateau in Northwestern States are others. These are correlated by similarity of structural relations to identified adjoining rocks and partly by age measurements based on radioactive minerals as described later in this chapter.

Metamorphic rock bodies. Correlation of metamorphosed rocks commonly encounters special problems that arise from obliteration in varying degree of the original rock characters. On the whole, methods of study are closely analogous to those suited to investigating sedimentary and igneous bodies, taking account especially of physical continuity, lithologic similarity, and structural relations to associated rocks, but conclusions must be cautious and qualified. Despite the importance of an effort to correlate metamorphic rocks in many areas, such as the Appalachian Piedmont province, New England, the enormously large crystalline-rock area of Canada, and the Pacific Border region of North America, discussion of applicable techniques and their limitations is inappropriate here.

Correlation Aimed at Establishing Age Equivalence

Classification of rock units in terms of their proper placement in geologic time is the most fundamental task of the historical geologist. Without knowledge of age relationships of sedimentary, igneous, and metamorphic rocks in many places, not even a beginning can be made in putting together the evidence of earth history that actually exists in accessible parts of the crust. Once age equivalences are established with varying precision, we can proceed.

Among criteria applicable to correlation aimed at establishing equivalence in geologic age, the following are arranged approximately in order of decreasing value: (1) nature and distribution of fossils; (2) stratigraphic characters and relationships, including such features as bedding planes, lateral intergradation and interfingering of different kinds of rock units, order of superposition, and relation to any widely traceable "key beds" and unconformities; (3) similarity of structural deformation, useful only within limits of rather small areas and under special conditions; (4) "absolute" age measurements based on radioactive methods; and (5) exceptional time-equivalent key beds such as volcanic ash deposits, widely transported dust deposits (loess), and the like. Evidence from paleontology is the most important, indeed indispensable, basis for correlation, directly or indirectly, of nearly all rocks from region to region and from continent to continent. This applies to definition of the so-called time-rock units of various ranks, as explained in a following section of this chapter. Also, information given in successive chapters of this book, particularly those describing parts of geologic history classed as belonging to the Phanerozoic Eon, substantiates the dependence on fossils.

Methods of Correlation

In conclusion, it is desirable to make a few general statements about methods of correlation, applicable to both syntopogenic and synchronogenic objectives.

Continuity. One of the simplest and most direct means of establishing correlation of sedimentary rock units is that of establishing their continuity. If rock exposures are sufficiently good, equivalence of individual strata a few miles or even some scores of miles apart may be determined by walking along all the intervening outcrops or perhaps more quickly and painlessly by observing outcrops from a car or tracing them on aerial photographs. By means of borings spaced at reasonably short intervals, beds may be traced reliably underground, and especially by use of techniques such as microscopic examination of well cuttings and correlation of electrical or radioactive well logs, continuity of strata may be es-

tablished for long distances. Correlation by such means, however, is obviously limited to the sedimentary basin or province in which the formations occur; they have no value for establishing relations among provinces or among different continents.

Lithologic similarity. Where absence of continuous outcrops and lack of intervening wells give no basis for correlation between two areas or where sedimentary strata are widely separated by older rocks, as on opposite sides of a broad anticline or mountain belt, similarity of lithology may support correlation. Unless very distinctive peculiarities are duplicated in the two areas, however, correlation on this means alone is very insecure. Observation shows that almost every type of sedimentary deposit occurs somewhere among deposits belonging to each part of past earth history. White sandstone representing a given age at one place is not necessarily represented by white sandstone at another locality 100 miles or even 10 miles distant. On the contrary, we have noted that some sediments, where continuously traceable, show marked lateral variation in lithologic characters.

Structural relation, including sequence. Similarity of structural relations has value for correlations, at least within a single sedimentary province. This refers not so much to the attitude of the beds, which also may have significance, as to the order of sequence of strata. If a succession of beds having differing lithologies and features of stratification is matched elsewhere by a like sequence—especially if thicknesses of respective units approximately correspond—equivalence of the two sections seems probable (Fig. 1.26). Again, correlation on such grounds is not to be expected outside a single sedimentary province.

Organic remains. Similarity of organic remains is useful locally in establishing correlations (Fig. 1.27) and generally is the sole basis of correlation applicable to deposits in different provinces or different continents. With varying precision it indicates equivalence in age. Some marine organisms of the geologic past had a relatively short geologic life span.

for their remains are nowhere found distributed through more than a few feet of sedimentary beds; yet identical forms are known from all the continents. Such short-ranging but widely distributed cosmopolitan types are especially valuable for establishment of tie points between rock successions of different parts of the globe. Many other organisms, including both marine and terrestrial types, are found to occur in two or more separated regions of sedimentation or on different continents, and these, too, are indispensable tools for interregional correlation.

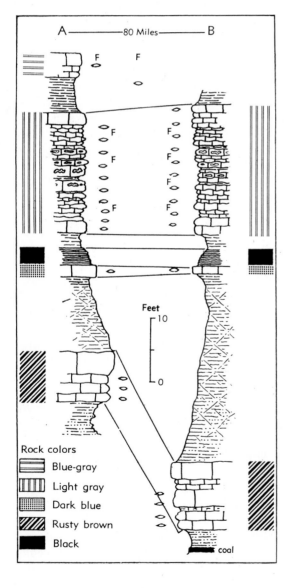

Rock colors

- ▦ Blue-gray
- ▥ Light gray
- ▨ Dark blue
- ▨ Rusty brown
- ■ Black

THE GEOLOGIC COLUMN AND TIME SCALE

Definition and Nature

The term *geologic column* refers to the entire succession of rocks, from oldest to youngest, that is known to occur in a given region or on the earth as a whole. Thus, we may speak of the geologic column of Pennsylvania or of Illinois, meaning all the rock divisions collectively that are known to occur in either of these states. Such a column comprises two types of rock units, as discussed later —one consisting of local rock units defined on a lithologic basis and the other of widely recognized rock divisions defined on a paleontological or time basis (time-rock units). The geologic column of a large area, such as a continent or the whole world, consists of time-rock units solely. It is made up by bringing together in proper order the time-rock divisions recognized in different places so as to represent as completely as possible all known geologic time. It is a composite yardstick.

The geologic time scale consists of major and minor time divisions arranged in proper order, corresponding to segments of the geologic column that are defined on a time basis.

The names applied to main time-rock divisions of the geologic column and to corresponding divisions of the geologic time scale are mostly derived from areas where they were first studied and named in Europe, despite the fact that not all these divisions are best developed on that continent. Ac-

Fig. 1.26 Correlation on the basis of lithologic similarities and identity of sequence. The two successions of Pennsylvanian stratified rocks in eastern Kansas, shown here plotted to scale, may be correlated on the basis of close correspondence of the nature of the rocks, supplemented by identity in the sequence of the strata. The occurrence of many intermediate outcrops of these rocks between *A* (near Melvern) and *B* (Atchison) and tracing outcrops by geologic mapping permit confirmation of the accuracy of the correlation shown. (See Appendix B for explanation of geologic symbols used in sections.)

cordingly, the span of some divisions is modified by data derived from other parts of the
world. The geologic columns of Pennsylvania
and Illinois, unlike this general column, entirely lack some divisions because rocks representing these are not found there.

Classification of Constituents

Rock units. All types of rocks may first be
classified in units that are defined primarily
by their physical nature—that is, lithology.
Usage in North America recognizes as the
basic element in this classification what is
known as a *geologic formation,* which is defined as an assemblage of rocks—igneous, sedimentary, or metamorphic—having generally
like characters of lithology and forming a
logically differentiated part of the rock succession for geologic mapping. A formation consists typically of rocks representing uninterrupted processes of origin. Formations bear
geographic names combined with a lithologic
term, as Coconino Sandstone (Permian, Fig.

1.28), Onondaga Limestone (Devonian),
Mancos Shale (Cretaceous), Milford Granite
(?Devonian). Also assemblages of varied
rocks may be classed as a formation without
mention of a lithologic type, as Jackson Formation (Eocene). Boundaries between adjoining formations should be those that any geologist may identify and trace in the field. They
may coincide with an unconformity or simply
mark the contact between one type of rock
and another. Neither the span nor the boundaries of a rock formation are defined by concepts of time. For example, sand deposited by a
transgressing sea may be classed as belonging
to a single formation despite evidence that
at one locality the sandy deposits are younger
than those at another (Fig. 1.25).

An important persistent subdivision of a formation is known as a *member* and may be
given a geographic name. A rather local subdivision may be designated as a *lentil,* and part
of a formation that extends laterally into a
different formation, eventually pinching out,

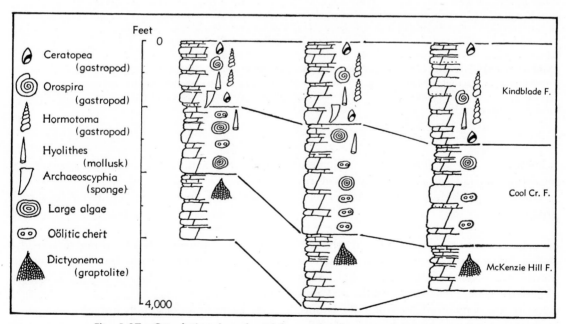

Fig. 1.27 Correlation based mainly on fossil zones. Successions of lithologically very
similar Lower Ordovician rocks in southern Oklahoma can be divided and correlated on the
basis of fossils, even though these are scanty and not highly specialized. (*Modified from C. E.
Decker, Oklahoma Geol. Survey.*)

Fig. 1.28 Rock units exposed in walls of the Grand Canyon. Exceptional opportunity for study of the classification of strata based on their distinctive lithologic characters is found in this region of northern Arizona; the hard rocks form cliffs and weaker rocks crop out in slopes. Successive units from oldest to youngest are as follows: (1) Grand Canyon Sequence, Precambrian, overlain with angular unconformity by (2) or locally by (3); (2) Tapeats Sandstone, followed conformably by (3) Bright Angel Shale and (4) Muav Limestone, all Cambrian; (5) Redwall Limestone, Mississippian, paraconformably on (4); (6) Supai Formation, (7) Hermit Shale, (8) Coconino Sandstone, (9) Toroweap Formation, (10) Kaibab Limestone, all Permian and all bounded below and above by paraconformities or locally by disconformities.

is known as a *tongue*. Two or more adjoining formations having certain important features in common may be assembled together as a *group*.

According to custom, the geographic names of rock units are nouns, and following the recommendation of the American Commission on Stratigraphic Nomenclature, the initial letters of both the geographic name and the rock-unit category are capitalized, as Colorado Group, St. Louis Limestone, Austin Chalk. Abbreviations used throughout the stratigraphic sections and charts published in this book are Dol., Dolostone; F., Formation; Gr., Group; Gyp., Gypsum; Ls., Limestone; Qtzt., Quartzite; Sh.,

Shale; Ss., Sandstone. Lithologic symbols are explained in Appendix B.

Time-rock units. Entirely different from rock units in basis of recognition are divisions of the geologic column known as time-rock units. These are differentiated from one another by the span of geologic time that they represent and are not defined in any way by lithologic characters.

A basic time-rock unit, termed *stage*, comprises beds representing essentially continuous deposition and containing distinctive organic remains that often may be recognized in widely separated parts of the world (Fig. 1.29). In places such beds may be bounded below and above by hiatuses in sedimentation. Seemingly abrupt changes in the nature of organic remains coincide in position with boundaries between adjoining stages.

Larger in span and composed of two or more stages is the time-rock unit called *series*. Variation in the sedimentary record in different continents or in different sedimentary basins of the same continent may lead to definition of series that are only regional in scope.

Major segments of the geologic column, which are deemed to have world-wide application, are known as *systems*. They comprise successive groupings of lesser time-rock units. Each system is broadly characterized by its assemblage of organisms, and in most parts of the world there are discernible breaks between adjacent systems. Owing to continuity of sedimentation in many places, however, problems exist in precise definition of boundaries between the systems in such places.

No generally accepted collective term has been proposed for the rocks of all sorts formed during an era. Accordingly, such units are spoken of simply as Paleozoic rocks or Mesozoic rocks.

For the purpose of distinguishing time-rock units from rock units, geographic or other definitive names employ an adjectival form, and the initial letter of the time-rock category is capitalized, as in Trempealeauan Stage, Croixian Series, Cambrian System.

Time units. Divisions of geologic time are based on the duration of time that corresponds to making of the time-rock units. The time unit corresponding to a stage is designated as *age*, that of a series as an *epoch*, and that of a system as a *period*. An *era* is a long time division comprised of two or more periods and recognized as forming a major chapter in earth history; the eras are partly differentiated and are named from dominant life characters, as Mesozoic, meaning medieval life, the age of dinosaurs.

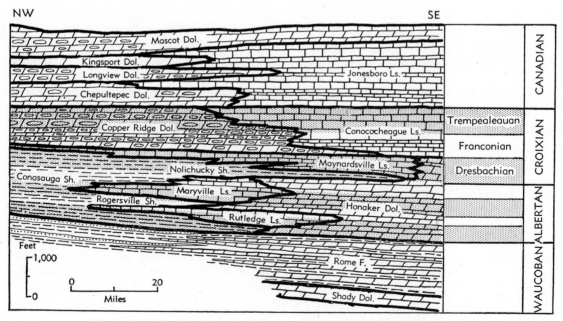

Fig. 1.29 Classification of strata in part of the Virginia-Tennessee region according to rock units and time-rock units. The diagram represents a succession of limestone, dolostone, and shale deposits of Cambrian and Early Ordovician age. The rock units vary in thickness and lateral extent, and in places the different rock units interfinger with one another. The time-rock units shown at the right are determined primarily by characters of fossils; as shown by the alternating light and shaded bands, they do not coincide with lithologic units. (*Data from Howell, Rodgers, and others.*)

The names of time units are written like those of corresponding time-rock units, as Trempealeauan Age, Croixian Epoch, Cambrian Period. Both of these groups of names advantageously employ endings in "-an" or "-ian." This helps to distinguish them from rock-unit names.

Measurement of Geologic Time

Various attempts to measure geologic time have been undertaken. For example, suppose we knew the average number of years required to make a layer of limestone 1 foot thick and likewise knew data for other sorts of sedimentary rocks; we could then multiply figures representing the total thickness of each rock type by appropriate years-per-foot factors and derive a product representing at least a large part of geologic time. Sedimentation rates are much too variable and little known, however, to put much reliance in such a method of computing geologic time.

During the past few decades, atomic research has led to important new methods of measuring geologic time which within reasonable limitations are reliable and definite. These methods depend on the observations that certain radioactive elements—chiefly uranium (U) and thorium (Th)—undergo a slow, spontaneous atomic disintegration, unaffected by any surrounding conditions of heat, pressure, chemical association, or the like. The end products of such decay are lead (Pb) and helium (He). Thus, given an initial quantity of $U = 1$ gram, after 1,000 million years we should have $U = 0.865$ gram and $Pb = 0.116$ gram (neglecting He). At the end of 2,000 million years, $U = 0.747$ gram and $Pb = 0.219$ gram. This is accounted for by the constant decay rate of U, stated in terms of "half life" amounting to 4,560 million years, which means that in this period one half of the original U atoms vanishes by disintegration and in a like period half of the remainder likewise disappears, and so on. Eventually, 1 gram of U yields $Pb = 0.865$ gram and $He = 0.135$ gram.

In principle, this radioactive clock may be compared with the old-fashioned hourglass, in which time is measured by the slow, steady fall of fine sand through a tiny orifice; a given moment within the hour is marked by the quantity of sand fallen to the bottom part of the glass.

Investigation of the age of radioactive minerals and rocks has been advanced materially in recent years by (1) more precise measurement of decay constants, (2) discrimination of different isotopes of elements concerned in radioactive distintegration, and (3) discovery that some substances other than U and Th furnish reliable means of making determinations of geologic age.

Numerous first-published computations of age based on study of radioactive minerals have proved to be erroneous, mainly because knowledge of decomposition rates was insufficiently accurate. Analytical techniques also were deficient. These difficulties now are almost gone. In early work the gross quantity of radioactive source elements (U and Th) in a sample was weighed and compared with the gross amount of radiogenic decay products (as Pb), a procedure that is very crude in the light of subsequent discovery of isotopes involved in radioactive decomposition. An isotope is the variant of an element distinguished by its own atomic weight, signifying the number of protons in each atom.

Now it is known that the isotope U^{238} breaks down to yield the stable end product Pb^{206} and produces no other Pb isotope. Isotope U^{235} decays into Pb^{207} and produces no other Pb isotope. The decomposition rates of U^{238} and U^{235} differ greatly. The isotope Th^{232} yields isotope Pb^{208} at still another decay rate. Thus, in a mineral containing a mixture of these pairs of isotopes ($U^{238} + Pb^{206}$, $U^{235} + Pb^{207}$, $Th^{232} + Pb^{208}$) age measurements based on the different pairs may be used to check each other. For example, in a sample from South Africa the ratio of U^{238} to Pb^{206} indicated an age of 2,675 million years, of U^{235} to Pb^{207} an age of 2,680 million years, and of Th^{232} to Pb^{208} the slightly smaller age of 2,645 million years. An independent computation based on the ratio of Pb^{207} to Pb^{206} in the sample yielded an age determination of 2,680 million years. This close agreement invites confidence as to accuracy of the analyses and computations based on them.

In addition to the so-called lead methods of age determinations, some others have demonstrated usefulness or give promise of yielding reliable measurements. A radioactive isotope of rubidium (Rb^{87}) disintegrates at constant rate to produce strontium (Sr^{87}). Radioactive potassium (K^{40}) decomposes similarly at a uniform rate to make an isotope of argon (A^{40}) and another of calcium (Ca^{40}). Because of their slow decay constants, both the rubidium and potassium methods are suited to study the age of relatively ancient rocks, 500 million years and older. Even though K^{40} amounts to only 0.012 per cent of the potassium found in nature, this element is so widely distributed as a constituent of feldspars and other rock minerals that age studies based on K^{40} should yield much new information of importance.

In quite a separate class is the carbon-14 (C^{14}) age-measurement method because of the relatively rapid rate of its radioactive decay. This adapts it for pin-pointed determinations of age within the last 25,000 years and for making somewhat less precise age computations to 40,000 years ago or a little more. In this part of earth history, the previously described radioactive methods of measurement are valueless. The isotope C^{14} is produced from nitrogen atoms (N^{14}) in the atmosphere by bombardment of neutrons (cosmic rays) coming from outer space. Each N^{14} atom yields one C^{14} atom and a proton. The C^{14} combines with oxygen (O) to make a radioactive carbon dioxide ($C^{14}O_2$), which eventually reaches the earth's surface and is absorbed by living matter. Extensive observations show that distribution of C^{14} around the earth is practically a constant, independent of longitude, latitude, and altitude. When incorporated in organic tissue, such as a piece of wood or fragment of bone, the quantity of C^{14} can be measured

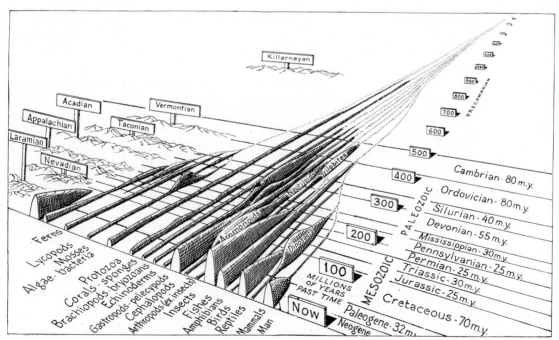

Fig. 1.30 Perspective diagram representing geologic time. The figure shows main divisions and indicates the evolutionary development of plants and animals in the course of earth history. Times of some important mountain building in North America are posted at the left.

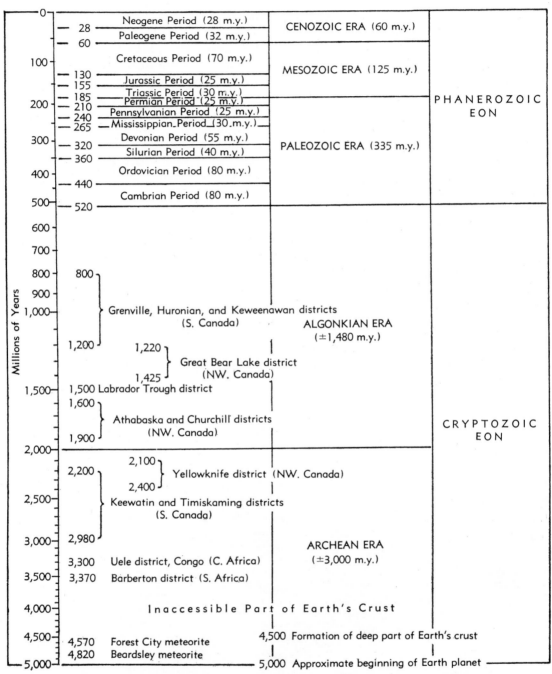

Fig. 1.31 Main divisions of geologic time, with indication of their duration in millions of years. Record of age determinations by radioactive methods is given for several important Precambrian rocks.

accurately. Determination that one half of the originally present atoms disintegrate in 5,720 years (half life) permits computation of the age of the sample.

Carbon-14 samples can be placed accurately in the geologic time sequence indicated by Recent sedimentary deposits containing fossils, but this is not true of the other known radioactive elements (possibly excepting K^{40}). Here lies the main difficulty in calibrating the early parts of geologic time. The U, Th, and other radioactive elements do not occur in fossiliferous stratified rocks but in igneous rocks that intrude the sedimentary strata. How long a time elapsed after the sediments were deposited before the igneous rocks invaded them generally is unknown.

Figures 1.30 and 1.31 show main divisions of geologic time and their approximate duration, utilizing the most reliable age determinations based on radioactive methods.

We may better comprehend the immensity of geologic time by changing its scale so as to bring it within mental grasp. Suppose that 1 year of earth history is represented by 1 second on this reduced time scale. Then 1 minute equals an average human lifetime and barely more than one half hour corresponds to time from the birth of Christ to the present. If we measure time on this scale, starting from January 1, 1960, the date of man's appearance on the earth would be approximately in mid-December, 1959; the beginning of the Mesozoic Era (age of dinosaurs) would fall in the neighborhood of January, 1956; and the beginning of the Cambrian Period would date back only to 1943. If the earth is 5,000 million years old, it originated—on our reduced scale —approximately 150 years ago when James Madison was serving as fourth President of the United States.

READING

Dunbar, C. O., and Rodgers, John, 1957, *Principles of stratigraphy*, John Wiley & Sons, Inc., New York, pp. 116–156, 257–307.

QUESTIONS

1. Referring to Fig. 1.1, explain how the relative age of intrusive igneous rocks with respect to associated rocks is ascertained and in what respects criteria for determining age relationships of intrusive igneous rocks differ from those applicable to extrusive igneous rocks.

2. Referring to Fig. 1.2, how can you account for the uniformity in mineral composition of the grains illustrated? Why are the grains nearly uniform in size and shape?

3. Explain how near- or offshore currents may be effective in concentrating deposits of gravel composed of pebbles and cobbles too coarse to be transported by such currents. What evidence, if any, can you suggest for distinguishing between gravel (conglomerate) deposits formed by streams on land and deposits of similar coarseness produced in shore belts of lakes and seas?

4. What is a bedding plane in stratified rocks, and how is it produced?

5. If crest portions of ripples are somewhat sharply curved in profile as compared with broadly concave profiles of adjacent troughs, as commonly observed, how does this serve to show that some ripple-marked strata are overturned instead of right side up? What features of cross-bedding and mud cracks similarly are usable for identification of upward direction in sequence of strata?

6. What conditions or actions of geologic agencies are requisite for making fossil molds? What is the distinction between internal and external fossil molds? What is a fossil cast? How is a natural fossil cast distinguished from a replacement?

7. How does the concept of time-rock units differ from that used for differentiation of rock units? What conditions or factors are involved in explaining that some rock units coincide in lower and upper limits with time-rock units or are wholly included within such time-rock units as fractions whereas other rock units contain parts of two or more time-rock units?

8. Why is the recognition that different isotopes of uranium exist and that these yield disintegration end products consisting of different isotopes of lead an important advance in making radioactive age determinations of uranium minerals? Why are age measurements based on analyses of carbon-14 valueless for study of Mesozoic and Paleozoic rocks?

2.

EVOLUTION OF LIFE

Primitive lizard-like reptiles (Casea) from Permian of northern Texas.

C. R. Knight, courtesy of Chicago Natural History Museum

The observation that organisms preserved as fossils in successive rock layers of the geologic column differ according to relative position of the layers is the essential basis for recognizing that sedimentary deposits at many different places in the world are equivalent in age. This is part of the foundation of historical geology, as discussed in the previous chapter.

We need now to extend our introductory study by noting the fact that geologic assemblages of plants and animals show an orderly progression in development from prevailingly simple at the start of the record to highly specialized at its present-day point. The nature of this progressive change and explanation of how it occurs are subjects of great importance.

In the early days of biological science, two centuries ago, no botanist or zoologist conceived that each kind of plant and animal was other than a sharply distinct species having characters given to it when the world began. Each such species, he thought, must have been created individually and separately. The host of extinct species represented by fossil organisms was mostly unknown, and the fact of indefinite boundaries of many species was unrecognized. Some naturalists of the eighteenth and early nineteenth centuries, however, noticed the variation of certain species in seeming response to environment and as a result of experiments in breeding. They suggested that differing forms of life could have evolved by some sort of transformation from preexistent organisms. The concept of organic evolution as the explanation of all variation in plants and animals did not have firm scientific footing, however, until 1859, when Charles Darwin published his epoch-making *Origin of Species*. This work contains voluminous incontrovertible documentation of the thesis that all known forms of life are not immutable but on the contrary are subject to evolutionary change. Darwin undertook to explain what he thought was the chief way of producing evolution—unceasing struggle of organisms for existence which leads to varyingly perfect adaptation to their environment and survival of fittest forms. There is need to distinguish between evolution (which Darwin demonstrated and which no competent modern biologist questions) and how evolution is accomplished (which Darwin did not prove and which is not yet adequately known).

Evidence of Evolution

Classification. The manner in which all known organisms can be arranged in categories based on varying degree of similarities conforms with their origin by evolution, as indicated by the treelike pattern which the categories fit. Related species correspond to twigs growing from a common branchlet (a genus), and related genera comprise branchlets of a single branch (a family); the branches are divergent parts of larger and larger branches (orders, classes, phyla) that in turn spread from main trunks (plant and animal kingdoms). The ascending series of organic groups that show increasing complexity of organization is readily explainable as the product of evolution but not rationally accountable otherwise.

Biochemical relationships. Living matter of whatever sort, as distinguished from nonliving, is characterized by the highly complex chemical structure of its basic constituent molecules, which are mainly formed of carbon, hydrogen, and oxygen. Also, living matter has the properties of growth, response to environmental stimuli, and reproduction. The substance of this matter, called *protoplasm,* is not a particular chemical compound but a mixture of interdependent molecular structures, of which some are in process of more complex organization and some are products of decomposition. These common attributes and the continuity in kind and degree of increasing specialization are strong evidence that all organisms are derived from preexisting living organisms without break. We are ignorant of the conditions of ultimate beginning of the physicochemical chain of life, but that it is an unbroken chain of unnumbered links and directions of branching we cannot doubt.

A biochemical proof of relationship among branches of the tree of life is the close correspondence between quantity of precipitate obtainable from the blood of one animal when tested with that of another and degree of kinship of these animals as inferred from their evolutionary differentiation. For example, the blood of man shows only a relatively small amount of precipitate when tested with serum from a lizard but a distinctly larger amount when the serum comes from a pig; progressively increased precipitates are obtained by testing human blood with serums from the lemur (a very primitive primate), monkeys, and anthropoid apes such as the gorilla.

Structural resemblance. The structural organization of plants and animals exhibits similarities in inverse proportion to their evolutionary differentiation. This is seen in structures of the stem, leaf, flower, and seed of various plants but is most readily apparent in comparative study of the anatomy of many animals. All limb-bearing vertebrates, for example, possess the same basic skeletal plan consisting of skull, backbone, shoulder and pelvic girdles, and four limbs formed of similarly arranged bones (Fig. 2.1). In proportion to their relationship, these animals also show exact correspondence in the nature of their musculature, digestive and reproductive organs, circulatory system, and nervous system. Such uniformity of pattern is readily explained as an inheritance of common evolutionary origin but is inexplicable otherwise.

Sequence of growth stages. It is an interesting fact that in varying degree early growth stages of animals reflect adult life forms of the stock from which they are descended. Thus, the human embryo, for example, passes through blastula and gastrula stages characteristic of fully formed primitive invertebrates, and subsequently it has well-defined gill arches like those of a fish; the development of the circulatory system repeats characteristic features seen in fishes, amphibians, and reptiles; the embryo is far advanced before it begins to take on characters that may differentiate it from other mammals. The generalization that the life history of an individual repeats racial history of the group to which the animal belongs is not wholly true because there are many necessary qualifications and variations. This so-called biogenetic law, that "ontogeny recapitulates phylogeny," does agree with many observations on the nature of successive growth stages and supports evolutionary concepts.

Vestigial structures. The organic world contains innumerable examples of once useful organs or other structures that in the course of evolution have become no longer functional. They persist as vestiges, like man's vermiform appendix, hidden little bony tail, ear-moving muscles, and the pineal body in the skull, which is remnant of a third eye that is still well developed in some lizards. Unless such structures become adapted to serve other needs, they are likely to disappear ultimately. These vestiges comprise one type of docu-

mentation of evolution because we can recognize them as traces of formerly useful parts.

Experimentation. Man has proved by trial and error, by breeding and selection, that he can change the characters of plant and animal species radically. Tulips and other kinds of flowers, hybrid corn, many special types of wheat, vegetables, shrubs, fruit, trees—all these have been modified in various ways because of commercial advantage, aesthetic appeal, or curiosity. Animals, too, have been specialized

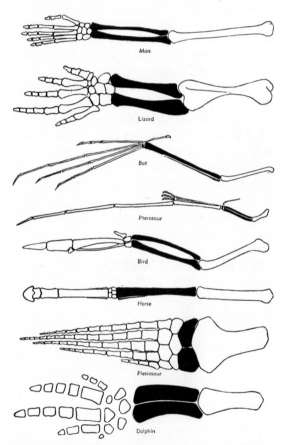

Fig. 2.1 Skeletal structure of the front limb of various animals showing correspondence (homology) of component bones. Each has a single upper limb bone (humerus), two bones or remnants of them (radius, ulna) which are represented in black on the diagram, wristbones, and fingers. The arm of man and the lizard is unspecialized, whereas that of the bat, pterosaur, and bird is modified for flight in the air, that of the horse for swift running, and that of the plesiosaur and dolphin for swimming.

in divergent ways. Differences between a large draft horse, like a percheron, a race horse, and a shetland pony are greater than between some species, but they are far surpassed by differences of every sort shown by innumerable breeds of dogs (Fig. 2.2). It is hard to imagine that a huge mastiff and tiny pomeranian, a greyhound and a dachshund, and many others are artificial derivatives of a common ancestral stock. If nature has done and does what experimentation by man has shown can be accomplished in changing organisms, this is in accord with evolution.

Paleontological evidence. More convincing than any other testimony as to actuality of the evolution of life forms from relatively simple to advanced types is afforded by fossils. These are the incontrovertible records of organisms that formerly lived on the earth (Figs. 2.3, 2.4). Their structural features, in so far as determinable from hard parts that have been preserved, show the sort of differentiation that had been attained by various plant and animal groups at a given stage in earth history, and comparison of this with earlier and later stages demonstrates the direction of evolutionary modifications (Figs. 2.5, 2.6).

The fossils may thus be viewed as documents having various degrees of antiquity that are found in the geological archives. They show that forms of life in the comparatively recent past are not greatly different from those living today; on land the dominant animals are mammals that differ in kind but belong to stocks living today, the plants include abundant flowering trees and shrubs, and marine life includes invertebrates that are closely similar to types represented by shells washed up on modern shore lines. More ancient deposits contain organic remains which differ obviously from living forms and which include only moderately specialized types of plants and animals. Still older rocks yield more primitive organisms, until among the oldest known are only marine plants and a few kinds of invertebrates.

The paleontological record thus furnishes samples of successive populations ranging in age from the distant past down to the present, and these populations show gradual change of

Fig. 2.2 Some types of dogs produced by breeding. Dogs well illustrate the range in shape, size, and various aptitudes produced by man under controlled conditions of evolution.

Fig. 2.3 Quarry site and some of the bones of extinct mammals excavated from Neogene strata in western Nebraska. Miocene deposits at Agate Springs, Nebraska, locally contain well-preserved skeletal remains of thousands of plains animals belonging to species that long ago disappeared from North America. (*Courtesy of American Museum of Natural History.*)

many sorts conforming to postulates of the theory of evolution. The forms of life have advanced from the simple to the complex and from the unspecialized to the specialized, but many primitive types of organisms have persisted with little change (Fig. 2.7). So-called missing links in the chain of evolutionary advance are represented by certain fossils, such as the half-lizard half-bird creature that helps define the reptilian ancestry of the birds.

Mode of Evolution

To know why organisms evolve and how evolutionary changes are accomplished is important because one who grasps these things can far better comprehend the history of life and varying physical conditions that make organic environments in past geologic periods. However, answers to these questions require appraisal of voluminous, complex data in the

Fig. 2.4 A fossil fish of Eocene age. Skeletons of the fishes and many types of higher vertebrates found in the rocks are invaluable paleontological documents that define the actual course of evolutionary development. Comparative study of such remains may lead to conclusions on the ancestral relationships of the organisms.

Fig. 2.5　Restoration of a fossil lobe-finned fish.
This fish (*Eusthenopteron*) of Devonian age undoubtedly represents the sort of ancestor from which amphibians and higher four-legged animals were evolved.
Like the modern lung fish, the lobe-finned fishes were
able to breathe air and thus could survive out of the
water. The fleshy fins are rudiments of limbs. (*Courtesy of American Museum of Natural History.*)

Fig. 2.6　Very early type of amphibian. The amphibians differ essentially from air-breathing fishes in
having definite well-developed limbs, with which they
can waddle about sluggishly on land. They cannot
travel far from streams or ponds, however, because
their eggs must be laid in water. This restoration
shows a small Pennsylvanian amphibian (*Diplovertebron*). (*Courtesy of American Museum of Natural
History.*)

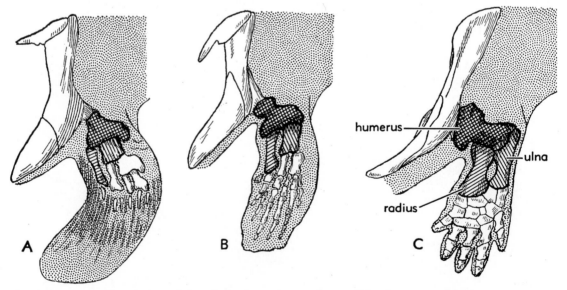

Fig. 2.7　Structural evolution of fore limbs in early vertebrates. The diagrams indicate
that no great change was needed in deriving the limbs of four-footed animals from appendages
of the lobe-finned fishes as ancestors.——*A*. Devonian lobe-finned fish.——*B*. Hypothetical
intermediate animal between fish and amphibian.——*C*. Late Paleozoic amphibian, which has
bone structure of the limbs essentially like that of reptiles, birds, and mammals. (*W. K. Gregory, from K. F. Mather, Sons of the Earth, W. W. Norton & Company, Inc., New York.*)

fields of genetics, ecology, biogeography, neo-biology, and paleontology, and despite much progress, there are still many uncertainties. We confine attention to organic variation, transmittal of variation by heredity, and natural selection.

Organic variation and heredity. No two individuals among plants or animals are precisely identical, however closely they may be related. Offspring differ slightly from parents, and members of any given generation vary among themselves. The bulk of population belonging to a species living at any time has characters, however, that are grouped closely around a mean, and only a small fraction deviates considerably from this average. It is recognized that two sets of factors are expressed in variation within a species or other systematic unit, one being the inherited characters (de-

pendent on features of the germ plasm) and the other being effects of environment. The latter may be repeated in successive generations but, according to tests by experimentation, are not (as postulated by Lamarck) transmissible as acquired characters. Features transmitted by the germ plasm reproduce themselves in successive generations, and if adapted to their surroundings, they tend to persist, thus leading to evolution. Much has been learned of the nature of chromosomes and genes and the mechanism of heredity, but it is not appropriate here to review studies in the field of genetics.

Natural selection. Just as the selection by man of plants or animals having desired sorts of variation permits segregation and propagation of these separately from rejected types, nature continually operates to favor the ex-

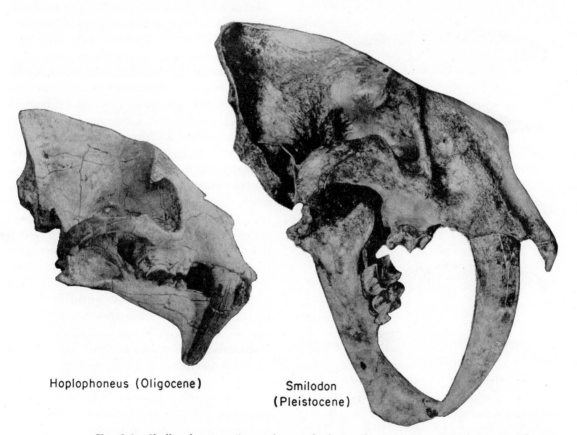

Hoplophoneus (Oligocene)

Smilodon
(Pleistocene)

Fig. 2.8 Skulls of two extinct saber-toothed cats from western United States. Adaptive specialization is shown especially by characters of the teeth, which are suited for grasping and tearing flesh. Also, the teeth were notably reduced in number as compared with earlier mammals that include their ancestors. (*Courtesy of American Museum of Natural History.*)

istence of organisms which are suited to their environment or which can best compete with their neighbors. Poorly adapted organisms and those which are weaker than their associates in any attribute (such as physical strength, protective features, intelligence, effectiveness in mating, and many others) are at disadvantage and tend to be weeded out by nature. This natural selection is unquestionably effective, as pointed out by Darwin, in developing and perpetuating differences in plants and animals, whatever may be the germ-plasm mechanism that leads to transmittal of characters. Populations may thus diverge so as to produce distinct species and genera, and such differentiation may be both contemporaneous and sequent in time; also, some systematic groups may exhibit progressive gradual change while maintaining comparative stability in the limit of variation of the successive populations. Fitness for a given mode of life and effective adaptation to environment are important factors in the operation of evolution.

Expression of Evolution

Adaptive divergence. Both plants and animals of many sorts show remarkable changes in form, structure, growth habits, and even mode of reproduction in becoming adapted to different climatic environment, type of food supply, or mode of living (Fig. 2.8). This divergence in response to evolution is commonly expressed by altering the form and function of some part or parts of the organism, the original identity of which is clearly discernible. For example, the creeping foot of the snail is seen in related marine pteropods to be modified into a flapping organ useful for swimming, and it is changed into prehensile arms that bear suctorial disks in the squids and other cephalopods. The limbs of various mammals are modified according to several different modes of life—for swift running (cursorial) as in the horse and antelope, for swinging in trees (arboreal) as in the monkeys, for digging (fossorial) as in the moles and gophers, for flying (volant) as in the bats, for swimming (aquatic) as in the seals, whales, and dolphins, and for other adaptations. The structures or organs that show main change in connection with this adaptive divergence are commonly identified readily as homologous, in spite of great alterations. Thus, the finger and wristbones of a bat and whale, for instance, have virtually nothing in common except that they are definitely equivalent elements of the mammalian limb.

Adaptive convergence. The opposite of adaptive divergence is an interesting and fairly common expression of evolution. This is adaptive convergence. Whereas related groups of organisms take on widely different characters in becoming adapted to unlike environments in the case of adaptive divergence, we find that unrelated groups of organisms exhibit adaptive convergence when they adopt simi-

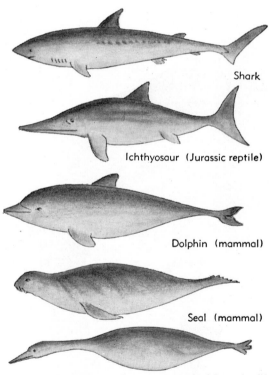

Shark

Ichthyosaur (Jurassic reptile)

Dolphin (mammal)

Seal (mammal)

Hesperornis (Cretaceous toothed diving bird)

Fig. 2.9 Adaptive convergence in the form of swimming animals. Fishes and other animals, such as reptiles, mammals, and birds, which have become specially fitted for life in the water tend to develop a streamlined cigar-shaped form. Except the shark, the animals shown here are air breathers, but none could get around efficiently on land.

Fig. 2.10   Restoration of part of a Pennsylvanian coal swamp. Except for their very large size, a majority of the plants correspond closely to living types of lycopods, horsetail rushes, and ferns. The giant dragonfly resembles modern insects of this sort but actually is much more primitive in structural features. (*Courtesy of Chicago Natural History Museum.*)

lar modes of life or become suited for special sorts of environments (Fig. 2.9). For example, invertebrate marine animals living firmly attached to the sea bottom or to some foreign object tend to develop a subcylindrical or conical form. This is illustrated by coral individuals, by many sponges, and even by the diminutive tubes of bryozoans. Adaptive convergence in taking this coral-like form is shown by some brachiopods and pelecypods that grew in fixed position. More readily appreciated is the streamlined fitness of most fishes for moving swiftly through water; they have no neck, the contour of the body is smoothly curved so as to give minimum resistance, and the chief propelling organ is a powerful tail fin. The fact that some fossil reptiles (ichthyo-saurs) and modern mammals (whales, dolphins) are wholly fishlike in form is an expression of adaptive convergence, for these air-breathing reptiles and mammals, which are highly efficient swimmers, are not closely related to fishes. Unrelated or distantly related organisms that develop similarity of form are sometimes designated as homeomorphs (having same form).

Trends of Evolution

Historical geology throws light on the trend of evolutionary changes that characterize both plant and animal groups. The record of life that is preserved in successive sedimentary formations shows how various stocks began as unspecialized offshoots of antecedent organisms, became gradually differentiated, and in general eventually vanished. The factor of time, stretching out through hundred-thousands or millions of years, may be observed in its effects on organic populations. Successful adaptations to the struggle of living under various conditions of physical environment, availability of food supply, interference by competitors and enemies, and abundance in survival of new generations commonly result in increase in average size of individuals and in a branching that gradually produces new species and genera. As divergent branches become specialized, they tend to be less and less alterable, and after reaching a certain culmination, they die out.

A survey of the record of life permits the following generalizations concerning evolu-tionary trends. Organisms having simple structures tend to persist; those characterized by complex structures tend to be short-lived. Loss of acquired structures is permanent; for example, air-breathing vertebrates, which are all indirect descendants of fishes, cannot revert to respiration by means of gills. On the whole, plant and animal stocks have advanced progressively in complexity of structure during geological history, but simple forms of life have persisted also (Fig. 2.10). Many specialized branches have prospered for a time and then disappeared. Among most organisms, the life history of the individual recapitulates with varying clearness and completeness the evolutionary changes belonging to its branch of the plant or animal world.

READINGS

BURNETT, R. W., 1947, *Life through the ages,* Stanford University Press, Stanford, Calif. (47 pp., illus.).
Nontechnical account of animals illustrating evolution.

COLBERT, E. H., 1951, *The dinosaur book,* McGraw-Hill Book Company, Inc., New York (156 pp., illus.).
Excellent and simple but authoritative descriptions of the dinosaurs, explaining evolutionary trends.

LUCAS, F. A., 1922, Animals of the past, *Handbook* 4, 6th ed., American Museum Natural History, New York (207 pp., illus.).
Widely read popular description of main groups of animals preserved as fossils.

LULL, R. S., 1931, *Fossils,* The University Society, New York (114 pp., illus.).
Brief popular presentation, well written.

———, 1947, *Organic evolution,* rev. ed., The Macmillan Company, New York (744 pp., illus.).
One of the best general works, containing numerous chapters specially worthy of reading.

MOORE, R. C., 1957, Modern methods of paleoecology: *Am. Assoc. Petroleum Geologists, Bull.,* vol. 41, pp. 1775–1801.
Discusses environmental factors affecting fossil organisms.

MOY-THOMAS, J. A., 1939, *Palaeozoic fishes,* Chemical Publishing Company, Inc., New York (149 pp., illus.).
Excellent treatment of early fossil fishes and their evolution.

SCHEELE, W. E., 1954, *Prehistoric animals,* The World Publishing Company, Cleveland (125 pp., illus.).
Good elementary presentation.

SIMPSON, G. G., 1953, *Life of the past,* Yale University Press, New Haven, Conn. (198 pp., illus.).
Excellent nontechnical descriptions with attention given to evolution.

———, 1953, *The major features of evolution,* Columbia University Press, New York (434 pp., illus.).
An authoritative, somewhat technical discussion based mainly on paleontology.

QUESTIONS

1. What is the readily determined basis for arranging kinds of organisms in a treelike pattern for expression of their mutual resemblances and differences? Why is such a pattern best explained as a consequent of evolution?

2. Referring to Fig. 2.1, what parts of the fore limbs are chiefly affected by adaptations to modes of living in the case of (a) bats, (b) pterosaurs, (c) birds, (d) horses, (e) plesiosaurs, and (f) dolphins? Why is the structure of the fore limb in lizards and man interpreted as unspecialized?

3. How does paleontologic evidence, taking account of morphologic characters and their record of occurrence in successive parts of geologic time, serve to confirm conclusions relating to lines of evolutionary differentiation?

4. Explain how adaptive convergence is distinguished from adaptive divergence, noticing especially the relation of each to zoologic affinities of the animals concerned.

3.

THE BEGINNING OF THE EARTH

One of the "island universes" lying far outside of
our stellar galaxy.

Courtesy of Lick Observatory, University of California

The Earth is a nearly perfect sphere, slightly flattened at the poles and bulging at the equator. It is one of a family of bodies that revolve about the Sun in the same direction and in nearly a common plane. This family comprises nine planets (including the recently discovered far-distant Pluto) and some 1,300 smaller bodies called *planetoids*. The four inner planets (Mercury, Venus, Earth, Mars) are smaller and denser than the outer ones (Jupiter, Saturn, Uranus, Neptune) except Pluto, which seems to have about the size of the Earth. Most of the planets are accompanied by one or more moons which revolve in nearly circular orbits in the direction of the planet's rotation and nearly in the plane of their equators. The Earth's moon is exceptional in magnitude as compared with its planet in that its orbital plane is distinctly inclined to the Earth's equator, lying nearly in the common plane of revolution of all the planets.

The dominant body in the part of the universe where the Earth moves through space is the Sun, 93 million miles distant from the Earth. The Sun is one of the lesser stars, a white-hot gaseous sphere having a diameter of 864,000 miles and a mass 332,000 times greater than that of the Earth. It rotates once in 25 of the Earth's days, turning slowly in the same direction as that in which the planets revolve about the Sun; the plane of the Sun's equator is inclined about 7 degrees to the mean plane of the planets' orbits. The huge energy and heat of the Sun's mass and its enormous radiation of energy into space are its outstanding characters. Measurements of the radiation show that the temperature near the Sun's surface is about 6000°C., but that of its center is estimated at 30 to 60 million degrees C. The surface heat is sufficient to vaporize any known substance and on Earth is matched only momentarily and microscopically on nature's scale by the explosion of an atom bomb. Explosive energies within the Sun are judged to represent a splitting and reforming of atoms with inconceivable rapidity and greatness of scale, explosive disruption of the Sun's mass being prevented only by its enormous gravity. Even so, energy radiated into space corresponds to a loss of mass amounting to more than 4 million tons per second—a radiation of which the Earth receives only one 2-billionth part. Truly, the planets are very minor objects as compared with this star, our Sun, that governs their motions. Also, the largest of the four inner planets, which is the Earth, is very small as compared with Jupiter, which has 318 times its mass and 1,312 times its volume (Figs. 3.1 to 3.5).

The Sun and planets, along with their attendant moons, comprise the main parts of the Solar System. Lesser bodies, such as a great flock of comets and a host of insignificant stony or metallic objects, termed *meteorites,* also belong to the system. The direction of infall of meteorites on the Earth, however, indicates that many of them are foreign to the Solar System. From the standpoint of Earth study, the most significant observation we may make about the Solar System is its essential unity, which is manifested in many features additional to those mentioned here. It is inconceivable that conditions or events that produced the Earth were not the same as those that made the other planets.

Origin of the Solar System

Two-star hypotheses. A plausible explanation of how our Solar System may have originated is given by two Americans—geologist T. C. Chamberlin, and astronomer F. R. Moulton—and two British scientists—astronomer James Jeans and geophysicist Harold Jeffreys. The basic feature of their hypothesis is that all the planets and lesser bodies of the Solar System that now move around the Sun were formerly parts of the Sun itself. They comprise fragments of Sun matter that have been explosively ejected from it as a result of disturbance caused by the passage of another sun —that is, a star—at a distance near enough to affect our Sun's gravitative pull. Such an event must have happened a long time ago, and the subsequent onward flight of this presumed visitor has now carried it so far that it cannot be identified among stars of the heavens (Fig. 3.6).

Known facts about the masses and constitution of stars, including our Sun, indicate that even if the closest approach of star to Sun was several billion miles, the effective inward pull of the Sun's gravity would be so weakened on the side facing the star and opposite to it (after the manner of tides) that explosive eruptions of some material in these directions would be inevitable. Some eruptions would begin as the star approached, reach culminating violence while the star was near it, and diminish as the star receded into space. Changing relative positions of the star with respect to the Sun would cause successive ejections of Sun matter to be thrown out in different directions much as when the nozzle of a hose is rotated sideward. The dispersed material would be distributed essentially in a plane

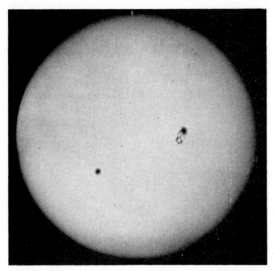

Fig. 3.1   The star that we call Sun, which controls movements of the Earth and other planets and which almost surely is their parent. The Sun is composed of materials that are identified also on the Earth, but at the enormously high temperatures prevailing in the Sun, all substances are incandescent gases in turbulent movement. Sun spots, such as the two large ones shown in this photograph, are centers of vortical disturbance in which upwardly projected matter is cooled by sudden expansion, so that it appears dark in comparison with adjacent parts of the Sun's face; they exhibit magnetic properties, and streams of electrons emitted at times of sun-spot activity affect atmospheric conditions on the Earth. (*Courtesy of Mount Wilson Observatory.*)

defined by the star's course with respect to the Sun. Undoubtedly, some of the ejected material would fall back into the Sun, but the Sun's own motion and the deflection due to the side pull of the star during its passage would cause much of the dispersed material to revolve in highly elliptical orbits around the Sun. The planes of these orbits would very nearly coincide.

Organization of the disrupted Sun material into definite planetary bodies and the evolution of near circularity of revolutionary motion are variously explained. According to Chamberlin and Moulton, centers of planetary growth were major masses or nuclei of Sun matter, which by reason of their own gravitative pull served to collect the lesser bodies, which they call *planetesimals*. Infall of planetesimals would gradually add to the mass of

planetary nuclei and eventually sweep up most of the independently revolving small bodies. Analysis of the net effect of infalling planetesimals proves that they would tend to throw the nuclei into more and more nearly circular orbits and induce forward rotation of the planets, features that characterize our observed system.

According to Jeans and Jeffreys, however, initiation of the planets is presumed to depend essentially on the breaking into segments of what were originally nearly continuous long streamers of incandescent gaseous matter. On this hypothesis, there is relatively little need for subsequent sweeping up of planetesimals. If, in agreement with the concept of successive solar ejections under the influence of the passing star, the largest volume of ejected matter should have been intermediate between the inner and outer parts, and if lighter elements tended generally to be expelled farthest from the sun, peculiarities in the distribution, size, and specific gravity of the planets would find reasonable explanation.

The Earth and neighboring inner planets are small, relatively heavy, and much more closely spaced than the large, light outer planets, dominated by Jupiter, which are widely spaced. Gradually acquired circularity of the planetary orbits is ascribed by Jeans and Jeffreys to the cumulating resistance effects of a gaseous atmosphere that is supposed to have surrounded the Sun and to have been composed mostly of light materials that leaked away from the bolts of ejected matter.

Satellites of the larger planets represent segregations of originally gaseous materials that were ejected from the planets by tidal disruption. This disruption was induced by the Sun during first passages of the planets in elliptical orbits that brought them relatively near the Sun. Thus, in miniature they represent processes that produced the planets themselves. Certain satellites that depart from rule, as to the plane and direction of their revolution, may be explained as the result of capture by one planet from another during early stages in development of the system.

The Earth's Moon, which has $\frac{1}{81}$ of the

mass of the Earth, is unusually great in relative magnitude—in fact, the Earth and Moon may be considered as a double planet, composed of two very unequal parts. Mathematical calculations show that the Moon may have been formed by splitting apart from the Earth as a result of tidal stresses when the combined body was in a liquid or semiliquid state. Recession of the Moon to its present distance of 283,000 miles from the Earth and slowing of its rotation until it keeps always the same face toward the Earth are effects of the mutual tidal retardation of the Earth and the Moon. The Moon is too small to hold an atmosphere, and its crater-marked surface and broad lava-like plains are unaffected by weathering. The larger craters have diameters exceeding 100 miles, and they have circular rims up to 20,000 feet in altitude. Radiating streaks extend outward for hundreds of miles from some of them. Perhaps these features denote a former stage of great volcanic activity, but they have been interpreted also as marks due to infall of bodies such as large planetesimals. A buckshot falling on mud may produce an identical pattern (Figs. 3.7 to 3.10).

One-star hypotheses. Explanation of the origin of the Earth and other planets by evolution of a single star—our Sun—without interference or disturbance of another heavenly body was generally accepted by scientists of the nineteenth century. A German philosopher Kant, in 1755, and a French mathematician LaPlace, in 1796, published closely similar hypotheses, which postulated that the Solar System was derived from condensation of an enormously dispersed gaseous atmosphere surrounding the Sun. Increased rotational velocity of this atmosphere during condensation was assumed to have produced a discoidal shape, the plane of the disk coinciding with that of the Sun's equator. When velocity at the periphery of the disk reached a critical point, it was judged that centrifugal force would throw off part of the gas as a ring and that breaking up of this ring would produce a planet. The planet would revolve around the Sun in the path of the former ring. Successive rings would make planets nearer to the Sun, and ultimately

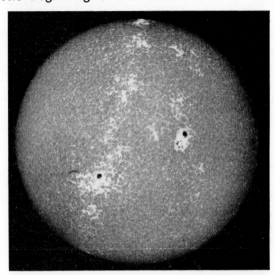

Fig. 3.2 Appearance of the Sun as photographed in the light of its incandescent calcium. The mottled aspect of the Sun's disk in this view records the uneven concentration of the element (calcium) in the Sun's atmosphere that furnished the monochromatic light selected for making the photograph. It indicates the agitated condition of matter near the Sun's surface, which is in contrast to the relative stability of the Earth's atmosphere. The same sun spots that appear in Fig. 3.1 are seen in this photograph. (*Courtesy of Mount Wilson Observatory.*)

nearly all gas not gathered to make the planets would condense into the Sun. According to this hypothesis, the Sun should possess almost all the energy of angular motion (moment of momentum) of the System, inasmuch as the Sun's mass is equal to about 99 times that of all planets put together. When it was learned that the planets possess 98 per cent of the total angular momentum of the System—not to mention other difficulties—it seemed necessary to abandon the hypothesis of Kant and LaPlace.

Recently, several European and American scientists (Alfven, 1942; Berlage, 1940; ter Haar, 1948; Weiszacker, 1944; Whipple, 1947) have developed hypotheses based on condensation of gaseous and solid particles in a greatly expanded envelope surrounding the Sun. Utilizing present knowledge of physics in relation to magnetism and condensation of heated vapors of varying composition and temperature, plausible explanations are being developed, for not only the distribution of angular momentum but the spacing and specific gravities of the planets and peculiarities of the satellites. So it may be that origin and evolution of the Solar System again will be judged to follow the general pattern of the hypothesis introduced by Kant and LaPlace.

The most abundant elements in the Earth's crust (98.6 per cent composed of oxygen, silicon, aluminum, iron, calcium, sodium, potassium, and magnesium) all occur in the Sun with relative proportions nearly the same, but as a whole, the Sun is composed much more largely of light elements (chiefly hydrogen and helium) and has a computed specific gravity

(1.4) amounting to only one-fourth that of the Earth (5.5). Accordingly, some hypotheses of the origin of the Solar System stress the conclusion that the Sun and planets are parts of a single evolutionary process, possibly duplicated by millions of other stars-with-planets in the galaxy of the Milky Way to which we belong. The postulate that the whole system developed by differentiation of an interstellar gas or dust cloud assigns nearly equal antiquity to the Sun and Earth, whereas supposition that the planets (with attendant satellites) are products of explosive eruption from the Sun indicates that the Earth was made millions of years after the birth of the Sun. Origin of the

Fig. 3.3 Explosively ejected prominences of Sun substances that reach a height of 140,000 miles. These eruptions are not visible when the intense sunlight of ordinary daytime is diffused by the Earth's atmosphere, but they may be seen during a complete solar eclipse or by artificially blocking out the Sun's disk in a telescope. The small white disk represents the size of the Earth. (*Courtesy of Mount Wilson Observatory.*)

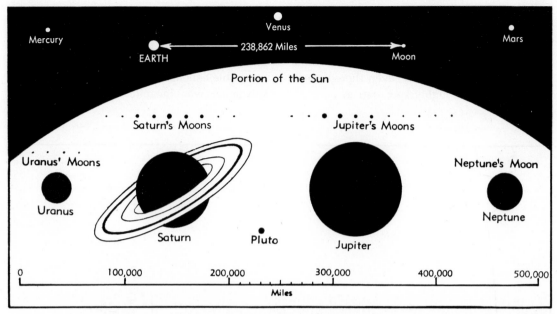

Fig. 3.4 The size of planetary bodies compared with a portion of the Sun. The four lesser planets, which are nearest to the Sun, are shown in the upper part of the diagram; they have relatively high density (3.7 to 5.5), whereas the large outer planets are low in density (0.7 to 1.4). The Earth's Moon is unusually large as compared with the planet around which it revolves, but it is matched in size by some of the moons of Jupiter and Saturn and by Neptune's lone moon.

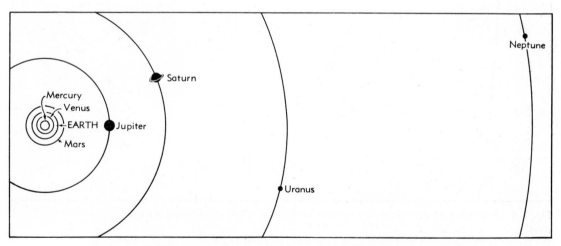

Fig. 3.5 Orbits of the planets, showing wide spacing of the outer planets in comparison to the inner ones. The planets revolve around the Sun in nearly circular orbits that lie in almost coincident planes. The size of the planets is exaggerated 100 times with respect to the scale of the orbits.

planets, not from the Sun, but from violent disruption of a much larger, hotter star that formerly made a binary pair with the Sun has been advocated and supported by plausible arguments from astronomy, even though some presumptions are highly speculative.

Molten Earth State

That our Earth passed through a molten state early in its history is a seemingly inescapable conclusion. Initially, its Sun-derived substance was incandescent and white-hot;

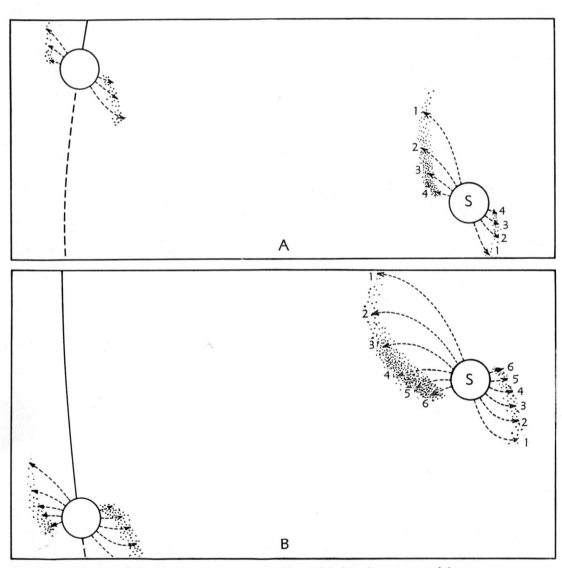

Fig. 3.6 Beginning of the planetary system caused by tidal disturbance exerted by a passing star on our Sun (S). Two stages (*A, B*) in the postulated passage of the star and Sun are shown in the diagrams, and movement of ejected matter from the Sun is represented by dotted lines that are numbered in order of ejection. Curvature of the lines reflects deviation of the ejected matter under influence of differential pull by the passing star. The dispersed Sun matter, consisting of planetesimals (Chamberlin-Moulton) or a gaseous streamer (Jeans-Jeffreys), is thrown into orbital movement around the Sun, and segregation into planetary bodies is inaugurated.

Fig. 3.7 Part of the Moon's surface. This photograph of the Moon in the first quarter shows the large relatively smooth dark areas called *seas* (although no water exists on the Moon) and lighter areas containing innumerable craters. (*Courtesy of Lick Observatory, University of California.*)

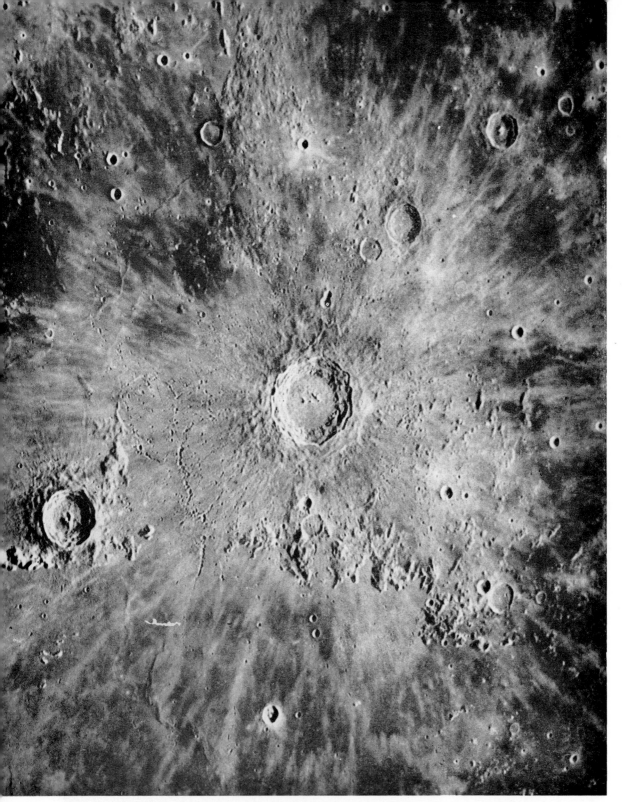

Fig. 3.8 Craters of the Moon. The large crater in the center of the view is Copernicus, nearly 100 miles in diameter and having a rim approximately 20,000 feet high. The central peaks in this and other craters and the prominent radiating streaks may reflect infall of planetary bodies; through absence of weathering, surface features on the Moon may be preserved intact indefinitely. (*Courtesy of Lick Observatory, University of California.*)

probably it was largely gaseous. According to one view, this earliest phase of Earth development was characterized by a total mass much smaller than that of the Earth today, and because of such small mass, it is thought to have cooled rather rapidly to a liquid and finally a solid state. Increase of size through infall of planetesimal matter, if rapid, would have developed such heat of impact that the Earth would have remained molten during most of its growth; on the other hand, if infall of matter was slow, as postulated by Chamberlin, the Earth may have remained solid during growth.

If the Earth's share of Sun matter was at outset essentially the same as its present mass, a molten state must have persisted for a considerable time. Jupiter and the other large planets are still molten, but the smaller planets have solidified. Strong indication that the Earth was molten at a time when it had attained about its present mass is found in the high degree of density stratification within its body, as indicated by seismic and other observations. The outer Earth crust has an average specific gravity of about 3.0, whereas deeper layers increase progressively in density to about 11.0 in the heavy core. The whole Earth averages 5.5 in specific gravity. The arrangement of densities is readily understood if the globe was once molten, for heaviest substances would come to accumulate below the lighter ones, just as in molten ore the metal sinks and the rocky slag rises.

Origin of Continents and Ocean Basins

Unevenness in surface configuration of the rock body of the Earth, or lithosphere, is represented by the differentiation of great land and water areas of the globe. Continents occupy about one-fourth of the Earth's surface and oceanic areas roughly three-fourths. The continents are protuberant parts of the lithosphere, and the oceans occupy relatively depressed parts. The vertical span from the top of the highest mountain peak (Mt. Everest in

Fig. 3.9 A nickel-iron meteorite from Texas weighing 1,630 pounds. Meteorites comprise metallic and stony masses that become incandescent and luminous by reason of friction in their passage through the Earth's atmosphere. Some millions of these bodies are reported to collide with the Earth daily, but a large majority of these disintegrate before reaching the Earth's surface. Some may comprise planetesimals, but the velocity and direction of others indicate origin outside the planetary system. (*Courtesy of Peabody Museum, Yale University.*)

Fig. 3.10 Meteor crater near Winslow, Ariz. This air view admirably shows the steep walls and floor of the bowl-shaped cavity, which is 550 feet deep and 4,000 feet across; the elevated rim rises more than 100 feet above the smooth plain that surrounds the crater. Many tons of metecritic iron have been found in and near the crater. The crater is judged to have been formed by impact and explosion of a large meteorite. (*Courtesy of Spence Air Photos.*)

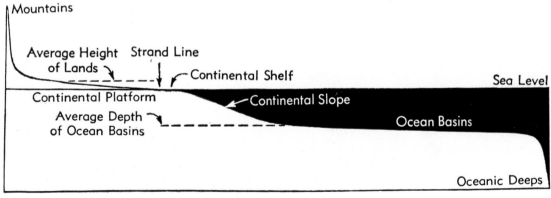

Fig. 3.11 Profile showing configuration of the surface of the lithosphere. The relative height of continental areas and depth of ocean basins are shown quantitatively, the width of the diagram representing 100 per cent of the Earth's surface. The small fraction of the surface comprised by mountains and ocean deeps is indicated, and the broad distinction between continental platform and ocean basin areas is emphasized.

the Himalayas) to the bottom of the ocean's greatest deep is about 13 miles, but the average height of continents above the average ocean bottom is only 3 miles. This 3-mile value of average vertical relief is seemingly large, and it has far-reaching importance in Earth history. Yet it is not a very significant feature in the shape of the Earth as a whole. On a 5-foot globe, the protuberant continental areas would be represented by a thickness of about $\frac{1}{50}$ inch, which might be represented by a layer of varnish spread over parts of the globe corresponding to areas of the continents. If the distribution of water and land did not serve to differentiate the elevated and relatively depressed parts of the lithosphere, an observer of this 5-foot globe probably would not be able to detect the slightest unevenness in its spherical surface (Fig. 3.11).

The facts just stated do not alter our interest in knowing how and when the continental and oceanic areas of the Earth became differentiated. If we note the values of gravity measurements that have been made at thousands of points on land and at widely distributed though lesser number of points in oceanic areas, it is evident that the protuberant parts (continents) of the lithosphere are light and that relatively depressed parts (ocean basins) are heavy. The respective, average specific gravities are about 2.7 and 3.3. As indicated by the following equation, a relatively light, thick block of continental Earth crust having an area of say 1,000 square miles corresponds

in mass to a relatively heavy, thin block of oceanic Earth crust of the same area.

$$\frac{\text{Continental area}}{1{,}000 \text{ square miles}} \times \frac{\text{crustal thickness}}{x \text{ miles} + 3 \text{ miles}}$$
$$\times \frac{\text{specific gravity}}{2.7} = \frac{\text{oceanic area}}{1{,}000 \text{ square miles}}$$
$$\times \frac{\text{crustal thickness}}{x \text{ miles}} \times \frac{\text{specific gravity}}{3.3}$$

Such masses are essentially in weight equilibrium, and accordingly we reason that the continents stand high because they are light. The continents thus represent segregations of relatively light rock material. Some features of their form and distribution suggest their origin in changing rotation rate of the globe, accompanied by slight shrinkage in cooling during a late formative stage in the Earth's early growth, probably in connection with solidification. In any case, it seems evident that no major change from continental to oceanic area, or vice versa, can occur without an accompanying radical shift of mass. Lack of any known mechanism competent to produce such change and evidence supplied by many features of geologic history, outlined in later chapters of this book, indicate that the continents and oceans are essentially permanent features of the Earth's surface. They were formed before the time of making any rocks now accessible to the geologist. It is significant that the oldest known rocks are metamorphosed sediments and that no vestige of an original igneous crust of the Earth has been identified.

READINGS

GAMOW, GEORGE, 1952, *The creation of the universe*, The Viking Press, Inc., New York (147 pp., illus.).

HOYLE, FRED, 1950, *The nature of the universe*, Harper & Brothers, New York (142 pp., illus.).

HYNEK, J. A. (ed.), 1951, *Astrophysics*, McGraw-Hill Book Company, Inc., New York, On the origin of the solar system, by G. P. Kuiper, pp. 385–417.

JEANS, SIR JAMES, 1929, *The universe around us*, The Macmillan Company, New York.

LEET, L. D., and JUDSON, SHELDON, 1954, *Physical geology*, Prentice-Hall, Inc., Englewood Cliffs, N.J., The earth's age and place in the universe, pp. 362–381 (illus.).

UREY, H. C., 1952, *The planets, their origin and development*, Yale University Press, New Haven, Conn.

WHIPPLE, F. L., 1941, *Earth, Moon, and planets*, The Blakiston Division, McGraw-Hill Book Company, Inc., New York.

QUESTIONS

1. How are the rotation period of the Sun and inclination of its axis to the plane of the ecliptic (common plane of planetary orbits) related to motions of the Earth and other planets? What is the significance of these relationships with respect to the hypotheses of planetary origin advanced by Kant and LaPlace?

2. In spite of extraordinary differences in size and specific gravity of the planets, why is explanation of the origin of the Earth considered to be inseparable from that of other planets?

3. How can the difference in the number of moons associated with various planets or absence of moons be explained?

4. What explanation can be offered to account for the marked dissimilarity of surficial features of the Moon, as seen from the Earth, as compared with the well-known surface characters of the lithosphere on our planet? What is the probable nature of the Moon's "seas," and why do they appear as dark areas?

5. What are meteorites? What conditions may account for the seeming preponderance of nickel-iron meteorites over stony meteorites contained in collections?

6. What explanation seems best to account for the average specific gravity of continental and oceanic areas in relation to their topographic expression as relatively protuberant or depressed parts of the lithosphere surface?

4.

CRYPTOZOIC EON

North-trending roots of late Precambrian Belcher Mountains in Hudson Bay region, Canada.

Courtesy of Royal Canadian Air Force

The first major division of earth history determinable from rocks exposed at the surface is called the Cryptozoic Eon. This name, signifying concealed life, is appropriate because the only preserved remains of organisms found in it are obscure and because the name suitably emphasizes the contrast between the almost unfossiliferous very ancient rocks of the earth's crust and the younger rocks called Phanerozoic (plainly visible life), which as a whole are characterized by abundance of well-preserved fossils. It is convenient also to designate the Cryptozoic rocks as Precambrian, a commonly used term indicating age older than the Cambrian Period, first division of the Paleozoic Era and of the Phanerozoic Eon.

OLDEST ROCKS OF EARTH'S CRUST

The oldest rocks of the earth's crust yet discovered are some from South Africa and the Congo region that contain lead-bearing minerals furnishing the basis for radioactive measurement of geologic age at approximately 3,300 million years. If we add a little to provide for probably existing still older exposed rocks and to give us a convenient round sum, we may arbitrarily set the beginning of Cryptozoic time as about 3,500 million years ago. It seems reasonable to confine Cryptozoic in this way, leaving unaccessible materials of the earth interior that originated in the 1,000 to 1,500 million years of pre-Cryptozoic time back to birth of the earth planet as an era that may be called Azoic (devoid of life). The conditions and events of Azoic earth history are so speculative that discussion of them is omitted here. So we turn to the Cryptozoic rocks and the study of history represented by them, but before we can proceed, definition of the Cryptozoic Eon must be completed. What limit in approach to the present shall be set for Cryptozoic time?

Base of Cambrian Rocks as a Historical Datum

One of the most important points of reference in the geologic time scale—comparable to the birth of Christ in reckoning time in years A.D. and B.C.—is the base of the Cambrian System of rocks. These strata are the oldest that in many parts of the globe contain somewhat numerous invertebrate fossils. Older sedimentary formations, belonging below the Cambrian, mostly lack organic remains, even though some of them contain abundant concentrically laminated deposits of calcareous algae (called *stromatolites*), trails and borings possibly made by worms, and some fairly well-preserved microfossils identified as blue-green algae and fungi. A fundamental distinction between the Cambrian and younger rocks on one hand and Cryptozoic formations on the other is the observation that whereas fossils occurring in post-Cryptozoic strata permit fairly exact correlations of them throughout the world, thus giving basis for determining

equivalence in age, none of the Cryptozoic rocks can be thus correlated reliably for any great distance. It is true that local successions of Precambrian rocks can be ascertained so as to allow inferences of early earth history in the regions concerned, but the prevailing absence of fossils that could indicate accurate placement in geologic time means that the local records of Cryptozoic history cannot be fitted together so as to give a connected story of the geologic evolution of a large region. Intercontinental correlations of Cryptozoic rocks can be made with some degree of assurance only where radioactive age determinations are available.

The unfossiliferous Cryptozoic rocks differ broadly from Cambrian and younger formations in physical constitution and structure. The old rocks are mainly crystalline. Bathylithic igneous rocks, such as granite, are very common, and there is an abundance of highly metamorphosed rocks. Structure generally is complex. The Paleozoic and later formations are dominantly composed of sedimentary strata in which well-defined bedding is a conspicuous feature. Except in mountain belts, where the original horizontal or nearly horizontal attitude of Cambrian and younger beds has been disturbed by folding and faulting and locally by metamorphism, structure is simple and the order of succession of beds is clear. It is natural, therefore, to separate the Cryptozoic from younger rock formations.

Upper limit of Cryptozoic rocks in the Grand Canyon. The boundary between Cryptozoic and overlying younger rocks is especially well displayed for many miles in the walls of the Grand Canyon of the Colorado River in northwestern Arizona (Figs. 4.1, 4.2). Here, flat-lying Lower Cambrian sandstone containing invertebrate fossils (trilobites, brachiopods) overlain by younger Cambrian and succeeding Paleozoic strata rests with pronounced unconformity on Cryptozoic rocks. In downstream (western) parts of the canyon, the Precambrian consists exclusively of crystalline rocks (Vishnu Schist) intersected by masses of granite and veins of pegmatite and other igneous rocks, together with some highly altered

Fig. 4.1 Great unconformity marking the boundary between Cryptozoic and Paleozoic rocks in the Grand Canyon of the Colorado River, Arizona. The rocks in the V-shaped "Granite Gorge" consist of granite, gneiss, and schist intersected by dikes of pegmatite and other igneous rocks, collectively called the Vishnu Schist, all of early Cryptozoic (Archean) age. The unconformity at the base of the Cambrian sandstone cliff defines a great pre-Paleozoic erosion surface that by evidence found elsewhere in the Grand Canyon can be dated as formed late in Algonkian (late Precambrian) time. (*N. W. Carkhuff, courtesy of U.S. Geol. Survey.*)

quartzite and slaty strata standing on end. The structural "grain" of the Vishnu rocks is expressed by northward-trending foliation and bands that stand vertically or at steep angles, a result of great metamorphism-producing stresses exerted at right angles to the trend of the structural grain. All these Cryptozoic rocks —granites, schists, and veins of various sorts— are truncated evenly by an ancient erosion surface that now is covered by the Lower Cambrian sandstone. The erosion surface, defined as a great unconformity, marks the upper limit of Cryptozoic rocks in this area. It is a prominent boundary having obviously great geologic importance.

At several places in the eastern part of the Grand Canyon, as near the mouth of the Little Colorado River and in the Shinumo area, a short distance west of the large hotels (El Tovar, Bright Angel) on the south and north rims of the canyon, respectively, the unconformity at the base of the Cambrian sandstone is found to cut across an inclined series of sedimentary strata in which unfossiliferous red-beds, thick quartzite layers, and basaltic lavas are prominent. These rocks differ from the Vishnu Schist in being unmetamorphosed and only moderately disturbed by tilting and local faulting. Collectively, they are called the Grand Canyon Sequence [1] of rocks, and although in places only lower strata of the suc-

[1] Actually, the term *system* has been employed by geologists for these rocks, but because they cannot be correlated reliably with divisions of Precambrian rocks in other regions, in this respect differing from Phanerozoic systems, *sequence* is a preferred designation.

Cambrian sandstone

ALGONKIAN

ARCHEAN

Fig. 4.2 Evenly inclined late Cryptozoic (Algonkian) sedimentary rocks belonging to the lower part of the Grand Canyon Sequence. The rocks dip eastward at an angle of about 30 degrees as a result of post-Algonkian deformation that produced block-fault mountains. Prominent unconformities at the base of the system and obliquely truncating the top furnish record of two periods of profound erosion that produced nearly flat peneplains. (*N. W. Carkhuff, courtesy of U.S. Geol. Survey.*)

cession are present as a thin wedge a few tens or hundreds of feet thick, the sequence has an exposed aggregate thickness of more than 12,000 feet. The base of the Grand Canyon Sequence is marked by an unconformity as prominent as that found at the base of the Cambrian beds in the western part of the Grand Canyon region. It consists of an erosion surface that cuts smoothly across complex structures of the underlying Vishnu Schist, and although now inclined at an angle of about 30 degrees paralleling strata of the Grand Canyon Sequence above it, it must have been nearly horizontal when formed. Resting on the post-Vishnu pre-Grand Canyon unconformity is a conglomerate containing coarse rounded boulders and cobbles of various kinds of Vishnu rocks. Evidently, this unconformity is not the same as the one next beneath the Cambrian sandstone but very much older, as is proved both by the occurrence of the thick Grand Canyon Sequence between them and

by the manner in which the younger unconformity cuts across the older one (Fig. 4.3).

In the eastern part of the Grand Canyon area two important chapters of the Cryptozoic Eon are represented by the highly metamorphosed, prevailingly crystalline Vishnu rocks below and the tilted, unmetamorphosed Grand Canyon Sequence above. The two divisions may be classed as representing eras that, respectively, have been named Archean and Algonkian.

Upper limit of Cryptozoic rocks in northern North America, Europe, and western Africa. On a scale geographically much larger than in the Grand Canyon region, the relations of Cryptozoic to Cambrian and younger formations may be studied advantageously by examining representative cross sections of shallow parts of the earth's crust in northern North America, Europe, and western Africa (Fig. 4.4). We see in sections extending southwestward and southward from Hudson Bay (*A–B*,

C–D) that crystalline rocks of complex structure classed as Precambrian are truncated by an unconformity that marks an erosion surface produced mainly in pre-Cambrian time, since in various places little-disturbed Cambrian deposits lie on this erosion surface. Where post-Cambrian strata lie directly on the truncated Cryptozoic rocks, we must conclude that either Cambrian beds never were formed in these places or, if deposited, were worn away before the younger deposits were laid down. Thus, erosion later than the beginning of Cambrian time is indicated in parts of the region,

but the planed surface so produced merges with that beneath the Cambrian, and the upper limit of Cryptozoic rocks is sharply defined.

The same sort of relations are shown in northern Europe (Fig. 4.4, sections E–F, G–H) where the upper limit of Cryptozoic crystalline rocks is a smoothly carved erosion surface that in places is buried by post-Cambrian formations and locally is deformed by folding and faulting of post-Cambrian date.

The upper limit of Cryptozoic rocks is not everywhere marked clearly and sharply by a great unconformity (assuming correctness in

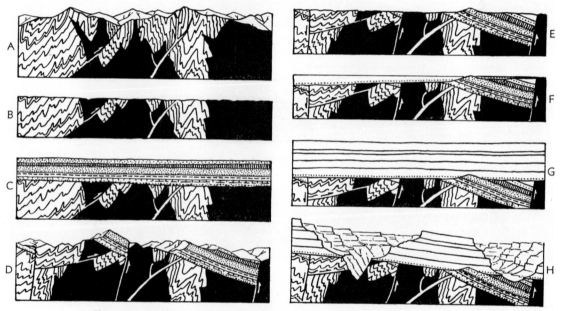

Fig. 4.3 Geologic history of the Grand Canyon region in northern Arizona illustrated by diagrammatic sections. Steps in the geologic evolution of this area are as follows.——*A.* Mountain-making deformation of Archean (Vishnu) sedimentary and volcanic rocks with accompanying metamorphism and intrusion of them by granite and other plutonic igneous rocks.——*B.* Profound erosion (Eparchean) producing a peneplain.——*C.* Deposition of Algonkian (Grand Canyon Sequence) sedimentary and volcanic rocks unconformably on the Archean. ——*D.* Uplift accompanied by faulting and tilting of crustal blocks, producing mountains mostly composed of inclined Algonkian strata but locally with exposures of Archean rocks.—— *E.* Profound erosion of the region forming a peneplain that in some places bevels the inclined Algonkian beds and elsewhere cuts deeply into the Archean crystalline rocks, obliterating parts of the previously carved Eparchean peneplain.——*F.* Beginning of Paleozoic sedimentation, recorded by the early Cambrian sandstone laid down unconformably on various Cryptozoic rocks.——*G.* Completion of Paleozoic sedimentation in the region with accumulation of flat-lying strata nearly 5,000 feet thick.——*H.* Slight warping of the Paleozoic and older rocks followed by stream cutting that has produced the Grand Canyon, these changes belonging mostly to recent geologic history.

defining the lower limits of the rocks called Cambrian in some areas). The problem is illustrated by a diagrammatic section of the rock succession in the Moroccan region of northwest Africa (Fig. 4.4, section *I–J*). Here, marine shale and limestone bearing numerous trilobites and other fossils that indicate age equivalence to oldest Cambrian of other regions are found to lie conformably on a very thick succession (up to 15,000 feet) of lime-

stones containing calcareous algae and on still older unfossiliferous rocks extending down to a profound unconformity. Beneath this unconformity are typical Cryptozoic crystalline rocks of complex structure and composition. It is thought that the sedimentary deposits between this great unconformity and the base of strata containing early Cambrian invertebrate fossils really belongs to a late part of Cryptozoic time (Algonkian Era) rather than

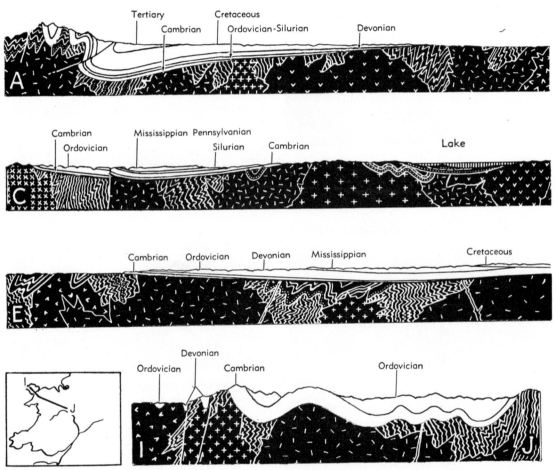

Fig. 4.4 Upper limit of Cryptozoic rocks illustrated by geologic sections in North America, Europe, and western Africa. Nearly everywhere the ancient Precambrian rocks are evenly truncated by a great unconformity that is overlain by Cambrian or younger strata.——*A–B*. Section from the Rocky Mountains in Alberta to Hudson Bay. Cambrian beds are confined to the western part of this section. Ordovician deposits, which overlie the Cambrian in the west but rest directly on the Precambrian in the east, may originally have been continuous across the area of Cryptozoic outcrops where now they are missing.——*C–D*. Section from the Ozark highland of Missouri to Hudson Bay, showing features similar to *A–B* but near Lake Superior intersecting Algonkian (Keweenawan) rocks.——*E–F*. Section from the margin of

to the Paleozoic Era. If this is true, no sharp boundary separates Cryptozoic from younger rocks in this region. A similar condition exists in China, where some 20,000 feet of unfossiliferous stratified rocks (Sinian Sequence) conformably underlies Lower Cambrian deposits. These exceptions to the general rule do not serve appreciably to lessen emphasis on the importance of the boundary between Cryptozoic and Paleozoic rocks (and time),

particularly in view of theoretical considerations that make explanation of a universal unconformity at the base of Paleozoic deposits impossible.

Duration of Cryptozoic Eon

Inasmuch as the beginning of Cryptozoic time is dated on the geological clock as belonging approximately 3,500 million years before the present and that of the Cambrian Period

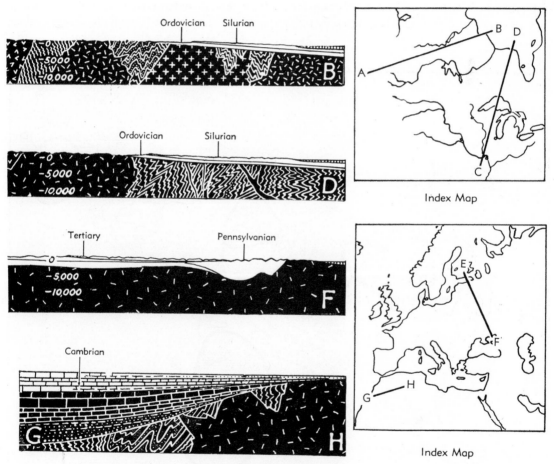

Index Map

Index Map

the Baltic Shield in Finland to the Black Sea, showing the structure of the Russian platform closely corresponding to that of the Mississippi Valley region in the United States.——*G–H.* Diagrammatic section of Lower Cambrian and conformably underlying rocks presumed to be of late Cryptozoic (Algonkian) age in Morocco, omitting effects of post-Cambrian structural disturbance (*modified from G. Choubert*).——*I–J.* Section from Anglesey Island, northwestern Wales, to Shropshire in England, crossing the type region of the Cambrian System. The unconformity that marks the base of Cambrian and top of Cryptozoic rocks is a smooth erosion surface that before folding was nearly horizontal.

is placed in the neighborhood of 520 million years ago, the difference, amounting to 2,980 million years, indicates the enormous magnitude of the Cryptozoic Eon (Fig. 1.31). Allowing latitude in estimation of the age of oldest rocks of the earth crust (4,500 million years) and of the beginning of our planet (5,000 million years), more than one-half of all earth history is embraced in the Cryptozoic. This is time enough for the building of tremendously thick successions of sedimentary rocks, for the uplift and subsequent complete obliteration of great mountain chains, and for erosion sufficiently profound to cut deeply into

the earth's crust, exposing great areas of granite and metamorphic rocks at the zone of flow. Again and again prolonged erosion produced widespread peneplains.

Continental Centers of Growth

Geological studies throughout the world have shown that each continent contains one or more exceptionally large areas of exposed Cryptozoic rocks that are characterized generally by low topographic relief. These areas have come to be known as *shields* because of their broad flattish surface and prevailing rigidity. Throughout geologic history they

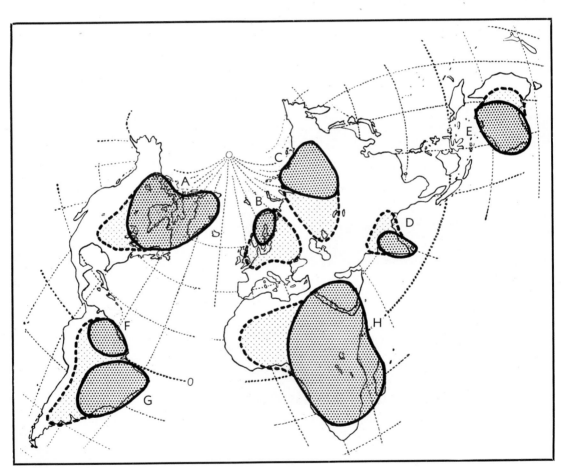

Fig. 4.5 Shields (coarse-stippled) and adjoining platforms (fine-stippled) composed of Cryptozoic rocks that form the ancient centers, or nuclei, of continental growth. The Cryptozoic formations, especially including large masses of granite, are widely exposed in the shields but prevailingly covered by flat-lying sedimentary strata on the platforms. The shields are designated as Canadian (*A*), Baltic (*B*), Siberian (*C*), Indian (*D*), Australian (*E*), Guianan (*F*), Brazilian (*G*), and African (*H*).

have tended to stand above sea level and to some extent have furnished the source of sediments deposited in areas around them. Also, the thrust of mountain-building forces at different epochs has been directed mostly from one side or another toward them. Thus, they are ancient-rock nuclei of the continents, which are bordered by younger-formed rocks. They are the chief cratons (ruling or dominant areas), so-called because they have stood firm as "positive" regions, tending to move differentially upward, in contrast to "negative" tracts such as basins and geosynclines that have progressively sunk downward.

Eight continental nuclear masses of Cryptozoic rocks are recognized (Fig. 4.5), of which the largest are in Africa (including adjacent Arabia) and northern North America. The smallest are in northern Europe and southern India. Inspection of Fig. 4.5 shows that the various nuclei are not centrally located in the continents but excentrically, although this relationship is slightly modified if account is taken of buried extensions (known as stable platforms) belonging to them. These platforms differ from the shields proper only in their lower structural position and concealment of Cryptozoic rocks by an extensive cover of nearly flat-lying sedimentary strata of post-Cryptozoic age. The platforms share the properties of the shields in standing as rigid masses that in later geologic time have not undergone profound compression or sunk deeply. They contain subordinate cratons that may be sufficiently strong to produce local exposures of Precambrian rocks, and they contain subordinate basins.

Chief outcrops of Cryptozoic rocks are in the continental nuclei or shields. Smaller ones occur in the stable platforms and outside these

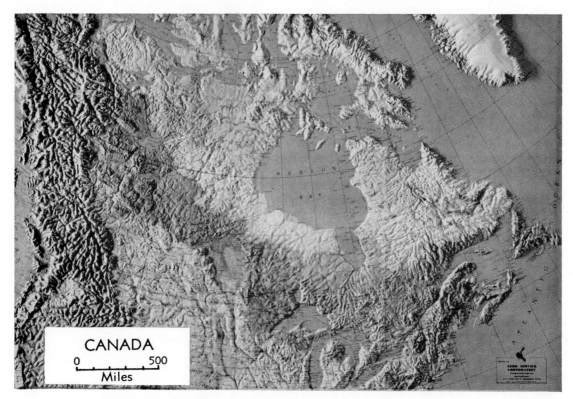

Fig. 4.6 Land surface of Canada. Most of the area east of the Rockies is a vast lowland that consists of peneplaned Cryptozoic rocks, but toward the northeast, uplift of the earth's crust in comparatively recent geologic time is responsible for rugged topography. (*Courtesy of Aero Service Corporation.*)

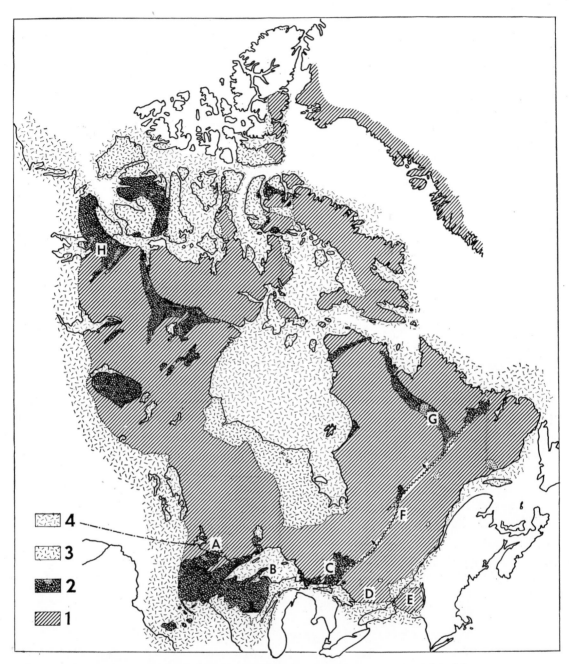

Fig. 4.7 Distribution of Cryptozoic rocks in the Canadian Shield.——1. Outcrops of Archean formations, locally including undifferentiated Algonkian rocks.——2. Algonkian (Proterozoic) formations.——3. Precambrian rocks thinly buried by younger formations.——4. Precambrian at shallow depth in areas covered by water.——*A.* Keewatin district.——*B.* Keweenaw district. ——*C.* Huronian district.——*D.* Grenville district.——*E.* Adirondack district.——*F.* Mistassini fault, rocks overthrust northwestward.——*G.* Labrador trough.——*H.* Great Bear Lake district.

in the axes of some mountain ranges that have undergone profound compression and uplift so as to bring older rocks to the surface.

CANADIAN SHIELD

By far the most extensive area of exposed Cryptozoic rocks in North America is in the northern part of the continent surrounding Hudson Bay (Fig. 4.6). This area, which includes parts of Arctic islands and reaches southward into the United States, lies mostly on the mainland of Canada and so has come to be named the Canadian Shield. This region has first importance for study of Cryptozoic history, not so much because of its size—only a small part has been fairly well explored—but because a more complete record has been worked out here than elsewhere on the continent. Also, rocks of the shield have great importance as sources of mineral wealth.

The Canadian Shield has a total area of 1,864,000 square miles, of which 93,000 square miles are located in the United States west and south of Lake Superior and in the Adirondack region of northern New York (Figs. 4.6, 4.7). Ignoring irregularities, the area has an elliptical outline, with the longer axis trending north-northeast. As a whole, the shield is somewhat saucer-shaped rather than bowed upward in the middle, for the depression of Hudson Bay is surrounded by a wide lowland that is mostly a nearly flat plain with many small lakes and marshes. Northeastward the land surface rises (according to present evidence because of uplift in Recent geologic time), reaching a maximum elevation of 8,500 feet above sea level in the eastern part of Baffin Island and 5,000 feet or more along the northern Labrador coast. Indeed, most of Labrador and adjacent parts of Quebec are rugged country with elevations of 1,500 to 3,000 feet. Except locally, the southern and western parts of the shield have lower elevations, ranging from

Generalized Classification of Cryptozoic Rocks of the Canadian Shield

ROCKS OF ERA	SEQUENCE	SUB-SEQUENCE	INTRUSIVE ROCKS
$\pm 1 \times 10^9$	Keweenawan		
	~~ Unconformity ~~~~~~~~~~~~~~~~~~~~~~~~~~~~~		
			?Killarney Granite
Algonkian (Proterozoic)		Animikie	
		~~	
	Huronian	Cobalt	
		~~	
		Bruce	
2×10^9 ~~~~~~~~~~~~~~~~~~~~~~~~~~~~~ Great unconformity ~~~~~~~~~~~~~~~~~~~~~~~~~~~~~~~~~~			
			Algoman Granite
	Timiskaming		
$\pm 2.4 \times 10^9$ ~~~~~~~~~~~~~~~~~~~~~~~~~ Unconformity ~~~~~~~~~~~~~~~~~~~~~~~~~			
Archean			Laurentian Granite
	Keewatin		
$\pm 3 \times 10^9$ ~~~~~~~~~~~~~~~~~~~~~~~~~ ?Unconformity ~~~~~~~~~~~~~~~~~~~~~~~			
	?Pre-Keewatin (local)		

little above sea level in coastal areas to slightly more than 1,000 feet; most of this country is a glaciated, lake-dotted peneplain on which features of rock structure are clearly indicated by differential erosion, especially as seen from the air (Figs. 4.8, 4.9).

Geological Divisions

Although reconnaissance investigations have been extended to much of the Canadian Shield area, detailed studies have yet been made only in a few districts such as the iron- and copper-bearing areas adjacent to Lake Superior, country northeast of Lake Huron, including rocks containing rich nickel and copper deposits near Sudbury, and in recent years, newly discovered iron-rich rocks in northeastern Quebec. No widely applicable detailed classification of the rocks has been worked out, even though nearly everywhere two main divisions of Cryptozoic rocks can be distinguished. The older of these main divisions is called Archean, and the younger is Algonkian (named Proterozoic by the Geological Survey of Canada), but it is recognized that rocks of Archean aspect in some areas may actually be younger than rocks classed as Algonkian in another. Generally, the Archean consists of "basement rocks" consisting of much metamorphosed sedimentary and volcanic rocks and granites, whereas overlying Algonkian formations are less altered and

Fig. 4.8 Peneplaned Cryptozoic rocks in the northwestern part of the Canadian Shield.
The structural grain of the smoothly beveled rocks is clearly marked by linear arrangement of the many elongate lakes (nearly black in the photograph). The area is near Artillery Lake, Northwest Territories. (*Courtesy of Royal Canadian Air Force.*)

strongly folded and in most places show much less evidence of metamorphic changes. In contrast to the Archean rocks, which are prevailingly crystalline, Algonkian formations are dominantly sedimentary.

Records of radioactive age determinations of numerous Precambrian rocks in the Canadian Shield region partly confirm the arrangement of divisions given in this table and partly give promise of important revisions and extensions of it. For example, a group of age measurements based on samples taken from Keewatin formations in country north and west of Lake Superior indicates a range in age from 2,200 million to 2,600 million years, which agrees with assignment of these rocks to an early part of Cryptozoic time. Huronian rocks from the district northeast of Lake Huron are recorded as 800 million to 1,200 million years in age, most of them being more than 1,000 million years old. Supposed Algonkian rocks from the vicinity of Lake Athabaska, in northwestern Canada, and the Labrador region, in the eastern part of the shield area, have indicated ages of 1,600 million to 1,700 million years. Several measurements of rocks called Grenville, in the St. Lawrence area in and adjacent to the Adirondacks of New York, yield figures of 800 million to 1,100 million years, comparable to determined ages of Huronian rocks and thus serving to disprove supposed Archean age of the Grenville strata.

Fig. 4.9 Fault in peneplaned Cryptozoic rocks near Great Slave Lake, northwestern Canada. The rock to the left of the fault-line scarp is Archean granite, and that to the right consists of gently folded Algonkian sedimentaries; consequently, the granite is on the upthrown side of the fault. Most of the displacement along the fault is very ancient, probably pre-Keweenawan and surely long before peneplanation of this part of the shield, but renewed elevation of the upthrown block in geologically recent time is indicated by the present topography. The water body with straight shore line defined by the fault-line scarp is Lake MacDonald. (*Courtesy of Royal Canadian Air Force.*)

Archean Rocks and History

Where best known, in the southern part of the Canadian Shield adjacent to the Great Lakes, Archean rocks include (1) a vast but unknown thickness of Keewatin sedimentary and volcanic strata, (2) a sequence of mainly sedimentary rocks called Timiskaming, and (3) large masses of granite (Laurentian, Algoman), as well as many intrusions of other igneous rocks of both light-colored (acid) and dark-colored (basic) nature that most commonly occur as dikes. Vast areas of the less explored parts of the shield area contain exposures of granite and highly metamorphosed and deformed sedimentary rocks of Keewatin or Timiskaming type. In some places these have been mapped as Archean, but mostly, divisions of the Cryptozoic rocks have not been separately distinguished.

Keewatin Sequence. The name Keewatin was first used for greenstones consisting of highly deformed lavas and associated minor amounts of sedimentary strata in the country surrounding Lake of the Woods and Rainy Lake, west-northwest of Lake Superior. Subsequently, rocks of similar nature in many other places have been called Keewatin, although they also bear local names in various districts (in Manitoba, Hays River, Rice Lake, Amisk, Wasekwan; in Northwest Territories, Yellowknife, Great Slave). Prominence of extrusive volcanic rocks is characteristic, as is also common occurrence of pillow lavas (Fig. 4.10), denoting flows that occurred under a cover of water, each pillow being formed by surficial chilling and quick cooling of small out-pushed masses of the molten lava. Between rocks that represent successive lava flows are altered rocks that originally were beds of ash

Fig. 4.10 Archean pillow lava. The peculiar structure of this volcanic rock is attributed to extrusion under water. The shape of the pillows as seen in this erosion-beveled section of the rock indicates that the top of the lava flow is toward upper left. Yellowknife Sub-sequence, Keewatin, southeast of Gordon Lake, Northwest Territories. (*J. F. Henderson, courtesy of Geol. Survey Canada.*)

and thin tuffs. Silica is common in the form of cherty beds and iron-rich jasper. Metamorphosed impure quartzite and siltstone (graywacke), crumpled thinly bedded limestone, and iron-bearing formations occur in the Keewatin (Figs. 4.11 to 4.14). At many places isolated patches of Keewatin-type rocks are found enclosed by granite; they must constitute small remnants of formerly much more extensive Keewatin rocks that were intruded and displaced by invading granites. Some greatly altered Keewatin is observed in the form of finely banded gneiss (Fig. 4.15). The original distribution and thickness of Keewatin lavas and sedimentary deposits are quite unknown, but in the southwestern part of the Canadian Shield alone they must have been enormous. The geologic history represented by their accumulation and later deformation accompanying intrusion of the Laurentian Granite, followed by erosion sufficiently prolonged to produce a broad peneplain, are illustrated diagrammatically in Fig. 4.16.

In two areas rocks of Keewatin type have been reported to overlie with great unconformity still older rocks that are predominantly sedimentary. One of these is near the Lake of the Woods (type Keewatin district) where the rocks thought to underlie the Keewatin are called Coutchiching; the greater age of the Coutchiching rocks and their separation from true Keewatin are advocated by some geologists but contested by others. Another area of presumed pre-Keewatin sedimentary rocks, named Pontiac, occurs in northwestern Quebec, where unquestionably the much deformed Pontiac rocks are separated from overlying beds by a major unconformity. However, the younger rocks, which also are much disturbed by folding, instead of being Keewatin, as supposed, may actually be late Archean (Timiskaming). Therefore, the existence of pre-Keewatin rocks has not been demonstrated. The most significant observation to make is that the oldest known rocks (Keewatin or possibly pre-Keewatin) are composed of lava flows and sedimentary deposits spread out on an older part of the earth's crust that is not exposed and thus is of entirely unknown na-

Fig. 4.11 Evenly stratified thin-bedded Archean quartzite. The dark-colored layers are relatively fine-grained and impure. In spite of regularity of banding seen in this view, the rock is much metamorphosed, comprising part of gneiss named Kissynew in northwestern Manitoba. (*J. D. Bateman, courtesy of Geol. Survey Canada.*)

ture. Nowhere in the Canadian Shield or elsewhere in the world are outcrops of rock known that may be interpreted as "original crust," meaning rock formed by the cooling of part of a molten globe.

Timiskaming Sequence. The younger part of the Archean division of Cryptozoic rocks, as defined in the "standard" succession, consists of the Timiskaming Sequence, named from Lake Timiskaming, located along the Ontario-Quebec boundary northeast of Lake Huron. At the base of the Timiskaming succession is a great unconformity representing an erosion surface that cuts evenly across complexly folded Keewatin rocks and large areas of granite (Laurentian) and other igneous rocks that intruded the Keewatin. Beds of conglom-

Fig. 4.12   Steeply inclined Archean sedimentary rocks. These are comparatively regular layers of quartzite and impure siltstone east of Lake Athabaska, Northwest Territories, Canada. (*F. J. Alcock, courtesy of Geol. Survey Canada.*)

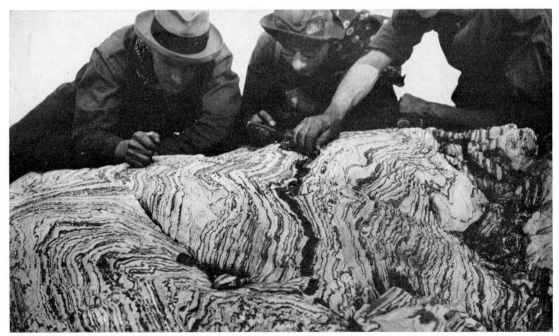

Fig. 4.13   Contorted folding in Archean cherty limestone. The outcrop shows beds of Steep Rock Limestone near Steep Rock Lake, western Ontario. (*T. L. Tanton, courtesy of Geol. Survey Canada.*)

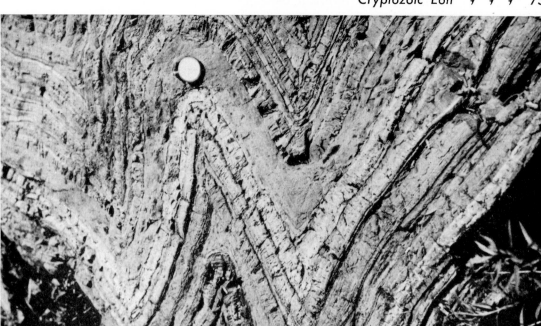

Fig. 4.14 Chevron-like folds in Keewatin iron formation. North of Lake Superior, near Mokomon, Ontario. (*T. L. Tanton, courtesy of Geol. Survey Canada.*)

Fig. 4.15 Finely banded Archean gneiss. The somewhat crinkled foliation surfaces are approximately vertical and denote great squeezing of the rock in the direction perpendicular to their strike. Near Embry Lake, Manitoba. (*J. W. Ambrose, courtesy of Geol. Survey Canada.*)

erate at the base and in the lower part of the Timiskaming Sequence contain not only pebbles and cobbles derived from Keewatin greenstones but pieces of water-worn granite ranging to boulder size (Figs. 4.17, 4.18). Nowhere does the granite that is the source of these boulders, cobbles, and pebbles intersect Timiskaming strata in the manner of an intrusion, with accompanying evidence of contact metamorphism of the sediments by the granite. Instead, the granite forms part of the floor on which the Timiskaming rocks were deposited, and it must be considerably more ancient than the oldest part of the Timiskaming strata, because very prolonged erosion was necessary to make the unconformity at the

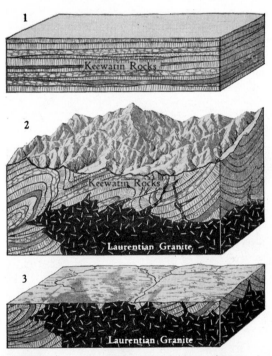

Fig. 4.16 Features of early Archean history in part of the Canadian Shield. The block diagrams illustrate successive steps in making the most ancient known rocks of the shield and structures associated with them.——1. Accumulation of Keewatin volcanic and sedimentary layers, originally approximately horizontal in position.——2. Mountain building, indicated by folding and metamorphism of the Keewatin rocks. This was accompanied or followed by intrusion of great bathyliths of granite (Laurentian). Erosion of the mountains must have begun as soon as they were uplifted.——3. Peneplanation of the mountain region.

base of the Timiskaming (Figs. 4.16, 4.21). As a whole, the Timiskaming Sequence contains large deposits of arkose (in which the feldspar content indicates derivation of the sediment from a granitic source), slate, quartzite, and conglomerate, with minor amounts of volcanic rocks (Fig. 4.19). Deposits of Timiskaming age are best known in northern Ontario and northwestern Quebec, but in other areas rocks presumed to be their equivalent are designated by local names (in Lake Superior region, Doré, Seine, Knife Lake; in Manitoba, San Antonio, Missi, Sickle). Widespread deposits of probable Timiskaming age are distinguished in northwestern Canada by the occurrence at their base of conglomerate with cobbles and boulders of iron formation of Keewatin type and of granite (Laurentian).

As now observed in many districts, the Timiskaming rocks are strongly folded and faulted and in places invaded by large bathyliths of granite that must be younger than the granite (Laurentian) that supplied boulders to the conglomerates of the Timiskaming. This younger granite is called Algoman. The deformation of the Timiskaming rocks, which was accompanied or followed by the granitic intrusions, produced mountains that probably were widely distributed geographically and prominent topographically (Fig. 4.24). As soon as uplifted, the mountains began to be eroded, and it is thought that this erosion continued for a very long time (called Eparchean Interval), until a thoroughly peneplaned land surface was produced. The appearance of this peneplaned surface carved across folded sedimentary strata intruded by granite must have been very similar to parts of the present Canadian Shield peneplain such as is illustrated in Fig. 4.20 (except for the presence of the numerous lakes which are due to glaciation). The Eparchean peneplain is represented by an unconformity that is interpreted to be the most widespread and important plane of partition in the Cryptozoic succession. It divides Archean from Algonkian (Proterozoic). The history of Timiskaming sedimentation, mountain building, and subsequent erosion is illustrated diagrammatically in Fig. 4.21.

Fig. 4.17 Timiskaming basal conglomerate resting unconformably on Archean igneous rocks. Outcrop east of Noranda, northwestern Quebec. (*M. E. Wilson, courtesy of Geol. Survey Canada.*)

Fig. 4.18 Water-worn pebbles and cobbles of Archean rocks, including Laurentian Granite, in Timiskaming Sequence. Near Noranda, northwestern Quebec. (*M. E. Wilson, courtesy of Geol. Survey Canada.*)

Algonkian Rocks and History

The later part of Cryptozoic time that (by radioactive age measurements) comprises approximately one-third of the era is distinguished as the Algonkian Era. It was characterized by very extensive accumulation of sedimentary deposits in basins and geosynclines, as demonstrated by widely distributed outcrops in the Lake Superior and Lake Huron regions, as well as in northwestern and eastern parts of the shield area, and locally there was important mountain building. Intrusive igneous rocks consisting of granitic bathyliths, masses of gabbro and other basic rocks, and

dikes of diabase are found in many places, and there are extensive flows of basaltic lavas, but sedimentary rocks of Algonkian age strongly predominate in bulk over igneous rocks. The sedimentaries are mostly divisible into geologic sequences separated by unconformities, and within some of the Huronian outcrop areas rocks of this sequence can be divided by important unconformities into subsequences. Generally speaking, early Algonkian rocks are more indurated and metamorphosed than later Precambrian formations, which usually dip at low angles or locally are found to be nearly flat-lying. Calcareous deposits consisting of both limestone and dolo-

Fig. 4.19 Fine-grained evenly bedded slate and siltstone of the Timiskaming Sequence. These beds, now standing nearly vertical, are exposed near Noranda, northwestern Quebec. (*M. E. Wilson, courtesy of Geol. Survey Canada.*)

Fig. 4.20 (*Opposite page.*) **Peneplaned Cryptozoic rocks near Duncan Lake, Northwest Territories, Canada.** Archean sedimentary rocks (light gray) are intruded by granite (nearly white) of Laurentian or Algoman age, both as bathylithic masses and thin dikes; Algonkian diabase dikes (dark gray) intersect the older rocks. (*Courtesy of Royal Canadian Air Force.*)

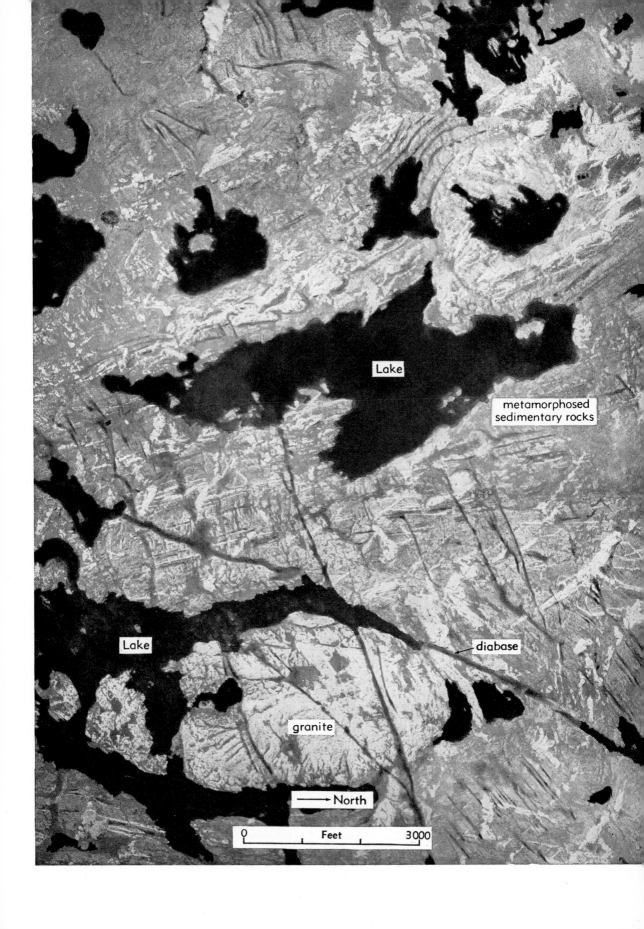

Lake

metamorphosed
sedimentary rocks

Lake

diabase

granite

North

0   Feet   3000

stone are relatively common, and in several regions these rocks are found to contain algal structures. Iron-bearing formations are prominent, giving rise to important ores in the southwestern and eastern part of the shield area. Locally, as in the Labrador trough, there are graphitic sedimentary rocks containing enough carbon to have the heat value of lignite (5500 B.t.u. per pound). Doubtless this carbon, as well as the widely spread limestones, accumulated through the agency of abundant life.

Huronian Sequence. One of the first areas of the Canadian Shield to be studied in some detail is the country northeast of Lake Huron where a thick succession of folded sedimentary rocks occurs. Pioneer investigations were

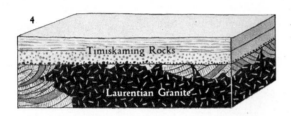

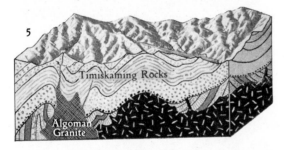

Fig. 4.21 Later Archean history of part of the Canadian Shield. The block diagrams, in continuation of Fig. 4.16, illustrate the following.——4. Deposition of the Timiskaming Sequence unconformably on older Archean sedimentary and volcanic rocks (Keewatin) and intrusive granite (Laurentian).——5. Post-Timiskaming mountain building accompanied or followed by intrusion of granitic bathyliths (Algoman). ——6. Peneplanation of Archean rocks as result of prolonged erosion (Eparchean Interval).

undertaken by Sir William Logan, first director of the Geological Survey of Canada, who recognized main features of the succession and named the rocks Huronian. Another classic area is the region in Minnesota, northern Michigan, and Wisconsin south of Lake Superior, where geologists of the U.S. Geological Survey, especially C. R. Van Hise and C. K. Leith, defined and described subdivisions of the Huronian Sequence.

Bruce Sub-sequence. In the type Huronian area, the lower part of the sequence, known as the Bruce Sub-sequence,[1] consists of approximately 5,000 feet of well-bedded quartzite that begins with a basal conglomerate resting unconformably on pre-Huronian schist and contains some other beds of conglomerate as well as limestones and siltstones. These deposits, which can be traced throughout a considerable area, are interpreted to have been laid down by a shallow sea in a basin produced by local subsidence of the Eparchean peneplain. After accumulation of the Bruce sediments there was temporary uplift that is recorded by uneven erosion of the upper beds of the sub-sequence, but because the next-following division (Cobalt Sub-sequence) lies parallel on the older Huronian, we must conclude that the uplift was not accompanied by appreciable deformation.

Cobalt Sub-sequence. The second division of the Huronian Sequence, named the Cobalt Sub-sequence, has an aggregate thickness of more than 12,000 feet, of which nearly two-thirds consists of quartzite (much of it arkosic) with well-developed cross-bedding and common ripple marks. The remainder is fine-grained impure silty rock that generally is well banded, and there are some iron-bearing cherty rocks. In places the Cobalt strata overlap on pre-Huronian crystalline rocks, probably indicating an enlargement of the area of sedimentation as compared with earlier Hu-

[1] Generally called *series* in Canadian reports, but because (like *system*) these Precambrian rock divisions cannot be correlated from one region to another, as is possible in classifying Phanerozoic rocks, the term *sub-sequence* is adopted here, written with a hyphen to avoid confusion with the common noun, subsequence.

ronian time but otherwise indicating complete removal of Bruce deposits before deposition of Cobalt sediments in areas where the Bruce rocks are missing. Of special interest is the occurrence of glacial deposits to a thickness of 500 feet or more in the lower part of the Cobalt Sub-sequence, distributed in an area extending nearly 1,000 miles from west to east. Deposits classed as indurated till (tillite) are heterogeneous unsorted accumulations of boulders, some of which show the distinctive smooth and striated surfaces produced by glaciation (Fig. 4.22). Banded silty deposits contain scattered boulders which must have been transported by being frozen in icebergs to places where they were dropped. When the ice melted, the boulders dropped into fine mud of the shallow sea bottom and, as fine sediments continued to be laid down, became buried. Although a glaciated rock floor belonging to Cobalt time has not been observed in southern Canada, we can hardly escape concluding that an ice sheet as large as or

larger than that which now covers Greenland existed during part of Huronian time in southern Canada. This record of glaciation, which is the oldest known, seemingly corresponds in age to Cryptozoic glacial deposits discovered in China and some other parts of the world, indicating that cold climate at this time was not confined to the North American continent (Fig. 4.38).

Cobalt sedimentation was brought to a close by uplift and folding of the Middle Huronian sedimentary rocks (Fig. 4.23). Igneous activity at about this time is indicated by common occurrence of intrusive masses (sills, dikes) of gabbro and diabase and less certainly of granitic rocks. South of Lake Superior there was somewhat intense folding of Middle Huronian and older sedimentary rocks accompanied by intrusion of granites.

Animikie Sub-sequence. Upper Huronian rocks are collectively designated as the Animikie Sub-sequence. This division is present only locally in country northeast of Lake

Fig. 4.22 Indurated glacial till (tillite) of the Cobalt Sub-sequence. This heterogeneous deposit of cobbles, some of which bear glacially polished and striated surfaces, and finely ground rock detritus between the cobbles was formed by an icecap-type glacier. Outcrop near Ville Marie, Quebec. (*Courtesy of Geol. Survey Canada.*)

Huron (Whitewater Sub-sequence of Sudbury district, formerly classed as basal Keweenawan). The Animikie division of rocks is defined and most typically developed in the Port Arthur district on the northwest shore of Lake Superior, where these rocks crop out in a southwest-trending belt that reaches into the United States. In this area the Animikie rests on pre-Huronian metamorphosed rocks, no Cobalt strata being present. Above a basal conglomerate is a considerable thickness of sandstone, shale, and limestone, but most important and characteristic are formations rich in iron. Concentrically laminated algal structures are common in the limestones. Rocks more or less reliably correlated with the Animikie occur in various parts of the Canadian Shield region from the far northwest to the northeast and east, reaching nearly to the Labrador coast. Commonly these rocks rest with great angular unconformity on Archean gneisses or granites, and in each district local names are applied. Prevailingly the Animikie rocks are not much disturbed by folding and faulting, but in many places they are intruded by igneous rocks. Also, undoubtedly they have been greatly reduced by post-Huronian erosion which in parts of the shield probably has been more or less continuous down to the present day.

Mountain building. Huronian and older rocks are found to be strongly folded and intruded by granite that clearly is younger than Laurentian and Algoman; the post-Huronian granite is named Killarney from outcrops on the northeast shore of Lake Huron. As noted later, the Killarney Granite and mountain building associated with its intrusion have previously been thought to be post-Keweenawan, but review of available evidence does not support this interpretation. The Killarneyan mountain building seems to have affected a large part of the southern shield reaching from Minnesota to southern Ontario (type Huronian and Grenville-Hastings district), and although the western part of the former mountains has been named the Penokeean Range (from the Penokee Hills in northern Wisconsin), the entire chain is better called the Killarneyan Range. Northeastward- and northward-trending mountains (Great Slave Range, Belcher Range, Labrador Range) that probably belong to the same time of orogeny are located farther north in the Canadian Shield (Fig. 4.24). Part of the roots of the Belcher Range are shown in the frontispiece illustration of this chapter.

Keweenawan Sequence. The youngest division of the Algonkian (Proterozoic) rocks, named Keweenawan from the Keweenaw Peninsula on the south side of Lake Superior in northern Michigan, consists chiefly of red to purple siltstone and ripple-marked sandstone associated with some beds of conglomerate and local cherty limestone. Both south and north of Lake Superior basaltic lava flows are prominent, some of them amygdaloidal (with scoriaceous vesicles filled by mineral deposits). In the Keweenaw area large quantities of metallic copper were deposited in gas-bubble cavities of the lavas and between pebbles of the Keweenawan conglomerates.

In the Lake Superior district Keweenawan sedimentary and volcanic rocks have an aggre-

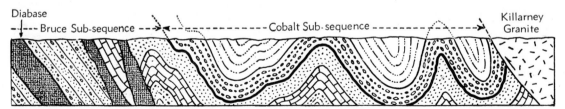

Fig. 4.23 Geologic section of Huronian rocks in the type Huronian area. The older (Bruce) sub-sequence is separated from next younger rocks (Cobalt) by a disconformity, both divisions being rather strongly folded. (*Modified from W. H. Collins and T. T. Quirke.*)

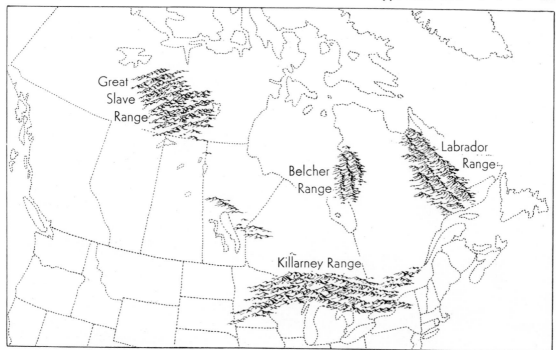

Fig. 4.24 Algonkian mountain ranges of the Canadian Shield. The roots of mountains consisting of much disturbed Huronian and older rocks are found in the southern and northern parts of the shield area.

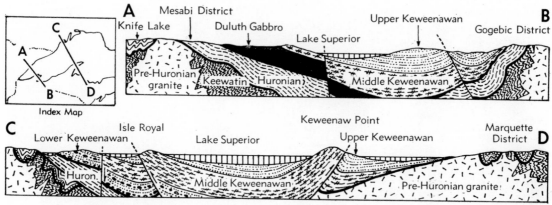

Fig. 4.25 Geologic sections of late Cryptozoic (Keweenawan) rocks in the Lake Superior region. The Keweenawan Sequence includes sedimentary and both extrusive and intrusive igneous rocks.——*A–B.* Section from northeastern Minnesota to northern Wisconsin across the western tip of Lake Superior near Duluth.——*C–D.* Section from the north edge of Lake Superior at Thunder Bay, Ontario, to northern Michigan crossing the Keweenaw Peninsula.

gate thickness of 50,000 feet or more. They form a broad, gentle syncline that underlies Lake Superior (Fig. 4.25). In the Duluth area is an enormous sill-like mass of gabbro that dips beneath the lake.

Especially in western and northwestern parts of the shield area, including large tracts bordering the Arctic, are nearly flat-lying sedimentary rocks and volcanics that closely resemble the type Keweenawan and are corre-

Fig. 4.26 Keweenawan diabase sills and associated nearly flat-lying sedimentary rocks. The relatively resistant igneous rocks form mesas near Nipigon, western Ontario. Part of the Trans-Canada highway is seen in the foreground. (*Courtesy of Royal Canadian Air Force.*)

lated with it (Fig. 4.26). One of these (Coppermine River Sub-sequence) in northwestern Canada includes 14,000 feet of basalts with thin interbedded conglomerates overlain by 34,000 feet of reddish-brown sandstone with some lava flows and sills of diabase. In all districts the base of the Keweenawan Sequence is marked by a prominent unconformity that separates this division from underlying Huronian rocks or throughout the western shield from Archean rocks.

Keweenawan time was brought to a close by a change from accumulation of sedimentary deposits and lava flows in various regions to a condition of general erosion that evidently was produced by moderate uplift of the shield area. Locally the occurrence of gentle folding is indicated by deformation of Keweenawan rocks, but contrary to former interpretation that postulated post-Keweenawan important mountain building accompanied by intrusion of granites (Killarney), no strong deformation of Precambrian rocks near the close of Cryptozoic time can be recognized in any part of the Canadian Shield. Certainly, no mountain building was involved in the downwarping of

the Keweenawan rocks that produced the Lake Superior syncline, for nowhere are the Keweenawan strata inclined more than very gently. The fact that lower Keweenawan beds dip lakeward more steeply than higher strata of the sequence indicates that the downwarp began during the time of Keweenawan sedimentation and was essentially completed by the close of the period. In large parts of the Canadian Shield, erosion must have been in progress during the time of Keweenawan sedimentation, thus contributing to peneplanation. When erosion of Keweenawan rocks began, this added to the degradation of the shield area, and judging by the even surface carved on Precambrian rocks, as indicated by smoothness of the surface covered by Cambrian and younger Paleozoic deposits along borders of the shield, we may conclude that virtually all the northern part of North America was a lowland plain by the time early Paleozoic sediments came to be laid down upon it in places.

Grenville and Hastings Rocks. In southern Ontario adjacent to the St. Lawrence River and extending eastward into the Adirondack

Fig. 4.27 Outcrop of strongly folded Algonkian (Hastings) quartzitic beds. Hastings district, southern Ontario. (*M. E. Wilson, courtesy of Geol. Survey Canada.*)

region of New York are very thick Cryptozoic sedimentary rocks consisting partly of hardened silty clay (argillite) but predominantly composed of limestone and dolostone. The lower part of this succession is called the Grenville Sub-sequence, and the upper part, separated from the lower rocks by a disconformity and a basal conglomerate, is known as the Hastings Sub-sequence. Both are named from localities in Ontario south of Ottawa. Outcrops of these rocks, as now observed, commonly show strong folding or extreme contortion as well as varying degrees of metamorphic alteration (Figs. 4.27 to 4.29). Rather commonly the Grenville and Hastings rocks are intersected by light- or dark-colored igneous rocks (Fig. 4.30), and in places they are invaded by moderately large stocks and batholiths composed of granite, anorthosite, and the like. The complex structure of these rocks and disturbance of them by igneous bodies denote important mountain building in the southeastern part of the Canadian Shield that

can be dated as post-Hastings because both Hastings and Grenville rocks are disturbed and no significant discordance in structure between them is observed. Formerly the Hastings and Grenville strata were thought to belong to an early part of Cryptozoic time, possibly contemporaneous with the Keewatin rocks of the Lake Superior region. Radioactive age measurements now demonstrate, however, that the calcareous deposits of the St. Lawrence area are at least 1,000 million years younger than most of the Keewatin and correspond closely to the age span recorded for Huronian rocks in the region northeast of Lake Huron. Accordingly, we may classify the Hastings and Grenville beds in the Algonkian rather than Archean division of Cryptozoic time.

What is the age of the mountain building that is indicated by the greatly disturbed Hastings and Grenville rocks? Except to say that it is obviously post-Hastings, this question cannot yet be answered firmly because efforts to trace Hastings-Grenville beds northwest-

Fig. 4.28 Banded limestone and impure siltstone of the Hastings Sub-sequence. The beds dip almost vertically. Hastings district, southern Ontario. (*M. E. Wilson, courtesy of Geol. Survey Canada.*)

Fig. 4.29 Cryptozoic sediments that have been metamorphosed into banded mica schist. Hastings Sub-sequence, southern Ontario. (*M. E. Wilson, courtesy of Geol. Survey Canada.*)

Fig. 4.30 Grenville Schist intruded by pegmatite dikes. The structure of both the schist and folded dike indicates a plastic type of deformation that denotes deep-seated origin within the earth's crust. Southern Ontario. (*M. E. Wilson, courtesy of Geol. Survey Canada.*)

ward so as to establish their continuity with Huronian rocks has not been successful, largely because a great thrust fault (Huron-Mistassini) separates the St. Lawrence and type Huronian areas (Fig. 4.7). Along this fault, which is traced 700 miles northeastward from Lake Huron, rocks of the southeastern much-disturbed province are pushed upward over the less deformed Huronian rocks. Included in the problem of dating is the Killarney Granite of southern Ontario and its probable correlatives north of the Huron-Mistassini fault, because these intrusions are associated with the structurally disturbed sedimentary strata. As already mentioned, the Killarney intrusives have been thought on insufficient evidence to be post-Keweenawan, and therefore mountain building called Killarneyan represented mainly by the disturbed Hastings and Grenville rocks has been inferred to belong near the close of Cryptozoic time. This interpretation cannot be defended because nowhere are rocks of Keweenawan age known to be affected by strong folding or intrusion of granitic rocks. Revised study indicates that the Killarneyan mountain building is simply post-Hastings and probably post-Huronian; also, it is most reasonable to conclude that it was pre-Keweenawan. This discussion emphasizes some of the difficulties that attend geologic investigation of the Cryptozoic rocks of the shield area.

CRYPTOZOIC OUTCROP AREAS IN THE UNITED STATES

In contrast to the enormous Cryptozoic outcrops in the Canadian Shield region (with which we have included the exposed areas in Minnesota, Wisconsin, northern Michigan, and northern New York), outcrops of Precambrian rocks in the United States are relatively small, isolated patches, the largest measuring only a few ten-thousand square miles (Fig. 4.31). Some are less than 100 square miles. All of them at one time may have been buried under Cambrian or younger rock formations, present-day outcrops being

due to removal of the former cover by erosion. As we might expect, this stripping away of younger deposits so as to expose the old crystalline rocks has occurred at places where the substructure of the continent has been most strongly pushed upward during deformative earth movements, some of which represent mountain building and others only upwarped bulges.

It is noteworthy that the rock successions observed in different Precambrian areas of the United States cannot be correlated in a reliable manner, even approximately, with one another or with main divisions of the Canadian Shield area. Age determinations by radioactive methods, however, indicate that some—as in the Black Hills of South Dakota—are very ancient, corresponding to early Cryptozoic rather than later divisions recognized in the Canadian region.

Appalachian Region

Along the eastern border of North America from Newfoundland southwestward to Alabama are discontinuous exposures of Cryptozoic rocks that are isolated both geographically and structurally from the Canadian Shield. This is the Appalachian belt, modified for convenience by including in it parts of the Maritime Provinces of Canada and areas in eastern New England that actually are separate from the Appalachians.

New York City, Philadelphia, Baltimore, Washington, and several other important eastern cities of the United States are located on or near Precambrian rocks belonging to the so-called Piedmont province, lying east of the Appalachian Mountains proper. This area is a low plateau that rises toward the west, culminating in the Blue Ridge. The area of Precambrian outcrops in the Appalachian belt shown on the geologic map of the United States (which is mainly the source of Fig. 4.31) is too extensive because it is now known that they include rather considerable areas of highly metamorphosed early Paleozoic rocks that are hard to distinguish from true Cryptozoic formations. In New Hampshire and adjacent parts of New England these Cryptozoic-like rocks are eliminated from the map, but southwestward from Pennsylvania it is not yet possible to do this.

This chief types of rocks in the Precambrian outcrops of the Appalachian belt are banded granite (gneiss) and highly metamorphosed sedimentary and igneous rocks (schist), some of which consist of lava flows. In Maryland and Virginia there are strongly folded beds of marble, and toward the south are thick deposits of black-colored slate that now mostly are considered to be Paleozoic. In spite of great alteration due to compressive forces and heat within the earth's crust that has almost destroyed original characters of the Cryptozoic rocks, they were once normal types of flat-lying sediments and volcanics associated with igneous rocks intruded into them. Details of the record cannot be deciphered clearly or completely; yet in kind, they denote a history corresponding to part of that read in the Canadian region.

Central States

Widely scattered small outcrops of Precambrian rocks occur (1) in northwestern Iowa and southeastern South Dakota near Sioux City, (2) in the structural center of the Ozark Uplift in southeastern Missouri south of St. Louis, (3) in the Wichita and Arbuckle Mountains of southern Oklahoma, and (4) in the Llano Uplift of central Texas near Austin and San Antonio. Thick red quartzite (originally sandstone), schist, and various sorts of igneous rocks, especially granite, are the chief litho-logic types observed. The contact of the Cryptozoic with overlying formations is mostly that of a smooth erosion surface, which indicates peneplanation of the Precambrian prior to its burial. Locally, however, as in the Ozark region, hills 1,500 to 2,000 feet high composed of Cryptozoic rocks have been revealed by the stripping away of the unconformably over-lying younger strata. Such topographic irregularity is unusual, but on observing it, one is not surprised to find pebbles and cobbles of igneous rocks derived from the hills included

in basal Cambrian sandy deposits that were deposited around the hills, partly burying them.

Rocky Mountains Region

Along the axes of uplift in the Rocky Mountains from far northwestern Canada to western Texas are many square miles of exposed Cryptozoic formations, mostly granite but in western Montana and the Canadian Rockies consisting of a great thickness of little-disturbed sedimentary rocks (Figs. 4.31 to 4.33). With the Rockies is included the outlying uplift of the Black Hills in southwestern South Dakota, where schists and granite have been brought to the surface and now stand topographically prominent (Fig. 4.34). Comparable to the Black Hills are isolated ranges of the Rockies in Wyoming such as the Big Horn, Wind River, Medicine Bow, where elevated masses of Cryptozoic granite are surrounded by upturned strata of Cambrian and later age. Some of the loftiest mountains of the Rocky Mountain chain, including Pikes Peak and Longs Peak in Colorado (Fig. 4.32), form parts of the ancient floor of the North American continent that have been lifted high by crustal deformation that occurred many millions of years subsequent to the close of Cryptozoic time. They furnish glimpses in random places of what must be the nature of the Cryptozoic floor on which sedimentary strata of the continental interior came to be deposited. Such information is supplemented by data for the continental interior from thousands of deep borings that have been drilled deeply enough to penetrate the Precambrian floor. Using knowledge accumulated in this way, it has been possible to map with varying degrees of accuracy not only the configuration but to some extent the geologic nature of this floor.

In the southern and central Rockies granite is a prevailing rock type in the Cryptozoic but there are also large areas of highly deformed and metamorphosed sedimentary rocks (Figs. 4.35, 4.36). In the Needle Mountains of southwestern Colorado and the Uinta Mountains of northeastern Utah are huge thicknesses

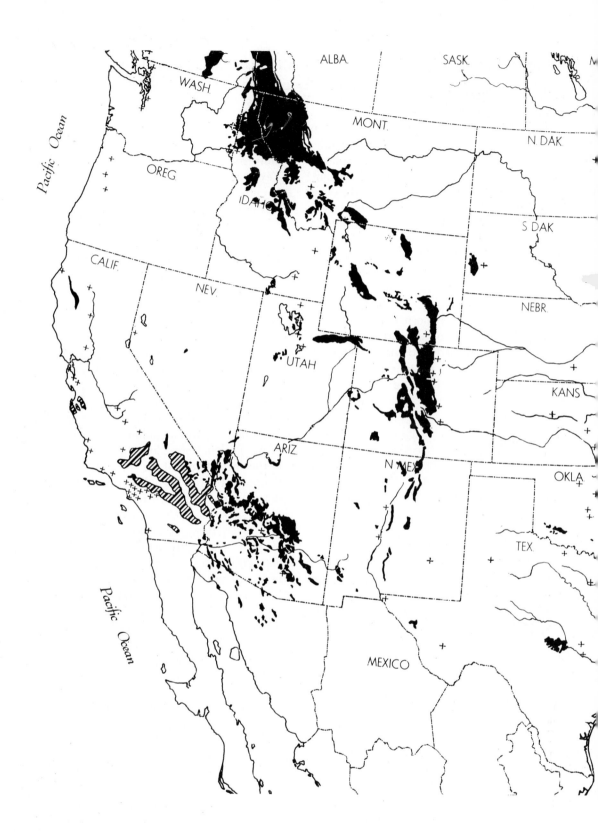

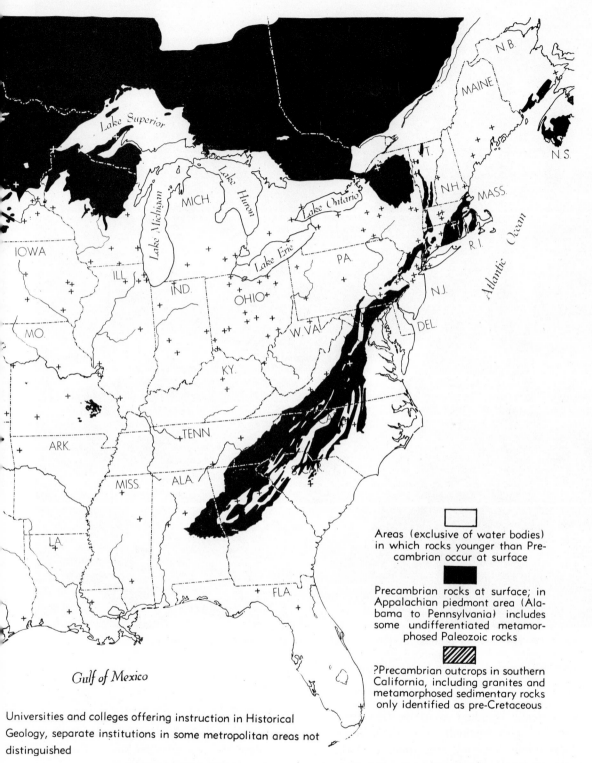

Areas (exclusive of water bodies) in which rocks younger than Precambrian occur at surface

Precambrian rocks at surface; in Appalachian piedmont area (Alabama to Pennsylvania) includes some undifferentiated metamorphosed Paleozoic rocks

?Precambrian outcrops in southern California, including granites and metamorphosed sedimentary rocks only identified as pre-Cretaceous

Universities and colleges offering instruction in Historical Geology, separate institutions in some metropolitan areas not distinguished

Fig. 4.31 Outcrops of Cryptozoic rocks in the United States, southern Canada, and northern Mexico. (*Data mainly from U.S. Geol. Survey, Geol. Survey Canada, and 20th Sess. Intern. Geol. Congr. in Mexico.*)

granite

Fig. 4.32 Precambrian granite forming part of the core of the Rocky Mountains. East face of Longs Peak and Chasm Lake in Rocky Mountains National Park, north of Denver, Colorado. (*Courtesy of Union Pacific Railroad.*)

of vertically standing quartzite that furnish record of what originally were thick deposits of essentially flat-lying sandstone. That these rocks are much older than Cambrian is proved by the presence of fossil-bearing Cambrian strata resting on the truncated edges of the quartzites, but no means are offered for de-

termining the part of Cryptozoic time to which the quartzites belong. In terms of divisions recognized in the Canadian Shield, they may be either Archean or Algonkian and equivalent in age to the Keewatin, Timiskaming, Huronian, or even Keweenawan; also quartzites of the Needle Mountains area may be older

Fig. 4.33 Late Cryptozoic (Algonkian) sedimentary rocks in the southern Canadian Rockies. The strata exposed in Vimy Mountain rising above Lake Waterton belong to the Belt Sequence, consisting of quartzite, thin-bedded argillite, and limestone: A, Waterton Quartzite; B, Altyn Limestone; C, Appekunny Formation; D, Siyeh Limestone. In spite of their nearly horizontal position, the rocks are displaced along two great thrust-fault planes: a, Lewis thrust; b, Crandall Mountain thrust. The Lewis thrust carries the Belt rocks across and over Cretaceous beds (E) from which in this view they have been eroded except locally along the distant skyline. Waterton Lakes National Park in Alberta. (*Courtesy of National Film Board of Canada.*)

or younger than those of the Uinta Mountains. No minerals suitable for making radioactive age measurements have been discovered.

Belt Sequence. The relatively undisturbed sedimentary rocks of the Montana and Canadian Rockies region which have been mentioned have an aggregate thickness of at least 15,000 feet, including some sills and flows of volcanic rocks associated with them. There are some quartzites, but especially prominent are thick limestones and well-laminated argillites that show red, green, and black bands parallel to bedding. Collectively, these rocks are known

as the Belt Sequence. They are exceptionally well exposed in many lofty cliffs along the mountain front and in canyons (Fig. 4.33). Because of the striking scenery in such regions as Glacier National Park (Montana) and Jasper Park (Alberta), where streams and erosion by ice have carved them deeply, they are objects of interest to many travelers. The tourist, however, is generally unaware of their great antiquity and their origin in a shallow sea, as indicated both by many features of the rocks themselves and by occurrence in the limestones of many colonies of calcareous

Fig. 4.34 Pinnacles of early Cryptozoic (Archean) granite in the Black Hills, South Dakota. These rocks are part of the Precambrian "basement" that has been pushed sharply upward in the core of the Black Hills. The outcrop area is surrounded by steeply dipping Paleozoic and younger sedimentary beds. (*Courtesy of Chicago and North Western Railway.*)

Fig. 4.35 Crumpled granite gneiss formed by profound metamorphism of Cryptozoic sedimentary layers. The rock belongs to the Idaho Springs Formation. Near Idledale, in the Rocky Mountains, a few miles southwest of Denver, Colorado. (*R. C. Moore.*)

Fig. 4.36 Precambrian quartzite showing beds turned up almost vertically. The structure of these rocks as now exposed is partly due to deformation associated with uplift of the Rocky Mountains long after Cryptozoic time (in fact, post-Cretaceous). Big Thompson Canyon west of Loveland, Colorado. (*W. T. Lee, courtesy of U.S. Geol. Survey.*)

1 foot

Fig. 4.37 Surface of mud-cracked Algonkian limestone. This rock belonging to the Belt Sequence is exposed near Missoula, Montana. (*Courtesy of L. R. Laudon, University of Wisconsin.*)

algae. Temporary emergence and drying of sediment are proved by well-defined mud cracks seen on the surface of some Belt strata, exactly as in many post-Cryptozoic formations and as may be seen today on recently exposed mud flats (Fig. 4.37). At many places the true base of this Cryptozoic rock succession is not seen because the strata are bounded below by a great thrust fault plane, along which these ancient rocks have been pushed eastward so as to rest on beds of vastly younger (Mesozoic, Cretaceous) age. Elsewhere, the bottom-most Belt rocks (basal conglomerate) are found to rest unconformably on granitic earlier Precambrian rocks.

Southwestern States and Pacific Border

Exposures in the bottom part of the Grand Canyon in northern Arizona already have been described. Especially in western Arizona and adjacent areas in southern Nevada, southeastern California, and northern Sonora (Mexico) are additional very numerous outcrops of Cryptozoic rocks (Fig. 4.31). The Precambrian rocks seen in all these areas consist of granite

and schist that is probably, but not certainly, of Archean age. Isolation of the many local outcrops is due to structural deformation (both folding and faulting) that has affected this region down to comparatively recent geologic time. As a result, various Paleozoic and younger sedimentary deposits have come to be laid down between the areas of present Cryptozoic outcrops that now occur as topographically prominent areas of local uplift. Thus, in general, exposed Precambrian rocks of this region show much-fragmented segments of the ancient basement rocks of this part of the continent.

CRYPTOZOIC ROCKS OUTSIDE NORTH AMERICA

Except where interrupted by post-Cryptozoic igneous intrusions, all the continents and undoubtedly the ocean basins also are underlain by Cryptozoic rocks. We may be sure of this because the solid-rock lithosphere must have been formed beneath the entire surface of the globe many hundred million years before the beginning of Cambrian time.

On land areas, the outcrops of Precambrian rocks are comparable to those observed in North America. That is to say, we find in each continent very broad areas of Cryptozoic exposures that resemble those of the Canadian Shield, and there are also numerous smaller areas of outcrops that commonly are found along the axes of mountain uplifts, just as in the Rocky Mountains and other uplifts of North America where the crust has been strongly elevated. The broad lowland outcrop areas constitute the so-called shields, which are nuclear parts of the continents bordered by nearly flat-lying sedimentary formations of the continental stable platforms.

Cryptozoic rocks exposed in the Baltic Shield of northern Europe include bodies of sedimentary and igneous rocks that are divisible on the basis of their structure and unconformities that separate them into successive sequences generally corresponding to those in the Canadian Shield. Precambrian rocks of shield areas in northern Siberia, India, Australia, Africa, and South America are of comparable nature. The most extensive outcrops of Cryptozoic rocks in the axes of mountain belts occur in the Alps, Himalayas, Andes, Urals, and several other chains. Almost universally they show the presence of granite, together with highly complex metamorphic rocks of many sorts. As a whole, wherever seen, Precambrian rocks are characterized by crystalline texture, general complexity of structure, and absence of fossils.

CLIMATES, LIFE, AND RESOURCES

Cryptozoic Climates

During earliest Cryptozoic time, climatic conditions must have been very different from anything now known on earth. After cooling had permitted condensation of water vapor, rains could fall on the still hot surface, but the globe must have been densely cloud-blanketed. This steamy sort of environment, which would permit the beginning of weathering and erosion, is a matter of guesswork. Later, we may be sure that climatic conditions approximating those now found on different parts of the earth made their appearance and persisted for very long periods of time. As judged by the nature of sedimentary deposits formed, the climate of some areas and of some parts of Cryptozoic time was prevailingly moist and warm. The existence of aridity or periodic wetting and drying is inferred from study of some extensive Precambrian redbeds formations like those attributed to desert climates in later geologic history.

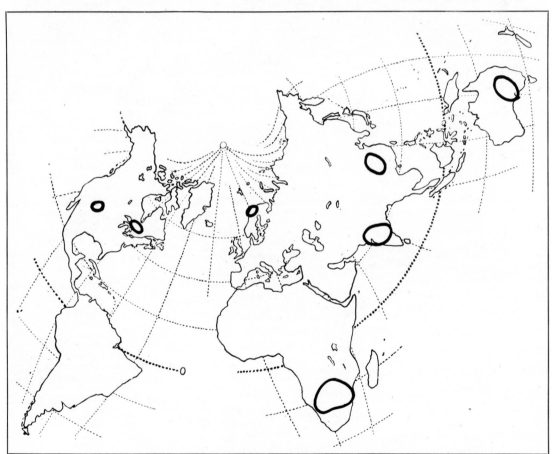

Fig. 4.38 Distribution of Cryptozoic glaciation. Probably the glacial deposits (tillites) found in the several areas outlined by heavy lines were formed by continental ice sheets comparable in size to the present Greenland icecap or larger. The indicated glaciations are not proved to have been contemporaneous, although all seem to belong to Algonkian time.

In late Precambrian time, parts of southern Canada show signs of having suffered continental glaciation. This evidence of cold climate very early in earth history is not unique, for glacial deposits dated as belonging to the late Cryptozoic have been reported also from China, India, Australia, South Africa, northern Europe, and western United States (Utah) (Fig. 4.38).

Life of Cryptozoic Time

Rocks of Cryptozoic age everywhere are characterized by the absence of fossils. The

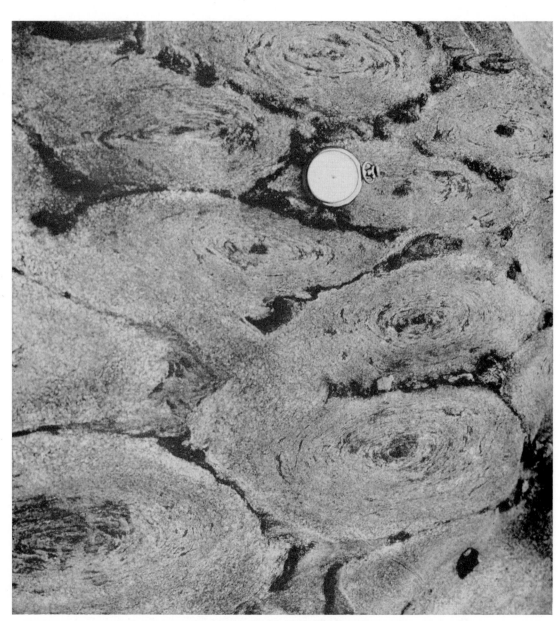

Fig. 4.39 Cryptozoic calcareous algae. The concentrically laminated masses occur in the Hastings Sub-sequence of probable early Algonkian age, in southern Ontario. (*M. E. Wilson, courtesy of Geol. Survey Canada.*)

predominance of igneous rocks in many areas partly accounts for this absence, and the prevalence of metamorphic alteration of sedimentary rocks may well explain the lack of organic remains in them. It is a striking fact, however, that many very little altered Precambrian strata, in which such features as cross-bedding, ripple marks, and mud cracks are well shown, have failed to yield fossils even to skilled and painstaking searchers in the field. If life existed, certainly not much trace of it has been preserved.

The record of Cryptozoic life is not entirely negative. Abundance of carbonaceous matter in many places strongly implies the existence of organisms, for no other agency of carbon fixation, having quantitative importance, is known. In rocks younger than Cryptozoic, abundant carbonaceous materials definitely are associated with life processes indicated by an abundance of various sorts of plants and animals.

Most common and best preserved among actual remains of Precambrian organisms are lime-secreting seaweeds, or algae (Figs. 4.39, 4.40). These built concentrically laminated subspherical or lobed structures, ranging from less than an inch to many inches in diameter;

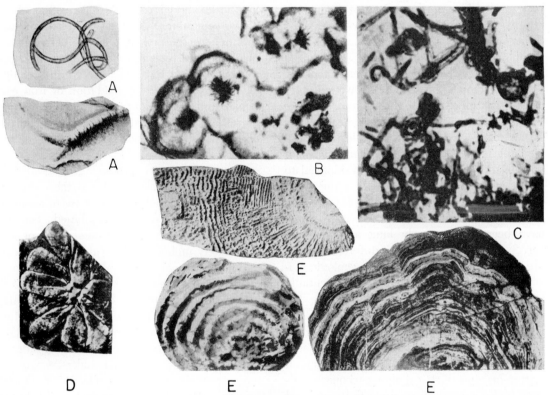

Fig. 4.40 Some types of Cryptozoic life.——*A.* Burrows probably made by worms from Belt rocks, Algonkian, in Montana (reduced). (*C. D. Walcott.*)——*B.* Blue-green algae from Gunflint Chert in southern Ontario. Undistorted remains of primitive plants consist of globose colonies containing short filaments in a jelly-like mass surrounded by a sheath and there are also unbranched threads, ×325. (*S. A. Tyler and E. S. Barghoorn.*)——*C.* Fungi; part of a mycelium and detached spores, ×725. From Gunflint Chert in southern Ontario. (*S. A. Tyler and E. S. Barghoorn.*)——*D.* Jellyfish (*Brooksella canyonensis*) from Algonkian limestone of the Grand Canyon in Arizona, ×0.5. (*C. E. Van Gundy.*)——*E.* Calcareous algae from Belt rocks, Algonkian, in Montana (reduced). (*C. D. Walcott.*)

they also formed colonial growths of various shapes. Surprisingly, some fossil blue-green algae and fungi authentically are reported from some Cryptozoic marine formations of the Canadian Shield. Fairly well-preserved fossils, representing creatures allied to sponges and corals, have been found in Cryptozoic rocks in the Lake Superior region, and a clearly identifiable impression of a jellyfish has been collected from limestone of Algonkian age in the Grand Canyon. We may complete the list by recording the presence of trails and burrows, like those made by worms and other invertebrates, and the finding of a very few traces of shelled invertebrates.

Forms of life abundantly represented in rocks next younger than Cryptozoic include relatively advanced, complexly organized forms of invertebrate life. Among these are marine crustacean-like animals (trilobites) having differentiated head, tail, many thoracic segments, jointed legs, and delicate respiratory organs. Inasmuch as the entire record of life from Cambrian time onward is marked by evolutionary change that includes development of more and more advanced types of animal and plant life, it is wholly illogical to entertain the thought that life on the earth began with such forms as are represented by fossils in Cambrian formations. There must have been an extremely long and virtually unrecorded slow evolutionary differentiation of life in Cryptozoic times. Why is geologic evidence of this inferred development essentially lacking? The best answer seems to be the guess that the primitive early forms of life nearly all lacked hard parts. If this is so, there would be almost no chance of their being preserved as fossils. When, at length, mineral matter of some sort—calcium carbonate, calcium phosphate, or silica—came to be secreted as parts of the body covering or other hard parts of the organisms, these remains, when buried in the sediments, were likely to be preserved. All of Cryptozoic time, judged to represent at least two-thirds of earth history, had elapsed before most sorts of organisms began to build and utilize a skeletal structure.

Economic Resources

Precambrian rocks are extremely important sources of mineral wealth, being chief suppliers of several metals.

Iron. First in importance among economic resources found in Cryptozoic rocks are iron-ore deposits. Although there are some important occurrences of iron-bearing minerals in younger formations, it is interesting to note that iron from Precambrian sources in various parts of the world far outweighs all others combined.

In North America, the Lake Superior district for several decades has been the chief source of iron supplied to huge steel plants of the Pittsburgh and Chicago areas, furnishing about 85 per cent annually of total United States iron production. In spite of previous withdrawals, production in recent years has averaged more than 90 million tons. The ore consists chiefly of hematite formed by oxidation of iron carbonate and iron silicate (greenalite) contained in sedimentary formations that crop out in northeast- or east-trending narrow belts called ranges (Fig. 4.41). The Mesabi Range in northern Minnesota, producing from Middle Huronian iron-bearing rocks, is the most important district, yielding about twice as much ore as the other districts combined. The ore deposits occur in near-surface parts of the moderately inclined iron formation where oxidation and leaching have altered the rock and concentrated the iron (Fig. 4.42). The Vermilion district obtains ore from Keewatin rocks, whereas others (Cuyuna, Gogebic, Marquette, Menominee) produce from the Huronian. Iron-ore bodies on the north side of Lake Superior (Steep Rock Lake, Michipicoten) occur in Keewatin rocks. Most of the iron, as along the Mesabi Range, at Steep Rock Lake, and elsewhere, is produced by steam shovels working in huge open pits (Fig. 4.43), but at Gogebic and other districts where ore extends to 3,000 feet or more below the surface, underground mining is carried on.

Outside the Lake Superior district, Cryptozoic iron-ore deposits are important in several

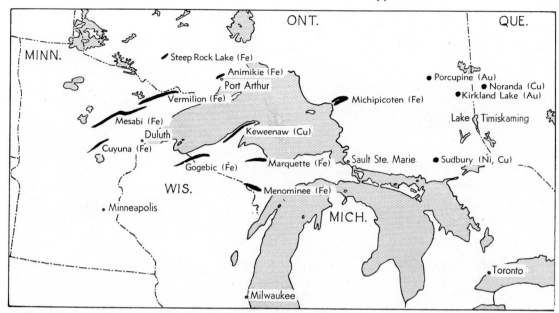

Fig. 4.41   Chief Cryptozoic metalliferous deposits in the southern Canadian Shield. Iron-producing districts include Vermilion, Mesabi, Cuyuna, Gogebic, Marquette, Menominee, Steep Rock Lake, Animikie, and Michipicoten. Copper-producing districts are Keweenaw, Sudbury, and Noranda. Nickel-producing district: Sudbury. Gold-producing districts: Porcupine, Kirkland Lake.

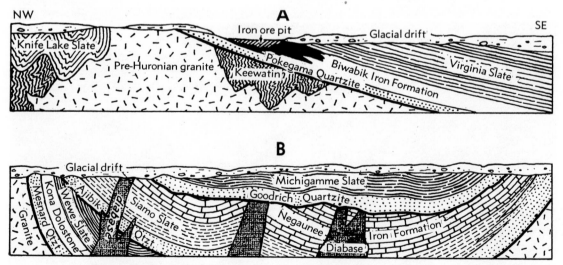

Fig. 4.42   Geologic sections of iron ranges.——*A.* Mesabi range in northern Minnesota. The iron ore comprises weathered parts of moderately inclined Algonkian (Huronian) rocks that lie with great unconformity on Archean (Keewatin) rocks.——*B.* Marquette range in northern Michigan showing the synclinal structure of the iron-bearing Huronian strata.

other areas, as, for example, high-grade ore (magnetite) obtained in northern Sweden (Kiruna), which is a main source of the steel manufactured by various European plants. Another iron-producing area is Knob Lake, 320 miles north of the St. Lawrence River in northern Quebec, where ore reserves amounting to several hundred million tons now have been proved, and after a 360-mile railroad was built in 1954, ore (12 million tons in 1956) can be brought for shipment to a port on the St. Lawrence. In South America are two major areas of Cryptozoic iron-ore deposits. One of these, already partly developed, is located in eastern Venezuela; it is computed to contain more than 6,000 million tons of reserves. The other, rated as possibly the largest iron-ore area in the world, is in the State of Minas Geraes, southern Brazil. Production from this district has been started, but the quantity of output does not yet rival that of Venezuela. Cryptozoic rocks in the Ukraine, western U.S.S.R., annually yield about 30 million tons of iron.

Copper. For many years Precambrian rocks of the Canadian Shield region have been one of the main sources of the world's copper, with aggregate production amounting to more than 11 million tons. The main producing districts are the Keweenaw Peninsula in northern Michigan, Sudbury in eastern Ontario, Noranda in western Quebec, and Manitoba and Saskatchewan with recently developed ore bodies (Fig. 4.41).

In the Keweenaw area native copper is found filling vesicular cavities in lava sheets and spaces between pebbles of conglomerate beds distributed through a thickness of approximately 25,000 feet of middle Keweenawan rocks. These crop out in a belt along the axis of the northeast-trending peninsula,

and the beds are inclined at angles of 30 to 40 degrees northwestward, forming part of the south limb of the broad syncline of Keweenawan rocks that underlies Lake Superior (Fig. 4.25). In places, mining has reached 9,000 feet downward along the copper-bearing layers (Fig. 4.44). No deposits of metallic copper comparable to these are known anywhere else in the world. During more than a century of copper mining in the area, a peak of annual production (135,000 tons of metallic copper) was reached in 1916, since which time the annual yield has dropped to less than one-fifth of this maximum.

At Sudbury, the copper ores are associated with nickel occurring along the outer borders of an elongate, elliptical intrusive mass (36 miles long, 16 miles wide) of basic igneous rock (norite) that has invaded Huronian sedimentary rocks. The igneous mass has been thought to be a sill but now is interpreted as a ring dike. The copper-bearing minerals are sulfides.

At Noranda and in Manitoba and Saskatchewan, the copper deposits occur in Keewatin volcanic and sedimentary rocks and the minerals are sulfides.

Nickel. The Sudbury district in Canada furnishes more than 80 per cent of the entire production of this mineral in the world and since 1887, when mining in the area began, has produced 3.6 million tons of nickel. The sulfide ores contain copper, as well as nickel and some platinum. Recently discovered nickel deposits in Cryptozoic rocks of northern Manitoba are estimated to allow 50 per cent increase of production by 1960.

Gold. Cryptozoic rocks far outweigh all others combined as a source of gold. The total value of gold production from these ancient rocks exceeds $12,000 million, and this sum

Fig. 4.43 (*Opposite page.*) **Open-pit iron mines in Cryptozoic rocks.**—*A.* Mine in Algonkian (Huronian) rocks, Mesabi district, northern Minnesota. (*Courtesy of Bucyrus-Erie Company.*) ——*B.* Mine in Archean (Steep Rock) rocks, Steep Rock Lake district, Ontario. (*Courtesy of National Film Board of Canada.*)

would be appreciably augmented if we added to it the large quantities of Cryptozoic-derived gold found in many placer deposits.

For many years the world leader in gold production has been South Africa, where, since mining in the Witwatersrand district began in 1886, more than 10,000 tons of gold, valued at approximately $8,000 million, has been produced, current annual production being at the rate of about $500 million. The gold is in metallic form, occurring in beds of conglomerate that alternate with quartzite, argillite, and some volcanic flows and iron formations in a series called the Witwatersrand Sequence, 25,000 feet or more in total thickness. This rock succession, now standing almost vertical, rests with great unconformity on granite and schist. Despite some observations pointing to deposition or alteration by the action of hot waters, preponderant evidence indicates that the gold deposits are of placer origin, but if so, the source of the gold in pre-Witwatersrand rocks is unknown.

In North America, gold from Precambrian rocks is obtained mainly from two areas located, respectively, in eastern Ontario and the Black Hills of South Dakota. The richest gold mines of eastern Ontario are clustered in the Porcupine and Kirkland Lake districts, 200 miles north of Sault Ste. Marie, between Lakes Superior and Huron (Fig. 4.41). In both of these districts, the gold, chiefly in metallic form, is found in Keewatin volcanics and unconformably overlying Timiskaming sedimentary rocks; it is thought that the gold-bearing veins are associated with intrusion of the Algoman Granite. Gold production in the Black Hills comes from the Homestake mine at Lead, South Dakota, which processes about 5,000 tons of ore daily and has been rated as the largest single producer of gold in the Western Hemisphere. The gold occurs as veins in Archean schist.

Other important occurrences of gold in Precambrian rocks are found in western Australia (Kalgoorlie and other districts) and in India (Mysore district), where mining has extended to a depth of 8,500 feet below the surface.

Uranium. Approximately 95 per cent of the world's production of uranium ores comes from Cryptozoic rocks in central Africa (Belgian Congo) and in northwestern Canada (Bear Lake district). In both regions the ore occurs as veins of pitchblende in deformed sedimentary and volcanic rocks associated with granitic intrusives.

Other mineral resources. Very important mineral deposits other than those described also come from Cryptozoic rock formations. Among these are platinum (U.S.S.R., Canada), silver (Ontario), lead and zinc (British Columbia, Idaho, New South Wales, New Jer-

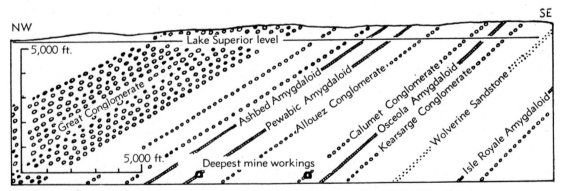

Fig. 4.44 Geologic section of copper-bearing rocks on the Keweenaw Peninsula, northern Michigan. The copper, in metallic form, occurs in conglomerate layers and lavas of the Keweenawan Sequence (late Algonkian). (*Modified from T. M. Broderick.*)

sey), chromium (South Africa, U.S.S.R.), cobalt (Ontario), manganese (India, West
Africa, Brazil), graphite (Korea, Siberia),
mica (U.S.S.R., India), and talc (eastern

United States). The quantity and variety of
all these sources of mineral wealth are impressive.

READINGS

COLEMAN, A. P., 1929, *Ice ages recent and ancient*, The Macmillan Company, New York, pp. 220–241.
COOKE, H. C., 1947, The Canadian Shield: in *Geology and economic minerals of Canada*, Geol. Survey Canada, Econ. Geol. Ser. 1, pp. 11–32.
FENTON, C. L. and FENTON, M. A., 1937. Belt Series of the North, stratigraphy, sedimentation, paleontology: *Geol. Soc. America Bull.*, vol. 48, pp. 1873–1970.
LEITH, C. K., LUND, R. J., and LEITH, A., 1935, Precambrian rocks of the Lake Superior region: *U.S. Geol. Survey Prof. Paper* 184, pp. 1–34.
PETTIJOHN, F. J., 1943, Archean sedimentation: *Geol. Soc. America Bull.*, vol. 54, pp. 925–972.
RAYMOND, P. E., 1935, Pre-Cambrian life: *Geol. Soc. America Bull.*, vol. 46, pp. 375–392.

QUESTIONS

1. Referring to Fig. 4.1, why is the boundary between Cryptozoic and overlying rocks inferred to represent an extremely long time of denudation? Since sediment derived from Cryptozoic rocks that is indicated by their erosion-truncated upper limit must have been deposited somewhere, what place or places are most likely sites for this sedimentation, bearing in mind the fact that strata deposited unconformably on the Cryptozoic cannot be parts of these deposits?

2. What successive times of erosion and sedimentation in pre-Paleozoic history are illustrated by the diagrammatic sections given in Fig. 4.3A to H?

3. What geologic characteristics distinguish the parts of continents designated as shields, illustrated in Fig. 4.5?

4. Referring to Fig. 4.9, what reasons can be suggested for concluding that most of the displacement along the fault is very ancient, long before peneplanation of this part of the shield?

5. Explain how shapes of the "pillows" that characterize subaqueous lava extrusions, as illustrated in Fig. 4.10, indicate upward direction in the flow.

6. Referring to Fig. 4.16, why is intrusion of the Laurentian Granite interpreted to have occurred during or shortly subsequent to deformation of the Keewatin rocks rather than prior to their folding and metamorphic alteration?

7. Why is profound erosion in pre-Timiskaming time indicated by the presence of Laurentian Granite pebbles and cobbles in basal Timiskaming deposits as illustrated in Figs. 4.17 and 4.18?

8. What evidence is seen in the air photographs reproduced in Fig. 4.20 for establishing the age relationships of different kinds of rocks that are distinguishable by their topographic expression and color?

9. Why is the rock illustrated in Fig. 4.22 identified as a tillite rather than a stream-formed gravel deposit or consolidated pebbles of a beach?

10. What sort of evidence is needed to support the mapped location and structural "grain" of Algonkian mountains in the Canadian Shield region shown in Fig. 4.24?

11. Referring to Fig. 4.31, what explanation can be given for the occurrences of Cryptozoic rock exposures in several parts of North America outside the Canadian Shield? Why are the relatively small outcrop areas not classed as diminutive shields, essentially equivalent to the great shield in Canada except for size?

12. How is the granite mass seen in Fig. 4.32 identified as Precambrian in origin? When first formed, was the granite now occurring at the summit of Longs Peak in its present position, and if not, how did it get there?

13. What geologic conditions account for distribution of important iron deposits in Cryptozoic formations as contrasted to those found in gold and nickel districts? In what respects do the Lake Superior copper deposits differ from those of most other copper-producing districts, such as Bingham, Utah; Bisbee, Arizona; and others?

5.

PALEOZOIC ERA:

CAMBRIAN PERIOD

Mt. Eisenhower in the Canadian Rockies is formed by Cambrian rocks.

Courtesy of Royal Canadian Air Force

The Cambrian rocks derive their name from *Cambria,* the Latin name for Wales, where, a century ago, this division of the Paleozoic succession was defined (Fig. 5.1). Together with outcrops in western England, this region furnishes the classic section with which deposits of equivalent age elsewhere in Europe and on other continents are compared and correlated.

Although the nature of the deposits belonging to the Cambrian in different regions is not the same, definition of boundaries belonging to the Cambrian System is based on the type section. Here, as elsewhere, the lowermost fossil-bearing Cambrian strata are underlain conformably by some unfossiliferous layers and then, beneath these, by a profound un-

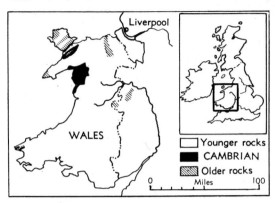

Fig. 5.1 Outcrops of Cambrian rocks in Wales.
The unconformable contact of Cambrian on Precambrian rocks is seen both in northwestern and southwestern Wales. The largest outcrop area has a broad anticlinal structure.

conformity that in parts of the Welsh region is a nonconformity and in other parts an angular unconformity. The rocks below the unconformity are classed as Precambrian.

The upper boundary of the type Cambrian System is less easy to define. Locally the Cambrian is overlain conformably (or ?paraconformably) by shaly beds called Tremadocian; these formerly were classed as uppermost Cambrian, but now, because of important new groups of fossils with Ordovician rather than Cambrian affinities occurring in them, and because in most parts of the world where deposits of this age are recognized the Tremadocian seems to be allied with younger rather than older beds, the upper boundary of the Cambrian System is drawn at the base of the Tremadocian division. At some places in the Welsh type region an angular unconformity marks the surface of separation between Cam-

brian and Ordovician (Fig. 5.2), indicating not only an important interruption of sedimentation near the close of Cambrian time but folding of the Cambrian strata. Parts or, locally, all of the Cambrian rocks were destroyed by erosion, as may be deduced from observing basal Ordovician deposited on various Cambrian beds from youngest to oldest and even on Precambrian (Fig. 6.2).

Study of the Cambrian System in Wales and western England has led to the recognition of three main divisions classed as series; these are called Lower Cambrian, Middle Cambrian, and Upper Cambrian. The boundaries between them are defined in some places by disconformities; elsewhere they are drawn on the basis of change in the fossil assemblages, generally at a more or less arbitrarily chosen marker bed. Instead of complete conformity of the strata, however, unrecognized paraconformities actually may be present, as suggested by abruptness of faunal changes. Each series has been subdivided into four to eight fossil zones, mostly defined by kinds of trilobites, and these serve to establish moderately detailed correlation with Cambrian sections in Scandinavia and other parts of continental Europe. Correlations with North America can be made also, as discussed in a later part of this chapter that considers the paleogeography of Cambrian time.

Distribution and Nature of Cambrian Rocks in North America

Rocks identified as belonging to the Cambrian System are widespread in North America (Fig. 5.3). They are exposed locally in easternmost Canada and eastern New Eng-

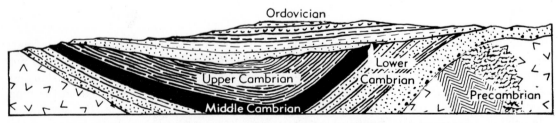

Fig. 5.2 Diagrammatic section showing structural relations and divisions of Cambrian rocks in Wales. Important unconformities occur below and above the Cambrian System. In places, however, Ordovician strata (Tremadocian) lie parallel on Upper Cambrian beds.

land; in a long, fairly continuous narrow belt in the Appalachian Mountains reaching south to Alabama; in a relatively broad, irregularly shaped tract in the upper Mississippi Valley region; and in small patches scattered through the Southwestern and Western States. Beneath the surface, Cambrian rocks extend uninterruptedly throughout territory between outcrops in the Appalachian Mountains belt and those in the Wisconsin-Minnesota region, Missouri, Oklahoma, and central Texas. Buried Cambrian deposits are very extensive also in western United States, western Canada, and northwestern Mexico, but once-present Cambrian formations in a wide belt extending from Saskatchewan and Manitoba in the north to western Texas and Mexico in the south have been removed by erosion. In Idaho, eastern Washington, and parts of other Western States, absence of Cambrian indicated by blank spaces on the map is inferred to be due to engulfment of Cambrian rocks in great bathylithic intrusions or removal by erosion after being displaced by these intrusions.

Eastern Canada and New England. Deposits of predominantly shaly nature several thousand feet thick in Newfoundland, New Brunswick, Maine, and eastern Massachusetts contain some of the same fossils that distinguish the Lower, Middle, and Upper Cambrian in Wales. Evidently a shallow-water connection between these regions existed in Cambrian time, permitting intermigration of marine invertebrate species that neither in larval stages nor as adults could have crossed oceanic deeps (Figs. 5.17 to 5.19). Also, the sea in which these deposits accumulated differed somehow from the contemporaneous shallow seas that spread over interior parts of North America in Cambrian time, because the kinds of trilobites and other invertebrates found in these respective areas differ. Formerly, this was explained by supposing that the New England and eastern Canada region was geographically isolated from other parts of North America in Cambrian time but connected with northwestern Europe, forming part of a so-called Atlantic Province. A land barrier was presumed to prevent migration of "Atlantic"

species into seas of the continental interior and western areas classified as Pacific Province. Added information obtained in recent years and accompanying revision of interpretation lead to the conclusion that the existence of a land barrier is fictitious, the inferred Atlantic and Pacific Provinces being merely expressions of different sedimentary environments, one ("Atlantic") being a mud-bottomed trough along the continental margins and the other ("Pacific") consisting of parts of the continental platform inundated by broad, very shallow seas. The differences are those of sedimentary environment to which the Cambrian invertebrates were sensitive.

The Cambrian formations, wherever seen in New England, the Maritime Provinces of Canada, and Newfoundland, are greatly disturbed, being folded, faulted, and locally metamorphosed (Fig. 5.4). Naturally, the deformation is post-Cambrian in age, because the youngest Cambrian rocks are affected as well as the older. This region has been affected by at least four epochs of mountain-making crustal movements, and therefore one should not expect to find undisturbed Cambrian strata.

Appalachian region. Beginning in Newfoundland and New Brunswick, at the southeast border of the Canadian Shield, outcrops of Cambrian strata are traced almost continuously along the eastern margin of the Appalachian Mountains as far southwest as Georgia and Alabama. Throughout this belt, the rocks have been strongly folded and in places greatly displaced by thrust faults; yet in many places the unconformable contact of the Cambrian System on the unfossiliferous Precambrian rocks may be observed. This statement takes account of the problem in defining the base of the Cambrian in various places, as discussed in the preceding chapter, and the view of some geologists who would exclude from the system all unfossiliferous rocks below the lowest discovered fossils. We do not so restrict the Cambrian, agreeing with most geologists who have worked in the Appalachian region by defining the base of the system as marked by the first major break in

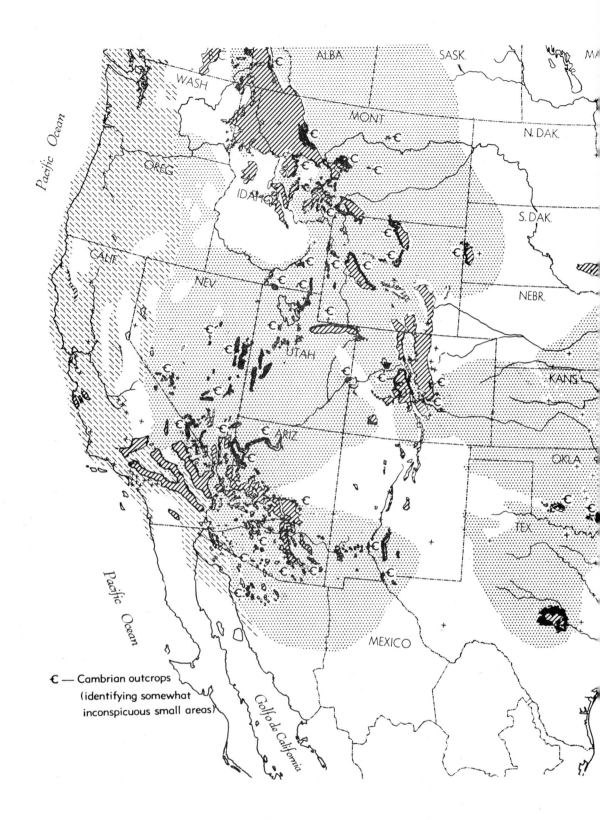

€ — Cambrian outcrops
(identifying somewhat
inconspicuous small areas)

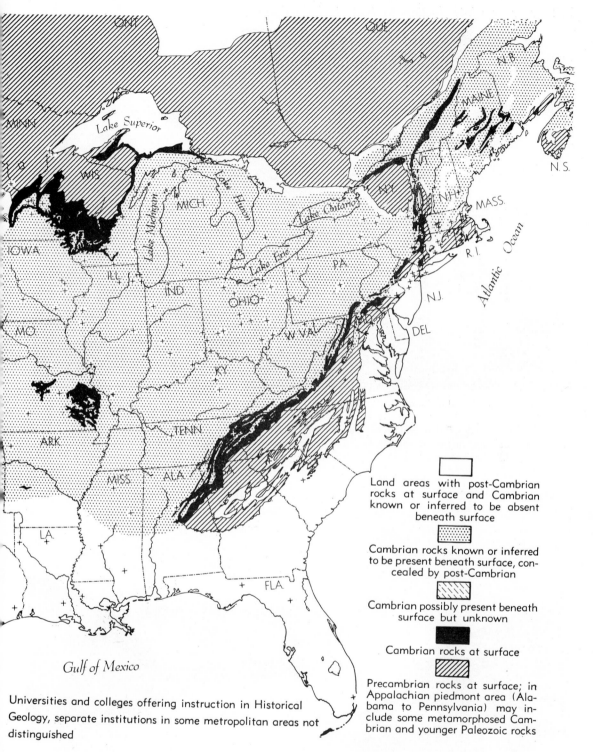

Land areas with post-Cambrian rocks at surface and Cambrian known or inferred to be absent beneath surface

Cambrian rocks known or inferred to be present beneath surface, concealed by post-Cambrian

Cambrian possibly present beneath surface but unknown

Cambrian rocks at surface

Precambrian rocks at surface; in Appalachian piedmont area (Alabama to Pennsylvania) may include some metamorphosed Cambrian and younger Paleozoic rocks

Universities and colleges offering instruction in Historical Geology, separate institutions in some metropolitan areas not distinguished

Fig. 5.3 Distribution of Cambrian rocks in the United States, southern Canada, and northern Mexico. The outcrops and subsurface occurrences shown indicate the original distribution of the system, altered by aggregate destruction of deposits resulting from post-Cambrian erosion or locally from effects of post-Cambrian bathylithic igneous intrusions.

Fig. 5.4 Crumpled Lower Cambrian limestone and dolostone. This outcrop, near Danby in west-central Vermont south of Lake Champlain, shows the typically disturbed nature of Cambrian and other lower Paleozoic rocks that prevails in New England and eastern Canada. The folding of these rocks probably is Taconian (near close of Ordovician). (*Arthur Keith, courtesy of U.S. Geol. Survey.*)

Fig. 5.5 Lower Cambrian quartzite on the Potomac River at Harpers Ferry, Virginia. The strata are steeply upturned as a result of mountain-making movements in late Paleozoic time. The hard rocks make ridges, and the weaker strata form valleys. The view is eastward downstream toward the Blue Ridge. (*Courtesy of Maryland Geol. Survey.*)

sedimentation beneath the lowest known Cambrian fossils. This is at the base of the Antietam Quartzite, Erwin Quartzite, and equivalents (Fig. 5.5). Still lower clastic formations (classed as Eocambrian on the chart, Fig. 5.7) may belong to the Cambrian, but this is doubtful.

Although Cambrian deposits of the Appalachian region commonly aggregate a mile in thickness, the outcrops do not cover broad areas; because of steep dip, they have the shape of long, narrow strips, running nearly straight for many miles and then changing direction abruptly as they follow the pattern of rock folding. The lower two-thirds or three-fourths of the section in most places consists of quartzite and sandy shale, whereas the remaining upper part is limestone (Figs. 5.5, 5.6). Well-preserved marine fossils are found in many places.

The Cambrian rocks are divided into many formations that are defined chiefly by lithologic characters (Fig. 5.7). Occurrence of unconformities and evidence furnished by fossils are the bases for recognizing lower, middle, and upper main divisions called *series,* and these in turn contain time-rock units classed as *stages* and *zones.*

Because of striking differences in the nature of sedimentary deposits at the same stratigraphic level (denoting equivalence in age) as they are traced laterally, classification in terms of rock units offers complex problems (Fig. 1.29). These variations reflect contemporaneous contrasted types of sedimentary environment which are expressed as facies that change most rapidly in northwest-to-southeast directions, at right angles to the Appalachian Mountains trend. In Early and Middle Cambrian time, clastic sediments consisting of fine sand and clay predominated toward the northwest, dolostone being laid down in southeastern areas; in the Late Cambrian, deposits in these two tracts consist almost exclusively of very cherty dolostone in the northwest and fine-grained limestone in the southeast.

Central States. Under the designation of Central States we include all territory between the Appalachians and the Rockies, which is geologically appropriate because

everywhere the Cambrian strata are found to be essentially flat-lying. Also, they are thin as compared with deposits belonging to the system in the Appalachian and Cordilleran belts. Finally, reference to the chart (Fig. 5.7) showing representative Cambrian rock successions brings to notice the fact that Lower and Middle Cambrian deposits are lacking in the Central States (although specialists in study of the Cambrian think that some beds now classed as Dresbachian, in the lower part of the Upper Cambrian, really may belong to the Middle Cambrian Series).

Easternmost outcrops of flat-lying Upper Cambrian border the Adirondack Uplift in northeastern New York. They show sandstone (called Potsdam) resting nonconformably on Precambrian, locally with prominent basal conglomerate composed of pebbles and cobbles of Precambrian rocks (Figs. 5.8, 5.9).

The Mississippi Valley region, in the interior of the continent, also contains exposures of Cambrian formations, mostly sandstone and shale, totaling less than 1,000 feet in aggregate thickness. Outcrops of nearly flat-lying strata, many miles in width, occur south of Lake Su-

Fig. 5.6 Ripple-marked limestone in eastern Pennsylvania. The ripple marks prove that this deposit (Conococheague) was made in shallow water. The steeply tilted attitude of the old sea bottom is due to late Paleozoic deformation. (*Courtesy of Pennsylvania Geol. Survey.*)

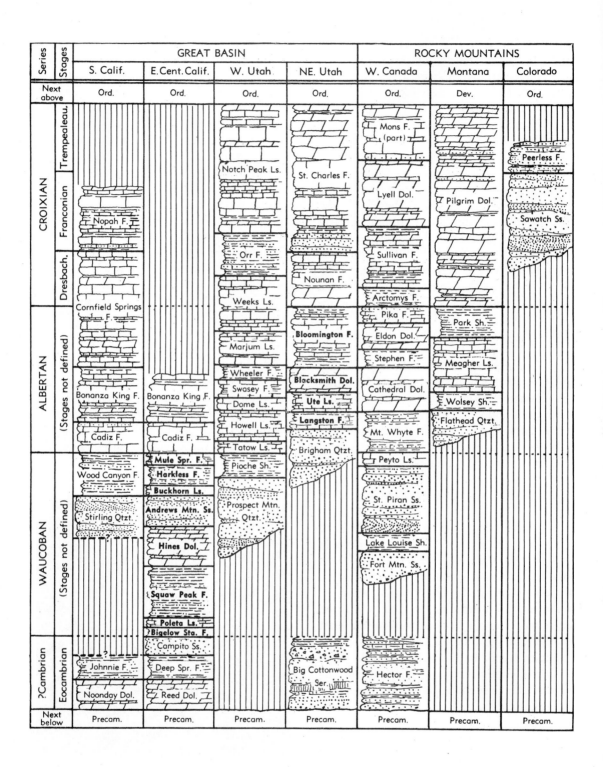

Series	Stages	GREAT BASIN				ROCKY MOUNTAINS		
		S. Calif.	E. Cent. Calif.	W. Utah	NE. Utah	W. Canada	Montana	Colorado
Next above		Ord.	Ord.	Ord.	Ord.	Ord.	Dev.	Ord.
CROIXIAN	Trempealeau.	Nopah F.		Notch Peak Ls.	St. Charles F.	Mons F. (part)	Pilgrim Dol.	Peerless F.
	Franconian					Lyell Dol.		Sawatch Ss.
	Dresbach.	Cornfield Springs F.		Orr F.	Nounan F.	Sullivan F.		
				Weeks Ls.		Arctomys F.		
ALBERTAN	(Stages not defined)	Bonanza King F.	Bonanza King F.	Marjum Ls.	Bloomington F.	Pika F.	Park Sh.	
				Wheeler F.	Blacksmith Dol.	Eldon Dol.		
				Swasey F.	Ute Ls.	Stephen F.	Meagher Ls.	
				Dome Ls.	Langston F.	Cathedral Dol.	Wolsey Sh.	
		Cadiz F.	Cadiz F.	Howell Ls.	Brigham Qtzt.	Mt. Whyte F.	Flathead Qtzt.	
				Tatow Ls.				
WAUCOBAN	(Stages not defined)	Wood Canyon F.	Mule Spr. F.	Pioche Sh.		Peyto Ls.		
			Harkless F.			St. Piran Ss.		
			Buckhorn Ls.					
		Stirling Qtzt.	Andrews Mtn. Ss.	Prospect Mtn. Qtzt.		Lake Louise Sh.		
			Hines Dol.			Fort Mtn. Ss.		
			Squaw Peak F.					
			Poleta Ls.					
			Bigelow Sta. F.					
?Cambrian	Eocambrian		Campito Ss.		Big Cottonwood Ser.			
		Johnnie F.	Deep Spr. F.			Hector F.		
		Noonday Dol.	Reed Dol.					
Next below		Precam.	Precam.	Precam.	Precam.	Precam.	Precam.	Precam.

114

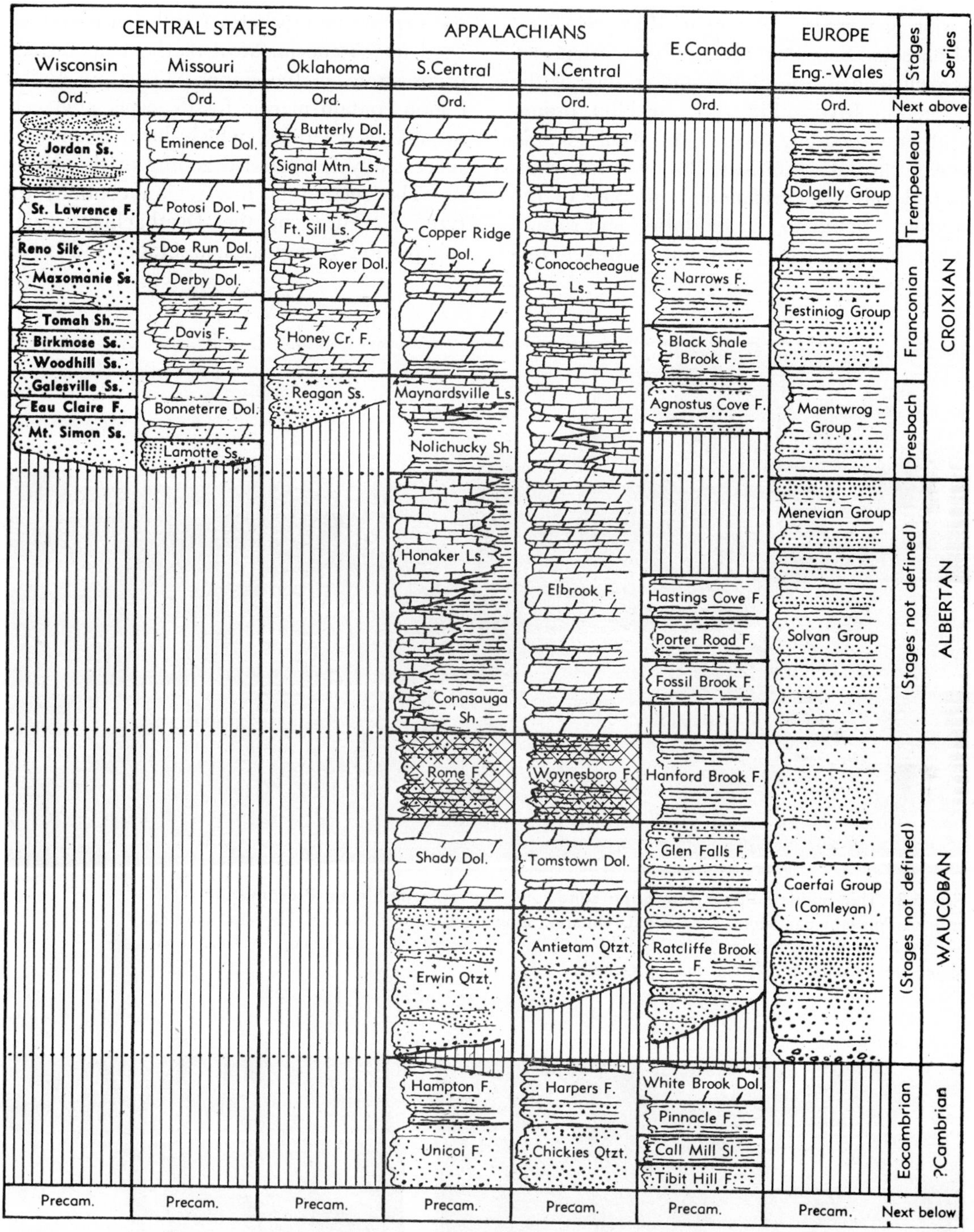

CENTRAL STATES			APPALACHIANS		E.Canada	EUROPE	Stages	Series
Wisconsin	Missouri	Oklahoma	S.Central	N.Central		Eng.-Wales		
Ord.	Ord.	Ord.	Ord.	Ord.	Ord.	Ord.	Next above	

Central States — Wisconsin: Jordan Ss.; St. Lawrence F.; Reno Silt.; Maxomanie Ss.; Tomah Sh.; Birkmose Ss.; Woodhill Ss.; Galesville Ss.; Eau Claire F.; Mt. Simon Ss.

Central States — Missouri: Eminence Dol.; Potosi Dol.; Doe Run Dol.; Derby Dol.; Davis F.; Bonneterre Dol.; Lamotte Ss.

Central States — Oklahoma: Butterly Dol.; Signal Mtn. Ls.; Ft. Sill Ls.; Royer Dol.; Honey Cr. F.; Reagan Ss.

Appalachians — S.Central: Copper Ridge Dol.; Maynardsville Ls.; Nolichucky Sh.; Honaker Ls.; Conasauga Sh.; Rome F.; Shady Dol.; Erwin Qtzt.; Hampton F.; Unicoi F.

Appalachians — N.Central: Conococheague Ls.; Elbrook F.; Waynesboro F.; Tomstown Dol.; Antietam Qtzt.; Harpers F.; Chickies Qtzt.

E.Canada: Narrows F.; Black Shale Brook F.; Agnostus Cove F.; Hastings Cove F.; Porter Road F.; Fossil Brook F.; Hanford Brook F.; Glen Falls F.; Ratcliffe Brook F.; White Brook Dol.; Pinnacle F.; Call Mill Sl.; Tibit Hill F.

Europe — Eng.-Wales: Dolgelly Group; Festiniog Group; Maentwrog Group; Menevian Group; Solvan Group; Caerfai Group (Comleyan).

Stages: Trempealeau; Franconian; Dresbach; (Stages not defined); (Stages not defined); Eocambrian.

Series: CROIXIAN; ALBERTAN; WAUCOBAN; ?Cambrian.

Bottom row: Precam. | Precam. | Precam. | Precam. | Precam. | Precam. | Precam. | Next below |

Fig. 5.7 Time-rock divisions of the Cambrian System and rock units assigned to them in representative important Cambrian sections of North America. The vertical scale does not represent time duration or thickness of rocks but is determined by suitability for plotting the various recognized rock units, placement of which indicates correlation in age. Lithologic character is represented graphically (explanation of symbols in Appendix B). Necessarily the plotted thickness, although approximating proportional values in many sections, is not to scale. Vertically ruled areas denote absence of deposits.

perior in northern Michigan, Wisconsin, and Minnesota. Some of the sandstone deposits, as well seen in the picturesque Dalles of the Wisconsin River (Fig. 5.10), exhibit prominent cross-bedding, which, of itself, simply proves current action; the discovery of wind-shaped pebbles (dreikanter) in some of the sandstone points to transportation and sorting of the sand by winds, without, however, fur-

nishing testimony that a Cambrian desert existed in Wisconsin. Most of the Upper Cambrian strata in the upper Mississippi Valley region contain marine fossils, especially well-preserved trilobites, which have been used successfully for detailed zoning of the deposits. The section of this region contains the type exposures of the Dresbachian, Franconian, and Trempealeauan Stages and is rec-

Fig. 5.8 Thin-bedded Upper Cambrian sandstone nonconformable on Precambrian. Outcrop of Potsdam Sandstone near Elgin, Ontario, showing the very smoothly beveled surface of Precambrian schistose rocks parallel to bedding planes of the sandstone, no basal conglomerate. (*Courtesy of Geol. Survey Canada.*)

Fig. 5.9 Basal conglomerate of Late Cambrian age in eastern Ontario.——*A.* Potsdam nonconformable on Precambrian (Grenville), near Lyndhurst.——*B.* Outcrop of Potsdam Sandstone with coarse basal conglomerate, near Brockville. (*Courtesy of Geol. Survey Canada.*)

Fig. 5.10 Cross-bedded Upper Cambrian sandstone in south-central Wisconsin. These outcrops occur along the Dalles of the Wisconsin River near Kilbourn.

ognized as the standard for correlation of Upper Cambrian strata in North America.

Outcrops of Cambrian rocks found on the flanks of structural uplifts, such as the Black Hills in South Dakota; the Ozark Highland in Missouri; the Ouachita, Arbuckle, and Wichita Mountains in southern Oklahoma; and the Llano Uplift in central Texas, are comparatively small in area, but they are broad in terms of thickness of the Cambrian rocks present. This breadth of outcrop pattern is most evident in the upper Mississippi Valley, the large width being due to the nearly flat-lying attitude of the strata and low topographic relief.

Correlations by means of marine fossils accurately determine equivalences of the widely scattered small exposed sections of Cambrian in the Central States. In addition, the Cambrian strata have been traced beneath the surface, utilizing information obtained from thousands of wells.

Cordilleran region. The Cordilleran region of the western United States and Canada contains fine sections of Cambrian strata in many places. The thickest deposits, locally exceed-

ing 10,000 feet, are found farthest west—in California, Nevada, Utah, Idaho, Montana, and the Canadian Rockies—where the lower one-fourth is made up of quartzite and the upper three-fourths chiefly of limestone. In most of the outcrop areas, the rocks are not strongly folded, and magnificent exposures of little-disturbed Cambrian strata may be studied by climbing the mountainsides (Figs. 5.11, 5.12, 5.13). Marine fossils are abundant in many places.

The Inyo Mountains, near Death Valley in eastern California, contain the thickest and seemingly most complete section of Lower Cambrian rocks known on the continent. Recent studies of these rocks by C. A. Nelson show that the trilobite *Olenellus* ranges through 14,900 feet of beds, representing the entire Lower Cambrian (unless 7,500 feet of unfossiliferous beds that underlie the *Olenellus*-bearing beds with seeming conformity also are classed as Cambrian) (Fig. 5.3). The name *Waucoban*, applied to the Lower Cambrian Series, is derived from this same region. Several very important Cambrian sections occur in Nevada and Utah, one of which is in

Ordovician

ambrian

UPPER

ambrian

MIDDLE

ambrian

Fig. 5.11 Cambrian strata forming Mt. Robson, highest peak (12,972 feet) in the Canadian Rockies. This mountain, located in eastern British Columbia, is capped by Lower Ordovician rocks and based on Algonkian (Belt Sequence) sedimentary rocks, but most of its mass is composed of nearly horizontal Cambrian strata. (*Courtesy of National Film Board of Canada; rock identifications by R. J. Douglas, Geol. Survey Canada.*)

the House Range of west-central Utah (Fig. 5.14).

Few regions, if any, offer such continuously well-exposed sections of Cambrian rocks as the Grand Canyon of Colorado River (Fig. 1.28), allowing not only reliable determination of Cambrian history of the region but recognition of important principles for study of sedimentary facies and geologic age of deposits that vary considerably in thickness from place to place (Fig. 5.15). More of Cambrian time is recorded by rocks found in western parts of the canyon than in the east, and contemporaneous differences in kinds of sedimentation in these areas are proved by interfingering of dolostone with limestone, limestone with shale, and shale with sandstone. Persistent fossil zones and the occurrence of

some widespread distinctive rock layers (key beds) help greatly in working out the geologic relationships.

Significance of Variations

Before we can interpret the history of Cambrian time in North America, we must examine the nature of Cambrian deposition in different parts of the continent more closely, taking note especially of the evidence furnished by fossils. We must learn also, as exactly as possible, the meaning of the great variations in Cambrian deposits that are found from place to place.

Does the greater thickness of Cambrian rocks in the Appalachian and Cordilleran areas, as compared with the Central States, signify a much longer and fuller record of

Fig. 5.12 Gently inclined Cambrian strata in the Canadian Rockies. This view of Mt. Temple, in western Alberta, shows more than 5,000 feet of Cambrian beds. They form part of the great accumulation of deposits that were laid down in the Cordilleran geosyncline.

Cambrian time than that found in Wisconsin or Missouri? Not necessarily. Sedimentation rates under varying conditions are by no means constant. If such average rate were ten times slower in Wisconsin than in Nevada during the Cambrian Period, 1,000 feet of Wisconsin Cambrian beds would represent as much geologic time as the making of deposits 10,000 feet thick in Nevada.

Let us postulate that rates of deposition were actually less uneven. Then the smaller thickness of Cambrian strata in the Central States would mean that a lesser part of Cambrian time is represented by the thinner deposits because of (1) absence of sedimentation during some portion of the period, (2) erosion that has obliterated part of the record, or (3) both.

Conceivably, the thin Cambrian of the continental interior might represent only the lower part of the whole Cambrian succession, middle and upper parts never having been laid down there, or perhaps Middle and Upper Cambrian, once present in this region, were entirely eroded before deposition of Ordovician rocks. Again, if the thin Cambrian represents some other part of the system, the case is entirely different. We need to know the age relations of the Cambrian sections in each region, and for this we must turn to the fossils and recognize divisions of the Cambrian that are based on fossils.

Cambrian Guide Fossils

Cambrian deposits of eastern Canada and part of New England are found to contain European species of Cambrian fossils associated with others that are restricted to the American side of the Atlantic. Thus, these sections can be divided and correlated. The

Labels on image: Eldon Dol. / ephen F. / athedral Dol. / Mt. Whyte F / St. Piran Ss.

Fig. 5.13 Middle Cambrian rocks in western Alberta, type region of the Albertan Series.
This view of Mt. Eisenhower, in Banff National Park west of Calgary, shows all but topmost strata belonging to the Middle Cambrian. (*Courtesy of National Film Board of Canada; geology by R. J. Douglas, Geol. Survey Canada.*)

dominant guide fossils are primitive marine arthropods called *trilobites*, characterized by prominently three-lobed body form (Fig. 5.16). These and all other groups of fossils having importance in historical geology are described in Appendix A, and the reader should consult the descriptions as often as needed. Also useful, but secondary in importance, are small, lime-phosphate-shelled brachiopods, which are forerunners of the great group of bilaterally symmetrical two-shelled marine invertebrates, that in later Paleozoic fossil assemblages came to have front rank. Lastly, there are a few snails and the steeply conical shells called *hyolithids*.

On the basis of these fossils, especially the trilobites, equivalents of Lower, Middle, and Upper Cambrian, as defined in the European section, are identified. For example, the Lower Cambrian is especially characterized by a group of trilobites (olenellids) having a sharp-spiked tail and large, narrowly crescentic eyes (Fig. 5.16). This form does not extend upward into Middle Cambrian rocks.

It is important to bear in mind that geographic factors almost universally affect or control distribution of different organic assemblages, and this has been true in the earth's past as it is today. Migration of bottom-dwelling, shallow-water marine invertebrates is impeded by very great distances, variations in temperature or salinity, changes in the nature of bottom sediments, and the like; it may be prevented entirely by deep water of ocean basins, if this must be crossed, or by a land barrier such as the Isthmus of Panama, which keeps present-day faunas of Atlantic and Pacific waters of this region apart.

Fig. 5.14 Western front of the House Range in west-central Utah. The view shows an unusually fine section of Cambrian strata. Rock units distinguished in this region are indicated in the western Utah column of Fig. 5.3.

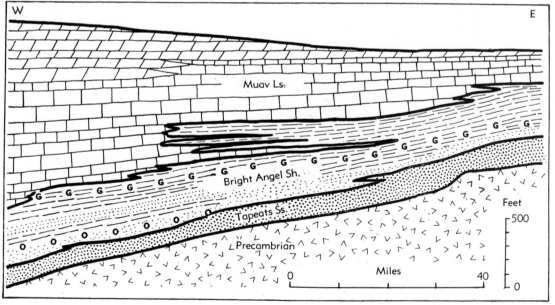

Fig. 5.15 Diagrammatic section of Cambrian rocks exposed in the Grand Canyon, northern Arizona. The rocks increase in thickness westward and exhibit changes of facies, age equivalence of beds from place to place being determined by their interfingering relations, by observing the distribution of persistent fossil zones (trilobites *Olenellus* and *Glossopleura* marked by *O* and *G* on the drawing), and by tracing numerous key beds. (*Modified from E. D. McKee.*)

The fact that European guide fossils of Cambrian rocks are found in Newfoundland, southeastern Labrador, New Brunswick, and eastern New England serves to identify the occurrence in eastern North America of Cambrian divisions equivalent to those in Wales. The animals represented by these fossils lived on the bottom of shallow seas, and accordingly we must conclude that in Cambrian time there was a shallow-water pathway of migration between what are today opposite sides of the North Atlantic (Figs. 5.17 to 5.19).

Lower Cambrian spike-tailed trilobites and other guide fossils, equivalent to those of Europe and northeastern North America, occur also in the lower part of the Cambrian throughout the Appalachian belt and in the Far West but are entirely unknown in the intervening country of the Mississippi Basin. This means that there must have been open shallow-water connections between areas where the faunas occur, passageway to the west probably being located around the northern margin of the continent.

The Middle and Upper Cambrian of northwestern Europe and northeastern North America contain similar fossils because the deposits of these regions were laid down in a connected trough in which the sedimentary environment was much the same throughout

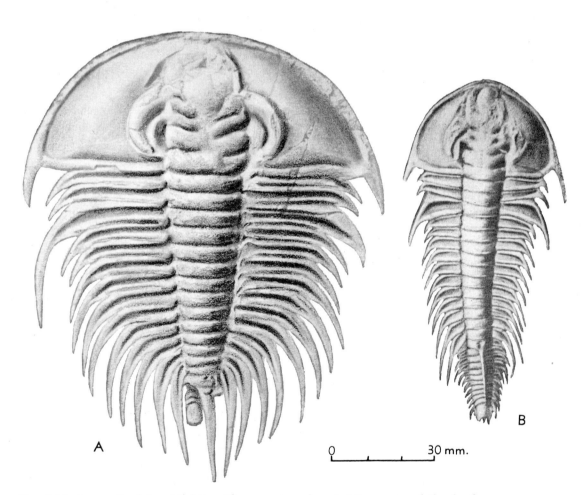

Fig. 5.16 Lower Cambrian trilobites. These are two characteristic species of the family Olenellidae, which includes index or guide fossils used throughout much of the world for identification of Lower Cambrian deposits.——A. *Olenellus thompsoni,* from Nevada, a characteristic western species.——B. *O. vermontanus,* from Vermont, an eastern species.

(Figs. 5.18, 5.19). The far western part of North America contains Cambrian deposits and faunas of like character, but the very wide shelf-sea domain in Middle and Late Cambrian time was quite different in the nature of its sediments and shallow-water faunas. As previously noted, the formations once were thought to denote a geographically separated "Pacific Province" with a land barrier barring passage into the "Atlantic Province." In the light of present knowledge, this interpretation must be discarded, for Pacific really means shelf-sea environment and Atlantic means trough environment. No barrier separated them. In fact, intermediate shelf and trough deposits occur where environments fluctuated.

Geographic Pattern of North America in Cambrian Time

Geosynclines and borderlands. The Cambrian deposits of the Appalachian and Cordilleran areas are thousands of feet thick, and the areas occupied by these thick deposits are very much greater in a general north-south direction than from east to west. They may be described as belts of thick sediments having trends roughly parallel to the borders of the continent. This concentration of deposition is a very interesting and important feature in the geologic history of our continent, for the pattern of Cambrian sedimentation is closely repeated by that of later Paleozoic periods.

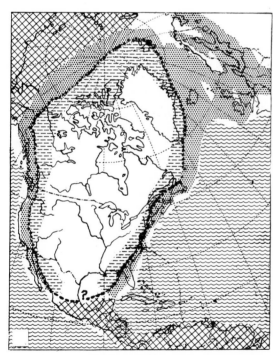

Fig. 5.17 Paleogeography of North America and northwestern Europe in Waucoban (Early Cambrian) time. The map is based on correlation of deposits that takes account of sedimentary environment (see Fig. 5.19 for explanation) as well as equivalence in age. In parallel pathways faunas adapted to the clear shallow water of shelf seas and those mainly restricted to mud-bottomed troughs were able to migrate as far as their preferred environment extended. (*Modified from Christina Lochman and James Lee Wilson.*)

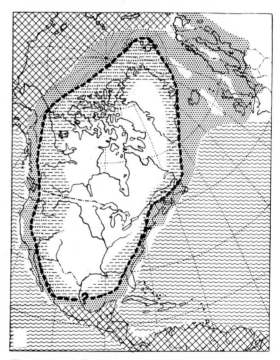

Fig. 5.18 Paleogeography of North America and northwestern Europe in Albertan (Middle Cambrian) time. This map resembles closely that given in Fig. 5.17 except that in the west a narrow belt of "mixed faunas" is recognized, these assemblages including some typical shelf-sea invertebrates associated with forms that mostly are restricted to mud-bottomed troughs. This is a help because it serves to establish the age equivalence of the dissimilar shelf-sea and trough faunas. (*Modified from Christina Lochman and James Lee Wilson.*)

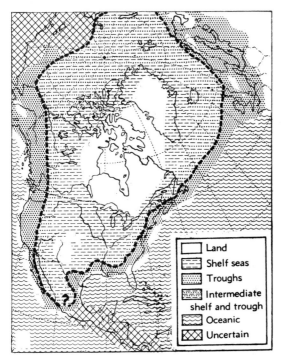

Fig. 5.19 Paleogeography of North America and northwestern Europe in Croixian (Late Cambrian) time. Great expansion of the shelf seas characterizes this part of Cambrian history; also, comparatively wide belts of intermediate shelf and trough faunas are recognized. Only the Canadian Shield region and a persistent land area in southwestern United States were unsubmerged areas in the interior of the continent, but on the outer side of the trough belt narrow land areas (exact location and size wholly conjectural) are represented, because clastic sediments in considerable quantity must have come from them. (*Modified from Christina Lochman and James Lee Wilson.*)

Legend:
- Land
- Shelf seas
- Troughs
- Intermediate shelf and trough
- Oceanic
- Uncertain

The belts of thick sedimentation define the location of crustal features called *geosynclines* (Fig. 5.20). These are elongate, relatively mobile tracts of the earth's crust that slowly subside to form troughlike depressions, thus inviting inundation by shallow seas that extend from ocean basins and furnishing natural sites for accumulation of sediment worn from adjacent land. Actually, they consist of a varying number of subordinate troughs separated by intervening narrow belts of relative uplift (or subsidence smaller than that of the subordinate troughs), and these structural elements within the geosyncline tend to become ac-

centuated in the course of time. Ultimately they come to govern the manner in which sedimentary deposits of the whole geosyncline are deformed by mountain-building forces. Considerable local variations in thickness of rock units and complex facies relationships are introduced as sediments accumulate in the subordinate troughs.

The gradualness of crustal sinking in a geosynclinal belt is proved by the prevailing shallow-water nature of the marine deposits laid down in the belt, and subaerial deposits are found also. In water-laid sediments the presence of cross-bedding, ripple marks, mud cracks, etc., gives reliable evidence of shallow water; moreover, the invertebrates preserved as fossils are nearly all types adapted to living on sea bottoms not far below the surface. Since physical and biological evidence of this sort is found throughout geosynclinal deposits having aggregate thickness of 30,000 to 60,000 feet or even more, the conclusion is inescapable that subsidence was slow.

As a complement of downwarping in a geosynclinal belt with its subordinate troughs, an adjacent part or parts of the earth's crust tend to rise. Uplift affects a linear tract running parallel to the geosyncline for distances of many hundred miles (possibly more than 3,000 miles), width of the raised belt being generally only a few scores of miles. This is a *geanticline*. Erosion of a geanticline furnishes sediment to the adjacent geosyncline, and study of the geosynclinal clastic sediments indicates that a preponderant part of them are derivatives of the geanticline rather than of stable platform areas on one side or other of the geosyncline. These observations have general validity.

A geanticline bordered the *Appalachian geosyncline* along its eastern side, forming a so-called borderland of the North American continent, this borderland being named *Appalachia*. It furnished most of the clay, silt, sand, and coarser rock detritus that was spread into troughs of the geosyncline from Algonkian time to the close of the Paleozoic Era. As interpreted by some geologists, including such authoritative stratigraphers as

Charles Schuchert (1858–1942) and E. O. Ulrich (1857–1944), Appalachia was a comparatively large land mass extending eastward well out into the Atlantic Ocean; it was a small subcontinent having the general attributes of the Canadian Shield region but tending periodically to be pushed upward and thus to have mountainous topography. This view now is rejected generally, and Appalachia is judged to have had the character of island arcs such as exist today along parts of the Pacific Ocean border. These arcs, probably formed by compression and uplift of marginal parts of the Appalachian geosyncline itself (or Precambrian antecedent of this geosyncline), may have had great linear extent but not great width, the volume of sediment derived from them being accounted for by repeated uplifts and denudations. Thus interpreted, Appalachia was located on the outer side of the extensive trough belt shown on the Cambrian paleogeographic maps (Figs. 5.17 to 5.19), not between the trough and shelf-sea area of the continent.

The long north-south geosyncline in western United States and Canada is known as the *Cordilleran geosyncline,* and the borderland on the Pacific side of North America is called *Cascadia.* Revised interpretation of Cascadia is exactly like that of Appalachia.

During Early Cambrian time, Cascadia furnished much sand and some finer clastic sediments to the Cordilleran trough, in the region of which thick Lower Cambrian quartzites and shaly rocks now are seen. In Middle and Late Cambrian time most deposits formed in the Cordilleran trough consist of limestones and dolostones. The unimportance of shale and virtual absence of sandstone in the middle and upper parts of the Cambrian succession indicate that adjacent lands must have been low-lying and therefore undergoing very little mechanical erosion.

Interior platform. The broad area lying between the Appalachian and Cordilleran geosynclines seems nowhere to have been submerged by the sea during Waucoban or Albertan time, because in this region Cambrian deposits older than Croixian have not been discovered. Accordingly, we conclude that the continental interior was then a land area, though evidently not much above sea level, because little sediment in the geosynclines seems to have come from this part of the continent. In the late part of the Cambrian Period, the Mississippi Basin area was gradually and somewhat uniformly depressed, or else the level of the sea was sufficiently raised to cause marine waters to flood this part of the continent broadly. Fine materials that had been weathered from the Precambrian rocks throughout the region during the time it had been land were sorted by the sea, and they form parts of the Late Cambrian deposits which now are exposed or lie buried under younger formations in this region. Some sediments also probably were carried into the Mississippi Valley area from the Canadian Shield. Unlike the Late Cambrian deposits in the geosynclines, which are largely limestone and dolostone, sediments of the interior platform are predominantly shale and sandstone, and their aggregate thickness is much less than in the geosynclines.

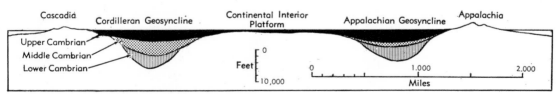

Fig. 5.20 Diagrammatic section across the middle part of North America in an east-west direction, showing Cambrian deposits and configuration of the Precambrian floor. This figure indicates important distinctions between Cambrian deposits of the continental interior platform and of the two adjacent north-south trending geosynclines. Repeated uplift of the borderlands called Cascadia and Appalachia furnished the source for most of the sediments carried to the geosynclines. The vertical scale is greatly exaggerated.

Cambrian Life

The nature of the dominant kinds of Cambrian marine invertebrates has already been noted in reference to guide fossils and in discussing differentiation of Cambrian seaways, as defined by the assemblages of life in them. Although several classes of invertebrates that make their first appearance in Ordovician rocks are unknown in the Cambrian, the variety of trilobite species (Figs. 5.16, 5.21 to 5.23) and of brachiopods is amazing.

Plant life is poorly represented among Cambrian fossils, and only forms adapted for life in the sea are known. We may be sure that aquatic plants (algae) were abundant and varied, because they are the source, direct or indirect, of all the food of animals. Therefore, an abundance of animals presupposes an abundance of plants. Most plants, however, are poorly adapted for preservation as fossils. The one type that has left a good paleontological record in Cambrian rocks comprises lime-secreting seaweeds (calcareous algae) that are marked by fine concentric laminae of calcium carbonate. They form rounded masses a few inches to several feet in diameter and locally are important rock builders (Fig. 5.24).

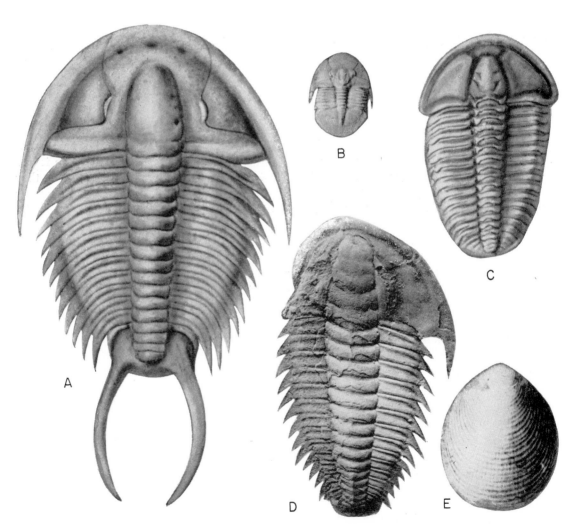

Fig. 5.21 Representative Cambrian invertebrate fossils.—A. *Tricrepicephalus* (Croixian). —B. *Cedaria* (Croixian).—C. *Conocoryphe* (Albertan).—D. *Redlichia* (Waucoban).—E. *Obolella* (Waucoban phosphatic brachiopod). Natural size.

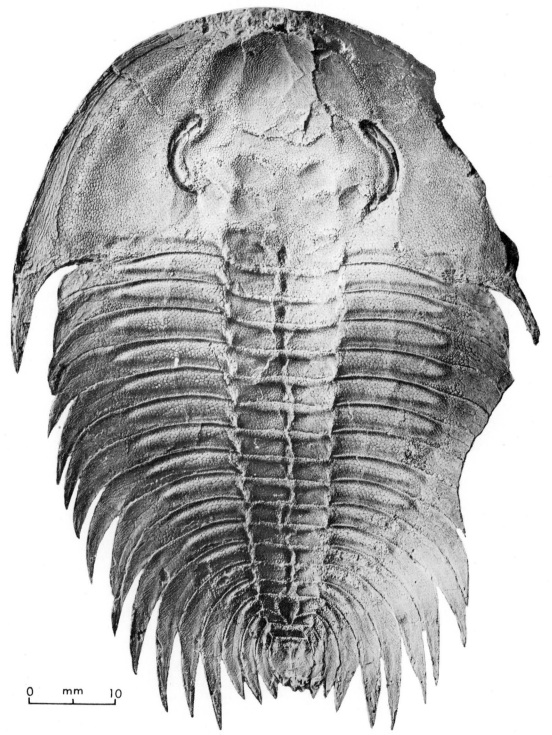

0   mm   10

Fig. 5.22 Lower Cambrian trilobite. Surface markings of the carapace are exceptionally well preserved. *Wanneria walcottana,* from the vicinity of Lancaster, Pennsylvania. (*Courtesy of U.S. National Museum.*)

No fishes or other animals having backbones are known from beds as old as Cambrian (record of a supposed fish, *Eoichthys*, from Middle Cambrian rocks of Vermont, not being accepted). It would not be very surprising, however, if they turned up somewhere in these rocks, inasmuch as Ordovician deposits containing abundant vertebrate remains of primitive type are known. Of course these Ordovician animals had ancestors. Exceptionally large trails made by an unknown kind of animal remind us of the incompleteness of our acquaintance with the forms of life that existed in Cambrian time (Fig. 5.25).

Exceptional fossil assemblage from British Columbia. An unusual glimpse of marine life that existed in an arm of the Pacific some 500 million years ago is furnished by layers of black Middle Cambrian shale near the town of Field, British Columbia, on the Canadian-Pacific Railway about 100 miles west of Calgary. High on a mountainside have been found thousands of specimens representing upward of 130 species of Cambrian organisms, most of which are entirely unknown elsewhere. They include a strange and varied assortment of arthropods, soft-bodied worms, jellyfish, sponges, and other invertebrates, in which minute details of structure are imprinted on bedding planes of the shale as tissue-thin films of carbon. Delicate external structures, such as bristles and scales, and even internal parts, such as the alimentary tracts of some creatures, are shown (Fig. 5.26). Ordinarily, the remains of such animals are destroyed by bacteria, or they are devoured by scavengers on the sea bottom, and thus all traces of them are lost. This local area of Middle Cambrian black shale shows a section of former sea bottom in which bacteria and scavengers evidently could not live, just as today they cannot survive in the stagnant unoxygenated waters on the floor of the Black Sea. The animals preserved as fossils could not have lived in this environment, but evidently they sank into it from above, being buried at length in the soft black

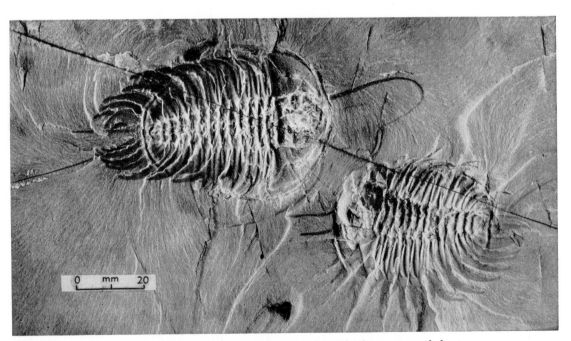

Fig. 5.23 Middle Cambrian trilobites with appendages preserved. The specimens belong to the species *Olenoides serratus*. They were collected from the Burgess Shale member of the Stephen Formation in British Columbia. In addition to walking legs that project from the carapace, long curved antennae and a pair of caudal cerci can be discerned. (*Courtesy of U.S. National Museum.*)

ooze. Flattened by the weight of sediments, the carbon of their bodies has been concentrated as the shiny film that now appears on the bedding planes of the shale. An interesting reconstruction of the Burgess Shale sea bottom, showing a few of the many known kinds of invertebrates, is given in Fig. 5.27.

Climate

The nature of climates in Cambrian time is largely a matter of guesswork, especially since inferences have to be made mainly from study of marine deposits. We know that glacial climates prevailed in different parts of the world near the beginning of the Cambrian Period, for deposits of glacial till of Late Precambrian or Early Cambrian age furnish evidence. However, widespread deposition of pure limestone and dolostone, especially in Middle and Late Cambrian time, and general similarity of the Cambrian marine organisms in high and low latitudes are interpreted to mean moderately warm equable conditions, without differentiation of prominent climatic belts. Some Cambrian limestones contain thick reef deposits that were built by coral-like organisms, and inasmuch as modern coral reefs are confined to warm waters, it is reasonable, lacking con-

Fig. 5.24 Rock mass made by lime-secreting seaweeds. Representative of Cambrian plant life is a large calcareous algal mass in Upper Cambrian marine deposits of central Texas. (*Courtesy of A. H. Deen, University of Texas.*)

trary evidence, to suppose that the Cambrian reefs also were formed in warm water.

Sandy deposits of Late Cambrian age in Wisconsin and Texas contain faceted pebbles that bear the characteristic marks of wind abrasion. These certainly point to subaerial

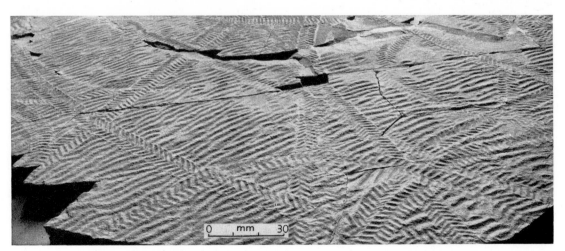

Fig. 5.25 Distinctive trails on ripple-marked Upper Cambrian sandstone. The pattern of these trails, found on a bedding plane in northeastern New York, suggests that they were made by some large arthropod, but since parts of the animal itself have not been found, the trail marker is unknown. (*Courtesy of U.S. National Museum.*)

drifting of sand, as in desert areas. The sandstone deposits associated with the wind-faceted pebbles are highly cross-bedded, and in part they may represent actual dune deposits, but other parts, judged by their bedding and by occurrence of marine fossils, were laid in water. At least local and perhaps temporary arid regions on land may thus be inferred to be a feature of Cambrian climate.

Close of the Period

Withdrawal of seas from the continents. In the latter part of Cambrian time the seas had spread widely over lands that had been worn low (Fig. 5.19). The period was brought to a close by withdrawal of these seas in many places, although it must be admitted that physical evidence of interrupted sedimentation in various parts of North America is obscure, the boundary between Cambrian and Ordovician rocks being a paraconformity or barely perceptible disconformity. Possibly some sections in the Appalachian and Cordilleran trough areas are continuous, without any interruption in sedimentation in passing from uppermost Cambrian into deposits classed as Lower Ordovician, but if so, this remains to be demonstrated. In other sections, as, for ex-

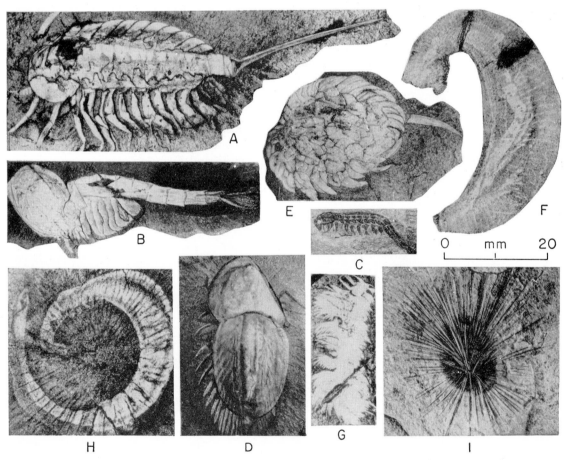

Fig. 5.26 Unusual fossils from Middle Cambrian shale in British Columbia. The occurrence of entirely soft-bodied invertebrates, some showing internal structures such as the alimentary tract, makes fossils from the Burgess Shale member of the Stephen Formation very exceptional. Among forms illustrated here, *A–D* are crustacean-like arthropods, *E–G* are worms, *H* is a holothurian (sea cucumber), and *I* is a siliceous sponge with needle-like radiating spicules. (*C. D. Walcott, courtesy of U.S. National Museum.*)

Fig. 5.27 Restoration of Burgess Shale invertebrate assemblage. This glimpse of a Middle Cambrian sea bottom in British Columbia shows two colonies of branching sponges, several kinds of crustacean-like arthropods, trilobites, sea cucumbers (*H* in foreground), and umbrella-like swimming jellyfishes. (*Courtesy of L. B. Kellum and I. G. Reimann, University of Michigan Museum of Paleontology; exhibit prepared by George Marchand.*)

ample, throughout most of western North America, a great hiatus occurs above the Upper Cambrian, the next younger deposits being Middle Ordovician or Upper Ordovician. In parts of Europe, South America, and other continents where Late Cambrian strata occur, earliest Ordovician (Tremadocian) deposits are missing and in some places an angular unconformity marks the boundary between Cambrian and Ordovician.

A reason, independent of physical evidence, for inferring general withdrawal of shallow seas from the continents before the beginning of Ordovician sedimentation is the abruptness and magnitude of paleontological changes observed in crossing the Cambrian-Ordovician boundary. Such changes, which include the introduction of important new main groups of invertebrates, could hardly have been produced suddenly and contemporaneously in widespread shallow seas that maintained their distribution over the continents. The fossil record can be explained more rationally on the premise that the depositional record actually is incomplete, seas being withdrawn extensively from the continental platforms and geosynclines for a time.

Mountain building. Geographic changes associated with the close of a period or with interruptions within a period that define epochs are commonly marked by mountain building in one or more parts of the globe. The crustal deformation involved in mountain building probably furnishes the mechanism that causes enlargement of marine basins and withdrawal of seas. As far as known, mountain building was not very important in any part of North America at the close of Cambrian time; therefore, in most places, the Cambrian strata lie parallel beneath younger beds. There was moderate deformation in New England and eastern Canada, however, that caused erosion to cut downward rapidly through the Cambrian; a basal Ordovician conglomerate in this region contains coarse angular blocks derived from different parts of the Cambrian, which are identifiable by the fossils in the blocks. This deformation has been termed the *Vermont disturbance* (Schuchert and Dunbar). In Europe, there was considerable volcanic activity near the close of Cambrian time.

Economic Resources

Rocks of the Cambrian System are not rich in mineral resources as compared with other parts of the geologic column, and most deposits of commercial value associated with Cambrian formations originated long after the close of this period. They are adopted children, so to speak, rather than true offspring of the system. In this category are petroleum, copper, lead, asbestos, iron, and ground water.

Petroleum. Oil production of real importance, measured in millions of barrels, has been discovered in Cambrian sandstone and dolostone of west-central Texas (Bronte trend) near San Angelo, in some fields of central Kansas near Russell, and in the Lost Soldier field of southwestern Wyoming near Rock Springs. In each of these places the oil is not indigenous to the Cambrian but migrated from younger strata.

Copper. Ores of copper introduced in Cambrian arkosic sandstone by veins originating in deep-seated post-Cambrian igneous rocks occur in the Ducktown, Tennessee, district; rich copper sulfide ores have been mined in this area since 1848. Copper also occurs in Cambrian formations of the Belgian Congo.

Lead. Lead-bearing minerals have been mined in Upper Cambrian sandstone and dolostone of southeastern Missouri since about 1800, chief deposits occurring in the Bonneterre Dolostone, in which large bodies of sulfide ore were introduced by solutions probably carried downward from younger rocks; annual production is approximately 150,000 tons, worth about $15 million.

Asbestos. Nearly 1 million tons of asbestos is produced annually from post-Cambrian veins in Cambrian rocks of southern Quebec.

Iron. Deposits of iron ore large enough to be worked commercially are found in Cambrian rocks of southeastern Pennsylvania, especially near Cornwall, 25 miles east of Harrisburg, the ore being found in a contact metamorphic zone bordering Triassic igneous intrusions. Iron comes also from Cambrian sources in Great Britain, France, Spain, and West Germany.

Ground water. The occurrence of ground water in various rock formations may be much more valuable than metallic or other mineral deposits. Cambrian sandstones are extremely important sources of ground water south of their outcrops in southern Wisconsin as far as the Chicago area, and the same is true in some other favorable districts.

Other resources. Indigenous to the Cambrian are stone, slate, and barite. *Stone* in blocks or as crushed rock is quarried at many places for use in construction of buildings, highways, and other structures, with aggregate value in the United States amounting annually to some millions of dollars. Some marble of excellent quality also comes from Cambrian sources. *Slate* is an important Cambrian product, the Penrhyn quarries in western Wales in Upper Cambrian of the type area of the system being the world's largest. For roofing purposes this slate is used throughout the British Isles and shipped in large quantities to continental Europe. *Barite* is a heavy white mineral ($BaSO_4$) used extensively as paint pigment, for heavy drilling muds, and as paper filler. Deposits formed by leaching from Cambrian and Lower Ordovician rocks are important in southeastern Missouri and Virginia (annual production about 200,000 tons).

READINGS

BARRELL, JOSEPH, 1925, The nature and environment of Lower Cambrian sediments in the southern Appalachians: *Am. Jour. Sci.*, ser. 5, vol. 9, pp. 1–20.

BELL, W. C., BERG, R. R., and NELSON, C. A., 1956, Croixian type area—Upper Mississippi

Valley: *Intern. Geol. Congr., 20th Sess.* (Mexico City), El Sistema Cambrico, su paleogeo-grafia y el problema de su base, vol. 2, pp. 415–446.

COHEE, G. V., 1948, Cambrian and Ordovician rocks in Michigan basin and adjoining areas: *Am. Assoc. Petroleum Geologists Bull.,* vol. 32, pp. 1417–1448.

DAKE, C. L., and BRIDGE, JOSIAH, 1932, Buried and resurrected hills of central Ozarks: *Am. Assoc. Petroleum Geologists Bull.,* vol. 16, pp. 629–652.

DEISS, CHARLES, 1941, Cambrian geography and sedimentation in the central Cordilleran region: *Geol. Soc. America Bull.,* vol. 52, pp. 1086–1114.

KAY, MARSHALL, 1942, Development of northern Allegheny synclinorium and adjoining regions: *Geol. Soc. America Bull.,* vol. 53, pp. 1601–1658.

———, 1951, North American geosynclines, *Geol. Soc. America Mem.* 48 (143 pp.), especially pp. 1–33.

KING, P. B., 1949, The base of the Cambrian in the southern Appalachians: *Am. Jour. Sci.,* vol. 247, pp. 513–530, 622–645.

———, 1950, Tectonic framework of southeastern United States: *Am. Assoc. Petroleum Geologists Bull.,* vol. 34, pp. 635–671.

———, 1951, *The tectonics of middle North America,* Princeton University Press, Princeton, N.J. (203 pp.), especially pp. 67–144.

LORD, C. S., HAGE, C. O., and STEWART, J. S., 1947, The Cordilleran region: in *Geology and economic minerals of Canada,* Geol. Survey Canada, Econ. Geol. Ser. 1 (Pub. 2478), pp. 220–260.

McKEE, E. D., 1949, Facies changes in the Colorado Plateau: *Geol. Soc. America Mem.* 39, pp. 35–48.

RODGERS, JOHN, 1956, The known Cambrian deposits of the southern and central Appalachian Mountains: *Intern. Geol. Congr., 20th Sess.* (Mexico City), El Sistema Cambrico, su paleo-geografia y el problema de su base, vol. 2, pp. 353–384, especially pp. 374–381.

———, 1956, The clastic sequence basal to the Cambrian System in the central and southern Appalachians: *Intern. Geol. Congr., 20th Sess.* (Mexico City), pp. 385–413, especially pp. 402–410.

WALCOTT, C. D., 1911, A geologist's paradise: *Natl. Geog. Mag.,* vol. 22, pp. 509–521. Cambrian formations of Canadian Rockies.

WHEELER, H. E., 1943, Lower and Middle Cambrian stratigraphy in the Great Basin area: *Geol. Soc. America Bull.,* vol. 54, pp. 1781–1822.

QUESTIONS

1. Referring to the section of Cambrian and associated rocks in the type region (Fig. 5.2), explain how the boundary at the base of the Lower Cambrian rather evenly extends across different sorts of Precambrian rocks, most of which actually consist of massive igneous or metamorphic crystalline rocks. Also explain why this contact between the Cambrian and older rocks is roughly parallel to stratification planes within the Cambrian succession and yet strongly tilted in different directions as traced from place to place. What geologic history is recorded by the nature of the contact between the Cambrian and Ordovician strata?

2. Referring to the map (Fig. 5.3) showing the distribution of rocks belonging to the Cambrian System in part of North America, can you account for the elongate linear belts of Cambrian outcrops in the Appalachian Mountains region? Why are outcrops of Cambrian rocks in Missouri irregularly shaped, rounded patches? Explain the great widening of Cambrian outcrops in southwestern Wisconsin as compared with the narrow belt in eastern Wisconsin and northern Michigan. What explanations can be suggested for the absence of Cambrian formations in central Nebraska and farther north? Similarly for absence of Cambrian outcrops on the east sides of the Black Hills (southwestern South Dakota) and Big Horn Mountains (northern Wyoming)?

3. If true (as it is) that the crests of ripple marks are sharply rounded as compared with the broadly concave nature of intervening troughs, how can you explain the appearance of the bedding-plane surface illustrated in Fig. 5.6?

4. What inference concerning land areas nearest to the Appalachian geosyncline in Late Cambrian time can be drawn from the prevailing nature of Upper Cambrian formations in the North Carolina-Tennessee-Virginia region (Fig. 5.7)?

5. Studying the contact between Cambrian and older rocks illustrated in Fig. 5.8, how can you account for the smoothness and comparative freshness of the Precambrian rocks next below the unconformity? Why is no material interpretable as an ancient soil seen?

6. Why are the Cambrian strata of Mt. Robson and Mt. Temple in the Canadian Rockies (Figs. 5.11, 5.12) judged to have been deposited in a geosyncline?

7. What features illustrated in the section of Cambrian strata in the Grand Canyon (Fig. 5.15) demonstrate the contemporaneity of different kinds of deposits found in different, though neighboring, parts of this region?

8. According to paleogeographic maps of North America in Early, Middle, and Late Cambrian time (Figs. 5.17 to 5.19), how does classification of marine invertebrate assemblages (especially trilobites) in terms of distinct environments to which they are adapted and mainly restricted serve to explain the distribution of the respective faunas that formerly were thought to denote quite separate provinces, one called the Atlantic Province and the other Pacific Province?

9. Why are most remains of trilobites fragmentary, consisting of isolated head shields (cephala) or parts of head shields, tail shields (pygidia), or thoracic segments? Why are specimens of trilobites with appendages preserved (Fig. 5.23) extremely rare as compared with whole carapaces (Figs. 5.16, 5.21, 5.22)?

10. Referring to Figs. 5.26 and 5.27, what invertebrates found preserved in the Burgess Shale fauna are extremely exceptional because of the absence of hard parts in the living organism?

6.

PALEOZOIC ERA:

ORDOVICIAN PERIOD

Highly fossiliferous Upper Ordovician beds near Cincinnati, Ohio.

R. S. Bassler, courtesy of U.S. National Museum

Like the Cambrian, the rocks called *Ordovician* have their type locality in Wales, the term being derived from the name of an early Celtic tribe (Ordovices) that resided in the region (Fig. 6.1). The section represented by outcrops there furnishes the standard for comparison with deposits of similar age elsewhere in Europe and on other continents, even though many features of the Ordovician record are more simply and fully recorded elsewhere. The base and top of the system are marked by important unconformities in most of the type region (Fig. 6.2) and in many other areas, these breaks denoting somewhat prolonged interruption of sedimentation accompanied by more or less erosion of pre-

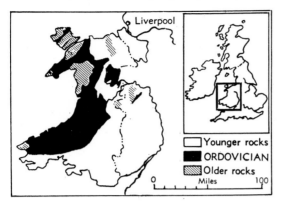

Fig. 6.1 Ordovician outcrop areas in the type region of Wales. This classic region contains many fine exposures of fossil-bearing Ordovician strata. On one side, the outcrops adjoin Cambrian or Precambrian rocks; on the other, they are bordered by younger rocks, mostly Silurian.

Ordovician deposits. As noted in the preceding chapter, throughout much of North America the boundary between Cambrian and Ordovician rocks is not very evident physically, for beds of the two systems lie parallel to each other with even or only slightly uneven contact. In many places the initial Ordovician deposit is a sandstone that lies on Upper Cambrian limestone or dolostone, the base of the sandstone coinciding with a disconformity or paraconformity. Also, an abrupt change in the nature of fossil assemblages is observed in comparing Lower Ordovician with uppermost Cambrian faunas, and this has much importance. At the top of the Ordovician sequence a hiatus occurs almost everywhere in North America, marked by absence of youngest Ordovician (upper Richmondian), as well as varying thicknesses of earliest Silurian (Figs. 6.5, 7.4); this boundary also is a disconformity or paraconformity in most places, but the unconformity is angular in parts of the Appalachian belt.

A noteworthy feature of Ordovician deposits in the type region is a decided contrast in the nature of the strata and their contained fossils in one part of the area as compared with another part that closely adjoins the first. These represent different environments of sedimentation or facies. Ordovician beds in the southeastern part of the outcrop belt are made up almost wholly of thinly stratified limestones, containing abundant trilobites, brachiopods, and many other shell-bearing marine invertebrates of shallow-water type; this is known as the shelly facies, and it is interpreted as having been laid down in off-shore clear but shallow water. Contemporaneous deposits in adjacent territory to the northwest consist almost exclusively of carbonaceous dark-colored shale that contains abundant carbonized remains of slender branching invertebrates called *graptolites* (Fig. 6.22) but very few other kinds of fossils; these beds are classed as the graptolite facies and are interpreted to represent deposits of a mud-bottom inshore belt where seaweeds grew thickly, furnishing the main source of the carbon.

Occurrence of Ordovician Rocks in North America

Recognition of the system. Deposits of Ordovician age, identified by their fossils, are found in many parts of North America. As in northwestern Europe, they are distinguished especially from the underlying Cambrian by the abruptness and pronounced nature of changes in the composition of fossil assemblages. Moreover, the same two dominant types of deposits occur on this continent; calcareous beds containing many trilobites, brachiopods, and additional varied kinds of invertebrates are found in certain areas, and black shale containing few fossils, except abundant graptolites, in other areas. Numerous Ordovician species of North America and Europe are identical or closely similar.

The upper boundary of the Ordovician is marked by a widespread unconformity that separates the system from younger deposits. However, equally pronounced unconformities occur within the Ordovician rocks of North America, and this serves to emphasize the point that definition of the major geologic divisions, called *systems*, depends largely on the adoption of a certain type section to serve as a world standard in classification. If the foundations of time-rock classification had been based on early geologic studies in North America rather than Europe, it is very probable that what we now class as the Lower Ordovician (Canadian) Series would have been defined as an independent geologic system. It is fairly well distinguished by the nature of the rocks (mainly cherty dolostones and limestones), by distinctness of widespread interruption in sedimentation above it (Fig. 6.5), and by faunal differences from underlying and overlying stratigraphic divisions.

General distribution and character. All parts of North America in which Cambrian deposits are found, including the eastern and western geosynclinal troughs and the interior continental platform region, also contain Ordovician deposits (Fig. 6.3). Like the Cambrian, the Ordovician in the geosynclines is measured in thousands of feet whereas that of the interior platform aggregates only hundreds of feet. Ordovician seas extended more widely over the interior of North America, however, than those of Cambrian time. We find Ordovician strata resting directly on Precambrian rocks in territory north of Lake Ontario (Fig. 6.4), in a large area along the southwest shore of Hudson Bay, and on many islands of the Arctic Archipelago west of Greenland.

Beneath the surface, Ordovician deposits are continuous westward from the Appalachian Mountains to states beyond the Mississippi River, and they underlie all the Great Lakes except Lake Superior. Without doubt they originally extended without interruption across the Ozark region of Missouri and the Llano Uplift in central Texas, but in many square miles they have been removed by post-Ordovician erosion. The system is known to be present in southeastern Nebraska, throughout most of Kansas and Oklahoma, and in the greater part of Texas, because Ordovician rocks have been penetrated in many thousand deep wells. Probably Ordovician deposits once spread over most of western United States but now are absent in large areas shown as blank spaces on the map and in oblique-ruled areas where pre-Ordovician rocks occur at the surface. Special attention should be called to the Southeastern States, where drilling in recent years has demonstrated the unexpected occurrence of marine Ordovician rocks in a large part of northern Florida and smaller areas in Georgia and Alabama. Whether or not these deposits formerly were connected with Ordovician rocks to the northwest, as seems probable, is not known.

Ordovician rocks of North America consist predominantly of limestone and dolostone, even though there are some widespread shale deposits and sheets of sandstone. In the Appalachian Mountains belt, New England, and eastern Canada, these rocks are strongly folded and faulted, but in much of the remainder of the continent they are mostly very little disturbed, being subhorizontal or dipping at very low angles.

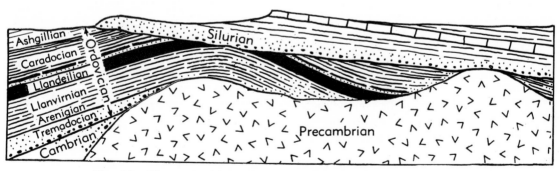

Fig. 6.2 Diagrammatic section of Ordovician rocks in Wales. The section shows the presence of Lower Ordovician rocks resting on truncated edges of Cambrian formations; successively younger Ordovician divisions overlap on Precambrian rocks also. Deformation and erosion of Ordovician strata, prior to deposition of Silurian sediments, are represented by the angular unconformity separating the Ordovician and Silurian rocks.

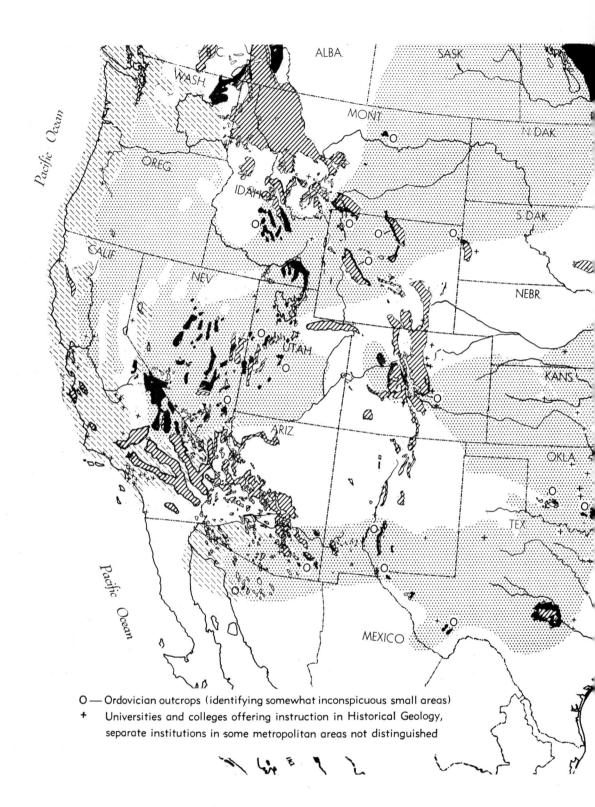

O — Ordovician outcrops (identifying somewhat inconspicuous small areas)
+   Universities and colleges offering instruction in Historical Geology,
     separate institutions in some metropolitan areas not distinguished

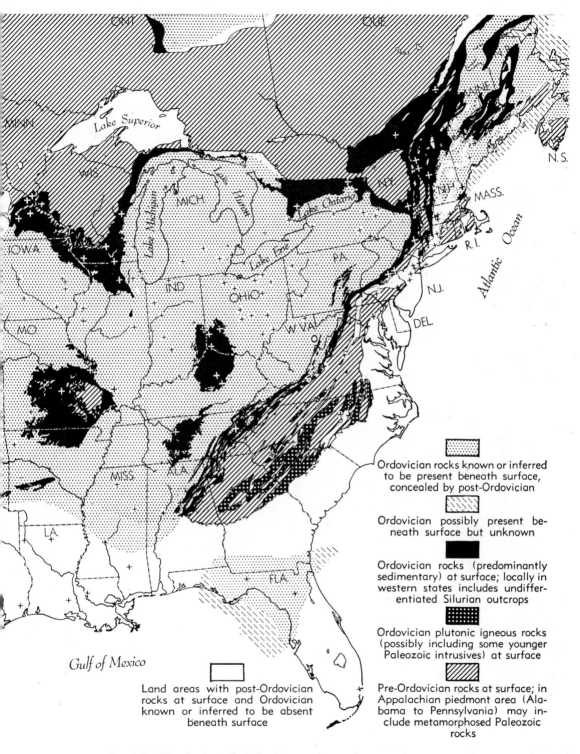

Ordovician rocks known or inferred
to be present beneath surface,
concealed by post-Ordovician

Ordovician possibly present beneath surface but unknown

Ordovician rocks (predominantly
sedimentary) at surface; locally in
western states includes undifferentiated Silurian outcrops

Ordovician plutonic igneous rocks
(possibly including some younger
Paleozoic intrusives) at surface

Land areas with post-Ordovician
rocks at surface and Ordovician
known or inferred to be absent
beneath surface

Pre-Ordovician rocks at surface; in
Appalachian piedmont area (Alabama to Pennsylvania) may include metamorphosed Paleozoic
rocks

**Fig. 6.3 Distribution of Ordovician rocks in the United States, southern Canada, and
northern Mexico.** The outcrops and subsurface occurrences shown indicate the original distribution of the system except as modified by destruction of deposits resulting from post-
Ordovician erosion or locally from effects of post-Ordovician bathylithic igneous intrusions.

Divisions. The Ordovician System in North America is clearly divisible into three or possibly four main time-rock units that are classed as series (Fig. 6.5). These are known as Lower, Middle, and Upper Ordovician or Canadian, Champlainian, and Cincinnatian Series. Formerly, the middle part of the system was classed as two series, Chazyan below and Mohawkian above. Because they are more closely related to each other in various ways

Fig. 6.4 Ordovician limestones nonconformably on Precambrian in eastern Ontario.——A. Late Middle Ordovician (Trentonian) limestone on granite; the camera case marks the slightly uneven contact. No basal conglomerate occurs in the lowermost limestone bed, which demonstrates that limemud was laid here on a clean-washed surface of the granite.——B. Lower Ordovician (Canadian) sandy limestone on granite gneiss. The erosion surface at the base of the limestone truncates the vertical banding of the gneiss. If Cambrian deposits ever were laid down in this area, they were removed before the Ordovician sea covered it. (*Courtesy of Geol. Survey Canada.*)

than to the Canadian and Cincinnatian, they are classed here as subseries of the Champlainian Series.

The main divisions just noted reflect major fluctuations of the Ordovician seaways that occupied much of the North American continent, and the boundaries between them represent times of emergence or at least physical changes that affected shallow-water marine faunas. During the emergent intervals of unknown duration that are indicated in various places, sedimentation ceased and at least locally there was erosion that removed previously formed deposits. Marine organisms underwent accelerated evolutionary changes, which may be correlated with changes in distribution of marine waters. Retreat of shallow seas, from broad areas that had been inundated, inevitably caused migration or extinction of the marine organisms that had been living in the inland seas, those that moved being crowded into peripheral areas of the continental shelf, which already had their own population. Under these conditions, competition for survival would weed out species least able to adapt themselves. Thus, organisms commonly represented among fossils in rocks below such an unconformity may fail to be found in strata belonging above the unconformity. During times of expanding seaways, when large areas of the continent again became suited as habitat for shallow-water marine creatures, the modified old stocks and immigrant new forms of life found maximum play for evolutionary differentiation. The organic assemblage of each main division of the Ordovician rocks accordingly is seen to differ materially from the others. In like manner, subordinate fossil groups characterize lesser time-rock units, classed as stages.

The Canadian Series is named from outcrops in southern Quebec along the shores of Lake Champlain, adjacent exposures in northeasternmost New York being included in the type region. Approximately equal in importance for study of Lower Ordovician deposits, however, are so-called standard sections in the northern, central, and southern Appalachians and the Ozark region of Missouri (Fig. 6.6). In addition, rocks of the Ellenburger Group in Texas, exposed on flanks of the Llano Uplift, are another standard succession, useful for identification and correlation of Early Ordovician deposits in the Southwest. The break that separates rocks of the Canadian Series from overlying deposits is perhaps the most important stratigraphic boundary within the system, for change in organisms and the general type of sedimentation is greater at this horizon than anywhere else in the Ordovician section.

Classic exposures of Middle Ordovician rocks are located in New York. They include the Lake Champlain region, from which the name Champlainian is derived; the Mohawk River Valley southwest of the Adirondack Mountains which contains the type Mohawkian sections (Fig. 6.7); and the Chazy area, on the west side of Lake Champlain in the northeastern corner of New York, which displays the type Chazyan. Studies of Middle Ordovician rocks and fossils in recent years have directed special attention to Appalachian outcrops in Pennsylvania, Virginia, and Tennessee, where many rock units have been named, and knowledge gained from this region has guided some reinterpretation of the New York Middle Ordovician deposits. Finally, the richly fossiliferous Middle Ordovician limestones of the Blue Grass district near Louisville, Kentucky, and the valley surrounding Nashville, Tennessee, are important for comparisons and correlations.

Upper Ordovician strata, comprising the highly fossiliferous Cincinnatian Series, are nowhere better exposed than in parts of southwestern Ohio, southeastern Indiana, and northern Kentucky adjacent to Cincinnati. Largely because of the abundance and fine preservation of the Late Ordovician marine fossils in this region, a number of leading American invertebrate paleontologists began as boys living in Cincinnati to make fossil collections and to study them.

Geosynclinal deposits. During Ordovician time, the Appalachian and Cordilleran geosynclines continued to sink slowly, the amount of subsidence being measured approximately

OHIO VALLEY	APPALACHIANS		NORTHEAST			EUROPE	Stages	Series
Ind.-Ky.-Ohio	Tennessee-Virginia		New York - Vermont		E. Canada	Eng.-Wales		
Sil.	Sil.	Sil.	Sil.	Pleisto.	Sil.-Dev.	Sil.	Next above	
Elkhorn Ls. / Liberty-Saluda / Waynesv. F. / Arnheim Ls.	Juniata F.		Queenston F.		Ellis Bay F. / Vaureal F. / English Head F.	Ashgillian	Richmondian	CINCINNATIAN
McMillan F. / Fairmount Sh. / Mt. Hope Sh. / McMicken Sh. / Southgate Sh. / Economy Sh. / Fulton Sh. / Cynthiana Ls.	Martinsburg F.		Oswego Ss. / Pulaski Sh. / Whetstone Gulf Sh. (Lorraine Gr.) / Utica Sh. / Cobourg Ls.			Caradocian	Maysv. / Edenian	
Tyrone Ls. / Oregon Ls. / Camp Nelson Ls.	Moccasin Ls. / Witten Ls. / Wardell Ls. / Ben Bolt Ls. / Peery Ls. / Ward Cove Ls.	Oranda F. / Edinburg F.	Sherman Falls Ls. / Kirkfield Ls. / Rockland Ls. / Chaumont Ls. / Lowville Ls. / Pamelia Ls.	Snake Hill Sh. / Normanskill Sh. (Graptolite-bearing)	Cowhead Breccia / Long Pt. Sh.		Trentonian / Blackriver,	CHAMPLAINIAN / Mohawkian
(Unexposed)	Lincolnshire Ls. / New Market Ls. / Lenoir Ls. / Mosheim Ls.	Whistle Cr. F.	Valcour Ls. / Crown Pt. Ls. / Day Pt. Ls.		Table Head Ls.	Llandeilian / Llanvirnian	Chazyan	
	Mascot Dol. / Kingsport Dol. / Longview Dol. / Chepultepec Dol.	Knox Group (part)	Bridport Dol. / Bascom F. / Cutting Dol. / Shelburne Ls. (Beekmantown Group)	Deepkill Sh. (Graptolite-bearing) / Schagticoke Sh.	St. George F.	Arenigian / Tremadocian		CANADIAN
Up. Cam.	Up. Cam.	Up. Cam.	Up. Cam.	Cam.	Up. Cam.	Up. Cam.	Next below	

142

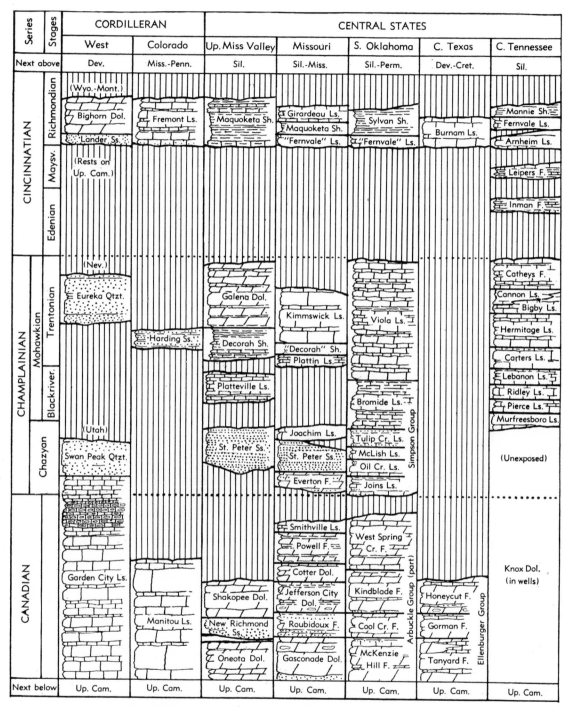

Fig. 6.5 Time-rock divisions of the Ordovician System and rock units assigned to them in representative important Ordovician sections of North America. The vertical scale does not represent time duration or thickness of rocks but is determined by suitability for plotting the various recognized rock units, placement of which indicates correlation in age. Lithologic character is represented graphically (explanation of symbols in Appendix B). Necessarily, the plotted thickness is not to scale, although it approximates proportional values in many sections. Vertically ruled areas denote absence of deposits.

by the thickness of Ordovician strata accumulated in these belts (Figs. 6.8, 6.9). The average thickness is 5,000 feet, and the maximum, in part of the Appalachian trough, is at least 12,000 feet. Inasmuch as this mile or more of Ordovician deposits rests on equally thick Cambrian strata, the Precambrian floor beneath parts of the geosynclines must have been depressed 2 to 3 miles below sea level by the close of Ordovician time. Even so, since the geosynclines are estimated to have been upward of 400 miles wide, the slope of the floor, after combined Cambrian and Ordovician subsidence, probably did not exceed an average of 60 feet to the mile, and of course, planes of stratification in the upper part of the geosynclinal deposits would be nearly horizontal. The Ouachita and Arbuckle Mountains, in Arkansas and southern Oklahoma, contain

Ordovician deposits of geosynclinal type some 10,000 feet thick (Figs. 6.10, 6.11).

The geosynclines are especially characterized by prominence of calcareous deposits of Ordovician age, which are thickest toward the axis of the troughs. The Lower Ordovician rocks consist mostly of massive dolostone, part of which contains much silica in the form of chert nodules and beds. Younger Ordovician calcareous deposits are mostly limestone. On the side of the geosynclines toward the interior continental platform, the dolostone and limestone formations merge with similar but thinner deposits that extend beyond the troughs.

The parts of the geosynclines adjacent to the outlying borderlands—that is, the eastern part of the Appalachian geosyncline and western part of the Cordilleran geosyncline—were

Fig. 6.6 Even-bedded Lower Ordovician dolostone (Beekmantown) in eastern Pennsylvania. Limestone and dolostone deposits of Ordovician age attain an aggregate thickness of approximately 4,000 feet in parts of the Appalachian geosyncline. They denote the absence of nearby highlands in Early Ordivician time, for if they had existed, considerable quantities of clastic detritus would have been deposited. (*Courtesy of Pennsylvania Geol. Survey.*)

the sites of extensive black-shale accumulation. These belts contain little sandstone (except in the Upper Ordovician of the Appalachian region) and virtually no limestone.

The black shales are carbon-rich graptolite-bearing deposits. Inasmuch as the varied kinds of invertebrates found in the calcareous deposits are mostly lacking in the black shale and since the graptolite faunas are mainly confined to the black shale, the contrasting environments represented by these deposits evidently exerted a controlling influence on the spread of marine organisms. An alternative assumption, that graptolites were carried into the shallow-water shelf-sea environment in about as large numbers as along the mud-bottomed troughs (for we are dealing with the same paleogeographic pattern of interior shelf seas and continental-border troughs as in the Cambrian), may be closer to the truth, for we do find graptolites in black shale, such as the Utica Shale, interbedded with limestones of the continental interior. Rarely, graptolites are preserved in limestone, as in the Viola Limestone of southern Oklahoma, being then unflattened by compaction. Therefore, distribution of the graptolites as fossils may reflect conditions of preservation, such as the presence or absence of scavengers on the sea bottom, more than original distribution. In any case, the shale represents muds derived from the borderlands, as shown by geographic position in the geosynclines and by interfingering with clear-water, calcareous deposits that extend uninterruptedly toward the continental interior. The graptolites did not live in the bottom muds but at or near the water surface, being attached to seaweeds or supported by their own floats. Shallow-water mud and sand, representing very near-shore equivalents of the graptolite-bearing Lower and Middle Ordovician deposits, are unknown, for the original easternmost part of the Appalachian geosynclinal deposits and the westernmost part of the Cordilleran deposits have been eroded away.

Late Ordovician rocks of the Appalachian geosyncline contain some conglomerate, much sandstone, and a considerable thickness of

Fig. 6.7 Middle Ordovician limestone at Trenton Falls, New York. This is the locality in the Mohawk Valley region from which Trentonian rocks are named. Numerous well-preserved fossils have been collected from these outcrops. (*Courtesy of D. W. Fisher, New York State Museum.*)

shale representing both marine near-shore and subaerial deposits laid down on land. They denote an important change from types of sedimentation just described. Much of the shale is red (Figs. 6.8, 6.12). This shale and the coarse sandy deposits lack marine fossils. They are judged to represent stream-borne materials carried westward from Appalachia and laid down above sea level. The conglomerate and coarse sand certainly reflect an uplift of the source country that supplied these sediments and, as noted later, furnish testimony of Late Ordovician mountain building in eastern North America. Upper Ordovician deposits of the eastern part of the continental interior also contain much shale, but this is fine-textured and is associated with many thin beds of limestone, which indicates deposition in muddy, shallow seas distant from the source of the silt and clay.

Continental interior. Throughout the Canadian Shield region and its structural continuation in the interior platform of the Mississippi Basin, the comparatively thin Ordovician deposits are made up largely of limestone and dolostone (Figs. 6.13 to 6.15). The sediments making these rocks were laid down in clear, shallow seas. There is one widespread deposit of very pure, even-grained sandstone (St. Peter, Fig. 1.2), and in the upper part of the section a small thickness of shale. The re-

mainder of the deposits is calcareous. There were no nearby lands high enough to be the site of appreciable mechanical weathering, which might have furnished considerable quantities of sand and mud.

That the shallow inland seas of Ordovician time somewhat shifted their position in different epochs, receding and advancing in some areas a number of times, is shown by the presence of minor unconformities in the rock succession. Seemingly, not much change in the relation of land elevation to sea level was required to produce considerable geographic fluctuations of the strand line. The dominantly

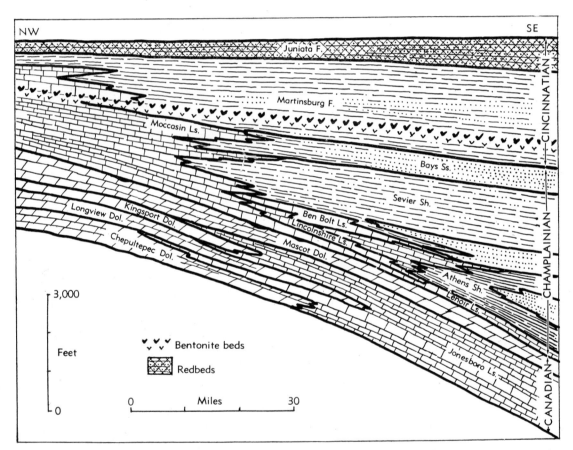

Fig. 6.8 Diagrammatic section of Ordovician rocks in the central Appalachians of eastern Tennessee and Virginia. The section is drawn approximately at right angles to the trend of the geosyncline, plotted thickness ranging from 5,000 to a little more than 10,000 feet. Bentonite beds are useful keys for determination of precise age equivalence because they are altered volcanic ash falls formed isochronously. Middle and Upper Ordovician clastic deposits plainly were derived from the eastern side of the geosyncline, for they grade or interfinger with contemporaneous carbonate strata to the west.

calcareous nature of the deposits and the varying distribution pattern of successive formations accord with the inferred very low-lying, nearly featureless nature of the continental interior during the Ordovician Period.

Especially widespread and uniform in lithologic character are early Ordovician deposits consisting mainly of dolostone. Silica occurs commonly in many layers, partly in the form of chert nodules and partly as scattered quartz sand grains. The latter indicate the existence during sedimentation of currents sufficiently strong to spread the sand from shore areas far out into the shallow basins. Successive layers mostly lie parallel on one another, or nearly so, but the absence of some deposits over large areas, coupled locally with evidence of temporary erosion, indicates disconformities or paraconformities. Thus, deposition of sediments was interrupted from time to time.

Outcrops of the older Ordovician dolostones and records of many thousand deep wells that penetrate these strata show that the formations

are distributed from the upper Mississippi Valley southward across Iowa, Missouri, Kansas, and Oklahoma as far as southwestern Texas (Fig. 6.5); they are extensively exposed in the Ozark region of Missouri. Correlation of formations and zonal divisions of formations has been made most reliably by dissolving samples of the rock or drill cuttings in acid and comparing the insoluble residues, which consist mainly of various sorts of silica. Porosity of these buried rocks in many places makes them an excellent reservoir rock for accumulation of oil and gas, much of which may have originated in the Ordovician deposits. The bulk of the oil obtained from the older Ordovician rocks in the midcontinent region, amounting to several hundred thousand barrels annually, probably originated in associated younger strata and migrated into the porous Ordovician strata.

Basins and domes. A structural peculiarity of the broad interior platform of North America is the differentiation of several wide

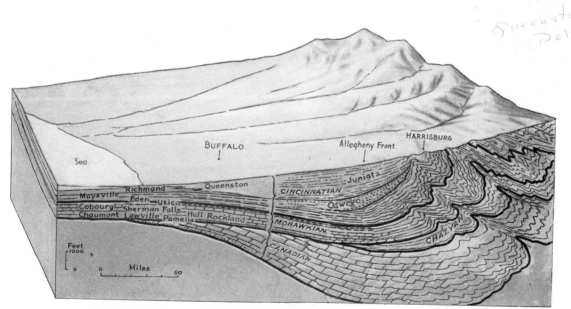

Fig. 6.9 Ordovician deposits in the Pennsylvania-New York region. The view across this block diagram is northeastward, and the section on the front of the block extends from southern Ontario (at left) to southeastern Pennsylvania beyond Harrisburg. Noteworthy features are the northwestward thinning of the sedimentary formations, prominence of shale and sandstone deposits toward the southeast, unconformities within the Ordovician sequence, and existence of mountainous highlands near the close of Ordovician time in Appalachia. These are the Taconian Mountains.

shallow depressions and intervening gentle arches or swells. These features are designated as *basins* and *domes* (Fig. 6.16).

The depressions are irregularly saucer-like, being mostly not much wider in one direction than in another. They represent sags of the Precambrian floor, and they are defined as synclinal basins in the structure of the layered Paleozoic rocks. Examples are the Michigan basin and Illinois basin, in which the beds slope inward from all sides to a low point centrally located in each state (Fig. 6.3). Out-

crops of different rock divisions are arranged in concentric belts, the youngest occurring in the middle.

The domes show the reverse of structure characterizing the basins. Rocks dip gently outward in all directions from a central high point, and the central outcrop area of old rocks is surrounded by concentric belts of successively younger formations. Typical examples are the Cincinnati dome in Ohio, Indiana, and Kentucky and the Ozark dome in Missouri (Fig. 6.3).

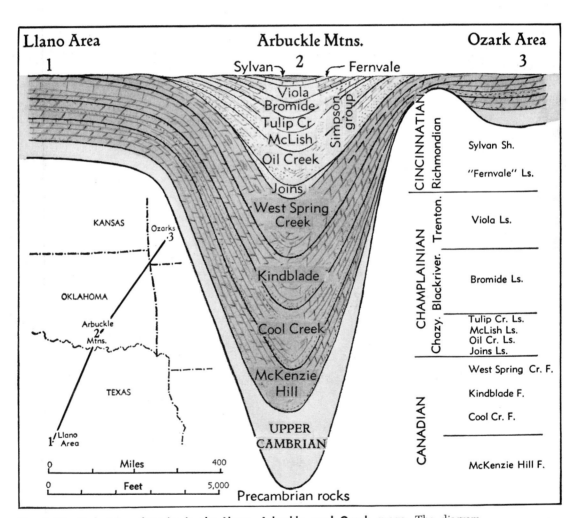

Fig. 6.10 Ordovician deposits in the Llano, Arbuckle, and Ozark areas. The diagram emphasizes the greater thickness and completeness of sedimentary records of the geosynclinal area that crosses southern Oklahoma as compared with sections in central Texas and the Ozark region of Missouri.

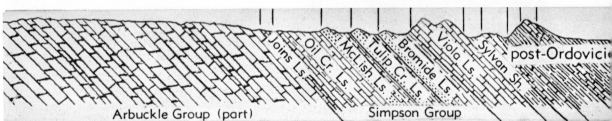

Joins Ls. | Oil Cr. Ls | McLish Ls. | Tulip Cr. Ls | Bromide Ls. | Viola Ls. | Sylvan Sh. | post-Ordovici

Arbuckle Group (part)

Simpson Group

Fig. 6.11 **Air view and geologic section of thick Ordovician deposits in the Arbuckle Mountains of southern Oklahoma.** The parallel outcrops of the steeply inclined strata are accented by such features as slightly differing hardness, variation in color, and associated vegetation. (*Soil Conservation Service.*)

Fig. 6.12 Upper Ordovician (Queenston) redbeds beneath nearly white basal Silurian sandstone. Exposures at Lewiston, New York, on the Niagara River below Niagara Falls. (*Courtesy of D. W. Fisher, New York State Museum.*)

Fig. 6.13 Lower Mohawkian limestones in east-central New York. The rock below *B*, which is a bentonite bed, is Lowville Limestone and that above is Hull Limestone, both of Blackriveran age. Outcrop at Middleville, about 10 miles east of Utica, New York. (*Courtesy of J. W. Wells, Cornell University.*)

The gently warped structural pattern, just described, has an important bearing on geologic history of the continental interior region. (1) The basins and domes are possibly very ancient features that persistently have influenced distribution of shallow seas and affected local sedimentation or erosion. (2) Alternatively, they are possibly much more recent features that were produced by deformation confined to time after deposition of the youngest rocks in the areas concerned. In such event the strata throughout most of the interior platform should be fairly uniform in thickness and should have remained essentially horizontal until the time of deformation that downwarped the basins and uplifted the domes. Prior to this deformation, seas could spread about as easily over one part of the interior as another.

Judgment as to which of these contrasted modes of origin of the basins and domes better accords with actual geological history requires information derived from field study. Are deposits essentially uniform, or do they differ significantly in distribution, thickness, and lithology? Are some formations confined to basins or thicker in the basins, whereas they are absent or thin in the area of domes? Observations of Ordovician deposits of the continental interior furnish clear answers to these questions and several correlated ones. The basins contain a distinctly thicker and more complete record of Ordovician sedimentation than the upwarped domes, which are characterized by numerous disconformities between Ordovician rock units (Fig. 6.17). Also, there is evidence that during part of Ordovician time, domal areas were subject to erosion, and they supplied sediment to adjacent basins, where it is incorporated in Ordovician deposits. The structural irregularities of the interior platform, such as the Illinois basin and Ozark dome, are therefore ancient features that are expressed in the geological record of Ordovician time and in part that of the Cambrian Period also.

Volcanic activity. Middle Ordovician deposits of the Appalachian geosyncline and the interior platform, as far west as the Mississippi, contain a number of distinctive clayey beds (bentonite) that are identified as altered volcanic ash falls (Figs. 6.8, 6.13, 6.18). Commonly, the beds are only 1 or 2 feet thick, but they are especially interesting because each single bed may be interpreted as a precisely contemporaneous deposit. Thus, it furnishes a useful datum plane for correlation of associated strata. Some of these altered ash beds have been proved to extend laterally at least scores of miles. The vents from which the explosive eruptions came have not been located, although in Pennsylvania lava flows have been observed in association with an ash bed. Considerable quantities of volcanic tuff, breccia, and submarine lava flows are found associated with Middle Ordovician deposits in eastern Canada and in Newfoundland.

Fig. 6.14 Middle Ordovician limestones in New York.——A. Weathered surface of Crown Point Limestone (Chazyan), near Chazy, New York, showing a straight cephalopod with internal curved partitions (septa) and part of the living chamber at left; the fossil is 18 inches long.——B. Beds of Lowville Limestone with typical white calcite bodies that resemble worm borings, east of Little Falls, New York. (*Courtesy of J. W. Wells, Cornell University.*)

Ordovician Life

Invertebrates. The variety of shallow-water marine life, represented by fossils found in Ordovician strata, considerably exceeds that known from Cambrian rocks. Probably this does not mean that Ordovician life was correspondingly richer but that more forms of invertebrates having hard parts adapted for preservation as fossils existed in Ordovician time. Some beds are literally made up of these organic remains, including especially calcareous-shelled brachiopods, colonies of the so-called moss animals or bryozoans, dismembered pieces or complete carapaces of trilo-

bites, corals, snails, clams, and still other classes of invertebrates (Figs. 6.19–6.23). All these groups must have had at least distantly related Cambrian ancestors, but most such inferred antecedents evidently had not acquired the capacity to secrete a protective hard covering. Development of a lime-secreting habit is thus responsible for the seemingly abrupt introduction of rather highly organized invertebrates that subsequently are well represented in the fossil record. The only plausible alternative to conclusions just stated is that these new types of calcareous-shelled invertebrates in the Ordovician rocks are immigrants descended from Cambrian shell-

Fig. 6.15 Crystalline Middle Ordovician limestone (Holston) composed chiefly of bryozoan fragments and crinoid remains. The bryozoans are recognizable by their generally elongate outlines and regular cells (zooecia); the gray rounded bodies that appear solid are crinoid fragments; the very light gray areas are clear crystalline calcite that cements the organic fragments together. The jagged dark line in the upper part of the photograph is a stylolite in cross section; by effects of solution and pressure, parts of the rock on opposite sides of the stylolite interpenetrate one another. Magnification approximately ×10. (*Courtesy of U.S. Geol. Survey.*)

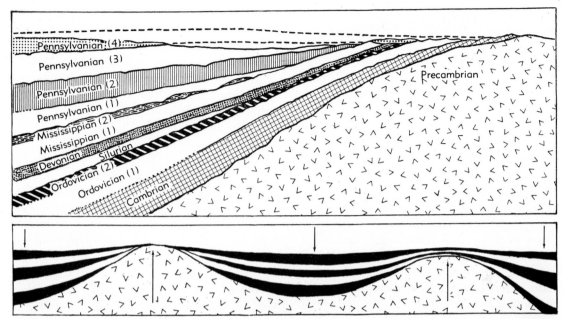

Fig. 6.16 Variation in thickness of sedimentary deposits in relation to basins and domes. The upper diagram represents strata on the west side of the Ozark dome extending into the Eastern Kansas Basin; some rock divisions reach farther toward the center of the dome than others, and nearly all are bounded by disconformities or paraconformities that increase in time value of the hiatus from the basin toward the dome. The lower diagram shows two domes and bordering basins, in which five rock divisions are distinguished; during geologic history the domes tend progressively to be uplifted (or subside less than basins) and the basins tend progressively to sink, as indicated by the directions of the arrows.

Fig. 6.17 Cross-bedded shaly Upper Ordovician limestone near Louisville, Kentucky. These deposits are typical of the very shallow oscillatory seas that transgressed and then retreated from regions of gentle uplifts, such as the Cincinnati arch and Nashville dome. Successive deposits, although parallel, are commonly separated by disconformities. (*Charles Butts, courtesy of U.S. Geol. Survey.*)

bearing ancestors that lived in some wholly unknown area. This is a very improbable explanation.

Trilobites reached the peak of their development during the Ordovician Period. They exhibit a striking variety in shape, and range in size. The largest known trilobite, 30 inches long, is a specimen of *Uralichas,* which comes from Ordovician rocks of Portugal.

Among brachiopods, the horny phosphatic-shelled types known from the Cambrian persisted, but they are greatly outweighed in importance by the newly introduced calcareous types, which are mostly much larger, more varied in shape, and more highly organized in structure. They especially distinguished Ordovician from Cambrian deposits and include many important guide fossils.

Ordovician time is preeminently the age of graptolites; although known from older and younger rocks, they are much more abundant and widespread in Ordovician black shaly deposits than in any other strata, and among them are a large number of index and guide fossils that occur in widely separated parts of the world. For example, some Ordovician graptolite species that originally were described from Europe have been collected from localities in North and South America, Asia, and Australia (Fig. 6.22).

Approximately 1,000 kinds of bryozoans have already been described from Ordovician rocks, and perhaps an equally large number is yet undescribed. Most Ordovician colonies are branching growths of slender or coarse type that are made up of innumerable microscopic calcareous tubes which were occupied by the individual organisms (Fig. 6.23).

Along with clams and snails, Ordovician strata contain cephalopods, which are an exclusively marine type of mollusk, represented in modern seas by the pearly nautilus and

Fig. 6.18 Altered volcanic ash (bentonite) bed occurring between layers of Middle Ordovician limestone. This deposit, derived from a volcanic ash fall, is traceable for many miles in southwestern Virginia near Bristol. Ultimately, it may be identified in a much larger area. The bed constitutes an interesting and useful geologic datum, since all parts of the bentonite bed are presumed to be exactly contemporaneous. (*Charles Butts, courtesy of U.S. Geol. Survey.*)

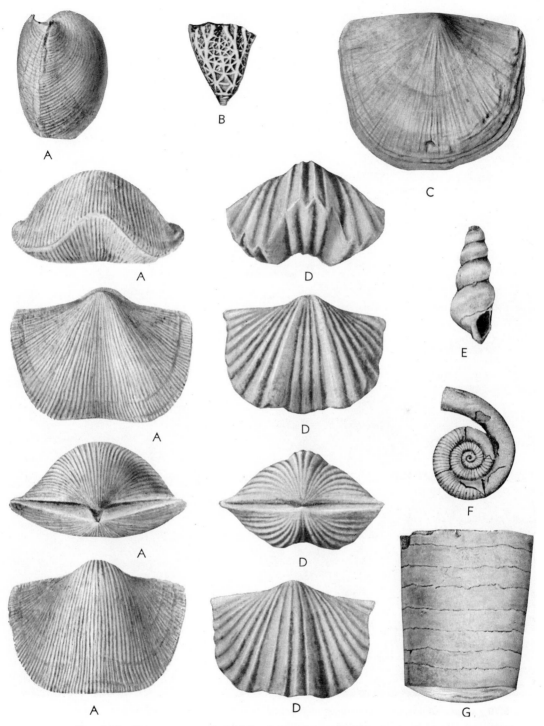

Fig. 6.19 Some common Ordovician invertebrate fossils. The fossils illustrated include calcareous brachiopods, having well-developed hinge lines (*A, Hebertella,* five views; *C, Rafinesquina; D, Platystrophia,* four views); a crinoid (*B, Glyptocrinus*) characterized by starlike ridges on the plates; a high-spired snail (*E, Hormotoma*); and two simple-sutured cephalopods (*F, Schroederoceras,* and *G, Michelinoceras*). All natural size.

Fig. 6.20 Upper Ordovician limestones composed mostly of brachiopod shells. These specimens from the Ohio Valley illustrate the profusion of fossils found in some layers. The nearly smooth semicircular shells (upper figure) are *Sowerbyella rugosa*, those with a pair of sharp ridges diverging from the beak being interiors. The rounded, strongly ribbed brachiopods (lower figure) are *Zygospira modesta*. Both ×2. (*Courtesy of G. A. Cooper, U.S. National Museum.*)

squids (Fig. 6.14). The shells of some were long, straight, and somewhat tapering; others had loosely or tightly coiled shells; all were divided into chambers of somewhat simple outline. The cephalopods were the largest invertebrates of their time, some having shells that attain nearly 1 foot in diameter and a length of more than 15 feet. A restoration of Middle Ordovician sea-bottom life, in which straight-shelled cephalopods are prominent, is reproduced in Fig. 6.24.

Plants. The calcareous laminated deposits formed by lime-secreting seaweeds are very common fossils in some Ordovician strata.

Fig. 6.22 Ordovician graptolites. Two specimens of black shale showing the carbonized impressions of graptolite colonies on bedding planes; natural size.—— A. *Climacograptus*, Mohawkian.——B. *Phyllograptus*, Canadian.

Fig. 6.21 A characteristic Middle Ordovician trilobite. This specimen of *Isotelus gigas* was collected from the Trenton Limestone at Trenton Falls, New York. The species shows evolution in the direction of losing the longitudinally trilobate character that distinguishes most trilobites; ×0.7. (*Courtesy of D. W. Fisher, New York State Museum.*)

They are the only plant remains definitely known from rocks of this age.

First known vertebrates. Bony plates and miscellaneous skeletal fragments of primitive fishes have been collected from Ordovician deposits in the Rocky Mountains region. Although the remains so far discovered are all fragmentary, there is no question as to their belonging to backboned animals, and for the present, they constitute the earliest record of vertebrates on the earth. The plates and bones occur in marine strata, but their highly localized distribution and fragmentary nature support the suggestion that the fishlike animals to which they belong actually lived in fresh waters of nearby land, from whence rivers carried them to the sea. If these animals had lived and died in the sea, traces of them ought to be much more widespread. We cannot be sure that vertebrates originated in the fresh waters of continental areas, but we shall observe that the great evolutionary advancement of this group of animals, to which man belongs, is associated with land areas rather than the sea.

Climate

Definite climatic zones, such as characterize the modern world, do not seem to have existed in the Ordovician Period. At any rate, there is hardly any observable difference in the composition of shallow-water marine faunas in Ordovician rocks from Ellesmereland and other parts of Arctic Canada and those from rocks of similar age in the southern United States. The sea is an equalizing climatic factor; large land areas, especially those having mountains, are characterized by climatic vari-

ations, in both temperature and humidity. We may infer that times of extremely widespread shallow seas and low-lying lands, on which mountains were conspicuously absent—and this applies generally to the Ordovician Period —were marked by relatively warm and even climate.

Close of the Period

Mountain building. Two sorts of evidence serve to establish the conclusion that in Ordovician time mountainous areas came into existence in eastern North America. These have been named the *Taconian Mountains,* from an area along the eastern border of New York. One sign of this uplift is the great quantity of gravel, sand, and mud that was furnished by erosion of the elevated terrain; these sediments comprise fluviatile and shallow-water marine Late Ordovician deposits in the Appa-

Fig. 6.23   Ordovician shale containing numerous lacy and ribbon-like bryozoans. This specimen, from the Baltic region of Europe, shows the presence of many colonies that are closely similar to forms in American Ordovician strata. Natural size. (*R. S. Bassler, U.S. National Museum.*)

Fig. 6.24 Mohawkian sea bottom in the neighborhood of Chicago. This restoration shows straight-shelled nautiloid cephalopods associated with snails, trilobites, colonial "honeycomb" and solitary corals (with outstretched tentacles), and seaweeds. The coloration of shells of the swimming nautiloids is based on fossils that show the pattern of original pigmentation, but the spotted tentacles of the large cephalopod lying on the limemud in the foreground obviously are conjectural. (*Courtesy of Chicago Natural History Museum.*)

lachian geosyncline. Some of the hard conglomerate deposits of Silurian age, derived from erosion of the Taconian Mountains, now form the resistant core of present Appalachian Mountains ridges. Late Ordovician streamborne sediment (Juniata, Queenston) consists of reddish alluvial sand and delta deposits.

Another evidence of the mountain building is the folded and faulted structure of Ordovician strata in the Appalachian Mountains region (Fig. 6.25), especially in places where these rocks, after being beveled by erosion, are found beneath Silurian deposits. Outcrops showing angular unconformity at the Ordovician-Silurian boundary occur at many places in Pennsylvania, New York, New England, and eastern Canada. At some localities a prominent basal conglomerate occurs next above the unconformity. These observations prove that Ordovician and older strata were subjected to mountain-making deformation, which occurred sufficiently long before the time of Silurian sedimentation in the region to permit deep erosion of the Ordovician rocks. Probably, the Taconian mountain building affected the entire length of the Appalachian

geosyncline. Granite bathyliths in the southern Appalachian Piedmont region that generally have been considered to be Late Paleozoic in age now have yielded radioactive age determinations of more than 300 million years, indicating that probably they are Taconian in age.

Continental emergence. The end of Ordovician time is signalized by general emergence of the North American continent after the very widespread transgression of the sea in Late Ordovician time. Even the geosynclinal areas were vacated by the shallow seas. Except in areas of mountainous relief in the east, however, elevation of the land seems not to have been enough to permit very much erosion of previously formed deposits. Nevertheless, the hiatus between Ordovician and Silurian strata is clearly defined.

Economic Resources

Products useful to man derived from Ordovician rocks have an aggregate value probably exceeding $1,000 million annually. These include petroleum and natural gas, lead, zinc, iron, manganese, gold, stone (including slate), glass and foundry sand, and ground water, although the very important last-named resource is not stated in terms of monetary worth.

Petroleum. Oil and gas were discovered in Ordovician rocks in the Ohio-Indiana-Ontario region in 1883, and later much larger quantities were found in the midcontinent area from Kansas to Texas. At present, formations of Ordovician age produce oil (and natural gas) in approximately 900 different pools in the United States which, counting past production and proved reserves, have a yield of approximately 4,500 million barrels; this amount is slightly more than 7 per cent of the country's total.

Metals. Metalliferous resources of the Ordovician are chiefly distributed as follows: (1) lead and zinc in Middle Ordovician dolostone of the Tri-State district in Illinois-Wisconsin-Iowa and in Lower Ordovician dolostone of southeastern Missouri, (2) iron in

Fig. 6.25 Strongly folded Lower Ordovician limestone in a quarry at Northampton, Pennsylvania. Under pressure of mountain-building forces, this limestone has been deformed in almost plastic manner. Ordovician formations along the northeastern border of North America have been affected by two or more epochs of mountain building, and their present structure reflects the sum of these movements. The Taconian orogeny, near the close of the Ordovician Period, was followed by deformations in Devonian and Permian time. (*Courtesy of Pennsylvania Geol. Survey.*)

eastern Newfoundland, (3) manganese in northern Arkansas and Virginia, (4) gold in the famous so-called "saddle-reef" anticlines of the Bendigo district in Victoria, Australia.

Nonmetals. Nonmetallic Ordovician materials are unusually important. These include (5) limestone for many purposes, some of high purity being produced for chemical purposes, as in large quarries at Bellefonte, Pennsylvania; (6) marble in the Rutland, Vermont, and eastern Tennessee areas, which furnish by far the largest part of marble supplies used in our country; (7) cement rock, both limestones having the properties of natural cement rock and formations used for making portland cement, especially in the northern and central Appalachian region but also in the Mississippi Valley; (8) slate in the Martinsburg Formation of eastern Pennsylvania, which is the chief producing area in the United States; (9) glass and foundry sand, coming mainly from the Ottawa district of northern Illinois and workings a few miles south of St. Louis, Missouri, both utilizing the well-sorted pure quartz sand of the St. Peter Sandstone, of Chazyan age; (10) silica bricks for lining kilns and other refractory purposes, manufacture being based also on St. Peter Sandstone; (11) ground water in Ordovician sandstones, notably in Illinois, the Ozark region of Missouri, Kansas, Oklahoma, and other parts of the midcontinent area.

READINGS

AGNEW, A. F., 1955, Facies of Middle and Upper Ordovician rocks of Iowa: *Am. Assoc. Petroleum Geologists Bull.*, vol. 39, pp. 1703–1752 (illus.).
Conditions of sedimentation interpreted from nature and distribution of lithologic characters.

CLOUD, P. E., JR., and BARNES, V. E., 1957, Early Ordovician sedimentation in central Texas: in *Treatise on marine ecology*, Geol. Soc. America, Mem. 67, H. S. Ladd, ed., vol. 2, pp. 163–214.

KAY, MARSHALL, 1937, Stratigraphy of the Trenton Group: *Geol. Soc. America Bull.*, vol. 48, pp. 226–235.
Classification and correlation of Middle Ordovician strata in eastern United States.

———, 1951, North American geosynclines: *Geol. Soc. America Mem.* 48 (143 pp., illus.).
Contains important general discussion (pp. 1–32) in addition to notice of Ordovician deposits (pp. 36–37, 52–53, 63–66). Excellent description and discussion of sedimentary environment in relation to bottom-dwelling invertebrates.

STOSE, G. W., 1946, The Taconic sequence in Pennsylvania: *Am. Jour. Sci.*, vol. 244, pp. 665–696 (illus.).
Selected from numerous papers on representative Ordovician areas.

WOODWARD, H. P., 1957, Chronology of Appalachian folding: *Am. Assoc. Petroleum Geologists Bull.*, vol. 41, pp. 2312–2327 (illus.).
Indicates that the Taconic disturbance was the most profound of orogenies in the Appalachian Mountains region.

QUESTIONS

1. Comparison of the outcrop areas of Ordovician and Cambrian rocks in the type region of Wales (Figs. 6.1, 5.1) demonstrates that the former are much more extensive than the latter. Does this mean that Ordovician seas spread over a larger territory than was submerged in Cambrian time? What other explanation can be offered?

2. What conditions of sedimentation and geologic history are represented diagrammatically by the presence of Late Ordovician strata resting directly on Precambrian rocks in part of Fig. 6.2?

3. Referring to Fig. 6.3, how does the map indicate the nature of regional structure in the areas of Ordovician outcrops surrounding Cincinnati (Ohio-Indiana-Kentucky), Nashville (Tennessee), and Rolla, Missouri (Ozark region)? Are these areas domal, basinal, linear anticlinal, or troughlike synclinal? Why is the occurrence of Ordovician rocks beneath the waters of the

Great Lakes (except Superior) reasonably certain, despite lack of proof obtained by drilling in the lake bottoms? What explanations can be suggested for the indicated absence of Ordovician deposits in a wide belt extending southwestward from Minnesota to Arizona?

4. Although Lower, Middle, and Upper Ordovician formations are found to be present in the Upper Mississippi Valley region (Minnesota-Wisconsin-Iowa-Illinois), their aggregate thickness is less than one-fourth that of Ordovician deposits in southern Oklahoma or in the central Appalachians (Virginia-West Virginia-Maryland-Pennsylvania). Can you cite three or more factors possibly contributing to this difference?

5. If the multitude of diverse fossils discovered in different parts of the rock units diagrammatically illustrated in Fig. 6.8 could be brought together in collections of a single survey or museum, what two main controlling factors would you expect to find expressed by assemblages from different parts of these Ordovician deposits? In what way or ways could the distinctions assignable to these factors be recognized and demonstrated?

6. How is the aggregate thickness of Ordovician rocks found in different areas indicated in Fig. 6.10 correlated with regionally dissimilar nature of the earth's crust? In what territory are the Ordovician strata strongly folded and faulted? What is the seeming significance of localization of the deformation?

7. Referring to Fig. 6.11, can you suggest at least three ways in which air photographs are very useful to geologists in field study of an area? Why does the value of air photographs as an aid to geologic investigations vary from region to region?

8. What is the evidence supporting conclusions that domal areas such as the Ozark and Cincinnati domes have become accentuated progressively during geologic history and that neighboring basins contain a more complete record of sedimentation than the domes (Fig. 6.16)?

9. How many noteworthy differences can you distinguish between the marine invertebrate assemblage illustrated in Fig. 5.27, representing the extraordinarily well-preserved Middle Cambrian fauna from the Burgess Shale of western Canada, and the restoration of Middle Ordovician bottom-dwelling invertebrates shown in Fig. 6.24?

7.

PALEOZOIC ERA:

SILURIAN PERIOD

Silurian strata in the Niagara River gorge below
Niagara Falls, New York.

The Silurian rocks are named from a region in western England and Wales, inhabited by an early tribe known as the Silures (Fig. 7.1). Here, as in many other parts of the world, an important unconformity marks the base of the Silurian System, but the top is less definite, because a transition into overlying continental deposits, known as the Old Red Sandstone, occurs at least locally (Fig. 7.2). Elsewhere in the British Isles and northwestern Europe generally, one of the most clearly marked unconformities in the Paleozoic succession defines the upper limit of Silurian deposits. Toward the close of the Silurian Period, great mountain-making movements, known as the Caledonian orogeny, affected northwestern

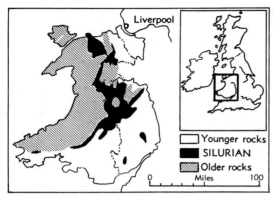

Fig. 7.1 Outcrops of Silurian rocks in Wales and western England where these rocks were named.

Europe and some other parts of the world. Greatly disturbed Silurian and older rocks were then eroded deeply, and the Old Red Sandstone, together with other post-Silurian deposits, was laid down across the truncated edges of older strata.

Occurrence of Silurian Rocks in North America

Recognition of the system. The occurrence of Silurian deposits in North America is proved by finding, at many places in the United States and Canada, stratified rocks that contain assemblages of marine shallow-water invertebrates very closely similar to those of the type region and neighboring parts of Europe. A considerable number of species found in America seem to be identical with those occurring in England and richly fossiliferous Silurian rocks of the Baltic region.

The rocks identified as representing Silurian time in North America lie unconformably on Ordovician strata. In the interior of the continent and Cordilleran geosyncline, there was no folding or tilting of Ordovician and older rocks before deposition of Silurian strata, and accordingly, these rocks lie parallel (disconformably or paraconformably) on older formations. In the northern part of the Appalachian geosyncline, however, an angular unconformity is observed at the base of the Silurian in many places, as noted in discussion of the Taconian mountain building given in the preceding chapter (Figs. 7.3, 7.4).

Distribution and general character of Silurian deposits. Outcrops of Silurian rocks occur mainly in the eastern and northern parts of North America (Fig. 7.5). In New York, where these rocks were first studied carefully and where the major divisions of the Silurian in North America were named, strata belonging to the system occur in a band that crosses the state in an east-west direction just south of Lake Ontario. Extensive exposures occur also in the Appalachian geosyncline as far south as Alabama and northeastward to Newfoundland.

The Silurian rocks lie nearly flat in the eastern Mississippi Valley region, where they form the surface of a large area extending from Kentucky, Ohio, Indiana, and Illinois into Wisconsin and Iowa. That the Silurian seas reached very far to the north in the central part of the continent is shown by the presence

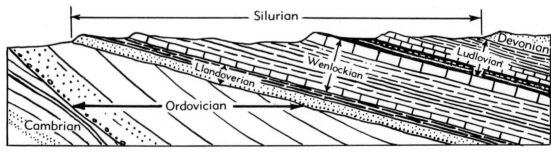

Fig. 7.2 Diagrammatic section of the Silurian System in the type region of England and Wales. The Silurian strata dip gently eastward, in general, the harder rocks forming west-facing escarpments. The basal Silurian sandstone rests on various parts of the Ordovician System and in places transgresses on to Precambrian rocks. The top of the system is less sharply defined, for nearly conformable fish-bearing beds lead up into continental strata of the Old Red Sandstone.

Fig. 7.3 Angular unconformity between Silurian and Ordovician rocks in eastern Pennsylvania. The structural relations of the light-colored Silurian sandstone that here shows stratification planes standing vertical and the dark-colored slaty Ordovician rocks that appear nearly horizontal prove the occurrence of two mountain-making deformations, as indicated diagrammatically in Fig. 7.4. (*N. H. Darton, courtesy of U.S. Geol. Survey.*)

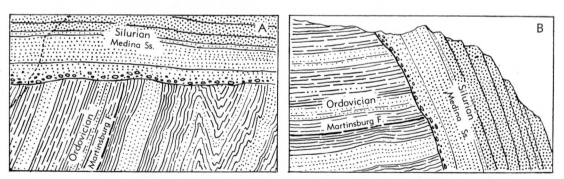

Fig. 7.4 Geologic history represented by the angular unconformity in Pennsylvania at the base of Silurian deposits.——*A.* Structure of the region illustrated in Fig. 7.3 as it was in Silurian time after folding of Ordovician strata (Taconian orogeny), truncation of upturned Martinsburg beds, and deposition subhorizontally of Early Silurian sandstone, which is conglomeratic at the base, containing pebbles of Martinsburg rock (profile of present surface as drawn in *B* shown by broken line at upper left).——*B.* Structure seen at present, in which both Silurian and Ordovician rocks have been disturbed by another mountain-making disturbance (Appalachian orogeny, at the close of Paleozoic); the angular unconformity now is tilted at a steep angle.

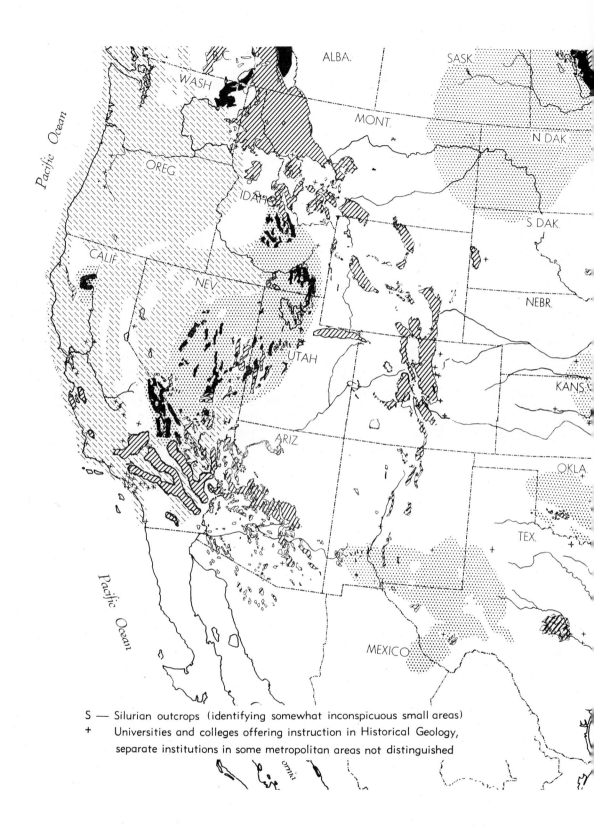

S — Silurian outcrops (identifying somewhat inconspicuous small areas)
+   Universities and colleges offering instruction in Historical Geology,
    separate institutions in some metropolitan areas not distinguished

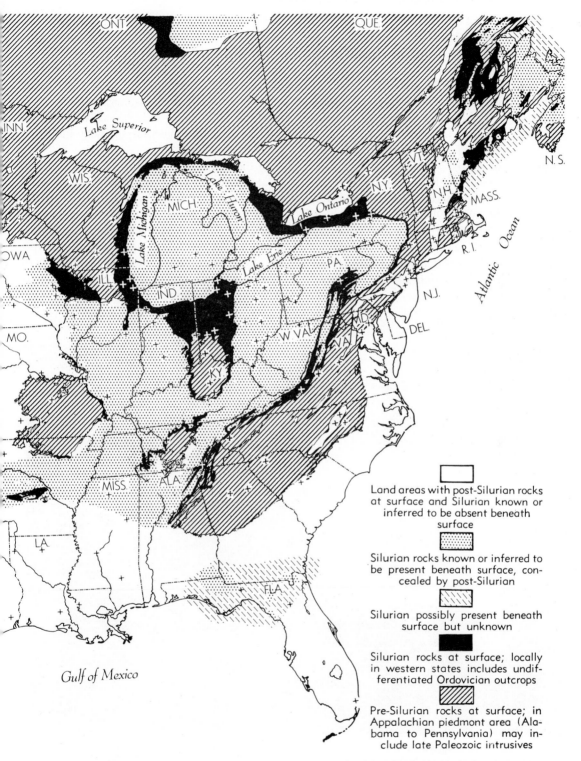

Land areas with post-Silurian rocks
at surface and Silurian known or
inferred to be absent beneath
surface

Silurian rocks known or inferred to
be present beneath surface, concealed by post-Silurian

Silurian possibly present beneath
surface but unknown

Silurian rocks at surface; locally
in western states includes undifferentiated Ordovician outcrops

Pre-Silurian rocks at surface; in
Appalachian piedmont area (Alabama to Pennsylvania) may include late Paleozoic intrusives

Fig. 7.5 Distribution of Silurian rocks in the United States, southern Canada, and northern Mexico. The outcrops and subsurface occurrences shown indicate the original distribution of the system modified by aggregate effects of post-Silurian erosion and probably in parts of the West by post-Silurian bathylithic igneous intrusions.

of outcrop areas of Silurian rocks in Manitoba, on the southwest shore of Hudson Bay, and in islands of the Arctic Archipelago almost to the pole.

In the western United States, Silurian deposits are thin, but they are found at intervals along the trend of the Cordilleran geosyncline from northwestern Canada to the El Paso region of western Texas. Silurian rocks are known also in Alaska.

Beneath the surface, Silurian formations extend from New York and eastern Pennsylvania throughout the upper Ohio Valley; the saucerlike structural basin of the lower peninsula of Michigan with marginal tracts covered by the waters of Lake Michigan, Lake Huron, and Lake Erie; the Illinois-Indiana basin extending into western Kentucky; and territory

farther south in Tennessee, Mississippi, Alabama, Arkansas, and southeasternmost Missouri. Study of the map (Fig. 7.5) of this area serves to show how subsurface distribution of Silurian rocks ties outcrop areas together in a readily intelligible manner, making clear also the relation of Silurian distribution to outcrop areas of pre-Silurian rocks indicated by oblique ruling.

In the Western States the Silurian is absent in at least half of the country, subsurface occurrence in Nebraska and Kansas being almost isolated from areas to the northeast. Patches of varying size and shape are known from drilling in Oklahoma, Texas, New Mexico, the Williston Basin of the Dakotas, eastern Montana, Saskatchewan, and Manitoba. Farther west, definitely known subsurface occur-

Fig. 7.6 Prominent escarpment made by hard Silurian conglomeratic sandstone (Shawangunk) near Kingston, in southeastern New York. These coarse sandy deposits were derived from Appalachia by erosion of the Taconian highlands during Early, Middle, and Late Silurian time. The age of the sandstone varies from place to place. (*N. H. Darton, courtesy of U.S. Geol. Survey.*)

Fig. 7.7 Appalachian Mountain ridges in eastern Pennsylvania. Topographic relief map of the Harrisburg Quadrangle showing parallelism of the ridges and intervening valleys made by hard and soft steeply dipping Paleozoic rocks. In northward order mountains on the east side of the Susquehanna River are made, respectively, by (1) Silurian, (2) Mississippian, (3) Pennsylvanian, and (4) Mississippian, same as (2), showing that the structure is synclinal. (*Courtesy of Aero Service Corporation.*)

rence of Silurian rocks is restricted to Idaho, Utah, Nevada, and small parts of California, but possible distribution includes most of the region westward to the Pacific.

The nature of Silurian deposits found in these different parts of North America varies greatly, as we should expect, this variation being expressed both in kind of rocks and their thickness. Along the Appalachian trough, adjacent to the Taconian Mountains formed near the close of Ordovician time, deposits belonging to the lower part of the Silurian System are thick and composed mainly of coarse quartzose sandstone and conglomerate derived from high lands to the east (Fig. 7.6). These rocks, turned steeply upward by later (Appalachian) deformation, form the easternmost even-topped ridges of the Appalachian Mountains (excluding the Blue Ridge) in Pennsylvania, Maryland, and Virginia (Figs. 7.7, 7.8). Study of Silurian deposits farther west in the geosyncline shows the existence of com-

plex facies changes, continental sediments in the east passing laterally westward into shallow-water marine deposits. Interfingering of strata of different origin proves the oscillating position of the shore line during the period.

An interesting and economically important feature of Silurian deposits in this region is occurrence of sedimentary iron ore. The iron oxide is presumed to have been precipitated through action of bacteria in lagoonal areas along the sea borders, but in many places the iron-bearing mineral replaces the original calcareous shell substance of marine fossils and other fragments of calcium carbonate.

Dolostone prevails in Silurian deposits of the Great Lakes and eastern Mississippi Valley area. It is this Silurian dolostone that forms the prominent north-facing escarpment in western New York over which Niagara River flows and in which the falls have been carved. Similar dolostone is widely exposed in Ohio, in Indiana, and in the vicinity of Chicago.

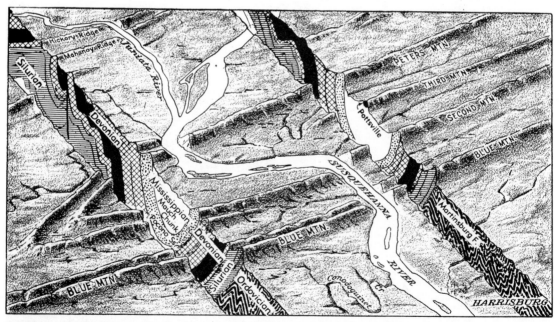

Fig. 7.8 Appalachian Mountain ridges and valleys in southeastern Pennsylvania. Blue Mountain, which is made by upturned hard Silurian sandstones, adjoins a plains region that is formed by much-folded, slaty Upper Ordovician rocks (Martinsburg Formation). The unconformable contact at the base of the Silurian represents erosion associated with the Taconian mountain building. The folded attitude of Silurian and younger Paleozoic rocks results from much later folding that occurred near the close of Paleozoic time. (*Modified from A. K. Lobeck, New York Academy of Science.*)

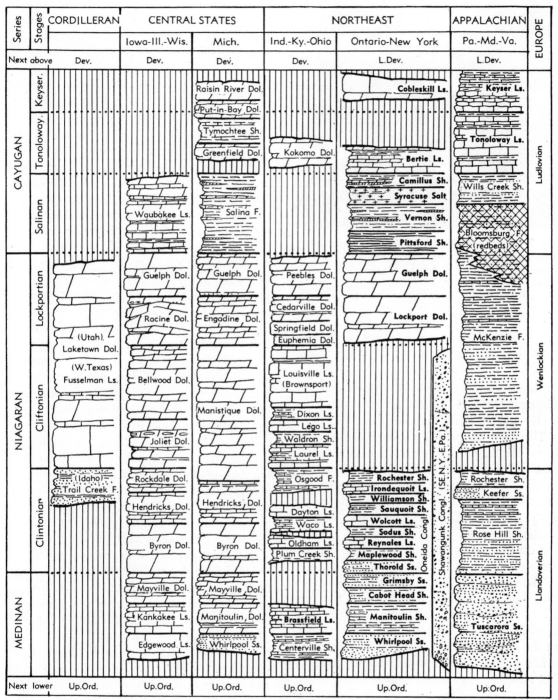

Fig. 7.9 Time-rock divisions of the Silurian System and rock units assigned to them in representative important sections of North America. The vertical scale does not represent time duration or thickness of rocks but is determined by suitability for plotting the various recognized rock units, placement of which indicates correlation in age. Lithologic character is represented graphically (explanation of symbols in Appendix B). Necessarily, the plotted thickness is not to scale, although it approximates proportional values in many sections. Vertically ruled areas denote absence of deposits.

Fig. 7.10 Fine-textured Medinan sandstone inter-bedded with silty to clayey sediment. This exposure is on the Canadian side of the Niagara River at Sir Adam Beck Station 2. (*Courtesy of J. W. Wells, Cornell University.*)

Divisions. Silurian formations of North America are divided into three series, named in order upward Medinan, Niagaran, and Cayugan (Fig. 7.9). All are defined from sections in the State of New York.

The Early Silurian, or Medinan, Series comprises sandy and shaly deposits mainly in the east and thin, rather discontinuous limestone in the Central States. The Middle Silurian, or Niagaran, Series is the most widespread division of the system. It contains various clastic formations in the Appalachian trough, but consists mostly of dolostone in the interior region.

The Upper Silurian, or Cayugan, Series is the most restricted main division of the system in geographic distribution, being confined mostly to the eastern and northern parts of the continent. It is characterized by evaporites and associated unfossiliferous deposits but also contains normal marine strata.

Early Silurian Sedimentation

Deposition derived from uplands of Appalachia. In western New York and throughout the Appalachian trough, from Pennsylvania to Alabama, the Lower Silurian deposits consist chiefly of coarse sandstone and conglomerate. The sand grains or pebbles are held tightly together in a siliceous cement, and the massively bedded white or gray rock is extremely resistant; it forms the backbone of many prominent mountain ridges in the present-day Appalachians (Figs. 7.7, 7.8). This deposit rests unconformably on folded Upper Ordovician rocks and in its composition furnishes a record of the erosion of elevated country lying east of the Appalachian trough. The source area of the sediments is interpreted as belonging to the Taconian Mountain system that had been formed in this region toward the close of Ordovician time. The thickness of the sandstone in places is nearly 1,000 feet. The sandy deposits become thinner and more fine-grained westward in the direction away from the Appalachian borderland (Fig. 7.10). The sandstone is almost entirely barren of any traces of organisms and seems mostly to have been laid down above sea level. In western New York and Ontario, however, lateral gradation and interfingering of the barren sandstone with marine fossil-bearing shaly deposits may be observed, and farther west there are limestone beds laid down in clear water. Thus, in Early Silurian time, we may picture somewhat rugged uplands in Appalachia along the eastern margin of a shallow sea that occupied the geosynclinal belt. Wearing down of the land was accompanied by alluvial deposition on a gently sloping coastal plain that merged with the sandy and muddy bottom of the sea.

Limestone deposition in the continental interior. Lower Silurian deposits of the continental interior are mostly limestone, but the maximum thickness is about 300 feet. The beds, which in many places are highly fossiliferous, rest paraconformably on various Upper Ordovician formations, but because the contact of the older and younger beds is even and the strata lie parallel, the unconformity is inconspicuous. The clear, shallow waters of Early Silurian time in which these limestone beds were laid down reached westward at least to Kansas and Oklahoma, and they are also identified far northward in central Canada.

Middle Silurian Marine Transgression

Geosynclinal deposits. After a time of continental emergence that is indicated by an unconformity at various places above the Lower Silurian rocks, the sea reoccupied virtually all the previously inundated territory and, in addition, spread widely over the western part of the Canadian Shield and into the Cordilleran geosyncline. In the Appalachian trough, especially in northeastern Pennsylvania and adjacent parts of New York, coarse sediments (Shawangunk Conglomerate, Figs. 7.6, 7.9) continued to be derived from the highlands of the Taconian belt and accumulated to a considerable thickness, but in the middle and western parts of the geosyncline, deposition of marine shale was predominant. The shale interfingers eastward with the coarse barren sandstone. Iron-bearing beds occur in this part of the Silurian, and especially in the vicinity of Birmingham, Alabama, they are of much economic importance.

Western New York and North Central States. A classic area for study of the Middle Silurian deposits is the Niagara River gorge, which marks part of the boundary between New York and Ontario (Fig. 7.11). From this section, the name Niagaran, applied to the Middle Silurian Series, is derived. The most prominent formation is the massive dolostone that forms the rim of Niagara Falls and occurs at the top of the bluffs along the gorge (Fig. 7.12). It is also the resistant rock unit that makes the prominent north-facing escarpment running parallel to the south shore of Lake Ontario (Fig. 7.13). Below the dolostone are fossiliferous shale and thin limestone beds that comprise the lower part of the Middle Silurian section. Their base approximately coincides with the river level at the foot of the falls, but downstream the beds occur at increasingly high level above the river, so that the entire Lower Silurian and the upper part of Ordovician red-shale deposits are exposed. The sea in which these sediments were laid down extended uninterruptedly westward

Fig. 7.11 Classic exposures of Niagaran strata in the gorge of the Niagara River below Niagara Falls, New York. The cliff-making rock at the top of the section is the Lockport Dolostone; beneath it are weak strata of the Clinton Group and beds belonging to the Medinan Series. (*F. B. Taylor, courtesy of U.S. Geol. Survey.*)

across the central Great Lakes region to Iowa, as shown by nearly continuous outcrops, by lithologic similarity of the deposits, and by occurrence of virtually the same assemblage of marine invertebrates throughout these strata (Fig. 7.14).

Coral reefs. A striking feature of the calcareous Middle Silurian formations, especially in parts of Indiana, Illinois, and Wisconsin, is the local presence of thick unbedded masses of dolostone containing abundant fossil corals. These masses are surrounded by somewhat

thinly stratified normal type of dolostone beds, which dip outward away from the structureless masses in such manner as to show that the latter were topographic prominences on the Silurian sea floor, just like many modern coral reefs. The reef characteristics of these rock bodies in the Niagaran dolostones of the Central States were recognized many years ago (1) by the massive, unstratified nature of parts identified as core rock, in which corals and other invertebrates were found to be most abundant and many of them obviously in undisturbed position of growth, and (2) by the presence of steeply inclined bedded deposits dipping outward from the cores and therefore appropriately distinguished as flank rock (Figs. 7.15, 7.16). Between adjacent reefs is normal horizontally bedded inter-reef rock. Although some of the reefs first studied are 2 or 3 miles across, they are not very thick, ranging to a maximum of approximately 75 feet. Now, many more reefs are known (Fig. 7.17), some of which are 6 miles in diameter and 1,000 feet in thickness and relief; these are buried but have been well explored by

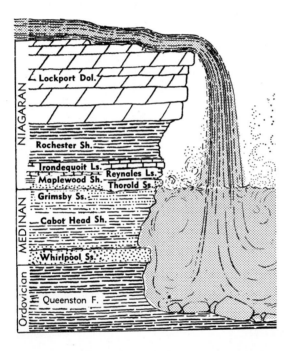

Fig. 7.12 Geologic section at Niagara Falls. The Lockport Dolostone and underlying Niagaran strata down to the contact with Medinan beds are exposed above water level just below the falls; the strata here represented below the water surface crop out downstream. (*Modified from Kindle and Taylor, U.S. Geol. Survey.*)

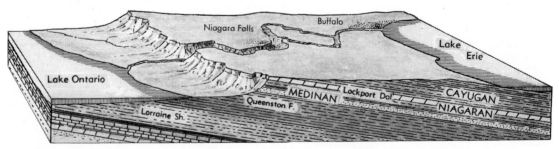

Fig. 7.13 North-facing escarpment made by Silurian rocks in western New York and southern Ontario. The diagram shows the territory between Lake Ontario and Lake Erie, looking slightly south of east. The Silurian (Medinan, Niagaran, Cayugan) and underlying Ordovician (Queenston, Lorraine) dip gently southward (toward right). The recession of Niagara Falls has led to making the gorge below the falls.

Fig. 7.14 Typical Niagaran dolostone of the Central States. Middle Silurian carbonate deposits closely resembling the rocks seen in this quarry in Chippewa County, Michigan, northeast of Mackinac, extend uninterruptedly to Iowa and beyond. The dolostone here exhibits very regular bedding and jointing. (*I. C. Russell, courtesy of U.S. Geol. Survey.*)

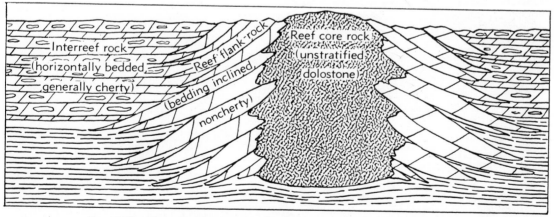

Fig. 7.15 Diagrammatic section of Niagaran reef. The distinctive features of the reefs are topographic relief on the sea bottom during growth and divisibility of the reef mass into two distinct parts: (1) massive core rock that lacks bedding and contains maximum concentration of the reef-building organisms and (2) flank rock that is bedded, more or less steeply inclined outward from the core rock, and less rich in fossils than the core. Between adjacent reefs is inter-reef bedded rock stratified more or less horizontally. (*Modified from E. R. Cumings and R. R. Shrock.*)

Fig. 7.16 Niagaran reef flank rock. The evenly inclined layers were accumulated along the edge of a reef, to the left of photograph, during lateral growth of the reef mass, here about a square mile in areal extent. Material Service Corporation quarry at Thornton, Illinois. (*Photograph made for this book, courtesy of J. C. Frye, Illinois Geol. Survey.*)

drilling, because some of them are rich oil producers. Exploration for such reefs continues.

Volcanism. Volcanic activity of some importance in Middle Silurian time is recorded by beds of basaltic lava, up to 4,000 feet thick in eastern Quebec and New Brunswick, and by similarly thick lava and ash beds in Maine.

Late Silurian Restricted Seas

Deposition of evaporites. The latter part of Silurian time is marked by a great restriction of marine waters on the North American continent and by deposition of much salt and gypsum in isolated Late Silurian basins. Associated with the gypsum, which is the hydrous

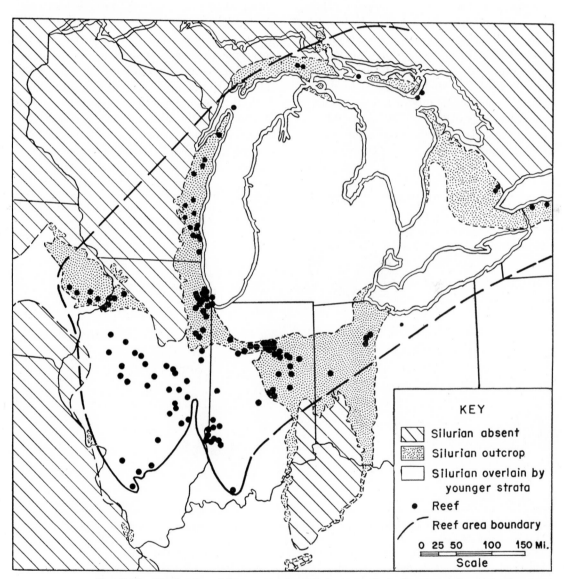

KEY

⬚ Silurian absent
⬚ Silurian outcrop
☐ Silurian overlain by younger strata
• Reef
⌐ Reef area boundary

0 25 50 100 150 MI.
Scale

Fig. 7.17 Distribution of known moderately large reefs in Niagaran deposits of western Great Lakes States. The map shows 126 reefs that range in diameter from approximately 0.5 to 6 miles and in topographic relief ranging to a maximum of 1,000 feet. Not only outcropping reefs but many beneath the surface, found in drilling, are shown; some of the buried reefs are prolific oil-yielding reservoirs. (*H. A. Lowenstam, Illinois Geol. Survey.*)

form of calcium sulfate, is much anhydrite, which is anhydrous calcium sulfate. These deposits indicate concentration of the mineral matter in sea water by evaporation to the point of saturation, at which continued evaporation produces precipitation. The southern peninsula of Michigan and adjacent country eastward to central New York contain thick deposits of Upper Silurian salt, gypsum, and anhydrite, which occur in numerous beds. There are much gypsum and anhydrite also in Upper Silurian deposits of the lower Mackenzie Valley in northwestern Canada.

The aggregate thickness of rock salt near the center of the Michigan basin is at least 1,800 feet, and a few miles south of Syracuse, New York, it is 318 feet (Fig. 7.18). Marine deposits associated with the evaporites consist of dolostone and gray to red unfossiliferous shale. It is probable that some of the shales are subaerial in origin, representing land deposits adjacent to the Late Silurian sea, laid down under a desert climate.

Deposition in unsaturated brines. The top part of the Upper Silurian Series in New York and the Great Lakes region is characterized by numerous fairly even layers of impure dolostone, called *water lime*. These beds contain organisms of specialized type, including a group of large arthropods (eurypterids) (Fig. 7.19). The rocks and fossils indicate that the sea was less saline than formerly, but not low enough in salt content to allow normal types of marine invertebrates to live in it. This interpretation of the environment agrees with the general picture of desiccation that stratigraphically adjacent salt deposits indicate, but some paleontologists think that the eurypterids lived in brackish-water lagoons or even fresh waters, and this does seem to

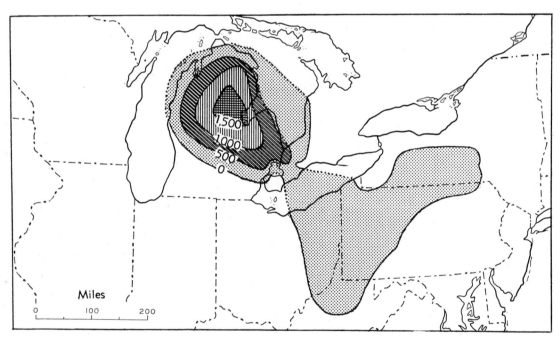

Fig. 7.18 Upper Silurian salt deposits in the eastern Great Lakes region. As shown by drilling, the salt deposits are known to occur throughout most of the southern peninsula of Michigan, with thickness ranging upward to 1,800 feet. In addition, Silurian salt beds aggregating 325 feet or less are distributed as indicated by the map in southwestern Ontario, eastern Ohio, northern West Virginia, western Pennsylvania, and southwestern New York. The total area, including some territory covered by the Great Lakes, exceeds 100,000 square miles. (*Data from U.S. Geol. Survey and Fettke, Martens, Pepper, and Alling, courtesy of Baltimore & Ohio Railway Co.*)

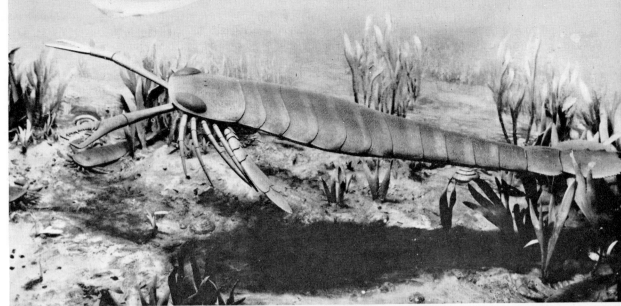

Fig. 7.19 Restorations of the large fossil arthropods called eurypterids. These joint-legged invertebrates, which were provided with a strong covering of horny shell, were fairly numerous in shallow Late Silurian seas of the Great Lakes region. They are thought to have fed largely on worms and perhaps small fishes. The water in which they lived was abnormal in salinity, as shown by absence of common types of marine invertebrates. (*Courtesy of Buffalo Museum of Science; model prepared by George and Paul Marchand, under the direction of Irving G. Reimann.*)

be true for some later species found in coal-swamp deposits. Although a few specimens have been collected in normal marine sediments (to which they could have been carried after the death of the animals), we can be sure that the eurypterids are creatures adapted to a nonmarine environment.

Late Silurian sedimentation in part of the Appalachian geosyncline was of essentially normal marine type, for limestone containing a varied assemblage of marine invertebrates comprises the youngest Silurian in Pennsylvania, Maryland, West Virginia, and Virginia.

Silurian Life

Invertebrates. The rich marine faunas, preserved in Lower and Middle Silurian rocks of North America, contain varied representa-

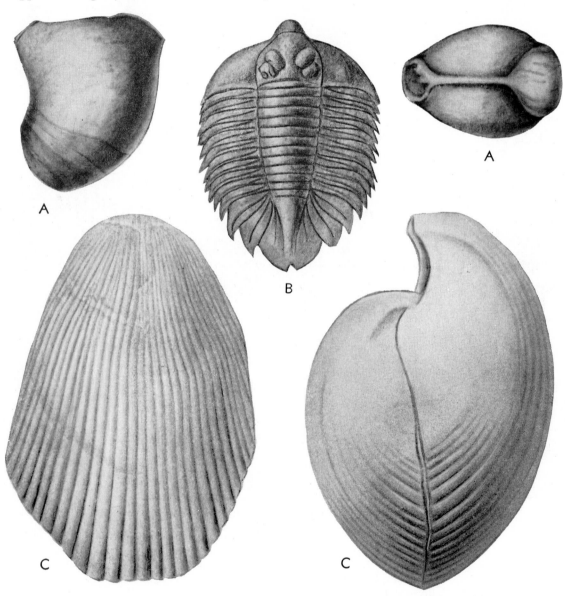

Fig. 7.20 Representative Silurian invertebrate fossils.——*A.* Two views of a simple-sutured cephalopod (*Phragmoceras*) that is specialized in having a partly closed living chamber.——*B.* A characteristic trilobite (*Arctinurus*) with large fluted tail shield.——*C.* Two views of a large, ribbed brachiopod (*Conchidium*). Natural size.

tives of all main classes. It is clear that a majority of the known forms of life are direct descendants of Ordovician organisms that had lived in American shallow seas, because the assemblages are similar. Many Ordovician and Silurian species belong to the same genera. Associated with old types are some in-

vertebrates that seem to represent immigrants or, at any rate, developments that are not readily traced to known Ordovician ancestors. A few representative species are illustrated (Figs. 7.20, 7.21). Brachiopods, corals, bryozoans, and cephalopods are the most important types in most Silurian faunas, but echino-

Fig. 7.21 Middle Silurian trilobite and unusual quadrangular type of coral. The trilobite (*A, Calymena*) has a moderately small head shield (cephalon) with strongly marked lobes along the sides of the axial part. The coral (*B, Goniophyllum*) is distinguished by its pyramidal form, as well as the arrangement of the internal radial partitions (septa). This is a silicified specimen in which the peculiarity of "beekite rings," produced by excessive deposition of silica around random centers of replacement, yields a pattern having nothing to do with the original appearance of the hard parts fossilized. Both fossils slightly enlarged. (*Courtesy of C. W. Collinson, Illinois Geol. Survey.*)

derms, trilobites, sponges, and the small bivalve crustaceans called *ostracodes* are valuable guide fossils in many formations. Graptolites, distinctly different in type from those characteristic of Ordovician horizons, are common fossils in some dark-colored Silurian shaly deposits.

A noteworthy feature of Silurian life is the very close similarity or identity of several highly specialized crinoids found in Niagaran deposits of the Mississippi Valley and Arctic islands north of Canada, and in Middle Silurian strata of the Baltic region of Europe (Figs. 7.22, 7.23). These occurrences clearly indicate a polar pathway of shallow-water marine migration by which species were interchanged between North America and Europe.

The arthropods called *eurypterids* or *sea scorpions*, which characterize Late Silurian deposits in the northeastern United States, were spike- or blade-tailed animals with jointed legs and claws, most of which had an over-all length of only a few inches. The largest attained a length of 9 feet from tip of tail to outstretched pincers, and this Silurian creature is the most gigantic known arthropod, living or extinct.

Vertebrates. Remains of fishes, which are very scanty and unsatisfactory, have been described from Ordovician deposits, but uppermost Silurian or lowest Devonian (Downtonian) rocks in Europe have yielded nearly complete remains of very primitive fishes. They had a length of about 6 inches and represent a type that lacks well-defined jaws.

Possible land plants and animals. Fossil land plants have been reported from Europe and Australia. Also the supposed first air-breathing animals, scorpions and thousand-leg worms (millipeds), are found in Upper Silurian rocks of Scotland. The Silurian scorpions are strikingly like living forms, which suggests, rather than proves, that they breathed air.

Climate

Generally warm, mild, and nearly uniform climatic conditions seem to have prevailed in Early and Middle Silurian times, as through-

out most of the Ordovician Period. This is mainly indicated by the near identity of marine faunas of polar areas and those of temperate latitudes in Europe and the United States. Corals are common as far north as the Hudson Bay region.

In the Late Silurian Epoch, desert conditions are indicated by deposits of the northeastern United States and Mackenzie Basin of far northwestern Canada.

Caledonian Mountain Building

One of the major mountain-building deformations of earth history affected northwestern Europe, northern Greenland, Alaska, and much of the Asiatic continent toward the close of Silurian time. It is known as the Caledonian revolution (from the Roman name for northern Scotland). In most of North America, conditions were very quiet at this time, for there is general absence of crustal disturbance near the boundary between Silurian and Devonian. Throughout the length of Norway and the bordering part of Sweden, however, Silurian and older formations were very strongly folded and pushed eastward along thrust faults; some of the displacements are measured in tens of miles (maximum about 80 miles). In Scotland, northern England, and Ireland, the Caledonian structures trend southwestward, and movement along faults was northwestward. Strongly deformed Silurian and older rocks are seen unconformably beneath the Old Red Sandstone (Devonian) or younger Paleozoic rocks that came to be laid down after erosion had truncated the folded and faulted strata.

Close of the Period

Except for parts of the northern border of the continent, North America was not disturbed by mountain-making movements at the close of Silurian time. Most of the land surface had become emergent at the beginning of the Late Silurian Epoch, but there is no evidence of highland areas. In the Appalachian geosyncline, limestone deposits of latest Silurian age are overlain by very early Devonian limestone, with signs of only a minor in-

Fig. 7.22 Silurian sea bottom with typical invertebrates. This reconstruction, representing an area in Bohemia, contains essentially the same kinds of bottom-dwelling animals as are found in strata of equivalent age in North America, some classified as belonging to identical species. The view shows solitary corals (*A, Omphyma; B, Xylodes*), trilobites (*C, Aulacopleura; D, Cheirurus*), straight- and curved-shell nautiloid cephalopods (*E, Michelinoceras; F, Cyrtoceras*), gastropods (*G, Murchisonia; H, Cyclotropis*), brachiopods (*I, Conchidium*), honeycomb colonial corals (*J, Favosites*), and crinoids (*K, Scyphocrinites*). (*By permission, courtesy of J. Augusta and Z. Burian, Praha.*)

terruption of sedimentation (or none at all) to serve in marking the boundary. Thus, in contrast to unrest such as is represented by the Caledonian disturbance elsewhere, the close of the Silurian Period in most of North America was very quiet.

Economic Resources

The Silurian System has great economic importance, although it is surpassed by several other systems. In approximate order of their value as measured by annual production, Silurian resources include deposits of iron, salt, gypsum, oil and gas, stone, mercury, and antimony.

Iron. The Silurian iron ores occur in the lower part of the Niagaran Series in rocks called the Clinton Group. The iron, chiefly in the form of hematite, is of sedimentary origin, as indicated both by constancy of occurrence stratigraphically and by petrographic examination of the ores, many samples of which show marine fossils replaced by hematite. The iron-rich beds of the Clinton are traced continuously along the Appalachian belt southward from New York to Birmingham, Alabama, where the greatest activity in mining these ores is found. The nearness to one another of easily worked iron deposits, abundant coal for fuel, and limestone for use as a flux in smelting is mainly responsible for development in the Birmingham area of the second largest steel-manufacturing district in the country, but favorable location for serving

Fig. 7.23   Middle Silurian sea bottom in the Niagara region of western New York and southern Ontario. The restoration shows typical crinoids (*A, Eucalyptocrinites*), trilobites (*B, Dalmanites; D, Arcturus*), straight-shelled cephalopods (*C, Dawsonoceras*), and brachiopods (scattered small bivalve shells). (*Courtesy of Buffalo Museum of Science; model prepared by George and Paul Marchand under the direction of I. G. Reimann.*)

southern markets calls for notice also. The so-called Big Seam of Clinton ore near Birmingham ranges to 30 feet in thickness, and mines extending along the dip of the bed (average 30 degrees) reach as much as 6,000 feet from the mine mouth. Annual production of Clinton iron amounts to approximately 20 million tons.

Salt. The Silurian salt deposits already have been cited in discussing the history of Late Silurian time. Here we may merely add statements that the earliest commercial production of these salt deposits was in New York, which continues to be a leader in salt mining, although surpassed by Michigan. The quantity of salt in Michigan is far greater than that of New York or other states containing Silurian deposits (Fig. 7.18), and the sum of all Silurian salt is exceeded considerably by Permian salt. Combined annual production of salt in the Great Lakes States is a little more than 6 million tons.

Gypsum. Associated with the Upper Silurian salt are important gypsum deposits, especially in New York, Michigan, and Ohio.

Production yearly is in the neighborhood of 2.5 million tons.

Petroleum. Clinton sandstones have been rather important producers of oil and gas for many years in Ohio, Kentucky, and West Virginia, and Silurian limestones (part of the so-called Hunton Group) are sources of petroleum in the midcontinent region. As a whole, however, Silurian rocks are not prolific oil and gas reservoirs.

Other resources. Like other systems containing abundant carbonate rocks and hard sandstones, the Silurian System is extensively worked for various sorts of construction stone, cement rock, and (from pure Medinan sandstone) material used in glass manufacture. The largest mercury-producing district in the world is at Almaden, Spain, where the deposits began to be worked in 1564. The area has produced approximately $250 million worth of quicksilver from Silurian quartzitic sandstone. One of the leading producers of antimony is China, which obtains it mainly from Silurian deposits.

READINGS

AMSDEN, T. W., 1955, Lithofacies map of Lower Silurian deposits in central and eastern United States and Canada: *Am. Assoc. Petroleum Geologists Bull.*, vol. 39, pp. 60–74 (illus.).
A study of regional variation in sedimentation.

GEIKIE, ARCHIBALD, 1905, *The founders of geology,* Macmillan & Co., Ltd., London (illus.), pp. 412–434.
Describes earliest work on Silurian rocks and definition of the system.

KINDLE, E. M., and TAYLOR, F. B., 1913, Geology of the Niagara Falls Quadrangle, New York: *U.S. Geol. Survey Geol. Folio* 190.
Gives maps, sections, and description of classic Silurian outcrops in the Niagara River gorge and vicinity.

LOWENSTAM, H. A., 1957, Niagaron reefs in the Great Lakes area: in *Treatise on marine ecology,* H. S. Ladd, ed., Geol. Soc. America, Mem. 67, vol. 2, pp. 215–248.
Excellent account of reef development in Middle Silurian shallow seas.

QUESTIONS

1. What sorts of evidence furnish a dependable basis for distinguishing Silurian from other geologic systems in the type region (Figs. 6.2, 7.2)? Which, if not all, sorts are reliable for the delimitation of Silurian in North America or other parts of the world distant from Wales and western England?

2. In what part of the Silurian succession in the Wales-England area are coarse clastic deposits (conglomerate, sandstone) found, and what explanation for this occurrence seems

to be most reasonable (Fig. 7.2)? Where are carbonate rocks chiefly found? How do these features correspond to the nature and distribution of Silurian rock types in representative North American sections (Fig. 7.9)?

3. Suppose that the contact between Silurian and Ordovician strata illustrated in Fig. 7.3 is postulated to be a fault rather than an angular unconformity (Fig. 7.4); how would you undertake to determine the true nature of this contact by examinations in the field? In and near the eastern Pennsylvania area containing the illustrated outcrops, fossils are virtually lacking in the rocks designated as Ordovician dark-colored slate and Silurian light-colored sandstone; in view of this, how is it possible to determine that the deformations of the strata belong to the Taconian and Appalachian orogenies?

4. (a) How does the distribution of Silurian outcrops in the eastern United States and Canada resemble that of Ordovician outcrops, and in what ways is it different (Figs. 6.3, 7.5)?

(b) How does the nearly closed circle of Silurian outcrops surrounding the southern peninsula of Michigan furnish indication of the geologic structure of this peninsula? Is it possible that Silurian rocks immediately underlie bottom sediments of Lake Erie in a belt extending much or all of the way from present outcrops at the western and eastern extremities of the lake? Explain your answer, giving reasons for estimation either that concealment of the Silurian here depends only on existence of Lake Erie or that it must involve also burial under several hundred feet of post-Silurian stratified rocks.

(c) Noting absence of Silurian, according to the map (Fig. 7.5), on the northern and western flanks of the Ozark Uplift in Missouri and in a belt crossing Kansas, is this lack of occurrence probably due to nondeposition or is it more likely due to removal by erosion of rocks once present? May it in part reflect both of these explanations? Can you state why positive answers to the last two questions are not possible?

(d) Buried Silurian rocks in western Texas and southeastern New Mexico are mainly marine. Explain the isolation of this Silurian area from others in North America. What is the probable explanation of missing Silurian in local spots within the mapped distribution area and in the narrow belt trending northwestward almost to the southeastern corner of New Mexico?

5. Referring to Fig. 7.7, how does the topography of this Appalachian Mountains area deny possibility of horizontal bed-rock structure? Can the direction of dip of the strata be ascertained from study of the topography alone, lacking information as to age of the rocks in different ridges and valleys? Using information given on the map, draw a diagrammatic geologic cross section along some selected line trending approximately at right angle to the strike of the ridges.

6. How do Silurian formations identified in representative sections (Fig. 7.9) generally differ from Ordovician rocks (Fig. 6.5)? In what respects are similarities observed? How are resemblances and differences related to geosynclinal and continental platform environments of sedimentation?

7. How do reef structures (Figs. 7.15 to 7.17) differ in lithology and fossil content as compared with ordinary stratified nonreef deposits? Can you suggest reasons for the common occurrence of Silurian reefs in the Great Lakes and Mississippi Valley States, taking account of their absence in the Appalachian geosyncline? If Silurian reef-dwelling organisms, like modern types, were mostly confined to shallow-water depths (100 feet or less), how can a reef having topographic relief of 1,000 feet (Fig. 7.17) be explained?

8. What are the conditions indicated by precipitation of anhydrite and common salt (halite) in an area as large as the Silurian salt basin of Michigan and Ontario? Especially, what does the extraordinary aggregate thickness of these Silurian deposits indicate?

8.

PALEOZOIC ERA:

DEVONIAN PERIOD

Lower Devonian escarpment southwest of Albany, New York.

N. H. Darton, courtesy of U.S. Geol. Survey.

The name of the Devonian Period is derived from the County of Devon in southwestern England, for it was in this place that fossil-bearing marine deposits belonging between Silurian rocks, below, and Carboniferous formations, above, first were recognized (Fig. 8.1). Continental deposits of equivalent age, known as the Old Red Sandstone, uncon-

formably overlie the Silurian in Wales and areas farther north, but such relatively un-fossiliferous beds were not deemed suitable as a basis for defining a major division of the geologic column. Actually, the marine Devonian strata of Devon are so folded and faulted that the exact nature of the rock succession is not yet wholly determined, and accordingly, the section of southern Belgium, northeastern France, and western Germany that comprises equivalent highly fossiliferous marine rocks, having somewhat simple structure, has come to be recognized as the European standard. Based on correlation with these deposits, rocks of Devonian age are recognized on all the continents.

Occurrence of Devonian Rocks in North America

Recognition and definition of the system. Characteristic guide fossils of the Devonian System, as represented in western Europe, are found in North America. These include various types of both marine invertebrates and organisms, such as fishes, that lived in streams and lakes of the land; therefore, essential equivalence in age of both marine and nonmarine deposits representing the Devonian Period is well established on opposite sides of the Atlantic.

Recognition of the lower and upper boundaries of Devonian deposits in most parts of North America, where interruptions in sedimentation defined by unconformities set these deposits apart from adjacent beds, is relatively simple and definite. There are places, how-

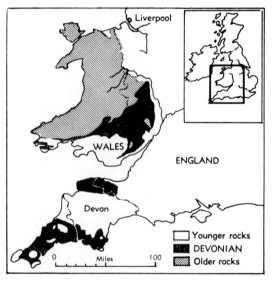

Fig. 8.1 Devonian outcrops in Wales and southwestern England where this system was named. The County of Devon contains marine deposits, whereas those in Wales are of continental type.

ever, in which the boundaries are not so fixed. In parts of eastern New York and farther south in the Appalachian geosyncline, sedimentation from Silurian into Early Devonian time seems to have been virtually continuous. Here, the beginning of Devonian time is reckoned by making correlations with nearby sections that record a break and by comparative studies of the fossil faunas. A similar problem in defining the top of the Devonian is encountered in the Ohio and Mississippi Valleys. These questions are not important, however, in so far as the broad features of historical geology of Devonian time in North America are concerned.

Distribution and character of formations. The outcrop areas of Devonian rocks in North America (Fig. 8.2) and areas inferred to have been covered by Devonian seas occupy a large part of the continent. In the east, they extend from the shore of the Gulf of St. Lawrence across New England and southward along the Appalachian geosyncline to Alabama. The thickest deposits are found in the classic area of Devonian studies in New York and Pennsylvania (Fig. 8.7). Both marine and nonmarine deposits are exceptionally well developed. The Lower Devonian and part of the Middle Devonian are made up mostly of limestone containing many marine fossils. In New York, these rocks make a north-facing escarpment that trends east-west a few miles south of the Middle Silurian (Niagaran) dolostone scarp; the beds dip southward at a gentle angle (Fig. 8.3). The limestone formations are overlain by highly fossiliferous marine shale, and this in turn by thick sandy continental deposits of predominantly reddish color that form the Catskill Mountains and cap the northern part of the Allegheny Plateau. In central and eastern Pennsylvania, the Devonian rocks are steeply but not complexly folded, and the beds are excellently exposed in many places. A noteworthy feature of the upper part of the Devonian succession in this area is the great thickness of continental deposits derived from erosion of a highland lying east of the Appalachian geosyncline.

Devonian rocks in western Ontario and Michigan and in the Ohio and Mississippi Valleys are comparatively thin and nearly flat-lying. They are entirely marine and consist of highly fossiliferous limestone and shale.

That Devonian seas covered western North America extensively is shown by limestone and other rocks of this age in many places in the Cordilleran geosyncline and overlapping on the platform area of the Canadian Shield. Outcrops occur at the south tip of Hudson Bay and extensively in the lower Mackenzie Valley in the far northwest.

Devonian formations are very extensive beneath the surface in eastern United States, being continuous throughout the upper Ohio River Valley east of the Cincinnati Arch, surrounding the Nashville Dome in Tennessee and occupying all the Michigan and Illinois-Indiana basins inward from girdling Devonian outcrops (Fig. 8.2). In western United States Devonian rocks are missing in a wide, irregularly bounded belt that stretches from eastern North Dakota to Texas and Mexico. The Williston Basin (from South Dakota and Montana northward into Canada) is underlain by continuous Devonian that is oil-productive, especially in western Canada. Devonian deposits are extensive in the Cordilleran region, extending in part definitely and in part conjecturally to the Pacific Coast. Because a majority of rock units belonging to this system are marine (in most sections all marine), the Devonian seaways are demonstrated to have been about as great in their extent as those of the Late Cambrian and Ordovician submergences.

The presence of Devonian rocks in Florida, entirely unknown a few years ago, is of special interest. The original distribution of the shallow sea in which these strata were deposited is as yet entirely a matter of guesswork.

Divisions. Devonian rocks of North America commonly are divided into three parts called Lower Devonian, Middle Devonian, and Upper Devonian, but these are not based on the occurrence of widespread unconformities reflecting major oscillations of the Devonian seas (Fig. 8.4). Rather, they define segments of the Devonian column based on comparison of assemblages of fossils with those occurring in the Lower, Middle, and Upper Devonian of Europe. It is convenient, for purposes of description and correlation, to divide the rocks in this manner. In addition, each series is divided into time-rock units called *stages*, all of which are based on deposits of the New York area.

Lithologic divisions of Devonian rocks, consisting of groups, formations, and members, are very numerous, and most of them are recognized only locally, that is, within 100 miles or less of the type outcrops from which these units are named. Geographic restriction in the use of lithologically defined units is imposed mainly by changes in the nature of the Devonian deposits from place to place, but to some extent it reflects uncertainty as to precise equivalence of differently named rocks. The local names tend to become fixed by their frequent use in geological reports and thus to persist even when it becomes recognized that they are synonyms of some other rock division.

Devonian History of North America

Early Devonian restricted seaways. At the beginning of Devonian time, the North American continent should be pictured as a land area somewhat larger than now but, so far as known, lacking mountainous elevations anywhere. There were then no large marine indentations like Hudson Bay. Also, the continent was many miles broader from east to west, for we know that the earth crust included in North America was squeezed and considerably shortened in making the Appalachians, Rockies, Sierra Nevada, and other mountain ranges, all of which were formed after the beginning of Devonian time.

In Early Devonian time, an arm of the Atlantic, somewhat resembling the Baltic Sea of Europe, reached southwestward from the present mouth of the St. Lawrence, extending virtually the entire length of the Appalachian geosyncline (Figs. 8.5, 8.6). Not much sand and mud accumulated on the bottom of this

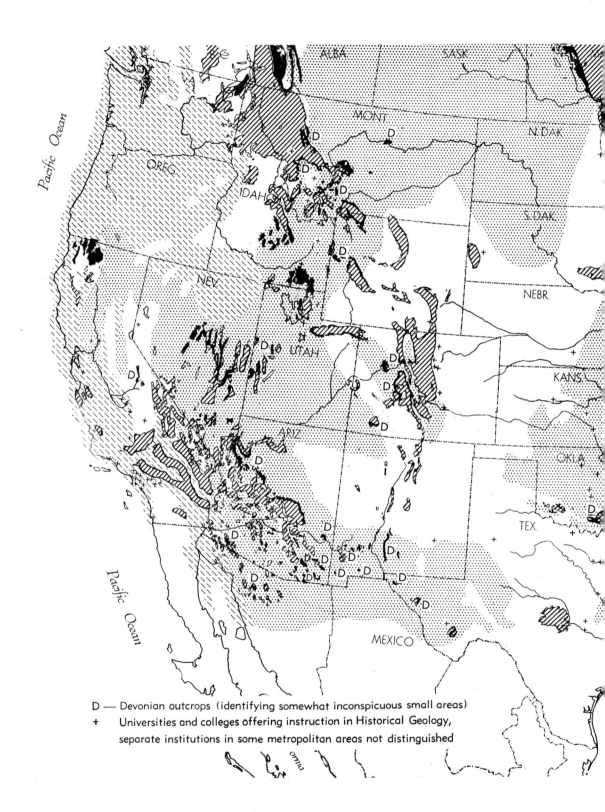

D — Devonian outcrops (identifying somewhat inconspicuous small areas)
+   Universities and colleges offering instruction in Historical Geology,
     separate institutions in some metropolitan areas not distinguished

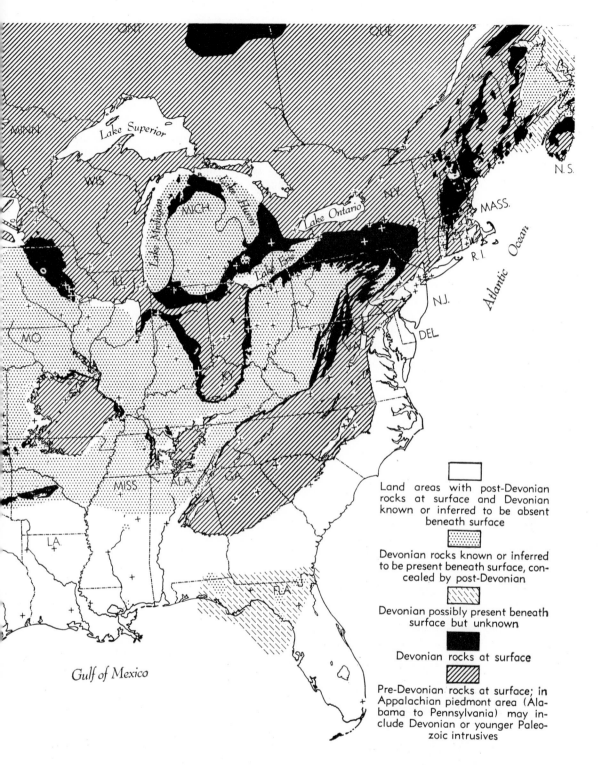

Land areas with post-Devonian rocks at surface and Devonian known or inferred to be absent beneath surface

Devonian rocks known or inferred to be present beneath surface, concealed by post-Devonian

Devonian possibly present beneath surface but unknown

Devonian rocks at surface

Pre-Devonian rocks at surface; in Appalachian piedmont area (Alabama to Pennsylvania) may include Devonian or younger Paleozoic intrusives

Fig. 8.2 Distribution of Devonian rocks in the United States, southern Canada, and northern Mexico. The outcrops and subsurface occurrences shown indicate the original distribution of the system, modified by aggregate effects of removal of deposits by post-Devonian erosion or locally by displacement due to post-Devonian bathylithic igneous intrusions.

sea, for the deposits found consist mostly of limestone. A westward extension of this sea, that existed at least temporarily, is recorded by Early Devonian limestones in central Tennessee, eastern Missouri, southern Oklahoma, and central Texas, but no Lower Devonian deposits are known in the northern interior or western parts of the continent.

Middle Devonian mountain building. Toward the close of the Early Devonian Epoch, the northern part of the Appalachian borderland began to undergo profound geographic change. The land (or chain of islands), which had been worn low after the Taconian mountain building, was strongly elevated at this time by crustal disturbances that produced new ranges of mountains, which have come to be known as the *Acadian Mountains.* Evidence of this mountain building is seen partly in the folded and faulted structure of Early Devonian and older rocks in eastern Canada; these lie beneath Late Devonian and Mississippian deposits with angular unconformity. Indirect more imperfect evidence is found in the tremendous accumulation of coarse detritus derived by erosion of the mountain-

ous area and carried into the geosynclinal depression to its west. The oldest of these deposits are conglomerates, coarse red and gray sandstones, and finer sediments that are excellently exposed in parts of eastern Canada, the Catskill Mountain region of New York, and east-central Pennsylvania (Figs. 8.7 to 8.9). The deposits are early Middle Devonian in age, as shown by marine strata farther west into which they grade laterally (Fig. 8.10). This proves that uplift of the source area and initiation of vigorous erosion had occurred not long after the beginning of Middle Devonian time. In part of the region that began then to receive coarse deposits, limestone (Onondaga) was being deposited late in Early Devonian time.

The mountain-derived sediments were laid down partly on land above sea level and partly in near- and offshore belts of the shallow sea that occupied the Appalachian geosyncline. This inference is supported both by physical characters of the deposits and by their fossil remains. Locally, the nonmarine beds contain stumps of trees standing in the position of growth, and these are associated

Fig. 8.3 Lower Devonian escarpment west of Albany, New York. The hard rocks that form this north-facing escarpment are Helderbergian limestones; they lie here on weak Silurian strata. (*Courtesy of J. W. Wells, Cornell University.*)

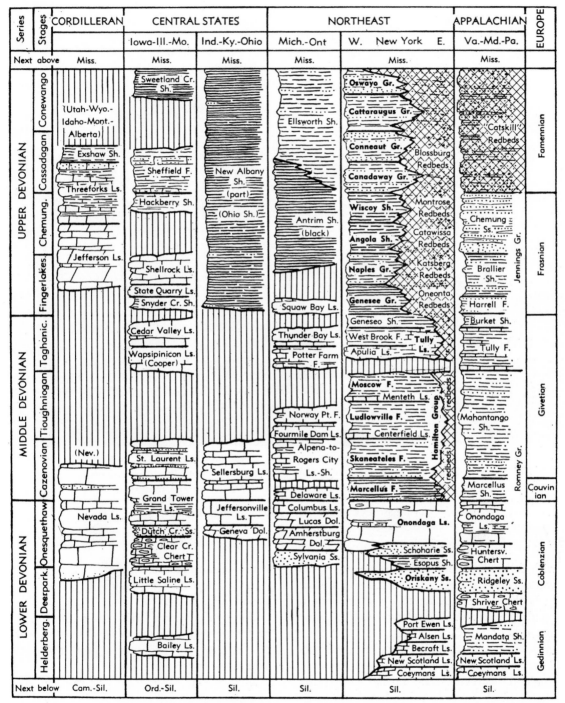

Fig. 8.4 Time-rock divisions of the Devonian System and rock units assigned to them in representative important Devonian sections of North America. The vertical scale does not represent time duration or thickness of rocks but is determined by suitability for plotting the various recognized rock units, placement of which indicates correlation in age. Lithologic character is represented graphically (explanation of symbols in Appendix B). Necessarily, the plotted thickness is not to scale, although it approximates proportional values in many sections. Vertically ruled areas denote absence of deposits.

Fig. 8.5 Remnant of formerly very extensive Lower Devonian limestone in eastern Canada. The view shows the small island of Percé, barely separated from the tip of Gaspé Peninsula, south of the St. Lawrence in easternmost Quebec. It is composed of massive Lower Devonian limestone containing fossils closely similar to those found in Helderbergian beds of New York, for a seaway joined these areas. (*Courtesy of National Film Board of Canada.*)

with fallen logs and leaf impressions; freshwater clams and fishes have been found in beds that were laid down by streams or in ponds. Adjacent marine deposits of the same age contain the stout shells of bottom-living invertebrates that were adapted to life in the sea not far from shore. Contemporaneous marine deposits several miles farther west consist of fine black muds and thin limestone layers formed in quiet water of somewhat greater depth (Fig. 8.11); these beds contain thin-shelled invertebrates that are adapted to such an offshore environment. The intergrading and interfingering deposits of different types in the Devonian area of New York, Pennsyl-

vania, and other eastern states constitute unusually interesting examples of sedimentary facies (Fig. 8.10).

The deposits here briefly described permit us to construct a reasonably definite picture of the Acadian Mountains belt, the plain sloping westward from its foothills, and the shallow sea at the margin of the plain. The mountainous country in western New England and reaching far northeast and south is judged to have attained elevations of several thousand feet above sea level, possibly comparable to those of the Alps and Rockies. The great alluvial fans and piedmont plain stretching westward from the foothills of this range were constructed by swift-flowing streams that became gradually sluggish before reaching the coast of the Appalachian seaway. As time elapsed, the sea was gradually filled in and the coastal plain extended farther and farther west, until in Late Devonian time, land conditions prevailed into western New York and western Pennsylvania.

Middle and Late Devonian seas. The central and western parts of the continent, including areas in the far north, were covered widely by shallow seas during Middle and Late Devonian time. Record of the abundant marine life of these epochs is given in the exceptionally well-preserved fossils that are found in many places (Fig. 8.12). The deposits consist mostly of limestone, which is commonly less than 300 feet thick in the interior areas but more than 2,000 feet thick in parts of the western geosyncline.

The study of Devonian deposits of the Central States has special interest from the standpoint of identifying and tracing thin rock units that commonly are bounded below and above by obscure unconformities (paraconformities) having a good deal of importance in working out the geologic history of the region (Figs. 8.13 to 8.15). Also, there are puzzling black-shale deposits in the upper part of the Devonian succession—puzzling because their mode of origin is very ill understood, considering all known features of thickness, distribution, peculiarities of lithology (including high radioactive content), and sparse but distinctive organic remains (Fig. 8.16). Furthermore, the boundary between Devonian and Mississippian in some sections seems rather definitely to belong within the shale section near its top.

Mention, at least, needs to be made of widespread, in part highly fossiliferous, Devonian deposits in the Cordilleran region, for example, the Canadian Rockies (Fig. 8.17). These strata are chiefly limestone and dolostone, but shale occurs also. Beneath the plains of Alberta and reaching far toward the Arctic are Devonian marine strata that include coral reefs; these rocks are the chief but not the only producers of petroleum and natural

gas in a vast area, as yet little explored, that promises to be an oil province rivaling Texas.

Finally, we come to the Devonian of Alaska and the Arctic Archipelago north of continental Canada. Here, recent field work using helicopter transportation for supplies has shown the occurrence of richly fossiliferous folded Devonian rocks that seem to extend along the entire northern margin of the continent (Fig. 8.18).

Devonian Life

The abundance and variety of marine invertebrates formed in Devonian rocks are striking, and in many places the preservation of these fossils is exceptionally perfect. The collection and study of specimens under these conditions are fascinating, not only for trained

Fig. 8.6 Lower Devonian limestone in the Helderberg escarpment southwest of Albany, New York. This formation (Coeymans) rests on Upper Silurian beds with little or no break. It is classified as Early Devonian on the basis of comparison of its fossils with those of the basal part of the Devonian System in Europe. (*N. H. Darton, courtesy of U.S. Geol. Survey.*)

geologists but for many who lack technical instruction. Localities in western New York, southwestern Ontario, northern Michigan, Indiana, and Iowa are famous for the richness of Devonian fossils.

Invertebrates. All main classes of invertebrates are well represented in Devonian deposits, although dominant groups of earlier Paleozoic times, such as the trilobites, are evidently on the wane (Figs. 8.19 to 8.22). Brachiopods were especially numerous, and among them are many highly useful guide fossils. Slender branching bryozoans and those of delicate lacelike network are very common in some formations. The variety and beauty

of fossil corals in Devonian rocks call for special notice. Also, there are numerous coral reefs, like those in Middle Silurian rocks; they occur chiefly in limestones. Associated with the corals are numerous colonies of lime-secreting coelenterates called *stromatoporoids*; they build laminated calcareous structures, some of which attain a diameter and thickness of several feet. Echinoderms are represented by many kinds of crinoids, including several exceptionally beautiful forms with ornamented plates; also there are blastoids and a few cystoids. Muddy and sandy deposits contain a host of pelecypods, gastropods, and cephalopods, which include many important guide

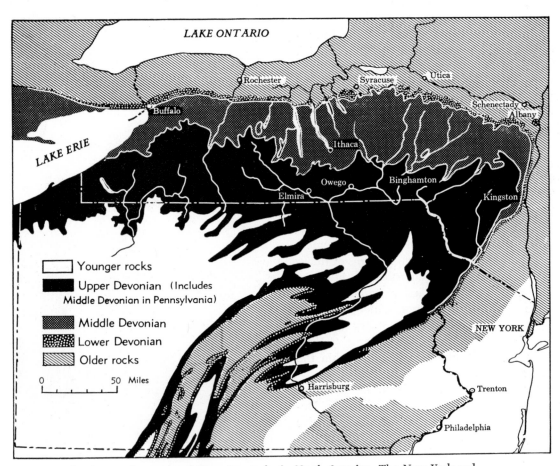

Fig. 8.7 Classic area for study of Devonian rocks in North America. The New York and adjacent Pennsylvania region takes first place in study of Devonian historical geology because time-rock classification used in North America is based on this part of the continent. Also, extremely fossiliferous formations and specially important features of Devonian sedimentation are illustrated in this region.

fossils, especially among the cephalopods; these molluscan groups also occur in limestones. Graptolites are gone, except for a single long-lived, relatively unimportant stock.

A noteworthy feature of some Devonian fossil assemblages, which is by no means confined to the Devonian, however, is differentia-tion of groups of organisms according to their environment. Thus, we find notable differences among faunas of black muds, clear limestones, gray shales, and other types of sediments.

Rise of fishes. The Devonian Period is sometimes termed the Age of Fishes. This does not mean that fishes are more prevalent as

Fig. 8.8 Devonian continental deposits in the Catskill Mountains. This view shows Kaaterskill Falls in the Catskill Mountains, one of many places where the irregularly stratified prevailingly red sandstone and shaly deposits of continental origin compose most of the mass of the Catskill Mountains. These sediments were formed as part of a great delta built westward from the Acadian Mountains formed in Middle and Late Devonian time.

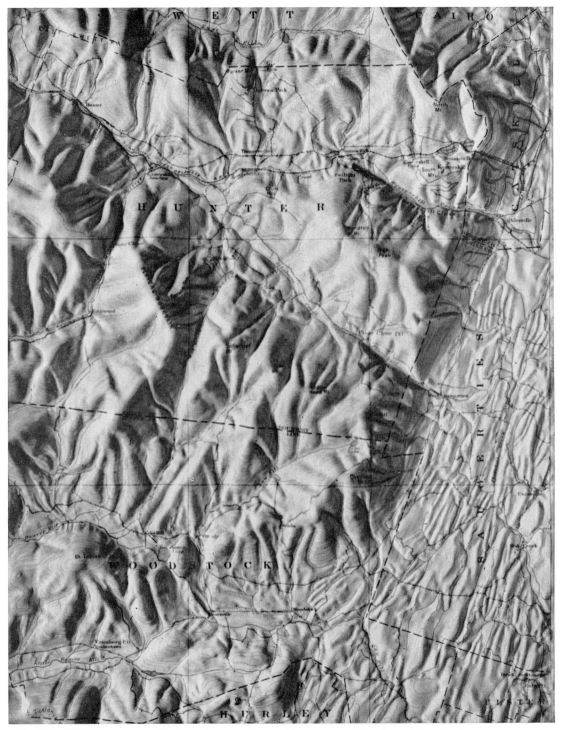

Fig. 8.9 Present eastern edge of Middle and Upper Devonian delta deposits in south-eastern New York. Topographic relief map of part of the Catskill Mountains (Kaaterskill Quadrangle), composed of Devonian continental deposits. The lowland bordering the mountain front (at right) is underlain by strongly folded early Paleozoic rocks. (*Relief map courtesy of Aero Service Corporation.*)

fossils in Devonian rocks than in any other part of geologic time, particularly later systems, for that is not true. Also, certainly it does not mean that the fishes reached the peak of their development thus early in geologic history. This designation signifies rather that, with seeming abruptness, a considerable

number and variety of well-developed forms of fishes are introduced in the fossil record. A majority of the known forms lived in fresh waters on land, and it seems not improbable that this lowest order of the vertebrates originated in fresh waters of the land. Marine fishes, especially primitive sharks, are also

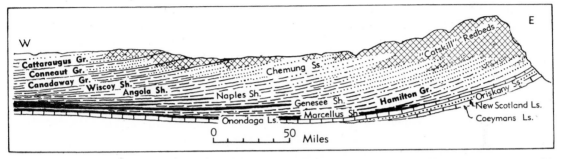

Fig. 8.10 Diagrammatic section of Devonian formations extending westward from the Catskill Mountains. The continental redbeds interfinger with near-shore marine deposits, and these, in turn, grade into offshore sediments. The progressive westward shift of these environments during Devonian time is indicated by the upward-lateral displacement of the different facies.

Fig. 8.11 Offshore evenly bedded limestone and black shale in the Devonian succession of New York. The limestone is Onondaga and the black shale above it is Marcellus, rock units indicated diagrammatically in the east-west geologic section given in Fig. 8.13. (*Courtesy of J. W. Wells, Cornell University.*)

Fig. 8.12 Middle Devonian limestone largely formed of fossil corals near Louisville, Kentucky. Coral-filled limestone (Jeffersonville) occurs in the bed of the Ohio River at the so-called Falls of the Ohio. The cylindrical objects weathered out on the limestone surface are horn corals. (*Charles Butts, courtesy of U.S. Geol. Survey.*)

known from Devonian strata, and some reached the respectable size of 20 feet in length. One group of Devonian fishes developed lungs and thus were able to breathe air, and among them we find types having bony supports for front and rear pairs of fins. This bony structure closely corresponds to that of leg-bearing vertebrates. Abundant remains of fish begin at the very base of the Devonian in beds (Downtonian) of the British Isles and Norway that have been classed as uppermost Silurian by some authors (Fig. 8.23). Fossil fishes are treated in the chapter on Paleozoic life.

First amphibians. The Devonian Period is the time when the first definitely known verte- brates higher than the fishes made their appearance. These are small amphibians found in Upper Devonian rocks of eastern Greenland. The collected remains of these creatures include numerous skulls and incomplete skeletons. We may note that, by the close of Devonian time, four-legged animals that are the ancestors of reptiles and mammals had appeared on the earth.

A single three-toed footprint, ascribed to an amphibian, has been reported from Upper Devonian rocks of Pennsylvania. Whether or not this fossil is indicative of an amphibian, we cannot doubt that one of the most important advances in vertebrate history had been made before the end of Devonian time.

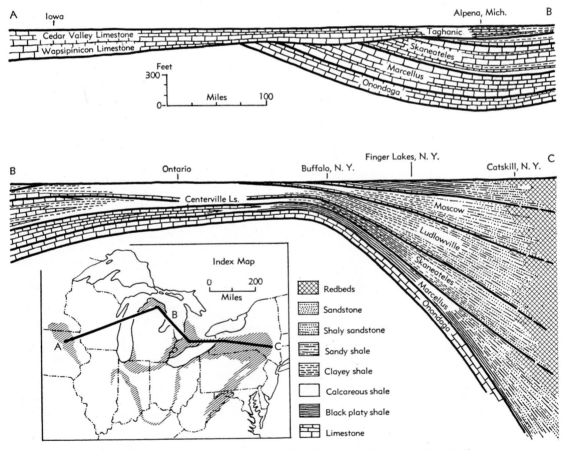

Fig. 8.13 Section of Devonian rocks from the Catskill region of southeastern New York to Michigan and Iowa. Westward changes of thickness and facies and unconformable relations of late Middle Devonian (Taghanic) rocks to older beds are main features illustrated; also noteworthy is the persistence of thin limestone units like the Centerville. (*Modified from G. A. Cooper.*)

Fig. 8.14 Paraconformable contact of Middle Devonian on Middle Silurian limestone at Louisville, Kentucky. This view of a quarry face on Bear Grass Creek shows a perfectly regular, seemingly conformable succession of limestone beds. Fossils establish the Silurian age of lower limestone beds and prove the Devonian age of upper layers. The intersystemic contact occurs just above the white streaks (chert) at mid-height of the photograph, marked by arrow. (*Charles Butts, courtesy of U.S. Geol. Survey.*)

Fig. 8.15 Devonian rock units in southern Indiana. This section in a quarry near Sellersburg shows about 60 feet of strata that include no less than five significant paraconformities, that between the Jeffersonville and Louisville Limestones representing a hiatus from lower Niagaran to near the top of the Lower Devonian. (Figs. 7.9, 8.4). (*Courtesy of Indiana Geol. Survey.*)

Fig. 8.16 Upper Devonian black shale near Columbus, Ohio. Large concretions, like that at lower left in the photograph, are common in the lower part of this formation, known as the Ohio Shale. (*Courtesy of Ohio Geol. Survey.*)

Fig. 8.17 Cliff-forming Devonian limestone in the Canadian Rockies. The Devonian rocks underlie Mississippian beds that form the higher parts of the mountain, which is Cascade Peak, between Banff and Lake Minnewanda, Alberta; the Devonian is overthrust on Cretaceous deposits. (*Geology by R. J. Douglas, Geol. Survey Canada; courtesy of National Film Board of Canada.*)

This evolutionary advance consisted in the development of limbs capable of being used for walking on land. The limbs of the amphibians were derived from fins of Devonian fishes of a type having the fins supported by a fleshy lobe.

Land plants. The oldest definitely known assemblage of land plants occurs in the Devonian, and even though isolated remains of such plants have been found in Silurian rocks of Australia, the spread of forests over land surfaces was accomplished in Devonian time. Plants of this period range from small herb-like forms of swamp-living habit to trees 40 feet or more in height. The trunks of tree ferns, some of which are $3\frac{1}{2}$ feet in diameter, have been found in Middle Devonian rocks of southeastern New York (Fig. 8.24).

Climate

The similarity of Devonian invertebrate faunas from high- and low-latitude belts indicates that an equable climate of fairly warm and humid type prevailed over much of the globe. No indication of any distinct climatic belts is found. On the other hand, existence

Fig. 8.18   Folded Devonian and older Paleozoic rocks on Bathurst Island, northern Canada. Prolonged erosion has developed a peneplain that smoothly bevels the inclined strata, but slight uplift in geologically recent time has allowed partial dissection of the peneplain by modern streams. Bed-rock divisions are plainly visible in this oblique air view looking eastward; units defined by recent exploration are (*A*) Cape Phillips Formation, Ord.-Sil.; (*B*) Bathurst Island Formation, ?L.Dev.; (*D, E*) Eids and Blue Fiord Formations, M.Dev.; (*F*) Okse Bay Formation, U.Dev.; (*G*) faults. Virtually every foot of the rock sequence is well exposed, showing fossiliferous marine sandstones, siltstones, shales, and thin limestones. (*Courtesy of D. J. McLaren, Geol. Survey Canada, who mapped the area; photograph by Royal Canadian Air Force, published by permission.*)

of rugged mountain chains—the Caledonian Mountains in Europe, Asia, and Arctic North America; the Acadian Mountains in eastern Canada and the United States; and mountains in eastern Australia—strongly implies attendant local variations in climate. Mountains cause air currents to move upward, lowering the temperature and causing precipitation. Thus, mountain slopes generally are well watered. In places where winds have a prevailing direction, such as the belts of westerlies in moderately high latitudes and the trade winds in low latitudes, climatic conditions may vary markedly on opposite sides of a mountain range running transverse to such winds. The Acadian Mountains may be presumed to have affected climates in eastern North America in this fashion. The prevailing wind in their latitude presumably was from the west, as now; therefore, the side of the range facing the Appalachian seaway should have been well watered, whereas that on the opposite side, toward the Atlantic, may have been fairly arid. No sedimentary deposits laid down on the eastern side of the Acadian chain are known.

Close of the Period

The end of Devonian time is marked by general retreat of seas from the continental areas, so that a well-marked break in sedimentation, in general, separates Late Devonian from succeeding sediments. The Acadian Mountains were still sufficiently elevated to supply much sediment to adjoining areas, but as far as known, there was no renewal of crustal deformation in North America that served to accentuate relief of the land surface. Mountain making (Bretonian) occurred, however, in parts of western Europe at or near the close of the Devonian Period (Fig. 8.25).

Crustal disturbance of local importance occurred toward the close of Devonian time on the east side of the Ozarks in southeastern Missouri. Devonian and older rocks here are found displaced at least 1,000 feet by faulting. After the faulting, the country was smoothed by erosion so that early Mississippian marine strata were laid down evenly across the fault lines, covering Devonian rocks on one side and lower Ordovician strata on the other.

One of the important times of mountain building in eastern Australia occurred at the close of the Devonian Period.

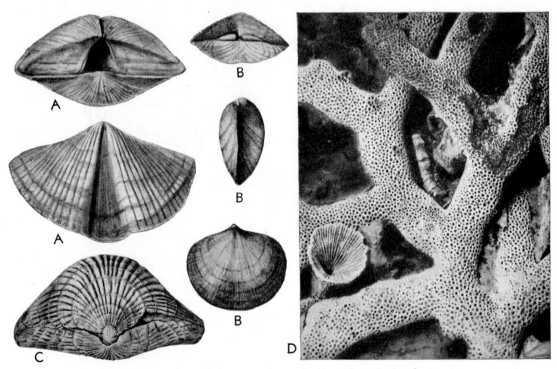

Fig. 8.19 Devonian brachiopods and honeycomb coral. Examples of abundant spire-bearing types of calcareous brachiopods are *A* (*Platyrachella*) and *C* (*Atrypa*); a small biconvex, finely ribbed brachiopod (*Dalmanella*) is represented by *B*. *D* illustrates a branching type of honeycomb coral (*Favosites*) with a small horn coral. Natural size.

Economic Resources

Petroleum. The Devonian System is entitled to special recognition from the standpoint of being the first oil-producing division of the geologic column discovered in North America, for it was Devonian oil that came from the earliest well drilled (at Titusville, Pennsylvania, in 1858) in search of petroleum, and after 100 years the district containing this well still yields significant production annu-ally. Other Eastern States, especially New York and West Virginia, have obtained considerable quantities of petroleum and natural gas from Devonian formations; far greater production from these rocks has been found in Kentucky, Michigan, Illinois, Kansas, Oklahoma, and Texas. At the present time, western Canada outranks all other parts of North America as an actual and potential producer of Devonian oil and gas, because major Devonian fields (Leduc, Redwater, Pembina, and

Fig. 8.20 Devonian trilobites. Although less numerous than in earlier Paleozoic time, trilobites were abundant locally in Devonian shallow seas. The unusual rock fragment here shown contains nearly two dozen specimens of a characteristic Devonian trilobite (*Phacops*), natural size. (*Courtesy of U.S. National Museum.*)

Fig. 8.21 Group of Onondaga Limestone invertebrates in habitat restoration. This assemblage, classed as belonging near the close of Early Devonian time (Fig. 8.4), is considered by some geologists to be early Middle Devonian; at any rate it is widely distributed from New York westward to the Mississippi. Corals (*A–F*), which are a prominent constituent of the fauna, include *Siphonophrentis gigantea* (*B*), one of the largest known solitary forms, and several colonial types. Nautiloid cephalopods are represented by a frilled *Gyroceras* (*G*) and the longitudinally fluted straight-shelled *Kionoceras* (*H*). Also shown are an unusually large spiny trilobite, *Terataspis grandis* (*I*), and the long-lived "Methuselah" brachiopod, *Leptaena rhomboidalis* (*J*). (*Courtesy of L. B. Kellum and I. G. Reimann, University of Michigan; model prepared by George Marchand.*)

Fig. 8.22 Restorations of life in a Devonian shallow sea. A sharklike fish (*Cladoselache*) is swimming toward a large coiled cephalopod that crawls about among the several sorts of sponges growing on the sea floor. (*Courtesy of Rochester Museum of Arts and Sciences; model prepared by George Marchand, under the direction of Irving G. Reimann.*)

Fig. 8.23 Restoration of Devonian fishes of the type called placoderms. The large fishes are a primitive armored kind (*Coccosteus*) with the head region covered by heavy bony plates; the smaller fishes are acanthodians, characterized by bony spines at the anterior edges of the fins. (*Courtesy of University of Kansas Museum of Natural History.*)

others with only initial development as yet) occur in this area. Furthermore, discoveries in the Peace River and Great Slave Lake districts, far north of Edmonton, serve to outline nearly 250,000 square miles as territory underlain by Devonian rocks that may yield huge quantities of oil and gas, and this does not take into account favorable prospects eastward to Manitoba.

Other resources. Other useful materials obtained from Devonian strata are chiefly parts of these strata themselves. Several large portland cement plants use Devonian limestone and shale. Reputedly the largest rock quarry in North America is located at Rogers City on the northeast coast of the lower peninsula

of Michigan; it produces dolostone and limestone that are shipped by water for construction uses and especially for flux needed by steel plants at the southern end of Lake Michigan. Exceptionally pure quartz sand, corresponding closely to the St. Peter (Ordovician) sand, is obtained from the Oriskany Sandstone (Lower Devonian) in the northern Appalachian area for glass manufacture, including high-quality optical glass; it is reported that the 200-inch lens of the world's largest telescope, at Mount Palomar in southern California, was made from Oriskany sand. The oldest commercially worked coal deposits are found in Devonian formations of Spitsbergen, Norway.

Fig. 8.24 Restoration of a Middle Devonian forest in western New York. Characteristic types of vegetation shown are (*A*) horsetail rushes, *Calamophyton;* (*B*) one of the earliest lycopods, *Protolepidodendron,* with trunk and branches covered by short spikelike leaves; (*C*) a primitive leafless plant, *Psilophyton;* and (*D*) an early tree fern, *Eospermatopteris,* which grew to a height of 40 feet. (*C. R. Knight, courtesy of Chicago Natural History Museum.*)

Fig. 8.25 Basal conglomerate of the Old Red Sandstone in the southwestern Highlands of Scotland. The photograph illustrates the effects of mountain uplift and erosion on ensuing sedimentation. The Devonian Old Red Sandstone comprises continental deposits derived from erosion of the Caledonian Mountains. Similar conglomerates were derived from the Acadian Mountains in eastern North America. (*Courtesy of J. W. Wells, Cornell University.*)

READINGS

ANDRICHUK, J. M., 1951, Regional stratigraphic analysis of Devonian System in Wyoming, Montana, southern Saskatchewan, and Alberta: *Am. Assoc. Petroleum Geologists Bull.*, vol. 35, pp. 2368–2408 (illus.).

Example of analysis of Devonian sedimentation describing relations of evaporite deposits to other strata.

COOPER, G. A., 1930, 1933, Stratigraphy of the Hamilton Group of New York: *Am. Jour. Sci.*, ser. 5, vol. 19, pp. 116–134, 214–236, vol. 26, pp. 537–551 (illus.).

Excellent description of classification and correlation of Middle Devonian deposits in a classic area.

———, 1957, Paleoecology of Middle Devonian of eastern and central United States: in *Treatise on marine ecology*, H. S. Ladd, ed., Geol. Soc. America, Mem. 67, vol. 2, pp. 249–277 (illus.).

Valuable interpretative study of regionally varying marine sedimentation of Devonian age.

GREGORY, W. K., 1941, Grandfather Fish and his descendants: *Natural History*, vol. 48, pp. 159–165 (illus.).

Good popular account of Devonian fishes.

WOODWARD, H. P., 1957, Chronology of Appalachian folding: *Am. Assoc. Petroleum Geologists Bull.*, vol. 41, pp. 2312–2327 (illus.).

Discusses effects of Middle and Late Devonian (Shickshockian) mountain-building deformations.

QUESTIONS

1. Why were rocks of the Devonian System not named from outcrops in Wales and western England (Fig. 8.1), where the type areas of pre-Devonian Paleozoic Systems are located?

2. (a) What relationship do outcrops belts of Devonian rocks in the eastern United States and Canada have to Silurian outcrops (Figs. 7.5, 8.2)?

(b) Can you explain why concealed Devonian is indicated to be present beneath parts of Lakes Michigan, Huron, and Erie but not extending throughout all the area of these water bodies?

(c) What is the probable reason for absence of Devonian strata in a large part of Kansas, Nebraska, and adjacent Plains States? What specific features of the map are observable as support of your interpretation?

(d) In spite of extremely widespread distribution of the Devonian System in the western United States, why are outcrop areas so much smaller and more localized than in eastern parts of the continent? Note especially the numerous, very diminutive Devonian exposures in Southwestern States.

3. Account for the different types of sedimentary deposits of Devonian age distinguishable in Figs. 8.10 to 8.13. What evidence is found to indicate that several of these types constitute contemporaneous facies?

4. What is the structural nature of Devonian rocks in the Catskill Mountains (Fig. 8.9)? Can you explain the origin of the lofty, relatively straight front of these mountains facing toward the Hudson River? Was the original distribution of Devonian deposits in this region only slightly larger than the present or considerably larger? What kinds of evidence bearing on this question can be cited? What was the source of Devonian sediments found in the Catskill Mountains?

5. Why are the contacts between formations shown in Figs. 8.14 and 8.15 identified as paraconformities? What is the distinction between paraconformity and disconformity? Does one signify any more "lost interval" than the other?

6. What conclusions concerning the time of folding the Devonian strata of Bathurst Island (Fig. 8.18) can be reached from features contained in the air photographs reproduced?

7. What groups of organisms illustrated in Fig. 8.21 are represented also in typical Silurian assemblages (Figs. 7.22, 7.23)?

9.

PALEOZOIC ERA:

MISSISSIPPIAN PERIOD

Mississippian limestone bluffs below Principia College chapel and campus, on Mississippi River near Alton, Illinois.

Photograph made for this book, courtesy of J. C. Frye, Illinois Geol. Survey

The Mississippian Period and the next following Pennsylvanian Period are the only widely recognized major geologic time divisions that are "made in America." These names have been almost universally adopted by geologists in North America and to some extent have been used on other continents, but most foreign maps and literature dealing with late Paleozoic deposits employ the term *Carboniferous* for rocks corresponding to Mississippian and Pennsylvanian. This name, which was first applied to coal-bearing rocks in England (1822), embraces two strongly contrasted main parts in almost all areas: rocks called Lower Carboniferous, corresponding closely to the Mississippian, and those classed

Fig. 9.1 Lower Mississippian limestone and shale in Mississippi River bluffs in northeastern Missouri. These outcrops are located just south of Hannibal. (*Courtesy of L. R. Laudon, University of Wisconsin.*)

as Upper Carboniferous, being approximately equivalent to the Pennsylvanian.

The Mississippian rocks were named from the central Mississippi Valley, where splendid exposures show relations of these deposits to beds below and above (Figs. 9.1 to 9.4). Almost all Mississippian strata of this region are of marine origin, and most of them are abundantly fossiliferous. The rocks are nearly flat-lying, so that the succession of formations can be determined with certainty. Both the base

Fig. 9.2 Lower Mississippian limestone and shale near Keokuk, Iowa. The limestone contains well-preserved crinoids and other marine fossils; the shale is noteworthy chiefly for its content of crystalline geodes. These strata are part of the type Mississippian section in southeastern Iowa.

and the top of the Mississippian System are marked by unconformities that generally are obscure at the base (consisting of discon-formities or paraconformities) but almost everywhere prominent at the top. These mark widespread interruptions of sedimentation accompanied by more or less erosion. In conjunction with contrasted features of lithology and paleontology below and above systemic boundaries, these breaks serve to define the Mississippian as an independent segment of the geologic column equivalent in rank with Devonian, Silurian, and other main time-rock divisions classed as systems.

Guide Fossils

The Mississippian rocks, like older Paleozoic Systems, are identifiable throughout North America by means of characteristic fossils, of which a few are illustrated in this book (Figs. 9.18 to 9.20). Many such organisms are identical with fossils in the Lower Carboniferous rocks of Europe, Asia, and other parts of the globe, and other forms, although distinct, represent the same organic stocks and show the same stage of evolution as are seen in foreign fossil assemblages. Accordingly, close equivalence in age can be determined reliably.

Mississippian sections in widely separated parts of the United States and Canada commonly can be correlated zone by zone by means of invertebrate species having short vertical range, which migrated laterally long distances. Thus, several species of crinoids that are confined to a few feet of beds in central Iowa occur also in a narrow zone in western Montana; bryozoans and brachiopods that characterize a small thickness of beds in Alabama and Kentucky occur also in Arizona and Idaho.

Character and Distribution of Mississippian Deposits

Two contrasting types of Mississippian deposits may be distinguished in North America. The first consists of marine deposits, mostly limestone, that are very widespread west of the Appalachian Mountains. The second comprises thick continental deposits,

Fig. 9.3 Lower Mississippian limestone on the east side of the Mississippi River near Alton, Illinois. All the rock shown here is Burlington Limestone, which is characterized by its uniform light color, coarse texture, general purity, and abundant content of crinoidal remains. The formation is widely traceable in the Ozark region. (*Photograph made for this book, courtesy of J. C. Frye, Illinois Geol. Survey.*)

which occur mostly within the Appalachian region.

The most important outcrop area of Mississippian rocks is that occurring along the Mississippi River from southeastern Iowa to southern Illinois, for the section here displayed embraces all parts of the system from the oldest to youngest and contains the type localities of most formations included in the standard reference section (Figs. 9.5, 9.6). The marine Mississippian strata of the type section may be traced southeastward as far as northern Alabama and eastward into West Virginia and Pennsylvania. Outcrops are traced westward across Iowa and around the Ozark dome in Missouri and Arkansas. In Oklahoma, Kansas, Nebraska, Texas, and elsewhere in the West, thousands of well borings

penetrate Mississippian strata, showing that these rocks continue under the Great Plains. Mississippian rocks reappear at the surface on the flanks of the Rocky Mountains uplift and in the Black Hills (Fig. 9.7). Thence they extend under cover to other outcrop areas in Western States from Arizona and Nevada northward to Alberta and Alaska. Thus, seaways of Mississippian time are seen to have been very extensive.

It should be noted also that Mississippian formations underlie the Appalachian Plateau, Michigan basin, and the Illinois-Indiana basin, which extends into western Kentucky (Fig. 9.5).

The continental deposits of Mississippian age in the eastern United States closely resemble the coarse red and gray sandstone and

Fig. 9.4 **Upper Mississippian limestones in southeastern Missouri.** The rock from the base of the exposure to the top of the two massive layers of subequal thickness (which are algal beds) just below the marked contact belong to the St. Louis Limestone. Overlying strata, including a thick cross-bedded oölite at the base, are part of the type section of Ste. Genevieve Limestone, for the outcrop is at the edge of Ste. Genevieve, Missouri. (*Photograph made for this book, courtesy of J. C. Frye, Illinois Geol. Survey.*)

silty redbeds of the underlying nonmarine Middle and Upper Devonian. This offers no surprise, for they have the same origin, consisting of erosion products carried westward from the still rugged Acadian Mountains belt. Aggregate thickness of the Mississippian continental beds in places exceeds 5,000 feet. From Alabama, in the vicinity of Birmingham, they are traced northward to southern New York, and some layers extend westward to southern Illinois. Like the Devonian, the Mississippian nonmarine beds become finer westward and interfinger with marine deposits.

Divisions. The Mississippian System is divisible into two major parts that are classed as series, and each series contains two main time-rock units that are designated as stages (Fig. 9.6). The successive stages are delim-

ited in many places by unconformities, and each is characterized by readily distinguished assemblages of fossils. The Lower Mississippian (Waverlyan) Series comprises the Kinderhookian Stage, below, and the Osagian Stage, above. The Upper Mississippian (Tennesseean) Series is made up of the Meramecian and Chesteran Stages, the latter forming the top part of the system.

The dividing line between Osagian and Meramecian deposits, which is the same as that separating Lower from Upper Mississippian, is judged to be more important than the boundaries between other stages, because it marks a more profound change in faunas and is inferred to represent a greater interruption in sedimentation, generally, than these other boundaries. Recently obtained information, derived partly from studies of outcrops in western Canada and partly from many wells drilled for oil in Montana and adjacent states, indicates that western North America contains widespread thick deposits of Meramecian age that have no equivalents in most other parts of the continent (Fig. 9.8).

The boundary between the Lower and Upper Mississippian Series corresponds to the break in the middle part of the rocks called Lower Carboniferous in Europe, Asia, Africa, and Australia. Thus, Lower Mississippian is equivalent in age to deposits called Tournaisian in other continents, and Upper Mississippian essentially corresponds to those named Viséan abroad.

History of Mississippian Time

Early Mississippian seaways. At the beginning of Mississippian time, the sea that invaded the continental interior transgressed a land that had been thoroughly peneplaned, so that basal Mississippian deposits are found unconformably on not only Devonian but also on Silurian, Ordovician, Cambrian, and Precambrian. This sea reached westward to the borders of Cascadian lands along the margin of the Cordilleran geosyncline (Figs. 9.9, 9.10). Probably we should express this in reverse manner, saying that the Cordilleran sea extended eastward into the Mississippi Valley region, for the Early Mississippian marine deposits are far thicker in the West and seemingly they represent a much longer record of limestone deposition than anywhere else on the continent. This thick succession of limestone beds, mostly light-gray massive and in part very cherty, is topographically prominent. It forms the crests of mountains, makes unscalable cliffs and steep canyon walls, and offers striking scenic features in many places.

From Kansas eastward to the Ohio Valley, the Early Mississippian deposits are relatively thin and lithologically somewhat variable. The prevailing lack of coarse sediments, however, indicates that adjacent lands were low. The basal deposit in most of this area consists of black shale, like that of Late Devonian age in the same region and farther east. The scanty

invertebrate fossils of the black shale are a specialized assemblage, and it is evident that normal types of marine organisms were unable to live in the environment represented by these deposits. Perhaps the blackness of the shale is due largely to occurrence of black, humus-rich soils on land near this sea, the fine carbonaceous material of the soil being the chief source of the shale; such black soils are common today in parts of Russia. Marine deposits overlying this shale, including highly fossiliferous limestone, contain a normal assemblage of bottom-living invertebrates. Local variations in the nature of the deposits surrounding the Ozark Uplift indicate that this area was an island during part of Early Mississippian time.

An unconformity, marking interruption of sedimentation and some erosion of the lowermost stage (Kinderhookian), is found in most places at the base of the second stage (Osagian), which represents the later part of Early Mississippian time. In some areas, Osagian deposits rest directly on pre-Mississippian rocks, which signifies that the sea of the second age invaded territory that had not been covered in the first transgression or else beds of the first stage, once deposited, were entirely eroded away before deposition of the second.

Two outstanding characteristics of deposits made in the latter part of Early Mississippian time are abundance of chert (Fig. 9.11) and a remarkable profusion of crinoid remains.

The chert occurs both as bedded layers and as nodules distributed in the limestone, in places forming at least half of the rock. Although some chert is undoubtedly a secondary deposit of silica, made by percolating ground water long after deposition of the limestone in which the chert occurs, the siliceous deposits in these Mississippian strata mostly accumulated on the sea bottom along with the calcareous materials. In this sense they are primary. The aggregate quantity of this silica that was carried in solution to the Mississippian seas is measured in cubic miles.

The sea in which the Early Mississippian limestones accumulated, extending from Ala-

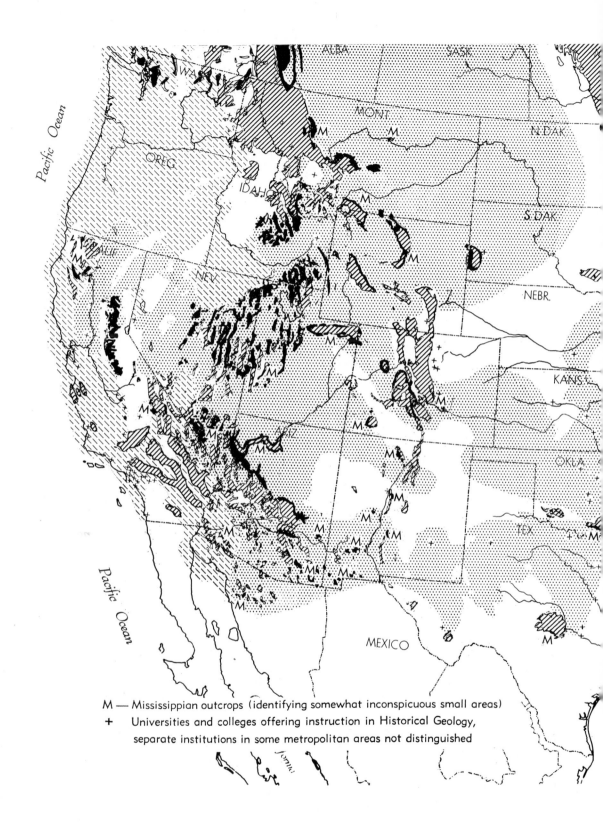

M — Mississippian outcrops (identifying somewhat inconspicuous small areas)
+ Universities and colleges offering instruction in Historical Geology,
separate institutions in some metropolitan areas not distinguished

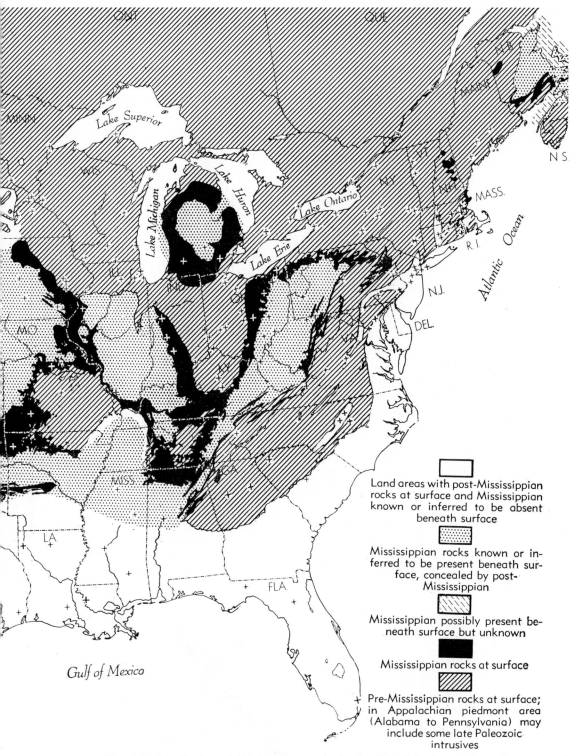

Land areas with post-Mississippian rocks at surface and Mississippian known or inferred to be absent beneath surface

Mississippian rocks known or inferred to be present beneath surface, concealed by post-Mississippian

Mississippian possibly present beneath surface but unknown

Mississippian rocks at surface

Pre-Mississippian rocks at surface; in Appalachian piedmont area (Alabama to Pennsylvania) may include some late Paleozoic intrusives

Fig. 9.5 Distribution of Mississippian rocks in the United States, southern Canada, and northern Mexico. The outcrops and subsurface occurrences shown indicate the original distribution of the system, modified by aggregate effects of removal by post-Mississippian erosion or locally from displacement by post-Mississippian bathylithic igneous intrusions.

217

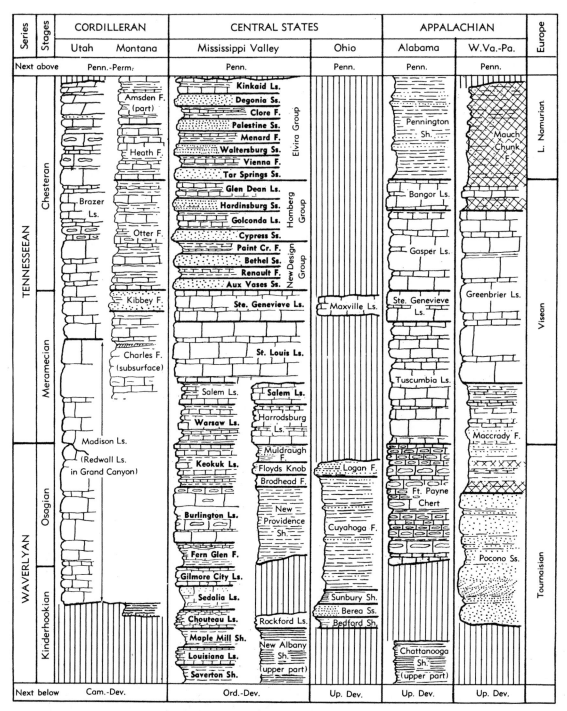

Fig. 9.6 Time-rock divisions of the Mississippian System and rock units assigned to them in representative important Mississippian sections of North America. The vertical scale does not represent time duration or thickness of rocks but is determined by suitability for plotting the various recognized rock units, placement of which indicates correlation in age. Lithologic character is represented graphically (explanation of symbols in Appendix B). Necessarily, the plotted thickness is not to scale, although it approximates proportional values in many sections. Vertically ruled areas denote absence of deposits.

bama to the Far West, was populated by crinoids in unprecedented numbers and variety. These stalked echinoderms secrete hard parts consisting of crystalline calcite, and their disarticulated fragments are a chief constituent of limestone beds 200 to 1,000 feet thick. That the warm waters were exceptionally clear is indicated by the purity of most of the limestone and almost complete absence of shaly or sandy deposits.

Continental deposits in eastern North America. The highland nature of Appalachia, lying east of the Appalachian geosyncline, has already been stated to characterize Mississippian as well as Middle and Late Devonian time. There is no proof of renewed folding in the land area, but elevation by strong upwarping is inferred from the nature of subaerial sediments laid down west of Appalachia. Such vertical movements are typical of the history of mountain areas, and they recur at intervals for a long time after initial folding. Whereas Late Devonian deposits in the geosyncline are predominantly red muds, silts, and fine sands, which are indicative of moderate relief in the source area of the sediments, Early Mississippian deposits contain large thicknesses of coarse conglomerates and very widespread, coarse, massive sandstone. These deposits are now tightly cemented and form some of the most prominent Appalachian Mountain ridges (Figs. 7.7, 7.8).

Late Mississippian continental deposits in the Appalachian geosyncline resemble those of Late Devonian age in showing a predominant red color and fine texture, but in this part of the period some widespread coarse sandstones and conglomerate beds were formed. In central Virginia, there are Mississippian coal beds of mineable thickness. These

Fig. 9.7 Mississippian rocks paraconformably on Cambrian sandstone in the Black Hills of South Dakota. The top of the Cambrian is at the summit of the dark-colored cliff in the lower part of the view. In the northern part of the Black Hills, Ordovician strata intervene between the Cambrian and Mississippian, but neither Silurian nor Devonian deposits are known in this region. (*N. H. Darton, courtesy of U.S. Geol. Survey.*)

Fig. 9.8 Mississippian limestones in the Canadian Rockies. The view shows Mt. Rundle and the Bow River Valley near Banff, Alberta; this is the type area of the Mississippian rock units called Banff and Rundle Formations, which here compose the upper part of Mt. Rundle. The Rundle Formation contains rocks of Meramecian age. (*Courtesy of National Film Board of Canada.*)

Fig. 9.10 Evenly layered Mississippian limestone in the Marble Gorge of Grand Canyon, Arizona. The sheer cliff, which rises about 400 feet above the Colorado River, is composed of the Redwall Limestone of Early Mississippian age. It is overlain disconformably (broken line) by Pennsylvanian and Permian red shale and sandstone, which form the stepped slope above the limestone cliff. (*R. C. Moore, courtesy of U.S. Geol. Survey.*)

Fig. 9.9 Steeply folded Mississippian limestone beds in the Bridger Mountains, western Montana. Some of the strata are highly fossiliferous, containing especially well-preserved crinoids. The deformation is of post-Cretaceous (Laramian) age. (*Courtesy of L. R. Laudon, University of Wisconsin.*)

indicate existence of swampy areas in which land plants accumulated in such quantity, unmixed with clay or silt, that carbonaceous material of the plants formed coal. Westward, the continental deposits graded into marine shale and limestone. The highly oscillatory nature of the sea border is shown by the varying extent to which marine layers reach eastward and interfinger with the continental sediments. The record of Mississippian time, from Alabama to New York, is thus essentially a continuation or repetition of conditions that had characterized Middle and Late Devonian time in this region, but plants living on the land and marine organisms inhabiting the sea serve readily to distinguish the Mississippian formations from those of Devonian age.

Late Mississippian marine oscillations. Less stability in distribution of shallow seas and less uniformity in the nature of sedimentation characterize Late Mississippian geologic history as compared with the early part of the period. Crinoids and many other invertebrates that had characterized the Early Mississippian marine waters are conspicuous by their absence or by relatively small numbers. Very fine-grained, dense limestone, largely noncherty, and much oölite are characteristic types of Late Mississippian deposits, which contrast to the coarse crystalline cherty Early Mississippian limestones (Figs. 9.12 to 9.16). Lateral variation also characterizes some of these deposits, which reflect gentle warping of the sea bottom and establishment of local basins of sedimentation. On the other hand, a few deposits in this part of the column are remarkably uniform and widespread. The limestones in which Mammoth Cave of Kentucky and innumerable smaller caves and sinks are carved are Late Mississippian deposits belonging to the Meramecian and Chesteran Stages. Likewise, the limestone that forms the highland rim surrounding the Nashville Basin of Tennessee is Upper Mississippian. In the Cordilleran geosyncline, the Late Mississippian seas extend far northward into Alberta, and deposits of this age are recognized in Alaska.

The Chesteran Epoch was a time of un-

Fig. 9.11 Chert nodules in Mississippian limestone. Beds of the Ste. Genevieve Limestone near Elizabethtown, Illinois, contain scattered small bodies of chert, which, because of relative insolubility and hardness, weather in relief. Other Mississippian strata, especially of Osagian age, may consist predominantly of chert. (*Charles Butts, courtesy of U.S. Geol. Survey.*)

Fig. 9.12 Upper Mississippian (Meramecian) limestones. Lower strata of extremely fine-grained texture (St. Louis Limestone, below arrow at mid-height of the view) and overlying cross-bedded oölite (Ste. Genevieve Limestone) are characteristic types of Meramecian lithology in central and eastern United States. This is a detail of the view shown in Fig. 9.4. (*Photograph made for this book, courtesy of J. C. Frye, Illinois Geol. Survey.*)

usual advance and retreat of the shallow seas in the central Mississippi Valley area. Deposits, which aggregate about 1,000 feet thick in this region, furnish a record of regularly rhythmic displacement of the strand line, showing that the sea margin shifted back and forth a distance of some hundreds of miles (Fig. 9.17). There are at least eight such cycles of submergence and emergence, the latter being marked by unconformities and by continental sedimentation that interfingers with the marine deposits. These changes in distribution of sea and land give rise to corresponding changes in the geographic boundaries of different sedimentary facies, so that complex lateral and vertical relationships must be worked out in field studies. Overlap and offlap of rock units are repeatedly shown. Rhythmic oscillations, like those recorded in Late Mississippian deposits, are very typical of sedimentation in Pennsylvanian time also.

Mountain building. Folding of Mississippian strata during this period is not recorded in any part of North America, although strong mountain building near the close of Mississippian time is recorded in parts of northwestern Europe. Existence of mountainous elevations in North America, approximately at this time, is proved indirectly by the enormous quantity of coarse land-derived detritus found in continental deposits of earliest Pennsylvanian time in the Appalachian and Ouachita Mountains. The part of the Appalachian area most affected by this uplift is inferred to have reached from Alabama to northern Virginia. The eastern interior and northern midcontinent areas remained low from the close of Mississippian sedimentation until the beginning of marine deposition in Pennsylvanian time. Erosion was widespread, but where the section is most nearly complete, the unconformity is inconspicuous.

Mississippian Life

Invertebrates. Marine life of the Mississippian Period was richly varied and included

Fig. 9.13 Cross-bedded Mississippian limestone in central Pennsylvania. This limestone (Loyalhanna), of late Meramecian age, differs from most limestone formations, which are evenly bedded, in being strongly cross-bedded. Granules of calcium carbonate were swept along by currents on the shallow sea bottom like sand grains. (*B. L. Miller, courtesy of Pennsylvania Geol. Survey.*)

Fig. 9.14 Fossiliferous Meramecian oölitic limestone. This specimen (natural size) shows individual oöids (grains of an oölitic rock) and an abundance of small low-spired gastropods. It represents a distinctive sedimentary environment that is characterized by association of mostly diminutive mollusks with oölitic rock. The sample is from the Salem Limestone of Indiana, which is identical with the so-called Indiana limestone of the building industry. (*Photograph made for this book, courtesy of Charles Deiss and J. B. Patton, Indiana Geol. Survey.*)

Fig. 9.15 Upper Mississippian (Meramecian) limestones in Indiana. Outcrop 40 miles west of Indianapolis showing Salem Limestone (the base marked by the head of the hammer held by the geologist) above Harrodsburg Limestone. An interesting unsettled question is whether the contact between these formations is conformable or paraconformable. The contact is even, and the change in lithology is abrupt. (*Photograph made for this book, courtesy of Charles Deiss and J. B. Patton, Indiana Geol. Survey.*)

Fig. 9.16 Limestone quarry near Mitchell, Indiana, source of virtually all stone used in constructing the Empire State Building in New York City. Since this working served the single purpose indicated in the title of the illustration, the pit may be termed the "Empire State hole-in-the-ground." The rock is Salem Limestone. (*Photograph made for this book, courtesy of Charles Deiss and J. B. Patton, Indiana Geol. Survey.*)

Fig. 9.17 Middle Chesteran strata in southern Indiana. The limestone and shale seen in this quarry exposure belong to the Glen Dean Limestone, which is traced very widely in states east of the Mississippi River. It is overlain disconformably by continental sandstone (Tar Springs), which in places is succeeded by thin coal. (*Photograph made for this book, courtesy of Charles Deiss and J. B. Patton, Indiana Geol. Survey.*)

numerous representatives of all main classes of invertebrates (Figs. 9.18 to 9.20). Most of the stocks clearly show their derivation from Late Devonian ancestors. Changes consist in the disappearance of many characteristic Devonian genera, in the evolutionary advancement of various persistent old types, and in the appearance of some new elements of unknown origin.

The outstanding group in Early Mississippian time is that of the crinoids, which in the Mississippi Valley region alone include more than 400 described kinds. A very remarkable feature of the record is the abrupt disappearance, at the close of Early Mississippian time, of all but a remnant of this great host. The budlike blastoids, which are close relatives of the crinoids, also culminated in Mississippian

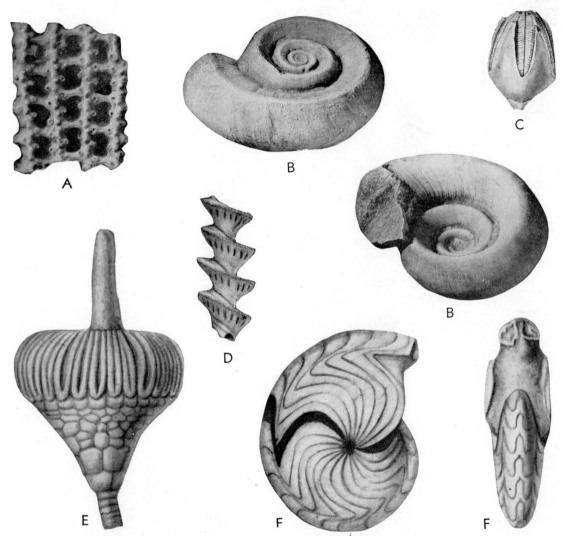

Fig. 9.18 Some representative Mississippian invertebrate fossils. Bryozoans include one of the lacy types (*A, Fenestrellina*) characterized by two rows of openings for the individual animals along each branch and part of the screw axis (*D, Archimedes*) of one type of lacy bryozoan. Echinoderms are represented by a blastoid (*C, Pentremites*) and a crinoid (*E, Eutrochocrinus*). A broad snail (*B, Euomphalus*) and an Early Mississippian ammonoid cephalopod (*F, Aganides*) are types of mollusks; the outer shell of the ammonoid is broken away so that edges of the chamber walls are exposed, and the space between two of these has been painted dark in order to emphasize the pattern. (*A*, enlarged; *B–F*, natural size.)

time, being especially abundant in the Late Mississippian marine beds.

A large group of spine-bearing brachiopods with concavo-convex shells, called *productids*, made their appearance and became world-wide in distribution (Figs. 10.22, 12.16). The brachiopods were a very important constituent of most marine faunas, but less numerous and varied than in the Devonian.

Bryozoans are very abundant in some beds

Fig. 9.19 Upper Mississippian limestone from Kentucky crowded with bryozoans. The observed fossils are mostly of lacy types, including axes of the screwlike *Archimedes;* slightly enlarged.

Fig. 9.20 Mississippian "sea lily" garden. Restoration of crinoid assemblage on the Osagian sea bottom in the Mississippi Valley region, with a blastoid (*C*) and brittle star (*G*) as accompanying echinoderms. All three main kinds of Paleozoic crinoids are represented: inadunate crinoids (*A, Cyathocrinites; F, Barycrinus*), characterized by the reduced size of the "dorsal cup" and free mobility of arms; camerate crinoids (*B, Uperocrinus; D, Gilbertso-crinus,* with peculiarly pendent arms and extensions of summit parts of calyx), characterized by large calyx; and flexible crinoids (*E, Forbesiocrinus*), with special articulations of the arms. (*Courtesy of L. B. Kellum and I. G. Reimann, University of Michigan; model prepared by George Marchand.*)

and show a predominance of delicate lacy types, along with small twiglike forms (Fig. 9.19).

Corals are common but not so varied as in Devonian time. Strangely enough, the Mississippian rocks are virtually devoid of coral-reef structures, although reefs formed by other organisms are well known in rocks of this system.

Among mollusks, clam and snails are very numerous but not especially noteworthy, whereas the cephalopods are represented by marked advancement in structural complexity as compared with forms known in older Paleozoic rocks. They include several important guide fossils that serve for correlating American Mississippian rocks with those in other parts of the world.

Trilobites persisted but had become a minor element of the fauna. There are only a few Mississippian species as compared with hundreds known from older Paleozoic rocks.

Vertebrates. Remains of fishes are fairly common in Mississippian marine strata. They consist chiefly of the teeth of sharks, especially types having a rounded surface adapted for crushing shells. Because fewer fresh-water fishes are known from Mississippian deposits, the variety of these vertebrates is seemingly smaller than that of the Devonian, but it is probable that this means simply a deficiency in preservation of these fossils.

Among leg-bearing animals, there is no question as to abundance of amphibians during Mississippian time, and it is possible that primitive reptiles had made their appearance.

Fig. 9.21 Southern Indiana quarry in Mississippian limestone. This is a typical stone-working operation near Mitchell. Large blocks of the limestone are cut by channelers (two on the upper level and three at the left below) and then hoisted by the large derrick. Sawing into slabs and cutting in various shapes are done in plants located near the quarries. (*Photograph made for this book, courtesy of Charles Deiss and J. B. Patton, Indiana Geol. Survey.*)

Numerous footprints are preserved in some continental Late Mississippian strata, but as yet no skeletal remains have been found in North America. On the other hand, rocks of Mississippian age in Europe have yielded entire skeletons of small salamander-like animals.

Climate

Climatic conditions of Mississippian time, as inferred from widespread distribution and general similarity of marine faunas, were probably fairly warm and uniform over large areas. Existence of coal swamps, at least locally, indicates humidity but not necessarily warmth. Widely distributed redbeds of Late Mississippian age, which contain numerous mud-cracked surfaces, are interpreted as indicating alternate drying and wetting, as on a coastal plain in temperate climates of the present day, but occurrence of gypsum and salt deposits in Virginia, Michigan, and Nova Scotia indicates evaporation of basins in a moderately arid climate.

Close of the Period

The end of Mississippian time was marked by withdrawal of the sea from most of the continent and by uplift that was perhaps of mountainous proportions on some of the land bordering geosynclinal troughs, as in the Appalachian and Ouachita belts. In a few places, sedimentation was resumed after only a very short interruption, whereas in most parts of the continent, the hiatus was long and erosion was extensive. On the continental shelf and possibly in parts of geosynclinal belts, sedimentation was uninterrupted from Mississippian into Pennsylvanian time.

Economic Resources

Mississippian rocks rank moderately high among the geologic systems in economic importance, for the annual value of nonmetallic and metallic materials obtained from them ranges from $300 million to $500 million. Chiefly important are petroleum and natural gas, stone, zinc and lead, gypsum, salt, phosphate, coal, gold, and silver.

Petroleum. According to a tabulation made in 1950 (O. B. Hopkins), Mississippian formations were oil producers in 1,610 different pools in the United States (nearly 22 per cent of the total pools) and were rated as having 3,377 million barrels of production and proved reserves. This is a large quantity, and the oil is mostly of high quality. Pennsylvania, West Virginia, Ohio, and Kentucky are Eastern States that have reported Mississippian oil and gas production for many years, but quantitatively Illinois and the midcontinent region extending from Kansas to Texas for two decades or more has been far in the lead. The Turner Valley field in Alberta and several areas in the Williston Basin of the northern Great Plains region produce from Mississippian rocks.

Stone. Use of Mississippian sandstone (Berea, from the Ohio region) and limestone (Salem, from Indiana, and Keokuk-Warsaw, from southwestern Missouri) for exterior and interior construction purposes has long given uncontested leadership in North America to this system. This is mainly because the quarried beds are sufficiently thick and uniform, as well as easily cut, to meet requirements of high-quality building and ornamental stone. The stone industry centers in southern Indiana, where many large quarries are located in the Salem Limestone (known commercially as "Indiana" or "Bedford" stone) (Fig. 9.21). The prepared stone is shipped all over the United States and even to foreign countries. In addition to cut stone, large quantities of Mississippian rocks are quarried for crushed rock, portland cement, hydraulic and chemical lime, and other uses.

Lead and zinc. One of the leading zinc- and lead-producing districts of the world for many years is the Missouri-Kansas-Oklahoma Tri-State district, where the ores have been mined at shallow depth in Mississippian limestone. Gradual exhaustion of the discovered deposits by working and competition with other districts, especially abroad, are responsible for the decline to present inactivity, but the whole area contains great piles of waste chert ("chat") brought from below ground with the ore (Fig. 9.22). The crushed chat is useful for road surfacing.

Gypsum. Mississippian formations of Michigan and Nova Scotia contain gypsum deposits of considerable commercial importance.

Salt. Mississippian salt production, amounting annually to 2 or 3 million tons, comes from Michigan, Ohio, West Virginia, and Virginia. A brine industry that produces bromine, magnesium, and some other chemicals is associated with the Mississippian evaporite deposits.

Other resources. We may group together phosphate from Mississippian rocks of Tennessee (about 2 million tons annually), coal from Virginia and other Appalachian states (about 80 million tons annually), and production of gold and silver, chiefly from the Leadville district of Colorado (still active but formerly a "boom" mining area).

Fig. 9.22 Lead- and zinc-mining area in northeastern Oklahoma. The piles of white material consist of chert ("chat") brought to the surface with the ore mined from Mississippian limestone at shallow depth. (*R. C. Moore.*)

READINGS

CHENEY, M. G., et al., 1945, Classification of Mississippian and Pennsylvanian rocks of North America: *Am. Assoc. Petroleum Geologists Bull.*, vol. 29, pp. 125–169 (illus.).
Considers criteria acceptable as guides in dividing Mississippian deposits into major units.

MOORE, R. C., 1935, Late Paleozoic crustal movements of Europe and North America: *Am. Assoc. Petroleum Geologists Bull.*, vol. 19, pp. 1253–1325 (illus.).
Discusses intercontinental correlation of Mississippian rocks.

SCHUCHERT, CHARLES, 1932, The Australian late Paleozoic glaciations: *Am. Jour. Sci.*, ser. 5, vol. 23, pp. 540–548 (illus.).
Describes evidence of Mississippian glaciation.

SUTTON, A. H., and OESTERLING, W. A., 1952, Lithologic character of Chester rocks in Illinois-Kentucky fluorspar district: *Am. Assoc. Petroleum Geologists Bull.*, vol. 36, pp. 1777–1801 (illus.).
Late Mississippian sedimentation in a classic region.

WELLER, J. M., et al., 1948, Correlation of the Mississippian formations of North America: *Geol. Soc. America Bull.*, vol. 59, pp. 91–196 (chart).
Discusses classification and correlation of Mississippian deposits.

WILLIAMS, J. S., 1957, Paleoecology of the Upper Mississippi Valley region: in *Treatise on marine ecology*, H. S. Ladd, ed., Geol. Soc. America, Mem. 67, vol. 2, pp. 279–324 (illus.).
Excellent analysis of marine sedimentary environments in relation to associated invertebrates.

QUESTIONS

1. In what ways do limestones composed chiefly of crinoidal parts, all composed of crystalline calcite (Figs. 9.1 to 9.3), differ from crystalline carbonate rocks classed as marble, which are metamorphic rocks?

2. What significance concerning the original distribution of Mississippian deposits may be attached to the occurrence of marine invertebrate faunas in deposits of this age observed in Michigan (Fig. 9.5)?

3. What explanation can be given to account for the presence of residual chert boulders containing Upper Mississippian fossils found lying on Ordovician rocks in the central part of the Ozark region of Missouri many miles distant from the nearest outcrops of Mississippian rocks of equivalent age on the flanks of this uplift?

4. What inferences can be drawn from the prevalence of limestone deposits in Mississippian formations found in most parts of North America?

5. What factors chiefly account for the preeminence of Indiana limestone production from Mississippian formations in the building-stone trade of the United States?

6. Some nodules and larger masses of chert in limestones and dolostones seem clearly to be secondary in origin, constituting replacements introduced long after sedimentation of the carbonate strata, whereas other siliceous deposits concentrated in the form of chert are judged to be primary, originating contemporaneously with the inclosing carbonates or essentially so. Which of these types of chert probably is represented in Lower Mississippian formations (for example, Reeds Spring in southwestern Missouri and Fort Payne in Alabama) characterized by extremely widespread occurrence of uniform chert beds in very numerous successive layers alternating with limestone beds or distributed as abundant nodules within the limestones? How does the observation that limestone formations next below and above the cherty strata are very low or lacking in chert content affect your conclusions in answer to the preceding question?

10.

PALEOZOIC ERA:

PENNSYLVANIAN PERIOD

Evenly bedded Pennsylvanian strata in southern Utah.

Courtesy of Spence Air Photos

The Pennsylvanian Period was a time of coal making on the greatest scale in earth history, and it is appropriate that the name of the period is derived from the leading coal-producing state of a country that furnishes nearly one-half of the world's annual coal output. Until 1869, coal production from the anthracite district of northeastern Pennsylvania alone exceeded all other coal mined in the United States, but today output of bituminous coal, both in Pennsylvania and elsewhere, greatly exceeds production of anthracite.

As originally defined, the Pennsylvanian rocks in Pennsylvania (Fig. 10.1) included some deposits (called Dunkard) that later generally have been considered to be of

Permian age, and they are here excluded from the Pennsylvanian. It is by no means certain, however, that the rocks in question are rightly classified in this way, since various specialists on plant and vertebrate fossils now think that after all the original definition of Pennsylvanian may be most appropriate. No significant interruption of sedimentation separates the restricted Pennsylvanian from Dunkard beds.

A prominent unconformity marks the base of the Pennsylvanian System in the type region, and the same is true almost everywhere else in North America (Fig. 10.2). Seeming conformity of sequence from Late Mississippian into earliest Pennsylvanian is found, however, at some places in southern Oklahoma and in various parts of the Cordilleran region, which may mean only that a break in sedimentation is too obscure to have been found. Such is the nature of paraconformities, for they can be overlooked easily.

In the midcontinent region and western United States, where Permian deposits are identified reliably throughout a vast area, they lie parallel on Upper Pennsylvanian beds, and therefore problems are encountered in

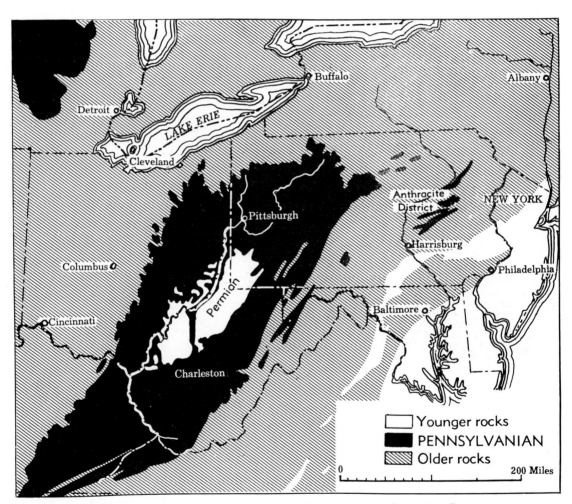

Fig. 10.1 Distribution of Pennsylvanian formations in the type region. In western Pennsylvania and adjoining parts of Ohio and West Virginia, the Pennsylvanian formations are nearly flat-lying and the outcrop area is very broad. Outcrops in the anthracite district of eastern Pennsylvania are elongate patches, owing to the steeply folded attitude of the beds. Pennsylvanian deposits of the Appalachian region are dominantly nonmarine.

defining a boundary between the two systems. No such difficulty exists in places, such as southern Oklahoma and western Texas, where an angular unconformity separates Pennsylvanian from Permian.

Rocks corresponding to Pennsylvanian in age are commonly called *Upper Carboniferous* in continents other than North America. Generally, the distinctness in character of the Lower and Upper Carboniferous is as strongly marked in Europe and Asia, for example, as that separating Mississippian from Pennsylvanian, but the position of the boundary dividing each pair does not correspond precisely.

Guide Fossils

Deposits of Pennsylvanian age are identified throughout most parts of the world, both by characteristic assemblages of fossil plants and by the nature of marine invertebrates. Not only do these organic remains serve for correlation of deposits from place to place in the United States, but many of them clearly define equivalence of deposits on different continents. Such widely distributed forms are unusually valuable guide fossils.

Since the plants lived on land and the invertebrates were marine, there is the problem of determining their precise age equivalence. If continental deposits were restricted to one region and marine beds to another, there would be no way of determining these exact relations. Fortunately, there are many places in which plant-bearing continental deposits interfinger or are interbedded with fossiliferous marine strata. For example, the Pennsylvanian sections of Illinois and Kansas contain dozens of such alternations of marine and nonmarine strata, furnishing an ideal record of the time relations of successive floras and faunas. The most important index or guide fossils among plants are various sorts of ferns, and among invertebrates the leading ones are the protozoans called *fusulinids*, shaped like large wheat grains (Fig. 10.3).

Fig. 10.2 Angular unconformity beneath Pennsylvanian basal conglomerate. This exposure in northern New Brunswick (Jacquet River) shows truncated vertical Silurian limestone deformed by the Acadian (Devonian) mountain building, beneath the Bonaventure Conglomerate, formerly thought to be a Mississippian deposit but on the basis of fossil plants now identified (W. C. Bell) as early Pennsylvanian. Similar coarse conglomerate occurs in many other places at the base of Pennsylvanian rocks, generally with disconformable contact rather than angular unconformity. (*F. J. Alcock, courtesy of Geol. Survey Canada.*)

Distribution and Character of Pennsylvanian Formations

Nature of outcrops. The outcrop areas of Pennsylvanian rocks in the eastern and central parts of the United States are large, irregularly shaped patches, some of which extend uninterruptedly across several states (Fig. 10.4). East of the Mississippi, the outer edges of the outcrops mark the contact of Pennsylvanian with older rocks. Except for a small area of Permian beds in the northern part of the Appalachian region, the Pennsylvanian deposits are not overlain by younger rocks, and they have a broadly synclinal structure. West of the Mississippi, however, Pennsylvanian outcrops, although many miles wide in places, are bands lying between older and younger formations, and there are great areas where Pennsylvanian rocks lie buried beneath the surface, concealed by younger rocks.

Distribution. Deposits of Pennsylvanian age in North America are known from Nova Scotia and New Brunswick, in eastern Canada, to Alabama; in the Central States they are distributed from Michigan to Texas; and in the West they are found in small areas along the Rocky Mountains belt and in all states between the Rockies and the Pacific.

Beneath Permian or directly overlain by deposits younger than Permian, Pennsylvanian rocks occur in the subsurface of almost the entire western United States (Fig. 10.4), proving that marine or nonmarine sedimentation, or both, was extremely widespread during at least part of this period. Most of the blank areas on the map in Oklahoma, Texas, New Mexico, Arizona, Colorado, and Utah represent territory in which Pennsylvanian strata probably once existed, but drilling shows that now they are absent. Also, Pennsylvanian deposits doubtless extended originally an appreciable but unknown distance northeastward and northward from their present subsurface limit in the Dakotas and Montana. If these inferences are true, erosion removed the Pennsylvanian rocks before the time of depositing the oldest post-Pennsylvanian sediments, whatever they are, that are found to be present in any given area of missing Pennsylvanian.

Lithologic features. Outstanding general features of the Pennsylvanian formations are the relative prominence of continental deposits, especially coal, and abundant variation in the nature of beds in vertical succession. The nonmarine stratified rocks include coarse to fine conglomerates, abundant sandstones, sandy to clayey shales, and redbeds (Figs. 10.5, 10.6). They contain remains of land plants in many places and tracks of land animals less commonly. Most of these deposits are marked by lack of any considerable lateral extent, and they vary in thickness much more irregularly than the marine lithologic units.

Marine deposits become increasingly abundant as one travels away from the geosynclinal belts toward the continental interior. These rocks include some sandstone, but the most persistent and characteristic marine strata consist of limestone and shale. Remains of marine invertebrates are very abundant in a

Fig. 10.3 Late Paleozoic wheat-grain-shaped fossils called "fusulinids." These relatively large foraminifers were abundant in Pennsylvanian and Permian marine rocks and are especially important index and guide fossils. The specimens (*Triticites*) show typical external and internal structural features (×8). (*Courtesy of Kansas Geol. Survey.*)

majority of the Pennsylvanian deposits that were formed in shallow inland seas.

An important feature of Pennsylvanian sections in many regions is the repeated occurrence of persistent thin marine layers between continental deposits and of extensive thin sheets of continental sediments between relatively thick marine strata. This variation in vertical succession is expressed by the occurrence of innumerable alternations of sandstone, shale, coal, fresh-water limestone, and marine limestone. The layers of different sorts of rock range in thickness from less than an inch to tens of feet, but the average thickness of most units is less than 10 feet.

Divisions. Pennsylvanian deposits are divisible into three main parts: Lower Pennsylvanian Series, Middle Pennsylvanian Series, and Upper Pennsylvanian Series (Fig. 10.7). The main coal deposits, but not all, belong in the Lower and Middle Pennsylvanian. On the basis of distinctions in the fossil faunas and floras that are associated with interruptions in sedimentation, the series are each divided into two time-rock units classed as stages. The breaks between successive stages, including those marking the boundaries between series, coincide with times of mountain building in parts of North America or Europe.

Features of Pennsylvanian History

Making of coal beds. Coal deposits, ranging in age from Devonian to Recent, are known, but the subject of coal making belongs naturally with study of Pennsylvanian history, because at no other time has such quantity of coal been formed in so many parts of the globe.

Everyone knows that coal is a moderately hard black rock which, when burned, leaves a deposit of ash (Fig. 10.8). Some coals ignite easily and burn with a yellowish flame and much smoke; others are ignited with difficulty, burn with a bluish flame, and give little or no smoke. Some have a low heating capacity, expressed in British thermal units (B.t.u.), and others a high value. These differences are some of the properties of different types of coal, such as lignite, bituminous coal, and anthracite. They denote differences in the coal-making substances or their physical alteration, or both.

Chemical analysis shows that coal consists mainly of carbon associated with varying quantities of oxygen and hydrogen, together with noncombustible mineral matter that produces ash. Low-grade coals contain a large proportion of hydrogen and oxygen in relation to carbon, whereas high-grade, or anthracite, coals have a relatively low content of hydrogen and oxygen and a large proportion of carbon.

Coal beds are commonly found interbedded with sandy or shaly strata of continental origin (Fig. 10.9). They vary in thickness from a fraction of an inch to several tens of feet locally, and some are known to be continuous laterally over areas of many thousand square miles. Very commonly the bed next beneath a coal is a sticky clay that may contain traces of roots and that seems to represent an old soil; it is termed *underclay*. Also, in many places strata just above a coal bed contain abundant well-preserved leaves of land plants. Microscopic study of the coal proves that it is composed largely of plant remains. Identifiable elements include leaves, flattened twigs or branches, and isolated cell structures of various sorts (Fig. 10.10).

The preservation of coal-making plant remains from the decay that occurs rapidly on dry land is ascribed to the presence of a protecting cover of water, such as in swamps, marshes, or shallow lakes. Even though complete decay is prevented in such environment, there is some decomposition through the agency of bacteria, and the plant materials, pressed together, form an organic deposit termed *peat*. The conversion of peat to coal is accomplished by slow chemical and physical changes in which compression, heat, and time are the most important factors. Oxygen and hydrogen are progressively driven off, leaving a residual concentration of carbon. Thus is explained the fact that most geologically young coals are lignites whereas coal of considerable age, like that in the Pennsylvanian System, is bituminous or higher grade.

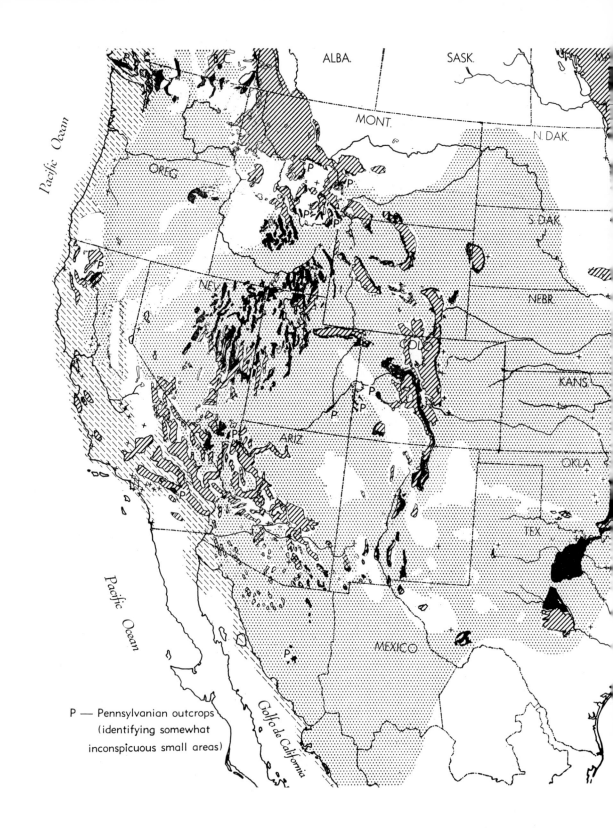

P — Pennsylvanian outcrops
(identifying somewhat
inconspicuous small areas)

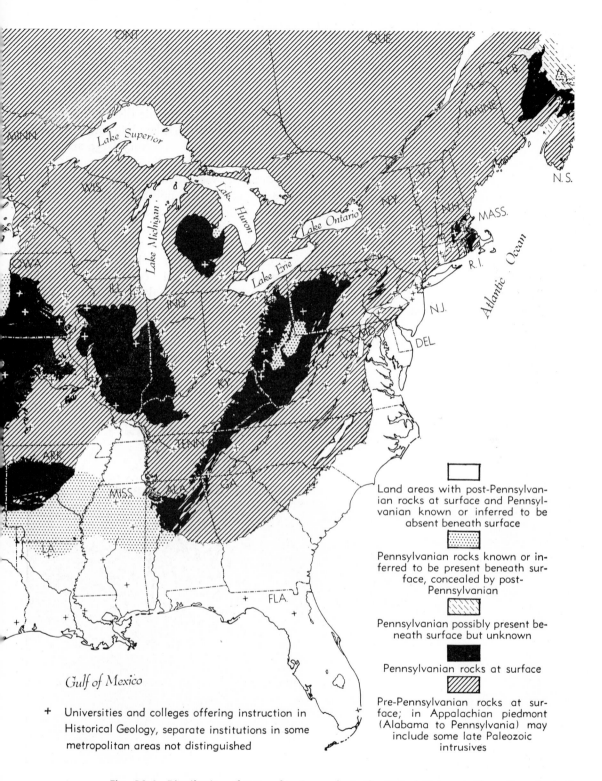

Land areas with post-Pennsylvanian rocks at surface and Pennsylvanian known or inferred to be absent beneath surface

Pennsylvanian rocks known or inferred to be present beneath surface, concealed by post-Pennsylvanian

Pennsylvanian possibly present beneath surface but unknown

Pennsylvanian rocks at surface

Pre-Pennsylvanian rocks at surface; in Appalachian piedmont (Alabama to Pennsylvania) may include some late Paleozoic intrusives

+ Universities and colleges offering instruction in Historical Geology, separate institutions in some metropolitan areas not distinguished

Fig. 10.4 Distribution of Pennsylvanian rocks in the United States, southern Canada, and northern Mexico. The outcrops and subsurface occurrences shown indicate the original distribution of the system, modified by aggregate effects of removal of deposits by post-Pennsylvanian erosion or locally from displacement by post-Pennsylvanian bathylithic igneous intrusions.

The effect of compression by geologic forces on coal beds is seen in areas such as northeastern Pennsylvania, where coal-bearing deposits have been considerably squeezed and folded. Here the coal beds have been altered to very hard anthracite. Extreme compression may drive off virtually all the volatile hydrocarbons, leaving a residue of nearly pure carbon (graphite). Pennsylvanian rocks in Rhode Island, which have been much more strongly compressed than those in Pennsylvania, contain graphitic coal that can hardly be burned.

The occurrence of several coal beds in a single section can mean only that swampy coal-forming conditions existed, disappeared, and then reappeared repeatedly. Where marine strata lie on a coal bed, we easily understand that swamp vegetation was drowned by sinking of the land or rise of sea level. Partial filling of the sea could permit reestablishment of coal swamp conditions and the making of a new coal bed. Pennsylvanian rocks are characterized by the remarkable number and incredibly large geographic distribution of coal beds. This means that low-lying swampy lands must have existed over very large areas during most of the period.

Geosynclines filled with continental deposits. Continued uplift of lands bordering the Appalachian geosyncline on the east and the Ouachita geosyncline in Arkansas and Oklahoma on the south supplied great quantities of stream-borne rock materials that now form Pennsylvanian continental deposits, which in places exceed 15,000 feet in thickness. The sea had access to the geosynclines only temporarily in the early part of the period. In spite of the steady subsidence that accompanied deposition of the continental

Fig. 10.5 Appalachian Plateau country, in which uplands are made by thick, hard, non-marine sandstone beds of Pennsylvanian age. The view shows part of the valley of Blue River in West Virginia. Owing to the ruggedness of the topography, the railroads, highways, and settlements are located almost entirely in the valleys. The stratified rocks lie nearly horizontal. (*J. K. Hillers, courtesy of U.S. Geol. Survey.*)

sediments, aggradation exceeded sinking, so that only now and then the shallow sea flooded the inland border of the old geosyncline for a short while.

The many-times repeated coal-forming conditions in parts of the geosynclinal areas and the equally numerous interruptions represented by the spreading widely over the coals of sand, shale, and other land-derived sediments point to many recurrent spasmodic uplifts in source areas of the sediments. These movements seem to have been accompanied by a corresponding downward displacement in basins of sedimentation. Thus, surfaces of erosion and deposition were steadily maintained in about the same relation to one another. These conditions, which obliterated the eastern and southern geosynclinal seaways, did not prevail in the Cordilleran geosyncline, although Pennsylvanian deposits, largely marine, attain a thickness of several thousand feet in parts of Utah and Nevada.

Oscillatory seas of the North American interior region. Pennsylvanian deposits of the Illinois-Indiana basin, Michigan, and the midcontinent region from Iowa to Texas furnish record of remarkably rhythmic advance and retreat of shallow seas. Dozens of times the sea spread over an area of several hundred thousand square miles, remained long enough to leave record of its existence in deposits of limestone and marine shale, and then retreated from the entire area (Fig. 10.11). Absence of the sea is marked by the spreading of continental deposits containing land-plant remains and, in places, tracks of land animals; also, disconformities generally, if not invariably, can be accepted as indicating subaerial erosion rather than submarine scour. Paraconformities probably are numerous, but it is difficult or impossible to demonstrate their existence in these deposits. The establishment of coal swamps over large areas signifies topographic position of the swamp at or above sea level because (with rare exceptions) the Pennsylvanian coal beds are autocthonous (formed in place), not allocthonous (formed by vegetation washed from more or less distant land).

Fig. 10.6 Cross-bedded conglomeratic sandstone of Early Pennsylvanian age in Tennessee. This deposit, of probable fluviatile origin, is the Sewanee Sandstone, belonging to the Pottsville Group. (*Charles Butts, courtesy of U.S. Geol. Survey.*)

Study of the whole body of deposits, taking account of characters observed both horizontally and vertically, leads inescapably to the conclusion that during Pennsylvanian time the interior platform of the continent must have stood just about at sea level. Then very small sinking of the platform or equivalent rise of mean sea level would result in extensive submergence, and conversely, very small elevation of the platform or depression of sea level would produce extensive emergence.

The cyclic sedimentation resulting from these oscillatory movements of sea and land is an outstanding feature of Pennsylvanian deposition, and it is observed in Europe and other continents as well as in North America (Figs. 10.12 to 10.14). On the whole, subsidence of platform areas (especially basin portions of them) gained over elevation, because the Pennsylvanian System is 2,000 to 4,000 feet thick in such areas. This gain of aggregate subsidence is accentuated in geosynclinal belts where Pennsylvanian deposits locally exceed 25,000 feet in thickness.

Sedimentation in the Western States. From the midcontinent region westward, Pennsylvanian deposits are characterized by virtually universal absence of coal beds and by a good

Series	Stages	CORDILLERAN						WESTERN INTERIOR			
		Ida.	Mont.	Wyo.	Colo.	S.D.	Tex.-N.Mex.	North Central Texas	South	Oklahoma	North
Overlying		Perm.	Perm.	Perm.	Perm.	Perm.	Perm.	Perm.	Perm.	Perm.	Perm.

CORDILLERAN — **WESTERN INTERIOR**

UPPER PENNSYLVANIAN

Virgilian

- Fresnal Gr.
- Avis Ss.
- Wayland Sh.
- Gunsight Ls.
- Keller Gr.
- Breckenridge Ls.
- Thrifty Gr.
- Graham Gr. — Cisco Ser.
- Vanoss F.
- Ada F.
- Elgin Ss. — Vamoosa F.

Missourian

- Hansonburg Gr.
- Veredas Gr.
- Home Cr. Ls. — Caddo Creek Gr.
- Ranger Ls. — Brad F.
- Graford F.
- Palo Pinto Ls. — Whitt Gr.
- Canyon Ser.
- Hoxbar Group
- Tallant F.
- Barnsdall F.
- Wann F.
- Iola Ls.
- Hogshooter Ls.
- Coffeyville F.
- Checkerboard Ls.
- Seminole F.
- Holdenville F.

MIDDLE PENNSYLVANIAN

Desmoinesian

- Wells F. (Wood River F.)
- Quadrant F. (part)
- Tensleep Ss.
- Hermosa F.
- Fountain F.
- Minnelusa F.
- Bolander Gr.
- Armendaris Gr.
- Capps Ls. — Lone Camp Gr.
- Brannon Bridge Ls.
- Kickapoo Falls Ls.
- Millsap Lake Gr. — Strawn Ser.
- Deese Group
- Wewoka F.
- Wetumka Sh.
- Calvin Ss.
- Senora F.
- Stuart Sh.
- Thurman Ss.
- Boggy F.
- Savanna F.
- McAlester F.
- Hartshorne Ss.

Bendian

- Amsden F. (part)
- Amsden F.
- + Paradox F.
- Glen Eyrie Sh.
- Derryan Ser.
- (Haymond F.)
- Smithwick Sh.
- Marble Falls Ls.
- Bend Ser.
- Lester Ls.
- Otterv. Ls.
- Dornick Hills Group
- Atoka F.

LOWER PENN.

Morrowan

- Dimple Ls.
- Wapanucka F.

Springeran

- Tesnus F.
- Springer Group
- Springer F.

| Underlying | | Miss. | | | Precam.-Miss. | Miss. | Dev. | Ord.-Miss. | Miss. | Miss. | |

NOTE. Recent studies of Springeran fossils of the type region in southern Oklahoma indicate Late Mississippian age of most, if not all, strata assigned to this division.

240

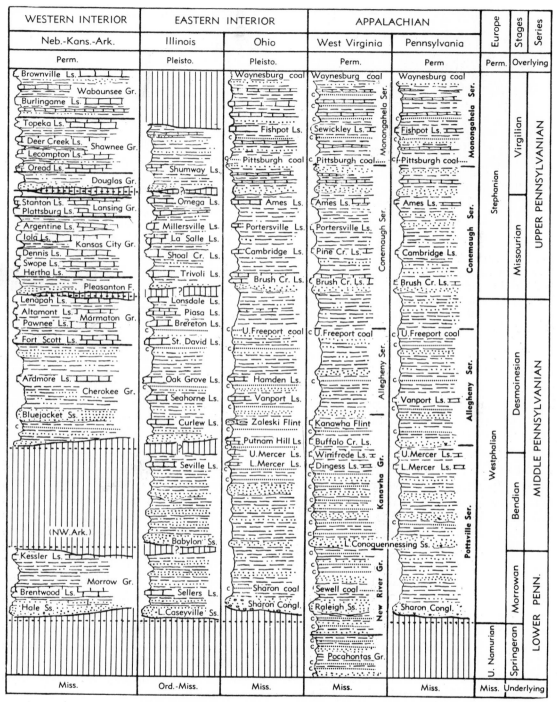

Fig. 10.7 Time-rock divisions of the Pennsylvanian System and rock units assigned to them in representative important Pennsylvanian sections of North America. The vertical scale does not represent time duration or thickness of rocks but is determined by suitability for plotting the various recognized rock units, placement of which indicates correlation in age. Lithologic character is represented graphically (explanation of symbols in Appendix B). Necessarily, the plotted thickness is not to scale, although it approximates proportional values in many sections. Vertically ruled areas denote absence of deposits.

Fig. 10.8 A chunk of coal from the Pittsburgh bed in western Pennsylvania. The many shiny streaks in this coal consist of altered woody plant tissue. The lighter colored material is made up of other sorts of decomposed plant matter. Natural size. (*R. Thiessen, courtesy of Illinois Geol. Survey.*)

deal of variation in lithology from place to place. In Colorado and adjacent parts of the Rocky Mountains are great accumulations of red arkosic conglomerate and sandstone (Fountain Formation), while farther west are variously named marine clastic deposits with some limestones (Figs. 10.15 to 10.18). Southeastern Utah and contiguous parts of Colorado, New Mexico, and Arizona contain locally thick deposits in what is known as the Paradox Basin that must have been a semiclosed sea area during a portion of Pennsylvanian time, because thick salt and gypsum beds were formed; commercial quantities of petroleum have been found in this basin.

Recurrent mountain building. Major interruptions in the making of Pennsylvanian formations are found to coincide with the building of mountains in some part of the earth, not always in North America. There was moderate crustal deformation in the Oklahoma and Kansas portion of the midcontinent region at the close of Early Pennsylvanian Morrowan time and strong folding in southern Oklahoma in the middle (post-Missourian) part of Late Pennsylvanian time (Figs. 10.19, 10.20). Mountain building also occurred in western

Texas at the close of Pennsylvanian time. These movements denote crustal instability during the Pennsylvanian Period that seems appreciably greater than in most preceding divisions of the Paleozoic Era. The accumulating stresses led to deformation that culminated in the Appalachian mountain building near the end of Permian time.

Comparable orogenic epochs are recorded in Europe, Asia, and northern Africa during Pennsylvanian time. These deformations were not simultaneous but occurred at different times. Collectively, they produced mountain ranges that are known as the Paleozoic Alps (or Variscan Mountains system). The Urals are an isolated chain that belongs with the Pennsylvanian mountains.

The boundary that separates the Middle Pennsylvanian Epoch from the later part of the period is marked by a widespread, though somewhat obscure, unconformity and by obvious difference in organisms occurring above and below the boundary. The magnitude of this break leads us to expect that the sea was absent for a much longer time than in ordinary oscillatory withdrawals during the period. We expect such a break to be associated with mountain building, yet none is known at this time in North America. Correlation of Pennsylvanian deposits with Europe, however, indicates that one of the important mountain buildings of the period in Europe fits the time of the sedimentary break in North America. This interesting observation and others like it suggest that sea level throughout the world may be affected by crustal deformation on any continent, and, if this is so, geologic effects may be recorded by simultaneous sea-and-land changes throughout the world. At any rate, it is important to observe that in Europe and Asia at least three distinct epochs of mountain building belong to the Pennsylvanian Period.

Pennsylvanian Life

Although land plants, including forest trees, are definitely known as far back as the Devonian, the luxuriant fast-growing vegetation of the coal swamps and adjacent lands in

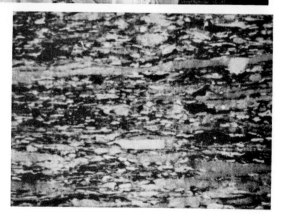

Fig. 10.9 Underground coal mining in West Virginia. The upper view shows a 4-foot coal bed of Pennsylvanian age that is overlain and underlain by sandstone. In the lower photograph is a thicker bed, divided by a shaly parting in the middle (just below shiny coal layers). (*Courtesy of Coal Age, McGraw-Hill Publishing Company, Inc.*)

Fig. 10.10 Very thin slice of coal cut at right angles to bedding. Viewed by transmitted light, only a small part of a thin section of coal is opaque. The light-colored constituents are various kinds of plant debris. Much magnified. (*R. Thiessen, courtesy of Illinois Geol. Survey.*)

Pennsylvanian time, which is abundantly represented by well-preserved fossils, gives the first fairly full picture of the earth's early vegetation (Fig. 10.21). As already noted, the close similarity or identity of many of these plants that lived on different continents in Pennsylvanian time greatly aids correlation of the deposits. Very widely distributed organisms of this type are termed *cosmopolitan*.

Some of the main types of Pennsylvanian plants are included in the review of Paleozoic life development (Chap. 12).

Marine invertebrates, although extremely varied and numerous in many Pennsylvanian formations, do not call for special comment here (Fig. 10.22). As a whole, the assemblage is intermediate between those characterizing Mississippian and Permian strata; several of

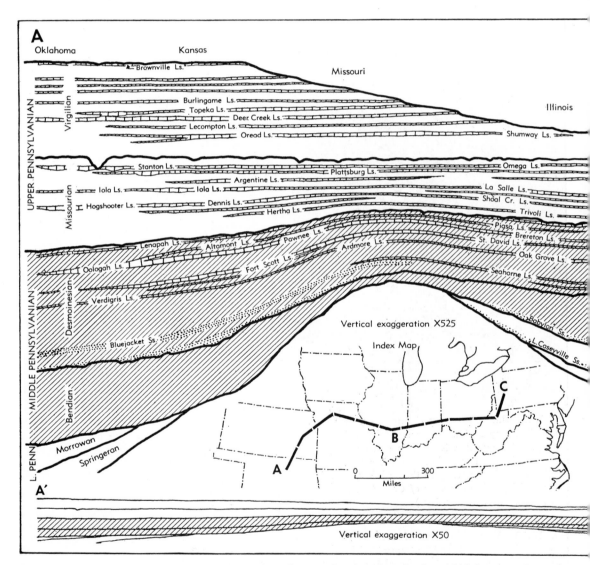

Fig. 10.11 Diagrammatic section of Pennsylvanian deposits from Oklahoma to Pennsylvania. The purpose of this drawing is to demonstrate graphically the extent to which numerous widely persistent rock units have been traced and the differently named local successions tied together. Even if some units are mismatched in proceeding from the midcontinent region to Illinois, for example, the second purpose of the diagram is fulfilled; this is to depict the

the most common shells collected from Pennsylvanian strata represent genera that occur also in adjoining systems, although the species are different. The shelled protozoans called *fusulinids* are extremely abundant in many Pennsylvanian marine deposits, especially limestones (Fig. 10.3). Forerunners of this group occur in Mississippian rocks, and specialized types abound in some Permian beds.

Among nonmarine animals, Pennsylvanian fossils include fresh-water clams, air-breathing snails, many sorts of insects, fishes, amphibians, and rarely a few primitive reptiles (Fig. 10.23). The presence of abundant cockroaches and flying insects, such as large dragonflies, and the occurrence of spiders are noteworthy. Richness of the vertebrate record is indicated by the fact that nearly 100 species of am-

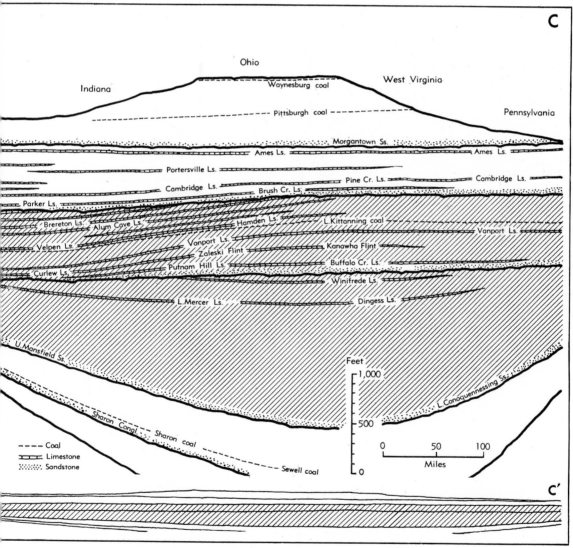

almost incredible persistence of thin marine strata, chiefly limestones in Pennsylvanian deposits of the continental interior. Between most of the successive marine units are nonmarine deposits, which indicates repeated transgression and regression of shallow seas over hundred thousands of square miles. Attention should be called to the vertical exaggeration of the upper and lower parts of the figure.

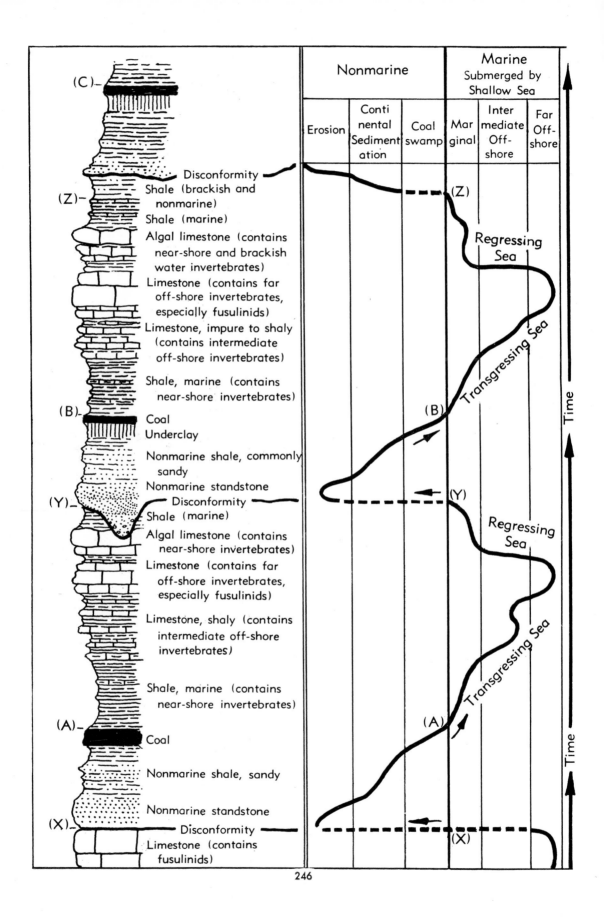

Nonmarine			Marine Submerged by Shallow Sea		
Erosion	Continental Sedimentation	Coal swamp	Marginal	Intermediate Off-shore	Far Off-shore

(C)—

Disconformity

(Z)—
Shale (brackish and nonmarine)
Shale (marine)
Algal limestone (contains near-shore and brackish water invertebrates)
Limestone (contains far off-shore invertebrates, especially fusulinids)
Limestone, impure to shaly (contains intermediate off-shore invertebrates)
Shale, marine (contains near-shore invertebrates)

(B)—
Coal
Underclay
Nonmarine shale, commonly sandy
Nonmarine standstone
Disconformity
(Y)—
Shale (marine)
Algal limestone (contains near-shore invertebrates)
Limestone (contains far off-shore invertebrates, especially fusulinids)
Limestone, shaly (contains intermediate off-shore invertebrates)
Shale, marine (contains near-shore invertebrates)

(A)—
Coal
Nonmarine shale, sandy
Nonmarine standstone
(X)—
Disconformity
Limestone (contains fusulinids)

(Z)
Regressing Sea
Transgressing Sea
(B)
(Y)
Regressing Sea
Transgressing Sea
(A)
(X)

Time

246

phibians are known from Pennsylvanian rocks of North America. They are mostly small creatures, a few inches long, but a few attained the size of a large crocodile.

Climate

The widespread rich vegetation of the Pennsylvanian Period strongly suggests warm, moist climatic conditions. Absence of growth rings in the woody plants points to lack of seasonal variation in climate, and occurrence of plants of subtropic type in high latitudes indicates mild, equable temperatures in these regions. Arid conditions are shown by occurrence of salt and gypsum in Pennsylvanian deposits of western Colorado and Utah, but this is local and exceptional. Glacial deposits such as those well known in the Permian of the Southern Hemisphere are found also in the Pennsylvanian succession of southeastern Australia (Fig. 10.24), thus indicating that climate was not universally warm in this part of earth history.

Close of the Period

The boundary between Pennsylvanian and Permian is ill defined in many areas where only slight interruption of sedimentation, if any, occurred at the end of Pennsylvanian time. Elsewhere, a strongly marked unconformity indicates interruption of sedimentation and considerable erosion. Mountain building occurred in western Texas. Coal-forming conditions largely disappeared in Permian time, and climate became increasingly arid, but generally speaking, the changes in these directions were gradual rather than pronounced and abrupt.

Fig. 10.13 Algal limestone of the type characteristically deposited as terminal calcareous sediment of a regressing sea. Top of a Lecompton cycle in southern Kansas, thin section, ×6. Algae are the light-gray laminated crusts surrounding shell fragments and cellular bodies, such as the elongate fossil at bottom of the view. (*R. C. Moore, courtesy of Kansas Geol. Survey.*)

Fig. 10.12 (Opposite page.) Diagrammatic section of Pennsylvanian rocks in Kansas showing cyclic sedimentation. Repeated like sequences of marine and nonmarine strata prove repeated submergence and emergence of continental interior regions. Alternative modes of defining boundaries between successive cycles are indicated: (1) at the horizon of change from nonmarine to marine conditions, indicated by letters *A, B, C* on the diagram, and (2) at the horizon of change from marine to nonmarine conditions or at disconformities, indicated by letters *X, Y, Z* on the diagram. European and some American geologists prefer the first method of marking cyclic limits, whereas some Americans choose the second method. Utility favors the definition of boundaries at top of coal beds.

Ss.	
———————	(X)
Sh.	
Ls.	
(A) Sh.————	
Coal	
Underclay	
Ss.	

Fig. 10.14 Cyclic Pennsylvanian strata in Illinois. Exposure near Harrisburg in southern Illinois showing the Herrin (No. 6) coal bed and associated strata; the Herrin coal is one of the chief sources of Illinois coal production. Parts of two cycles are seen, the boundary between them used by the Illinois Geological Survey being marked at X (Fig. 10.12, *X-Y-Z* method), whereas with propriety it may be drawn at A (Fig. 10.12, *A-B-C* method), as is done in Kansas and Missouri. (*Courtesy of J. C. Frye, Illinois Geol. Survey.*)

Fig. 10.15 Coarse arkosic redbeds of Pennsylvanian age in Colorado. The outcrop, known as Red Rocks, is in the Denver Mountain Parks, a few miles southwest of Denver. The strata (Fountain Formation, see Fig. 10.7) are tilted eastward by post-Cretaceous crustal movement (Laramian) that uplifted the Rocky Mountains. (*Courtesy of D. L. Hopwood, Denver.*)

Fig. 10.16 Regularly alternating layers of Pennsylvanian limestone, shale, and sandstone in southwestern Colorado. Lower part of mountain slopes above Ouray, Colorado, are composed of gently tilted Pennsylvanian deposits, mostly of marine origin. Sandstone beds, which alternate with limestone, contain much feldspar, denoting rapid mechanical weathering of adjacent exposed granite.

Economic Resources

The Pennsylvanian System is one of the most important of all major divisions of the geologic column as a source of materials useful to man, and this is because of the enormous fuel resources found in these rocks. They consist first of coal and (in spite of great volume) secondarily of petroleum and natural gas. Valuable but distinctly lesser products are stone, clay, and iron ores.

Coal. The nature and origin of coal have been discussed earlier in this chapter; here are

cited main features relating to occurrence and production.

Pennsylvanian coal deposits are widespread on all continents except Africa and South America and supply nearly one-fourth of the world's fuel energy. Producing areas in the United States comprise approximately 250,000 square miles, most important fields being located in the Appalachian region extending from Pennsylvania to Alabama and in the eastern interior region of Illinois, Indiana, and western Kentucky. Large quantities of Pennsylvanian coal are mined in the midcon-

Fig. 10.17 Light-colored Pennsylvanian sandstone in east-central Wyoming. The cliff-forming sandstone (Tensleep, Fig. 10.7) rests on older Pennsylvanian limestones and shaly rocks (Amsden), both of these units disappearing beneath Permian and Triassic formations in the background. Alcova Canyon of the North Platte River west of Casper. (*N. H. Darton, courtesy of U.S. Geol. Survey.*)

Fig. 10.19 (Above) Parallel ridges and furrows formed by lower Paleozoic strata upturned during Late Pennsylvanian mountain building. The view shows Lower Ordovician limestone and shaly beds in the Arbuckle Mountains of southern Oklahoma. The folding of these rocks occurred near the close of Missourian and beginning of Virgilian time. (*R. C. Moore.*)

Fig. 10.18 (Left) Evenly bedded Pennsylvanian strata in southern Utah. Canyon of the San Juan River near Goodridge. The hard rocks are sandstones and limestones, the weak ones shales. (*Courtesy of S. A. Wengerd, University of New Mexico.*)

Fig. 10.20 Angular unconformity in western Texas separating Cretaceous from upturned Pennsylvanian rocks. Mountain-building movements at the close of Pennsylvanian time disturbed Pennsylvanian and older rocks in the vicinity of Marathon, Texas (Glass Mountains region). These rocks are evenly truncated beneath overlapping Lower Cretaceous strata. (*C. L. Baker, courtesy of Texas Bureau of Economic Geology.*)

Fig. 10.21 A Pennsylvanian conifer twig (A, *Walchia*) and leaves of the horsetail (B, *Annularia*). Natural size. (*M. K. Elias, courtesy of Kansas Geol. Survey.*)

tinent region from Iowa to Texas, but production in this area is far less than from eastern fields.

The anthracite district of northeastern Pennsylvania, where compression due to mountain folding has partly metamorphosed the coal into high-carbon, low-volatile coal, is small in area (less than 500 square miles) but has produced approximately one-fourth of all coal mined in the United States, the total output from this district amounting to about 4,500 million tons. Numerous coal beds occur, one

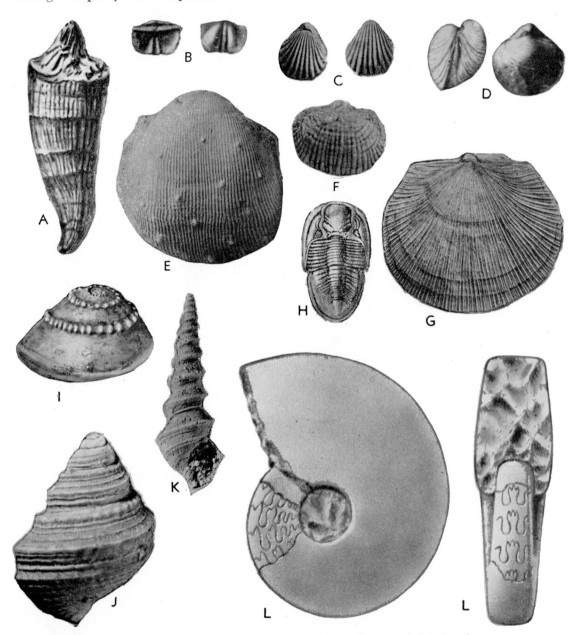

Fig. 10.22 Some representative Pennsylvanian invertebrate fossils. A coral (*A, Lopoh- phyllidium*) having a solid axis; several brachiopods (*B, Mesolobus; C, Hustedia; D, Squamu- laria; E, Linoproductus; F, Marginifera; G, Derbyia*); gastropods (*I, Trepospira; J, Baylea; K, Goniasma*); a trilobite (*H, Ameura*); and an ammonoid cephalopod (*L, Prouddenites*). All natural size (except J, ×6).

Fig. 10.23 Pennsylvanian reptiles and associated organisms on an eastern Kansas sea-shore. This restoration shows one of the earliest known well-developed reptiles (A, *Petrolaco-saurus*) with contemporaneous invertebrates (B, *Garnettius*, a scorpion; C, *Phyloblatta*, a cockroach; D, *Parabrodia*, a dragonfly) and Permian-type plants (E, *Dichophyllum*, probably related to the ginkgos; F, *Walchia*, a conifer; G, *Taeniopteris*, H, *Sphenopteris*, I, *Pecopteris*, ferns). The assemblage is based on fossils collected from Upper Pennsylvanian (Stanton) beds near Garnett, Kansas. (*Courtesy of Frank Peabody; restoration by Hermine Newcombe under direction of Dr. Peabody.*)

Fig. 10.24 Pennsylvanian glacial deposits in southeastern Australia. The conglomeratic rock contains glacially shaped and striated cobbles. The exposure is at Currabubula, New South Wales. (*Courtesy of J. W. Wells, Cornell University.*)

Fig. 10.25   Mining Pennsylvanian coal in Indiana by stripping the overburden. Coal beds
lying within 75 feet of the surface are economically mined by open-cut methods, in which the
overlying strata are dug away by power shovels. These views show such coal pits in Indiana.
(*Courtesy of Coal Age, McGraw-Hill Publishing Company, Inc.*)

(Mammoth bed) averaging 35 to 40 feet in thickness and locally ranging to more than 100 feet.

The bituminous fields yield excellent coal that is more easily mined than the anthracite deposits, both underground and surface stripping methods being employed in obtaining the huge quantity of this coal produced annually (Fig. 10.25). A specially important bituminous deposit is the Pittsburgh bed at the base of the Monongahela Series (Fig. 10.7), which has an average thickness of 10 feet in an area of approximately 6,000 square miles in Pennsylvania, West Virginia, and Ohio and which has already produced coal valued at more than $1,000 million. How much of the original deposit has been lost by erosion is conjectural, but this easily may be more than the amount that existed when mining began.

Petroleum. Pennsylvanian rocks have been leading producers of oil and gas for many years. The compilation of data for 1950 by Hopkins, previously cited, indicates that Pennsylvanian oil pools in the United States then numbered 1,960, which was one-fourth of the country's total, and fields producing from these rocks had a rated total yield (past production added to proved reserves) amounting to 10,097 million barrels. The producing areas are distributed in many states, from the Appalachian belt westward to Utah, largest quantities coming from Midcontinent States.

Stone and clay. Like several other geologic systems, the Pennsylvanian furnishes large quantities of stone for crushed rock, portland cement, lime, and other uses. Clay deposits are specially noteworthy, because they include inexhaustible supplies of high-refractory clays suitable for manufacture of fire brick and clays adapted for making porcelain, as well as raw materials for common brick and tile.

Iron. Production of iron from carbonate and oxide ores obtained from Pennsylvanian formations during many years is reported from areas in Ohio, Pennsylvania, and West Virginia. This is quantitatively unimportant, of course, as compared with the main sources of iron in Precambrian rocks.

READINGS

BERRY, E. W., 1920, Paleobotany, a sketch of the origin and evolution of floras: *Smithsonian Inst. Ann. Rept.* 1918–1920, pp. 289–407 (illus.).
Gives authoritative and readable descriptions of all main kinds of Pennsylvanian plants.

CAMPBELL, M. R., 1917, The coal fields of the United States: *U.S. Geol. Survey Prof. Paper* 100A, pp. 1–33 (illus.).
Excellent concise presentation of nature and distribution of Pennsylvanian coal-producing areas.

SIEVER, RAYMOND, 1951, The Mississippian-Pennsylvanian unconformity in southern Illinois: *Am. Assoc. Petroleum Geologists Bull.*, vol. 35, pp. 542–581.
Interesting description of stream-carved topography developed on Mississippian rocks and buried beneath Pennsylvanian deposits.

WANLESS, H. R., 1955, Pennsylvanian rocks of Eastern Interior Basin: *Am. Assoc. Petroleum Geologists Bull.*, vol. 39, pp. 1753–1820 (illus.).
Valuable summary of observations on an important area of Pennsylvanian deposits.

WELLER, J. M., 1957, Paleoecology of the Pennsylvanian Period in Illinois and adjacent states: in *Treatise on marine ecology*, H. S. Ladd, ed., Geol. Soc. America, Mem. 67, vol. 2, pp. 325–364 (illus.).
Gives detailed description and interpretation of cyclic deposits.

WHITE, DAVID, and THIESSEN, REINHARDT, 1913, The origin of coal: *U.S. Bur. Mines Bull.* 38, pp. 67–75 (illus.).
Concise, well-written description of characters of coal with an interpretation of their significance.

QUESTIONS

1. In what chief ways are sedimentary deposits of the Pennsylvanian System unlike those of the Mississippian System in general (compare Figs. 9.6, 10.7, and others)? In parts of North America where Pennsylvanian strata lie on Mississippian, what is the nature of the contact most commonly (conformable, paraconformable, disconformable, angularly unconformable)? What does this signify? Can you cite more or less extensive areas in which Pennsylvanian rocks lie directly on pre-Mississippian rocks (including Precambrian)?

2. What are the distinguishing characters (shape, size, internal structure, shell composition) of the fossils called fusulinids (Fig. 10.3)? Why are they exceptionally useful as means of identifying and correlating Pennsylvanian (and Permian) rocks that contain them? The fusulinids are exclusively marine invertebrates, and accordingly they are found normally only in various marine deposits (chiefly limestones). Can you give reasons for their absence in some undoubted marine Pennsylvanian strata? Rarely, a few "strays" are discovered in Pennsylvanian (or even post-Paleozoic) nonmarine conglomeratic, sandy, or shaly beds, such fossils tending to be broken or abraded. How are these occurrences explainable?

3. In relation to adjoining rocks, how do the Pennsylvanian rocks mapped in eastern Canada, New England, Michigan, and the so-called Eastern Interior region (Illinois, Indiana, western Kentucky) differ from those of other outcrop areas in North America (Fig. 10.4)? What is the probable explanation of the areas in western and northern Texas, New Mexico, and Colorado where Pennsylvanian rocks are absent beneath post-Pennsylvanian?

4. Why do the specimens of bituminous coal illustrated in Figs. 10.8 and 10.10 exhibit distinct horizontal laminae? Pennsylvanian coal beds commonly contain rich assemblages of spores that by their kinds and relative proportions are useful in correlating the coals from place to place. Can you suggest reasons for this usefulness?

5. Since nonmarine shale, sandstone, and coal beds commonly occur between the persistent marine limestones diagrammatically shown in Fig. 10.11, what inferences as to very widespread submergences and emergences of the continental interior are inescapable? Does study of the section indicate that marine sedimentation in some areas generally was contemporaneous with nonmarine sedimentation elsewhere or, alternatively, that accumulation of marine deposits repeatedly was contemporaneous everywhere or nearly so and that nonmarine deposition similarly was coincident over large areas during many successive time intervals?

6. What are the essential features that serve to prove beyond doubt the cyclic nature of Pennsylvanian sedimentary deposits in many places (Figs. 10.12 to 10.14)? What significance is attached to the observation that cyclic sedimentation is equally well developed in strata of Pennsylvanian age on opposite sides of the Atlantic, in North America and Europe (and probably, when adequately studied, in many other parts of the world)? Can you suggest explanation for variations in the nature of successive subdivisions of individual cycles found in different main parts of the Pennsylvanian System in almost any selected region or found in different regions in the same main part of the system?

7. Especially in parts of Colorado and Wyoming, Pennsylvanian deposits consist of arkosic redbeds that lie nonconformably on Precambrian crystalline rocks or unconformably on pre-Pennsylvanian Paleozoic strata (Fig. 10.15). What is the significance of these features in terms of Pennsylvanian historical geology?

8. What is the evidence that important mountain building occurred during Pennsylvanian time in southern Oklahoma and near the close of the Pennsylvanian Period in western Texas?

11.

PALEOZOIC ERA:
PERMIAN PERIOD

Continental Permian deposits in Monument Valley, Arizona.

Courtesy of Atchison, Topeka & Santa Fe Railway

The Permian Period, which comprises the final portion of the Paleozoic Era, derives its name from the province of Perm in northeastern Russia, where highly fossiliferous marine beds and associated continental deposits rest on Carboniferous rocks of Pennsylvanian age. Although the section of this region serves as standard for definition of Permian throughout the world, it is now known that the most richly fossiliferous succession of marine deposits belonging to this period occurs in the western Texas and southeastern New Mexico region of the United States.

Guide Fossils

Identification and correlation of Permian deposits depend mainly on three groups of fossils: first in importance, as defined by general use, are the marine invertebrates; next are remains of land plants; and third are skeletal remains of land vertebrates. Other organic remains, such as calcareous marine plants, marine vertebrates, and land invertebrates, are known, but these fossils are either too scanty and local in distribution or insufficiently differentiated as markers of certain zones to have much practical value for correlation.

One of the most important groups of guide fossils in marine deposits is that of the fusulinids, because they include many distinctive short-ranged types and are very widely distributed geographically. Those occurring in Permian rocks are more specialized than forerunners that characterize many Pennsylvanian marine deposits. Complexly sutured cephalopods are also important zone indicators but are less common fossils (Fig. 11.1). Corals, brachiopods, bryozoans, and, in restricted areas, crinoid remains are also valuable.

Continental deposits of Permian age are distinguished especially by certain types of ferns and conifers that are lacking in Pennsylvanian strata, and wherever land vertebrates are found, these fossils are especially valuable as guides.

Distribution and Character of Permian Deposits in North America

Midcontinent and southwestern regions. The most complete and important Permian deposits on this continent, for purposes of historical study, occur in the midcontinent and southwestern regions. Permian outcrops are continuous from Nebraska to central Texas, occupying an area many thousand square miles in extent (Fig. 11.2). Exposures in western Texas and southeastern New Mexico, which also are very large, are separated from the midcontinent outcrops by intervening younger formations, but records furnished by many thousand deep borings show that the Permian strata are continuous from one region to the other. In this central portion of the continent, highly fossiliferous marine strata compose an important part of the Permian section. There are also unfossiliferous marine

deposits, such as dolostone, anhydrite, and salt, that were formed by chemical precipitation in supersaline waters and extensive continental deposits consisting mainly of red sand and shale. The aggregate thickness of Permian strata in the region extending from Nebraska to western Texas ranges from about 3,000 to 7,000 feet. Nowhere have the beds been much disturbed from their original near-horizontal attitude.

Western States. Marine Permian formations cap a large part of the Colorado Plateau country in northern Arizona and are known in Nevada, California, Utah, Idaho, Wyoming, Montana, British Columbia, and Alaska. Their fossils are closely similar to forms found in Permian rocks of the midcontinent and western Texas; limestone is the dominant type of deposit. Permian outcrops in Oregon and Washington, on the other hand, contain fossils of strong Asiatic affinities, belonging to the very late part of the period.

Eastern North America. Eastern North America contains small outcrops of supposed Permian rocks, mostly continental, that are very small remnants of originally widespread deposits (see preceding chapter). These outcrops occur in an area surrounding Wheeling, West Virginia, in northern Nova Scotia, and possibly in the vicinity of Boston. The rocks are mostly redbeds.

Divisions. Three main divisions are recognized in the section located in western Texas that is taken as the standard of reference for study of American Permian formations (Fig. 11.3). These divisions, which are classed as series, are only locally and partly delimited by clearly marked unconformities, but mostly they are distinguished by both paleontological and lithological characters. The rocks classed as Middle Permian are divided into two main parts that are assigned rank as stages. Some geologists think that the separation between lower Middle (Leonardian) and upper Middle (Guadalupian) parts of the Permian is more important than any other in the section, and accordingly, they would divide the system into two series, each with two stages, or treat the four so-called stages as independent series.

We may notice that in Germany the old name for latest Paleozoic rocks now called Permian is *Dyas,* meaning twofold, for the succession of deposits there is most naturally classified into a lower thick redbeds series (Rotliegend) and an upper series (Zechstein) containing marine deposits associated with gypsum and salt beds.

In western Texas, where the best section is found for study and correlation of the whole Permian System in North America, the lower and middle series contain many fossils, but the Upper Permian (Ochoan Stage) is composed of unfossiliferous redbeds and evaporites (Fig. 11.3).

Features of Permian History

Varied marine sedimentation of the Texas-New Mexico region. The lower boundary of the Permian deposits in western Texas is very sharply defined, for in this region mountains had been formed late in Pennsylvanian time and eroded away before the beginning of Permian sedimentation. Thus, the lowermost Permian strata, in places containing thick basal conglomerates, are found resting on the upturned truncated edges of Pennsylvanian and older rocks, including both lower Paleozoic and Precambrian formations. The Early Permian seas that spread over this region were clear and warm, as judged by prevalence of limestone deposits and from the nature of bottom-dwelling invertebrates. Reefs were

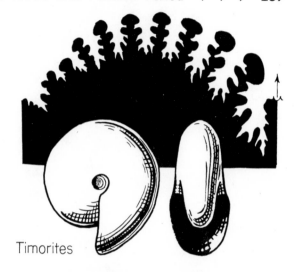

Timorites

Waagenoceras

Perrinites

Fig. 11.1 Index ammonoid cephalopods of Middle Permian age. The genera illustrated, with enlarged drawings of their suture patterns, which are diagnostic characters used in identification, give their names to successive zones of the Middle Permian that are recognized throughout the world. *Perrinites,* which defines with other fossils the lowermost of the three zones, is known from Canada to Mexico and South America, U.S.S.R., Asia Minor, and the East Indies. *Waagenoceras,* which is an index fossil of the middle zone, occurs in western Texas, Mexico, Europe, Asia, and the East Indies. *Timorites,* of the uppermost Middle Permian zone, occurs in western Texas, Mexico, and the East Indies. (*From Moore, Lalicker, and Fischer, Invertebrate Fossils, courtesy of McGraw-Hill Book Company, Inc., New York.*)

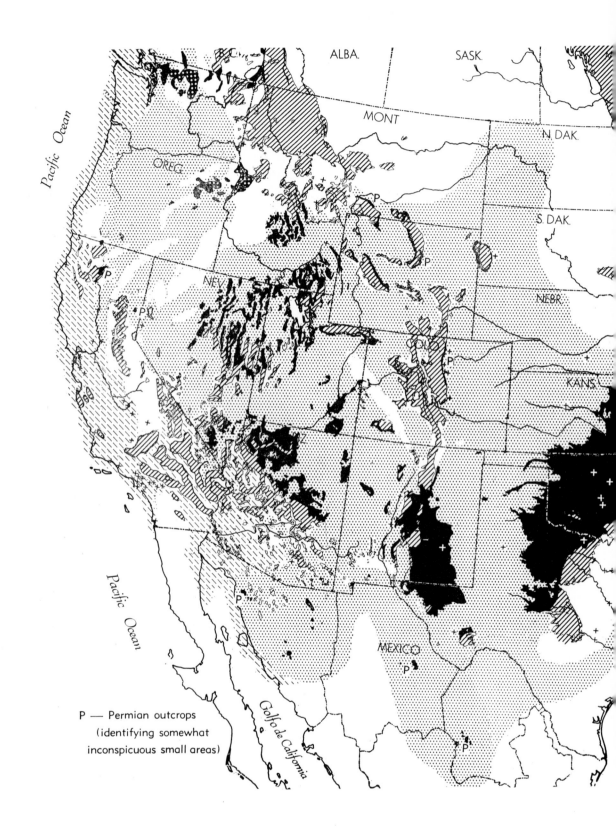

ALBA.　SASK.

MONT

N. DAK.

OREG.

P

S. DAK.

NEV.

P

P

NEBR.

P

COLO.

P

KANS.

P

MEXICO

P

P — Permian outcrops
(identifying somewhat
inconspicuous small areas)

Pacific Ocean

Pacific Ocean

Golfo de California

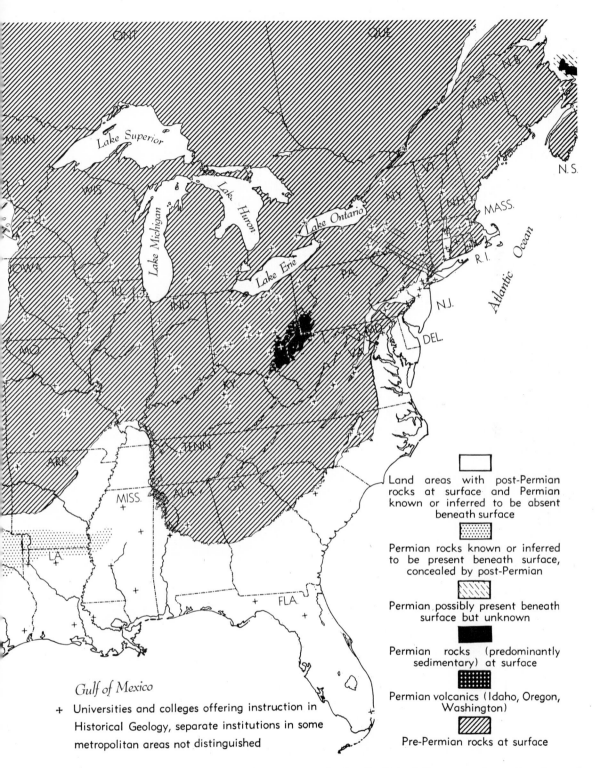

Land areas with post-Permian rocks at surface and Permian known or inferred to be absent beneath surface

Permian rocks known or inferred to be present beneath surface, concealed by post-Permian

Permian possibly present beneath surface but unknown

Permian rocks (predominantly sedimentary) at surface

Permian volcanics (Idaho, Oregon, Washington)

Pre-Permian rocks at surface

+ Universities and colleges offering instruction in Historical Geology, separate institutions in some metropolitan areas not distinguished

Fig. 11.2 Distribution of Permian rocks in the United States, southern Canada, and northern Mexico. The outcrops and subsurface occurrences shown indicate the original distribution of the system, modified by aggregate effects of removal of deposits by post-Permian erosion or locally from displacement by post-Permian bathylithic igneous intrusions.

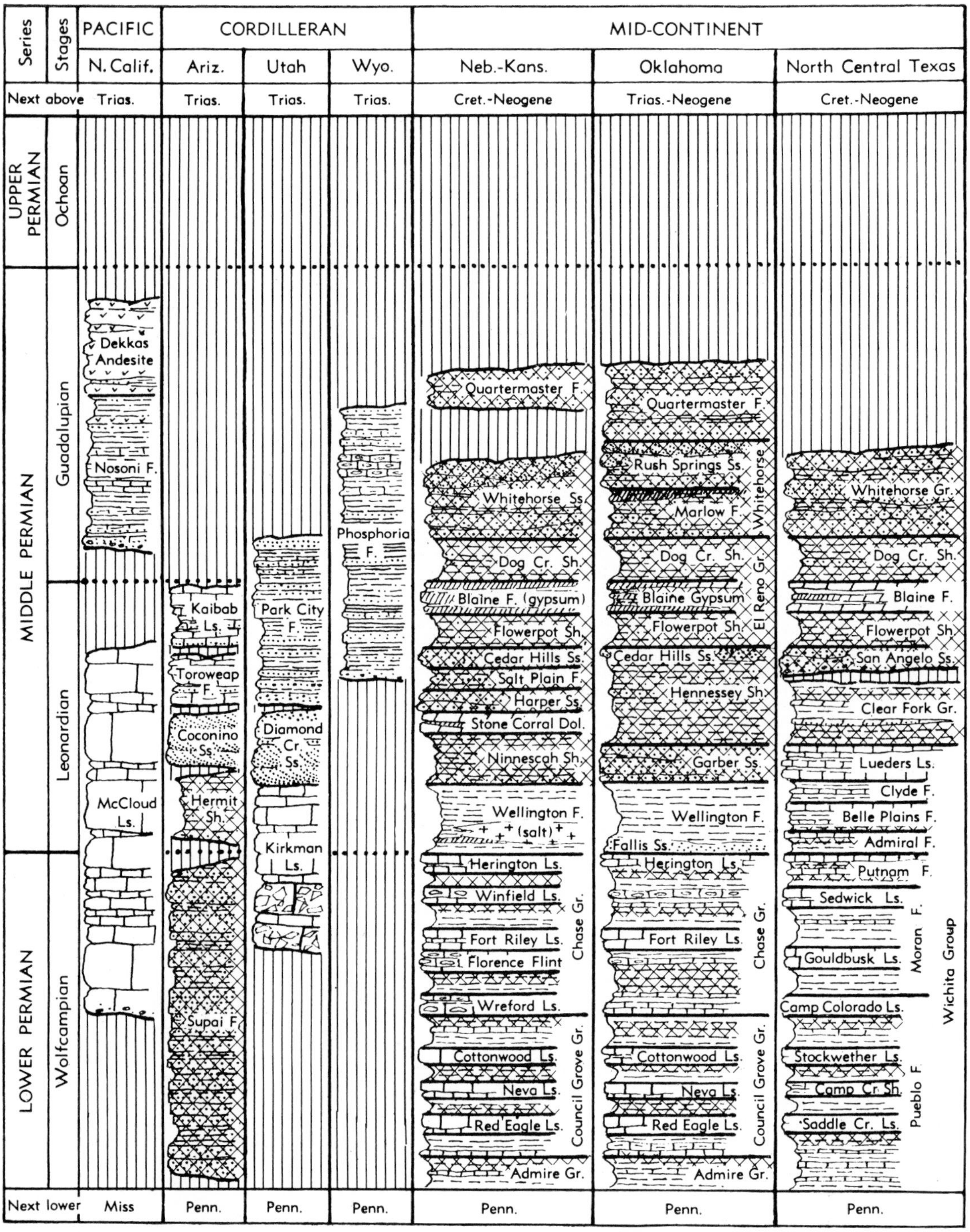
Series
Stages
PACIFIC
CORDILLERAN
MID-CONTINENT
N. Calif.
Ariz.
Utah
Wyo.
Neb.-Kans.
Oklahoma
North Central Texas
Next above
Trias.
Trias.
Trias.
Trias.
Cret.-Neogene
Trias.-Neogene
Cret.-Neogene
UPPER PERMIAN
Ochoan
MIDDLE PERMIAN
Guadalupian
Leonardian
LOWER PERMIAN
Wolfcampian
Dekkas Andesite
Nosoni F.
McCloud Ls.
Kaibab Ls.
Toroweap F.
Coconino Ss.
Hermit Sh.
Supai F.
Park City F.
Diamond Cr. Ss.
Kirkman Ls.
Phosphoria F.
Quartermaster F.
Whitehorse Ss.
Dog Cr. Sh.
Blaine F. (gypsum)
Flowerpot Sh.
Cedar Hills Ss.
Salt Plain F.
Harper Ss.
Stone Corral Dol.
Ninnescah Sh.
Wellington F.
(salt)
Herington Ls.
Winfield Ls.
Fort Riley Ls.
Florence Flint
Wreford Ls.
Chase Gr.
Cottonwood Ls.
Neva Ls.
Red Eagle Ls.
Council Grove Gr.
Admire Gr.
Quartermaster F.
Rush Springs Ss.
Marlow F.
Whitehorse
Dog Cr. Sh.
Blaine Gypsum
Flowerpot Sh.
El Reno Gr.
Cedar Hills Ss.
Hennessey Sh.
Garber Ss.
Wellington F.
Fallis Ss.
Herington Ls.
Fort Riley Ls.
Chase Gr.
Cottonwood Ls.
Neva Ls.
Red Eagle Ls.
Council Grove Gr.
Admire Gr.
Whitehorse Gr.
Dog Cr. Sh.
Blaine F.
Flowerpot Sh.
San Angelo Ss.
Clear Fork Gr.
Lueders Ls.
Clyde F.
Belle Plains F.
Admiral F.
Putnam F.
Sedwick Ls.
Gouldbusk Ls.
Moran F.
Camp Colorado Ls.
Wichita Group
Stockwether Ls.
Camp Cr. Sh.
Saddle Cr. Ls.
Pueblo F.
Next lower
Miss
Penn.
Penn.
Penn.
Penn.
Penn.
Penn.

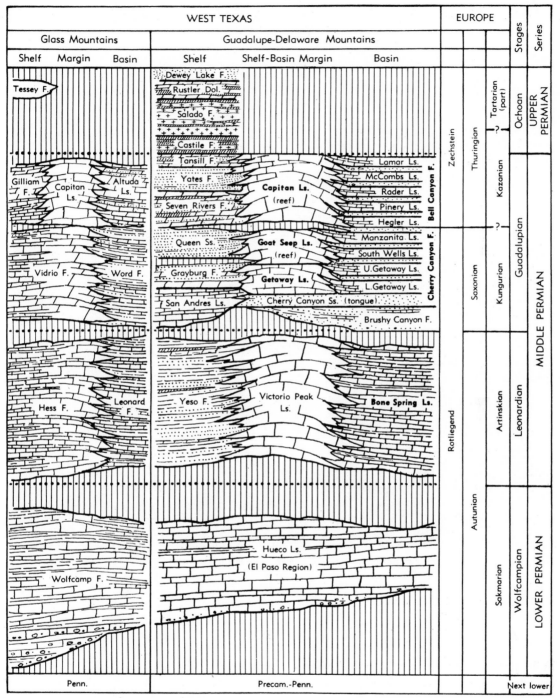

Fig. 11.3 Time-rock divisions of the Permian System and rock units assigned to them in representative important Permian sections of North America. The vertical scale does not represent time duration or thickness of rocks but is determined by suitability for plotting the various recognized rock units, placement of which indicates correlation in age. Lithologic character is represented graphically (explanation of symbols in Appendix B). Necessarily, the plotted thickness is not to scale, although it approximates proportional values in many sections. Vertically ruled areas denote absence of deposits.

Fig. 11.4 Permian marine deposits in western Texas. This northwestward air view of the south end of the Guadalupe Mountains, about 90 miles east of El Paso, shows Leonardian and Guadalupian shale and limestone. The cliff-making cap rock beneath the cloud bank is the Capitan Limestone, which is a reef deposit. (*Courtesy of Robert Muldrow, III, Kargl Aerial Surveys, Inc.*)

built, some having topographic relief of several hundred feet, but corals played only a minor role in building these reef deposits (Figs. 11.4, 11.5). The first three stages each contain such structures, associated with thinly and evenly bedded siliceous or dark calcareous sediments laid down in lagoonal areas. Also, in basin areas near the reefs, there was thick accumulation of fine sand. Broad depressions

northeast of the reefs, in Late Permian time, became filled, through evaporation, with concentrated brine in which dolostone, anhydrite, and salt were precipitated. Ultimately, the thickness of such deposits amounted to many hundred feet.

Three distinct sedimentary environments are recognized to have existed contemporaneously, one adjoining another. These are (1) *basin,*

Fig. 11.5 Southern extremity of Guadalupe Mountains, in western Texas. This view from the foot of the mountain slope supplements the air photograph reproduced in Fig. 11.4, showing at the right beyond the prominent high point, which is El Capitan, east-dipping limestones that include reef talus. The slope on this side of the mountains closely approximates the original eastward slope from the shelf-basin margin into the basin. (*P. B. King, courtesy of U.S. Geol. Survey.*)

(2) *shelf*, and (3) an intermediate belt between these that may be designated *shelf-basin margin* (Fig. 11.6). The basin was moderately deep (1,000 to 2,000 feet or even more), as may be judged from the height of the shelf-basin margin above the basin bottom near by as shown by topographic relief that persists in the deposits themselves. The slope into the basin was steep. Partly exhumed by erosion, this slope can be seen today along the eastern front of the Guadalupe Mountains and in comparable places elsewhere. The shelf areas were shallow seas and lagoons with abnormally high salinity, as shown by dolostone and evaporite deposits laid down in them and virtual absence of fossils (Fig. 11.7). The shelf-basin margins were the site of reef growths, the reefs consisting of thick unbedded

Shelf   Shelf-Basin Margin   Basin

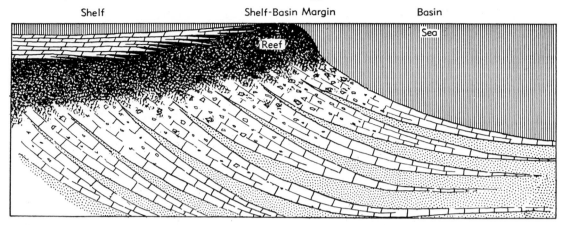

Fig. 11.6 Diagrammatic section of Permian deposits in western Texas in relation to sea level at the time when the youngest beds shown were formed. The structure indicates that the reef deposits grew somewhat upward but chiefly sideward toward the basin with lapse of time, signifying gradual rise of sea level or equivalent general subsidence of the accumulating mass of sediments. (*Modified from N. D. Newell.*)

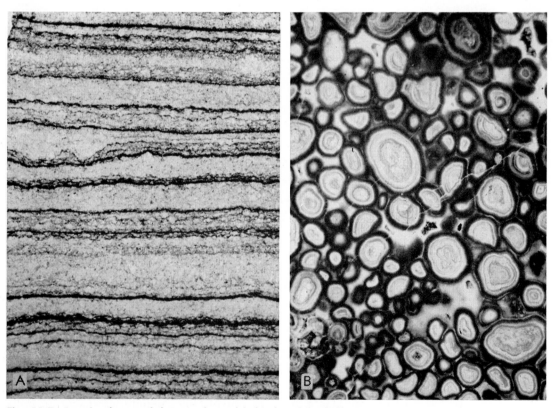

Fig. 11.7 Permian lagoonal deposits formed behind reef in shelf environment. Two common rock types of shelf sediments laid down in hypersaline waters.—*A.* Laminated anhydrite, possibly denoting seasonal accumulations, from the Castile Formation, ×1.7.—*B.* Section of pisolitic limestone, probably an algal deposit, Seven Rivers Formation, ×0.8. (*P. B. King, courtesy of U.S. Geol. Survey.*)

limestone that contains numerous marine organisms. Fragments broken loose from the reef by waves slid down the slope toward the basin, and such talus is incorporated in reef-flank limestones that interfinger with fine sandy basin deposits. The differences in the Permian deposits here briefly described naturally present problems in classifying, naming, and correlating them (Fig. 11.3). A great deal of study devoted to both surface and subsurface geology has been necessary in order to arrive at present understanding of the deposits and the geologic history they represent.

In north-central Texas, beyond the basin environment of western Texas that has been described, widespread normal shallow-sea deposits resembling those in the northern midcontinent region are found. The persistence and general uniformity of thin layers are characteristic of these Permian strata (Fig. 11.8).

End of normal seas in the midcontinent area. Shallow seas, in which invertebrate life was prolific, occupied the northern midcontinent, from northern Oklahoma into Nebraska, during earliest Permian time (Wolfcampian). Cyclic sedimentation, in which fossiliferous limestone and shale are found to alternate in rhythmically regular manner with unfossiliferous redbeds, indicates that the sea advanced and retreated repeatedly, as it had done in Pennsylvanian time (Fig. 11.9).

During the second age (Leonardian) of the Permian, normal marine sedimentation ceased, although a sea continued to occupy the region. Evaporation concentrated the salt in this sea to such extent that most forms of marine life could not survive, and eventually, when gypsum and thick beds of salt began to be deposited, virtually all life in the seas vanished (Fig. 11.10).

The later part of Permian history in this region includes the making of several hundred feet of fine silty and sandy redbeds, which in some horizons contain extensive thin beds of dolostone and gypsum. These deposits indicate the work of sluggish streams and the existence of very shallow bodies of saline water that spread over the nearly flat land surface.

End of deposition in the Appalachian geosyncline. Geologic history of the Appalachian geosyncline during Permian time (remembering that question has been raised about recognizing the rocks called Dunkard as Permian) is very incompletely known, for at best only small remnants of deposits, mainly continental, persist in the Pittsburgh, Pennsylvania, area, Nova Scotia, and Prince Edward Island. It is very possible, or indeed probable, that beds equivalent in age to the true Permian once were widespread in eastern North America as well as continuously westward to the midcontinent. It is evident that if post-Permian erosion had been only a little greater, even the questioned Lower Permian of eastern areas would now be gone.

Marine and continental Permian deposits in western United States. That shallow seas spread widely across parts of the western United States during different epochs of Permian time is shown by the presence of fossiliferous limestone and shale in Arizona, Nevada, California, and areas farther north reaching to Alaska. In Wyoming and Idaho, these Permian deposits include commercially valuable beds of rock phosphate. The fossils all show some provincial variation of the marine faunas, indicating lack of free intermigration between these areas and the Texas and midcontinent regions, but fusulinids and some other guide fossils give basis for correlation with subdivisions of the marine Permian farther east.

Small areas in Oregon, Washington, and British Columbia, recently discovered, contain marine Permian fossils unlike others known from North America but closely resembling those in very late Permian rocks of eastern Asia. These organisms are evidently Asiatic migrants that reached the western border of North America but did not penetrate far into this continent, probably because seas in this latest part of the period did not then submerge much of the Western States. Uppermost Permian deposits of the Texas-New Mexico region, which may be equivalent in age, are unfossiliferous beds made up largely of salt and gypsum laid down in an inland

Fig. 11.8 Vertical air view of Permian marine strata in north-central Texas. The light bands are limestone outcrops, and intervening dark bands are shaly slopes. Air photographs in country such as this in Runnels County east of Ballinger are very useful for geologic mapping, because individual layers can be traced for long distances; of course, work on the ground is necessary also. (*Courtesy of U.S. Soil Conservation Service.*)

sea of very high salinity. This marine remnant certainly was not connected with normal oceanic waters to the west.

Continental deposits of Permian age are widespread and thick in many parts of the western United States. They consist mostly of redbeds, but there are light-colored sandstones also. Some of the best-exposed and most scenic outcrops of these rocks are found in the Southwest (Figs. 11.11 to 11.14).

Appalachian mountain building. Crustal unrest near the close of the Paleozoic Era is recorded by mountain building that belongs at least partly to Permian time, perhaps near

the Paleozoic-Mesozoic boundary when very pronounced changes in the organic world took place. In central Europe deformation that produced moderate folding of stratified rocks can be dated as Middle Permian, but in North America the precise age of mountain building that gave final shape to Appalachian Mountains structures cannot be pin-pointed (Fig. 11.15). The deformative movements must have been later than the time of depositing Pennsylvanian strata that, as in the anthracite district of northeastern Pennsylvania and bituminous coal fields of Alabama, are strongly folded; probably, but not certainly, they post-

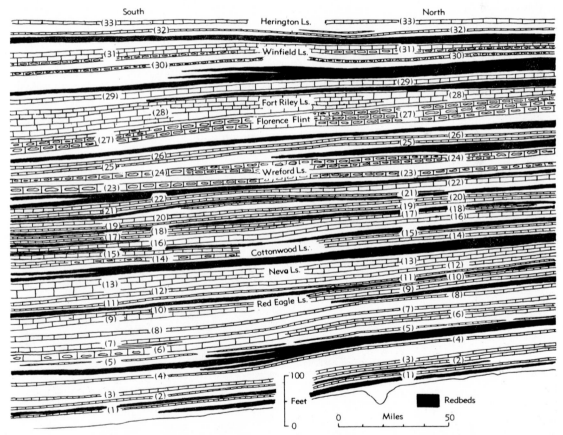

Fig. 11.9 Diagrammatic section of Lower Permian strata from north to south across Kansas. The thin limestones and intervening shales, including red zones, are extremely persistent and uniform. To facilitate identification of units across the diagram, limestones are numbered in upward order but only units named on the chart (Fig. 11.3) are here named also. Note that aggregate thickness of these deposits is nearly uniform for a distance of 240 miles, indicating remarkable evenness of sedimentation on a very stable part of the continenal platform.

date the making of topmost undisturbed Paleo-zoic deposits (Dunkard) in western Pennsylvania and adjacent states. Also, the Appalachian folding took place long enough before Late Triassic sedimentation in Atlantic Border States to allow great erosion of the uplifted Paleozoic rocks. This much we know, but there is leeway of perhaps 50 million years (Fig. 1.31) in trying to date this mountain building. We must recognize that it is pure assumption to say that the Permian Period (and Paleozoic Era) was brought to a close by the Appalachian mountain building.

A main reason for assigning the mountain revolution to the closing part of Permian time is the change in forms of life represented by fossils found on opposite sides of the Paleozoic-Mesozoic boundary. Comparison of Late Permian and Early Triassic organisms found in various regions shows that marine and non-marine life assemblages were profoundly altered, and such great, seemingly abrupt biologic change must reflect great physical change in environment. Only as a result of unusual al-

teration of physical surroundings can we account for the extinction of previously well-established, long-enduring plant and animal stocks and replacement of them by new types. Accentuating the effect of these changes in most places is a lost time interval of unknown duration. Since the Appalachian orogeny surely brought about important geographic changes that include alteration of climate, it is reasonable to conclude that this may be expressed in the nature of the fossil record. All things considered, the close of Permian time seems to have been an unusually critical period in earth history.

Without reference to its exact date in earth history, the crustal disturbance that produced the Appalachians is important. Throughout its entire length of more than 2,000 miles, the Appalachian geosyncline was greatly compressed by earth forces, which pushed previously undisturbed Paleozoic deposits northwestward against the rigid interior platform of the continent. The rocks were folded into great anticlines and synclines, and in many

Fig. 11.10   Middle Permian redbeds in southwestern Kansas. This view, near the Oklahoma line in Barber County, Kansas, shows a typical outcrop of red shale and thin-bedded sandstone capped by a layer of gypsum. These are water-laid sediments, but they are unfossiliferous. Probably they were made by sluggish streams and in shallow salt-water lakes on a nearly flat plain that was alternately subject to wetting and drying. (*Courtesy of Kansas Geol. Survey.*)

Fig. 11.11 Permian marine and continental deposits in the Grand Canyon. The rocks in the foreground that furnish a vantage point for outlook are cherty limestone (Kaibab) that caps the plateau in which the canyon is carved. The sunlighted light-colored rocks capping the spurs in the middle distance are Coconino Sandstone (Fig. 11.12), and strata forming slopes below the sandstone are red shale and sandstone, all continental deposits like the Coconino. (*Courtesy of Union Pacific Railroad.*)

places they were broken by thrust faults having the upthrow side on the southeast. Crustal shortening that amounted to 200 miles or more is estimated. Erosion must immediately have begun to attack the uplifted rock strata, carving canyons and making rugged mountainous topography. By restoration of eroded parts of the folded pattern in the Appalachian Mountains, the structural relief may be determined (Fig. 11.16). Although this cannot be accepted as a measure of topographic relief at any given stage, it supports judgment that, in the early part of their history, the Appalachians may have been as lofty as the present-day Rockies.

Much igneous activity doubtless accompanied the mountain-making deformation of the Appalachian geosyncline. Large granitic bathyliths exposed in the southern part of the piedmont area have been interpreted as representing such activity, because the mineral grains of the granite show little distortion such as may be expected if the rock had been subjected to compressive earth forces. These granites occur nonconformably beneath Triassic deposits, which shows that they are considerably older than Late Triassic. Recently, radioactive measurement of the age of minerals from some of the granites has yielded figures far greater than 185 million years, which is roughly what would be expected if the granites were intruded at or near the close of Paleozoic time. At least those measured seem to be Taconian, and they are so represented in Fig. 6.3.

Volcanism along the Pacific border. No record of Permian folding is found in the western United States, but crustal unrest is indicated by association of fossiliferous Permian strata with volcanic deposits, which in some areas total thousands of feet. Such rocks occur in California, Oregon, and Idaho, and each area includes lava flows, ash beds, and tuff. This evidence of volcanism is noteworthy, inasmuch as Paleozoic rocks older than Permian in the western United States are not associated with volcanic rocks.

Permian Life

Climatic and regional variation of plants. The chief difference between floras of Permian time and those known from the Pennsylvanian

Fig. 11.12 Cross-bedded Permian sandstone near Flagstaff, Arizona. This sandstone (Coconino) is a wind-laid deposit ranging to 1,000 feet in thickness. It is preserved in an area of about 32,000 square miles in north-central Arizona. (*N. H. Darton, courtesy of U.S. Geol. Survey.*)

Fig. 11.13   Massive continental sandstone of Permian age in northeastern Arizona. This view in the Canyon de Chelly shows cross-bedded sandstone that is correlated with part of the Coconino Sandstone. (*Courtesy of Atchison, Topeka & Santa Fe Railway.*)

Fig. 11.14 Permian red shaly rocks overlain by cliff-making sandstone. Part of Monument Valley National Park in the Four Corners Area where Arizona, New Mexico, Colorado, and Utah meet, now a region of oil and gas development. (*Photograph by Mel Coston, courtesy of Humble Oil & Refining Company.*)

Period is the diminished variety of plant types. This is associated with evidence of climatic variation and regional differentiation of distinct plant groups. Unlike the warm, moist climate of Pennsylvanian time, when identical types of lush vegetation grew thickly in coal swamps and on lands in widely separated parts of the globe, the greater dryness and variability of conditions in Permian time are reflected by plant groups adapted to these changed conditions. Although little coal is associated with Permian continental deposits in North America, mineable coal beds are important in some other parts of the world, such as Australia and Siberia. The flora associated with these deposits most nearly resembles typical Pennsylvanian plant assemblages. Plants in other areas were adapted to drier and probably somewhat cooler climates; these are characterized especially by prominence of conifers and by certain types of ferns and fernlike plants that are not known from the Pennsylvanian.

Permian floras of the Southern Hemisphere are distinguished by a broad-leaved fernlike plant that is not known from North America or western Europe, although in part of Permian time it migrated into the U.S.S.R.

Nonmarine animals. Permian rocks are the oldest in which a fairly abundant representation of land animals is known. Fishes that inhabited streams and ponds are found locally in continental Permian deposits, and they are associated with skeletal remains of amphibians. As described in the following chapter, these amphibians are marked especially by their broad, heavily armored skulls, and they represent considerable advancement over forms known from older rocks.

The most striking and interesting land animals are the reptiles, which are represented by many complete skeletons collected in Permian rocks of North America—especially Texas—South Africa, Russia, India, and Brazil. All were four-legged creatures of somewhat lizard-like form that averaged 3 or 4 feet in length. The beginning of successful conquest of the lands by reptiles, which culminated in

the great development of this group in Mesozoic time, is shown by skeletal advancement and specialization as compared with their amphibian ancestors (Figs. 11.17, 11.18).

Although found only very locally, remains of insects in Permian rocks are varied and abundant. The richest known Paleozoic insect locality in the world is a small outcrop of Lower Permian soft limestone in central Kansas, where about 12,000 beautifully preserved specimens have been collected. These fossils prove that most of the main divisions of insects had made their appearance on the earth before the close of Paleozoic time.

Marine invertebrates. All main classes of marine invertebrates, except trilobites, are common in marine Permian faunas. Especially important from the standpoint of geologic correlation are the abundant fusulinids, which show complex internal structures. The other most important elements are cephalopods, brachiopods, bryozoans, and corals. Each of these groups includes distinctive forms that are highly characteristic of the Permian System.

Permian deposits on the flanks of the limestone reefs in western Texas contain a great variety of shells which in the course of fossilization have been changed to silica. When the limestone matrix is etched away in dilute acid, the silicified fossils, which are not affected by the acid, are freed from the rock; the majority of these fossils show delicate structural features even more perfectly preserved than average shells picked up on a beach. The fauna includes several highly

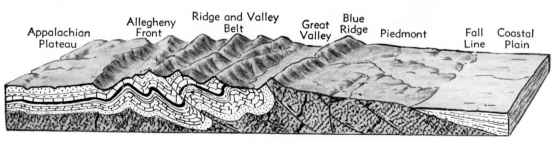

Fig. 11.15 Structural and physiographic units of the Appalachian Mountains region. The block diagrammatically shows relations of structure to characteristic surface features of the Appalachian Mountains and adjoining belts. The folding and faulting occurred near the close of Paleozoic time.

specialized brachiopods, some of which bear long delicate spines, and a great variety of bryozoans, along with corals, clams, snails, ammonoids, crinoids, sponges, echinoids, and fusulinids (Figs. 1.13, 11.19 to 11.21). When paleontologic studies now in progress have been completed, the marine life of Permian time in the western Texas region will be one of the best known among Paleozoic faunas of the world, for knowledge will be based on about 5 million beautifully preserved specimens that have been collected. Besides scientific interest in learning about past forms of life on the earth, this study of Permian fossils has practical value in furnishing accurate means for correlation of the Permian rocks, parts of which are prolific sources of petroleum and natural gas in this region. Beds associated with the great deposits of salt, gypsum, and potash, however, are unfossiliferous.

Climate

The climate of the Permian Period was undoubtedly drier and more varied than in Pennsylvanian or most of preceding Paleozoic time. Conditions favorable to growth of abundant coal-forming plants existed, especially in parts of Asia and Australia. Contemporaneously, in other areas there were warm, alternately wet and dry climates, semiarid climates, true desert climates, and frigid climates. Evidence of these conditions is derived partly from study of fossil organisms and partly from the physical nature of the Permian strata.

Glaciation. Continental glaciation occurred during Permian time in Australia, India, South Africa, and Brazil. Thick deposits of glacial till belonging to the Permian System are found in all these regions; in some, the glacially eroded surface over which the ice moved is also seen clearly. This glaciated surface shows well-preserved striae and other characteristic marks of ice cutting. The direction of ice movement can be determined in some of the glaciated areas, and it is surprising to learn that the centers of ice accumulation were on the equatorward side of the area of glacial deposition and that the glaciers moved away from the equator rather than toward it. In

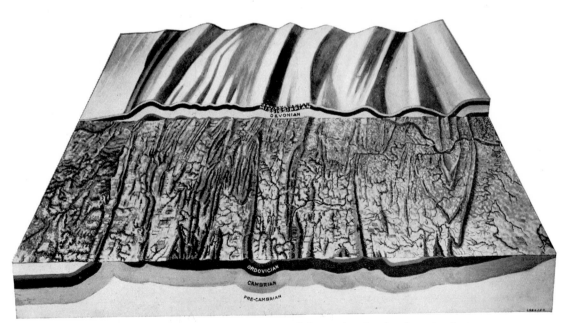

Fig. 11.16 Model of Appalachian Mountains in central Pennsylvania showing structure. The folded rocks removed by erosion are restored in part of the model. (*Courtesy of Chicago Natural History Museum.*)

Fig. 11.17 A connecting link between the amphibians and reptiles. This animal (*Seymouria*), which is represented by fairly abundant skeletal remains from Permian redbeds of north-central Texas, attained a length of about 2 feet and is chiefly interesting because it combines many typical characters of amphibians with those of unspecialized reptiles. Some paleontologists think that *Seymouria* should be ranked among amphibians, but the nest of eggs in a hollow on land, as shown in this restoration, implies that the creature is a reptile, because the eggs of amphibians must be laid in water. (*Courtesy of American Museum of Natural History.*)

Fig. 11.18 Fin-backed Early Permian reptiles. These animals, called *Edaphosaurus*, attained a length of 11 feet. As shown by their teeth, they were plant-eaters, not carnivorous. Remains belonging to them have been found in both North America and central Europe in Late Pennsylvanian as well as Early Permian deposits. (*Courtesy of J. Augusta and Z. Burian, Praha; published by permission.*)

eastern Australia, glaciation is recorded in the early part of Permian time by ice deposits interbedded with marine strata; coal-forming conditions were established subsequently and persisted for some time; then there was renewed glaciation, represented by another series of glacial-till deposits above the coal-bearing strata. All these deposits belong to the Permian.

Gondwanaland

In the Southern Hemisphere, a large continental mass that has received the name "Gondwanaland" is presumed by many geologists to have spread from Australia through what is now India and Africa to South America, occupying areas now covered by waters of the Indian Ocean and South Atlantic.

Main evidence for support of this postulate is the remarkable similarity of sedimentary deposits and their contained fossils as observed in these regions. Intermigration of land plants and animals, if freely allowed, would explain satisfactorily the many resemblances, and this is provided by Gondwanaland. On various grounds, however, the concept of such a continent is difficult to accept, especially since it runs counter to indications of the permanence of the ocean basins. That land connections of some sort between these now-separated parts of the globe did exist in Permian time seems probable, or islands may have provided partial and temporary means for migration of land organisms. A vast continent named Gondwanaland seemingly is a fiction.

Fig. 11.19 Permian invertebrates from western Texas. These are all silicified fossils from the Glass Mountains. They include a pleurotomarian gastropod (*A*); bryozoans (*B, Thamniscus; C, Polypora*); corals (*D, E, Lophophyllidium*); brachiopods (*F, Neospirifer; J, Prorichtofenia; K, Meekella; L, Leptodus*); pelecypods (*G*, nuculid showing exterior and interior with rows of teeth, *H*, scallop); and sponge (*I*). Natural size. (*Photographs courtesy of G. A. Cooper, U.S. National Museum.*)

Close of the Period

The close of the Permian Period and the end of Paleozoic time were marked by an emergent condition of the continents throughout the world. Shallow seas retreated. Nowhere are transitional marine deposits connecting Late Permian and Early Triassic known, and the hiatus in the record is of unknown duration. Most land areas probably were subject to erosion, but in some regions unbroken continental sedimentation so connects Permian with Triassic that a satisfactory boundary cannot be determined. South Africa and eastern Russia are regions in which the proper age assignment of some fossil-bearing continental deposits is unsettled, and such deposits are sometimes designated as Permo-Triassic. Nevertheless, the end of Permian time is marked by profound changes in the record of life.

Economic Resources

Rocks of the Permian System have large economic importance, exceeding all other systemic divisions of the column in quantity of some useful substances, such as salt, potash, and phosphate, although not now leading in

Fig. 11.20 Colony of coral-like Permian brachiopods in position of growth. The group of *Prorichtofenia* shells from the Glass Mountains, western Texas, is seen from the side; note the anchoring spines; ×1.4. (*Photograph courtesy of G. A. Cooper, U.S. National Museum.*)

Fig. 11.21 Restoration of Permian marine invertebrates from western Texas. Many of the animals shown belong to yet unnamed new genera. Forms marked by letters include sponges (*A, B*), brachiopods (*C, D, G*), nautiloid cephalopod (*E, Cooperoceras*), pelecypod (*F*), and seaweeds (*H*, algae). (*Courtesy of L. B. Kellum and I. G. Reimann, University of Michigan; model prepared by George Marchand with the guidance of G. A. Cooper.*)

commercial production of some (for example, salt and phosphate). The chief resource, based on dollar value of annual production, is petroleum; then come the evaporites (salt, potash, and gypsum), coal, phosphate, and stone for various uses; copper and gold occur but are relatively unimportant.

Petroleum. Permian oil production in the United States accounts for approximately 13 per cent of the total, counting proved reserves (an aggregate amount in 1950 of 7,904 million barrels). The so-called Permian Basin region of western Texas outranks other producing areas located in the north-central Texas, Oklahoma, and Kansas parts of the midcontinent and in various western states.

Salt. With little doubt, the greatest volume of salt deposits in a single region known anywhere in the world is found in the Permian salt beds extending southward from Kansas into New Mexico and western Texas, underlying an area of approximately 125,000 square miles with average thickness in the neighborhood of 400 feet. These figures are translatable into the incomprehensible sum of 95.5 million million (95.5 trillion) tons of rock salt. Although common salt has been mined in central Kansas for many years and now is produced also in Texas, combined Permian salt production annually in the United States is only a little more than half of Silurian production. On the other hand, potash salt from the New Mexico-Texas area is not matched by production elsewhere, even the famous Stassfurt region of Germany, where the potash and common salt also is Permian. Large amounts of Permian gypsum are produced in Kansas, Oklahoma, Texas, and West Germany.

Coal. Deposits of coal are unimportant in Permian rocks of North America, even counting appreciable production from Dunkard beds in Pennsylvania and West Virginia, but Permian coals in Africa, India, Australia, and especially the Kuznetsk Basin of east-central Siberia are produced in large amounts (annually more than 75 million tons).

Phosphate. Permian phosphate deposits are commercially important in Wyoming, Idaho, Utah, and Nevada but have only begun to be developed in recent years (current annual production from Idaho about 2 million tons). The ore occurs in marine deposits named the Phosphoria Formation.

Other resources. Copper has been obtained for many years from the "copper shales" (Kupferschiefer) of Germany, of Permian age. Significant gold production comes from Permian granodiorite in Queensland. Stone products from Permian formations are obtained for local uses at many places, but these do not rival such materials from other systems.

Fig. 11.22 Thin even layers of pure rock salt in a mine at Lyons, Kansas. The salt here being mined is part of a succession about 400 feet thick, occurring 1,000 feet below the surface in central Kansas. (*Courtesy of American Salt Corp.*)

READINGS

CASE, E. C., 1915, The Permo-Carboniferous redbeds of North America and their vertebrate fauna: *Carnegie Inst. Wash. Publ.* 207 (176 pp., illus.).
Excellent description of Permian terrestrial sedimentation and associated reptiles.

COLBERT, E. H., 1955, *Evolution of the vertebrates*, John Wiley & Sons, Inc., New York (479 pp., illus.). [1] Amphibians, pp. 85–105. [2] Advent of the reptiles, pp. 106–120. [3] Mammal-like reptiles, pp. 121–136. [4] Conquest of the land, pp. 137–145.
Most interesting accounts of Permian vertebrates.

JONES, T. S., 1953, Stratigraphy of the Permian Basin of West Texas: *West Texas Geol. Soc. Guidebook*, Midland, Tex. (63 pp., illus.).
Summarizes regional data usefully.

NEWELL, N. D., 1957, Paleoecology of the Permian reefs in the Guadalupe Mountain area: in *Treatise on marine ecology*, H. S. Ladd, ed., Geol. Soc. America, Mem. 67, vol. 2, pp. 407–436 (illus.).
Excellent discussion of sedimentary environments in relation to organisms.

———, et al., 1953, *The Permian reef complex of the Guadalupe Mountains region, Texas and New Mexico*, W. H. Freeman & Company, San Francisco (236 pp., illus.).
An indispensable general description containing important chapters on classification of deposits and conditions affecting life.

WOODWARD, H. P., 1957, Chronology of Appalachian folding: *Am. Assoc. Petroleum Geologists Bull.*, vol. 41, pp. 2312–2327 (illus.).
Points out that so-called "Appalachian orogeny" (renamed Allegheny orogeny by author) involves deformations ranging from Mississippian to possibly mid-Triassic and that these are minor in importance as compared with earlier folding in the Appalachian region.

QUESTIONS

1. What considerations chiefly influence selection of fossils classed as index fossils (Fig. 11.1)? Can you suggest reasons for the superior fitness of some organisms, such as the ammonoid cephalopods, for recognition as guide fossils in stratigraphic correlation as compared with other groups preserved as fossils?

2. If the strata in the Ohio-Pennsylvania-West Virginia area classed as Permian (Fig. 11.2) really belong to this system, what reasons can be given for concluding that the original thickness and area of occurrence of Permian deposits in this region must have been very much larger than the now-observed remnants? What differences are noteworthy in comparing the distribution of buried Permian and Pennsylvanian rocks (Fig. 10.4) in the western United States, and what do they signify as to geologic history?

3. What are the main differences in types of sedimentary deposits found in Permian successions of representative regions (Fig. 11.3) as compared with those of Pennsylvanian sections (Fig. 10.7)? What are important differences in economic products derived from these systems?

4. What are the characters that support identification of some Permian limestone deposits of western Texas as reefs and as lagoonal sediments laid down behind the reefs (Figs. 11.4 to 11.7)?

5. How do features shown by the section of Permian strata across the Kansas region (Fig. 11.9) demonstrate remarkable stability of the earth's crust in this part of the continent during Early Permian time? Why is it necessary to conclude that gradual subsidence of the crust took place very evenly as sedimentation proceeded? How can you account for the alternation of marine limestones with red shaly deposits formed under nonmarine conditions?

6. What are reasons for interpreting the Coconino Sandstone of the Colorado Plateau country as a wind-formed deposit (Figs. 11.12, 11.13)?

7. Can you explain the progressively higher stratigraphic position (and consequently indicated younger age) of salt deposits in Permian formations proceeding from Kansas to western Texas and New Mexico? Why should potash salts, which are more soluble than common salt (halite), occur in the western Texas-New Mexico region though absent in Kansas?

12.

NATURE AND EVOLUTION
OF PALEOZOIC LIFE

Devonian sea bottom in New York.   *Courtesy of Rochester Museum of Arts and Science*

The Paleozoic rocks are the oldest that contain abundant evidence of life. Remains of this life form an essential part of the geologic record, and the character of the life of these remotely ancient times has much intrinsic interest. Invertebrate marine animals constitute the predominant element in Paleozoic organic assemblages as a whole, and consequently, the era is well designated as the Age of Invertebrates. It is the purpose of this chapter to review the nature and evolution of plants and animals as recorded by fossils found in the Paleozoic formations.

PLANTS

That plant life was fairly abundant from the very beginning of Paleozoic time, and doubtless long before, is a safe presumption because of (1) the prolific fossil remains of animals, all of which are directly or indirectly dependent on plants for food, (2) the appearance of highly organized plant remains in the Devonian and later Paleozoic rocks, and (3) the widespread presence of calcareous algae. Bacteria, which are assigned an important role as precipitating agents of calcium carbonate, may have contributed greatly to accumulation of the thousands of feet of calcareous strata that were made in Paleozoic time.

Marine Plants

The only certainly known plants from the early Paleozoic part of earth history are seaweeds (algae). Some of the most interesting of these are remarkably preserved specimens of gelatinous and membranous algae that appear as shiny black films on bedding planes of Middle Cambrian shale in British Columbia. On the basis of form and mode of growth, 20 species have been distinguished. Since none of these algae shows a point of attachment, presumably they were floating forms.

Lime-secreting algae are especially abundant and characteristic of some Late Cambrian and Early Ordovician formations (Fig. 5.24). The algal remains consist of calcareous masses that are varied in size and irregularly rounded in shape. They show a finely laminated concentric structure, closely resembling that of some modern blue-green algae. Algal deposits occur in marine later Paleozoic rocks also.

Land Plants

First land plants. The oldest known land plants occur in Silurian rocks of Australia. They include at least two genera and several different types that in some respects resemble ferns and in others the lycopods; one of the genera is known also from Lower Devonian deposits of Maine. No doubt as to the Silurian age of these Australian fossils is allowed, because some of them are associated with diagnostic Silurian graptolites, presumably from

having been floated into marine waters; likewise, their well-preserved structures establish classification among the so-called woody plants that grow on land.

Succession of land floras. Devonian rocks contain a peculiar group of leafless land plants (psilopsids), which are quite unlike any others but give evidence in their generalized characters of ancestral relationship to various later forms of vegetation. These strata also show ferns of several types and scale trees having trunks more than 3 feet in diameter and probably 40 feet tall. The Mississippian and Pennsylvanian Periods mark the culmination of this ancient land flora, when there was greatest variety and when maximum sizes in plants of low orders were attained. Many of the shale deposits near coal beds furnish an extremely rich and beautifully preserved record of these plant growths. Permian time is chiefly characterized by the waning or disappearance of earlier plants, the expansion of early types of conifers, and the development, especially in the Southern Hemisphere, of a cool-climate flora, in which certain rather coarse fernlike plants dominated. This was a time of great change, leading up to the different-looking floras of the Mesozoic Era.

Devonian leafless plants. The first well-known land flora comes from Devonian rocks of eastern Canada, Maine, Wyoming, Scotland, and central Europe. A typical representative (*Psilophyton*) of this assemblage was a naked, leafless plant, having a woody stem ½ inch in diameter and numerous branches rising 2 feet or more (Fig. 8.24). The tips of young branches twisted in a coil, like new fern leaves, and some bore small, elongate pods, containing the reproductive spores. The stems have breathing pores, such as occur in the leaves of higher plants, and the cell structure shows the presence of a vascular system, which serves for transmitting water and nourishment derived from the underground portion of the plant. The latter did not consist of true roots but was a horizontal runner bearing small rootlets. Clearly, we find here the adaptation of an originally algal type of aquatic plant to a moist environment on

Fig. 12.1 Restoration of Devonian plants. The tallest plants are tree ferns (*Eospermatopteris*). Others are horsetails (right foreground). (*C. R. Knight, courtesy of Chicago Natural History Museum.*)

land and a beginning of the all-important structures that make it possible for land plants to thrive.

Ferns. Ferns (pteridophytes), which are generally distinguished by their numerous branching leaflets and by the presence of spore clusters on the underside of leaves or on specialized fronds, are now represented by some 6,000 species that range from tiny plants to tropical tree ferns 50 feet high. The spores are produced in almost incredible numbers, a single plant sometimes liberating 1,000 millions. The ferns made their appearance in Devonian time, and one type (*Archaeopteris*) was world-wide in distribution. Some of the fernlike types of Pennsylvanian time include climbing plants of tropical aspect, many of which suggest lianas. Other climbing forms were of filmy delicacy.

The oldest known tree ferns come from Middle Devonian rocks of southeastern New York, where fossil tree trunks were found in 1869 near the little town of Gilboa. It was not until a half century later that extensive quarrying in 1920 brought the discovery that a veritable fossil forest existed at this locality, for scores of stumps ranging to 3.5 feet in diameter were uncovered, in one part of the area 18 of them in a space 50 feet square. The trees were named *Eospermatopteris* (dawn seed fern), because they exhibit some resemblances to Carboniferous seed ferns, but it has not been demonstrated that they really bore seeds, and they are now classed with the ferns rather than seed ferns (Fig. 12.1).

The leaves of many Pennsylvanian ferns were strikingly similar in form to some of the present day (Fig. 12.2), and a few were 12 feet in length. Leaves of this type were borne at the tops of long trunks, which attained diameters of 30 inches or more. These tree ferns were provided with an extremely thick outer zone of protective, water-storing, root-like appendages.

Seed ferns. A surprising paleobotanical discovery was made in 1905 when fossils that looked like ordinary ferns proved to have true seeds instead of spores. Separated seeds are not uncommon in some late Paleozoic beds, but it was not suspected that any of these belonged to ferns. Now, it is clear that many seeds of previously unidentified origin belong to the seed fern, and it is possible that some of the fern species, known at present only by their foliage, may prove ultimately to be seed-bearing and not true ferns at all.

Lycopods. Dominant elements in the late Paleozoic floras were the plants called Lyco-podiales by botanists (or sometimes termed lepidophytes, signifying scale trees, in reference to the scalelike nature of the leaves).

They are represented by the modern diminutive evergreens known as club mosses (*Lycopodium*), but in Pennsylvanian time the group contained splendid trees more than 100 feet high, and there are tall forerunners (*Protolepidodendron*) in the Devonian (Fig. 8.24). The lycopods are distinguished by short, stiff, scaly or needle-like leaves that densely cover all the stem or trunk and branches, except parts from which the old dead leaves have dropped away. The leaves of large fossil species not uncommonly attained a length of 6 to 7 inches and were as much as ½ inch wide at the base, which was roughly diamond-shaped. The place of attachment of each leaf was marked by a distinctive scar (Fig. 12.3). In some (*Lepidodendron*), the scars were

Fig. 12.2 Slab of Pennsylvanian nonmarine shale containing a well-preserved fossil fern. This specimen (*Neuropteris*, one-third natural size) is from Lower Pennsylvanian (Pottsville) beds of Alabama. The original plant tissue is preserved as a thin carbonaceous film. (*Charles Butts, courtesy of Alabama Geol. Survey.*)

arranged in regularly intersecting oblique rows; in others (*Sigillaria*), they were in vertical series. Some were short, stocky, and unbranched, a trunk 6 feet in diameter at the base tapering to the top less than 20 feet above ground. Others were tall and slender (Fig. 12.4). One unbranched specimen 200 feet long is known. Branches were far less numerous than in modern trees. The scale trees are first known from Devonian rocks and are common in later Paleozoic swamp deposits, especially those of Pennsylvanian age.

Horsetails. The so-called horsetail rushes (sphenopsids) are plants having numerous unbranched, hollow, jointed, and ribbed stems. Most modern species are less than 3 feet tall, but one in South America has stems 1 inch in diameter and 30 to 40 feet tall. This group was very well represented in the late Paleozoic floras of all parts of the world (Figs. 12.1, 12.5). Most of the ancient horsetails were very much larger than their living descendants, some attaining a diameter of 3 feet and a height of fully 100 feet. The upright trunks grew from a prostrate, horizontal stem, and it is evident that they thrived in wet sandy soils. At the nodes along the stem were small branches that bore circlets of leaves (Fig. 10.21). Jungle-like areas of these plants were probably like the dense southern canebrakes on an enlarged scale and comparable to bamboo thickets of today.

Early conifers (Cordaitales). Another conspicuous late Paleozoic plant is an unfamiliar tree known as *Cordaites*, which was distinguished by a tall, slender trunk, rarely 2 feet in diameter but 30 to 100 feet high. Branches occurred only near the top, and they bore a thick mass of leaves up to 3 feet long and as much as 6 inches wide. They are exceedingly widespread in Pennsylvanian and Permian rocks of both hemispheres.

Fig. 12.3 Leaf impressions on the trunk of Pennsylvanian lycopods. The specimen at the left, with scars arranged in vertical rows, is *Sigillaria;* that at the right, with rhombic scars arranged in oblique intersecting rows, is *Lepidodendron.* Natural size. (*Courtesy of Chicago Natural History Museum.*)

Fig. 12.4 Restoration of Pennsylvanian coal-swamp plants. Large fronds of ferns and (in center of view) a seed fern are seen between the trunks of large lycopods (mostly sigillarias, with longitudinal rows of leaf scars but including lepidodendrons such as the prostrate nearest log, surmounted by a large cockroach). (*Courtesy of Chicago Natural History Museum.*)

Classified with the Cordaitales and like them, considered to belong in the ancestral line of the conifers, are many specimens of well-preserved fossil wood from the Upper Devonian; these are called *Callixylon* (beautiful wood). Trunks belonging to this plant with a diameter of 5 feet have been found in southern Oklahoma, although logs 2 or 3 feet across are more common. *Callixylon* is widely distributed, for it is known from several parts of the United States and from southern U.S.S.R.

Conifers. The plant group that is represented in modern times by the pines, spruces, and many other cone-bearing trees contains several primitive Permian types and a few of Pennsylvanian age. One type (*Lebachia*),

which was abundant and very widely distributed in Permian time, had numerous slender branchlets growing in the same plane, all densely clothed with short needle-like leaves (Fig. 10.21).

INVERTEBRATES

Protozoans

We might suppose that the oldest fossil-bearing beds would be especially characterized by prominence of protozoans, because these are the most primitive and simply constructed of all animals. On the contrary, fossil protozoans are rare in rocks older than Mississippian. This may be owing partly to conditions unfavorable for preservation of their minute delicate structure, but more probably, the scanty fossil records mean that most of the early protozoans lacked hard parts. A few poorly preserved specimens are known from the Upper Cambrian of England, and about 50 species of siliceous-shelled simple foraminifers have been discovered by dissolving samples of Ordovician and Silurian limestone in hydrochloric acid.

The delicate siliceous tests of radiolarians have been reported from Precambrian rocks, but they are not definitely identified in early Paleozoic faunas.

Fusulinids. Protozoans are first important as an element in later Paleozoic fossil faunas in Pennsylvanian time, when the "wheat-grain" shells termed *fusulinids* occurred in such vast numbers that they form a considerable part of many rock layers (Fig. 10.3). Other kinds of protozoans are present also. The fusulinid shells of Pennsylvanian and Permian time are

Fig. 12.5 Stem of a Pennsylvanian horsetail rush. This fossil, named *Calamites*, is distinguished by its hollow, jointed, longitudinally ribbed form. Natural size. (*Courtesy of Chicago Natural History Museum.*)

spindle-shaped, some of them long and thin, others nearly spheroidal, and they range in length along the axis from $\frac{1}{16}$ to more than 1 inch, the average being about $\frac{3}{8}$ inch. They are distinguished from microscopic foraminifers by their shape and much greater size, and by their complex internal structure. The Middle Pennsylvanian fusulinids (*Fusulina*) have mostly simple, nearly plane walls that divide each spiral turn of the shell into chambers; those of Late Pennsylvanian time (*Triticites*) are distinguished by moderately wrinkled walls, and several belonging to Permian time have highly fluted walls. There is thus a well-marked evolution of this stock during its existence, and most of the very many species are valuable index fossils. The fusulinids were bottom-dwelling foraminifers, but they spread very widely over the world, being abundant not only in America but throughout most of the Old World. These fossils are extensively used by paleontologists as an aid in identifying and correlating the Pennsylvanian and Permian formations penetrated by the drill in the midcontinent oil fields. It is interesting to find many perfect, unmutilated specimens of these delicate fossils in well cuttings.

Archaeocyathans

Archaeocyathans are invertebrates with calcareous hard parts that have been interpreted as peculiar primitive sponges or possibly corals, but now they are ranked independently as an extinct phylum. They have world-wide distribution in Lower and Middle Cambrian rocks. Their shape is subcylindrical to conical, and they range in size from greatest dimensions of less than 1 inch to a length of nearly 1 foot. The archaeocyathans are specially distinguished by the thick, porous nature of the outer and radial walls and the presence of a sort of plate that floors the calyx. Locally, they make large reefs, as in Australia, where a limestone 200 feet thick and at least 400 miles in lateral extent is largely composed of them. The presence of these coral-like forms in Labrador, islands north of Siberia, and Antarctica suggests that high latitudes were at least not frigid at this time.

Sponges

Among Cambrian fossils, siliceous sponges
are well represented by several types, including many with a delicate netlike skeleton,
that resembles the modern glass sponge known
as Venus's-flower-basket (Figs. 5.27, 12.10).

Sponges were common in Ordovician time,
and many of them are valuable index fossils.
One of the most important types (*Receptaculites*), which, however, may represent an
entirely distinct class of organisms, resembles
the large center of a sunflower.

The Silurian rocks contain a somewhat similar genus (*Ischadites*), and there are large
numbers of apple-shaped (*Astylospongia*) and
saucer-like (*Astraeospongia*) siliceous sponges
in some beds (Fig. 12.6). In parts of Tennessee, sponges weather out of the rocks in such
profusion that they may be gathered by the
bushel.

Sponges of several sorts are known from
each of the later Paleozoic periods. Some
formations are specially characterized by
abundance of sponge spicules or the presence
of certain species of sponges. The massive
stony types (lithistids) are much less common
than the beautiful, delicate glass sponges
(hexactinellids), of which many are found
in Devonian rocks (Figs. 12.7 to 12.9). Both
siliceous and calcareous sponges are common
in Mississippian, Pennsylvanian, and Permian
faunas, especially in some deposits that belong to an environment of a particular sort,
which is indicated by abundance of sponges
with sparse numbers of other invertebrates
(Fig. 12.9).

Coelenterates

Jellyfishes. In classification of the coelenterates, several distinct main groups of animals
loosely termed jellyfishes are recognized, some
being the umbrella-like free-swimming generation (medusae) of colonial attached polyps
and others being persistently free from attachment. Comparative study of coelenterate structural features, combined with observation of
the fossil record, indicates that some types of
jellyfishes are probably the ancestral stock
from which coelenterates as a whole de-

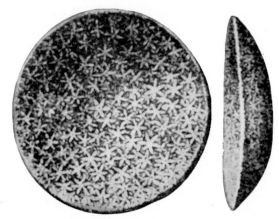

**Fig. 12.6 A saucer-shaped siliceous sponge from
Silurian rocks of Tennessee.** The star-like markings
on the surface of the fossil (*Astraeospongia*) are large
spicules. Top and side views, natural size.

Fig. 12.7 Devonian glass sponge from New York.
This fossil (*Hydnoceras*) clearly shows the pattern
of rectangularly intersecting spicules that resembles
a net; it belongs to the class of siliceous sponges called
Hyalospongea. (*Courtesy of American Museum of
Natural History.*)

veloped; at any rate, they are much the oldest known representatives of the phylum, examples being found in Precambrian (Algonkian) rocks (Fig. 4.40) and both Lower and Middle Cambrian strata (Fig. 12.10). Because jellyfishes lack hard parts, they are not common fossils, yet several interesting kinds are known from Ordovician, Devonian, and Pennsylvanian beds.

Stromatoporoids. The lime-secreting hydrozoans, called *stromatoporoids*, flourished during parts of Paleozoic time, when they were important as rock builders. The principal representatives of this class in the Ordovician period are columnar growths with external fluting (*Beatricea*); rounded, hemispherical growths (*Stromatocerium*); and flat expanding forms (*Labechia*). The Silurian species are mainly large, irregularly laminated masses, in which the vertical pillars extend only between the layers rather than continuously across several layers (*Clathrodictyon*). In Devonian time, they reached the peak of their career in numbers and variety. Some colonies

were truly gigantic in size, forming calcareous deposits several feet thick and as much as 10 feet across. Locally, they make reefs and may be accounted important as rock builders. The stromatoporoids disappeared suddenly, for they are not found in post-Devonian beds, unless possibly certain Cretaceous fossils belong in this group.

Corals. Corals are abundantly represented by fossils in Paleozoic formations, and they have been very important as rock builders. Many are good index fossils. If the ancient coral polyps were affected by temperature conditions like the modern, the common occurrence of fossil corals in a geologic formation may be interpreted to signify that the deposit was laid down in moderately warm, shallow waters.

For some reason, corals are rare or lacking in the Middle and Upper Cambrian, but they appear at various horizons in the Ordovician. Characteristic types include both colonial and horn corals. The chain coral (*Halysites*) is typically a Silurian fossil, but a closely related

Fig. 12.8 Restoration of fossil sponges from Late Devonian rocks of New York. Only sponges in which the skeletal elements (spicules) are knit together are preserved so as to show the form of the animal. (*Courtesy of New York State Museum.*)

Fig. 12.9 Reconstruction of Permian sponges and associated invertebrates. This assemblage is based on shallow-water fossils of a near-reef environment represented by collections in western Texas. The tall cylindrical organisms at the left (*A*) are siliceous sponges, and the slender beaded types at the lower right (*B*) are calcareous sponges. Other invertebrates are (*C, D*) productid and leptodid brachiopods, (*E, F, G*) three kinds of cephalopods, (*H, I*) gastropods, and (*J*) pelecypods. (*Courtesy of Chicago Museum of Natural History; prepared by George Marchand under direction of I. G. Reimann and guidance of G. A. Cooper.*)

form (*Catenularia*) has been found in rocks as old as mid-Ordovician. About 35 species of Ordovician corals have been described in North America.

The first really abundant development of corals occurred in Middle Silurian time, when at many places in North America they made reef limestones. About 400 species are recognized. Well-exposed sections of the ancient reefs may be seen in Wisconsin, Iowa, Illinois, and Indiana. Colonial corals are of many types, a few with large individual polyps (*Strombodes*) but the majority with units of small size. Especially interesting are the chain coral and the honeycomb. Horn corals are numerous. A strange coral (*Goniophyllum*), shaped like a four-sided pyramid provided with a cover of four plates, is a characteristic

fossil in the Silurian of northern Europe (Figs. 7.21, 12.11).

At no time in the Paleozoic were horn corals so numerous or varied as in the Devonian Period. They ranged in size from less than ¼ inch in length and width to more than 2 feet in length and about 4 inches in width. Some of the very common kinds (*Cyathophyllum, Heliophyllum*) had numerous, evenly spaced radial walls, without a fossular depression in the calyx; others (*Zaphrentis, Aulacophyllum*) are distinguished by the presence of well-defined fossulae. There are variously specialized forms. For example, one long-ranging genus (*Amplexus*), which is represented by several Devonian species, has extremely short radial walls and very numerous horizontal platforms; another (*Cystiphyllum*), which

Fig. 12.10 Middle Cambrian jellyfishes and associated invertebrates. This reconstruction shows a bit of Burgess Shale sea bottom in British Columbia. The jellyfishes (*A, Peytoia*) are mostly shown settled on the mud; other invertebrates include colonial hyalosponges (*B, Chancelloria, Vauxia*); trilobites (*C, Olenoides*); trilobite-like arthropods classed as Trilobitoidea (*D, E, F*); sea cucumbers (*G*); and worms (*H*). (*Courtesy of Chicago Museum of Natural History; prepared by George Marchand under direction of I. G. Reimann.*)

appeared in the Silurian and died out in the Late Devonian, had almost all the space inside the outer wall filled by a vesicular growth of curved plates. One of the peculiar and interesting horn corals is a slipper-shaped form (*Calceola*), which is abundant in some of the European Devonian strata but is uncommon in this country (Fig. 8.21).

Compound corals were remarkable in their variety, beauty, and profusion. Two groups are distinguishable, one having relatively large individuals provided with well-developed radial walls, and the other (Tabulata) having small individuals that lack distinct radial walls but have numerous platforms. The first group differs from the solitary or horn corals only in the colonial mode of growth; indeed, there are some genera that include both types of growth. The individuals in many types of colonies are sufficiently separated to permit development of the normal cylindrical form of each coral (*Diphyphyllum, Cyathophyllum*). There are also many types in which the individuals were crowded so closely together that the cross section of each coral became polygonal (*Hex-*

agonaria, Phillipsastrea). The tabulate corals include a variety of forms, among which the honeycomb coral (*Favosites*) is most common and generally known (Figs. 8.19, 12.12).

At many places in the shallow inland seas, the corals grew in profusion and were largely instrumental in building reefs. Some of these are now seen in the Devonian areas of Michigan, Wisconsin, Indiana, Ohio, and Kentucky. One region that is famous because of the beauty and variety of silicified fossil corals that have been collected from it is located near Louisville, Kentucky. The coral reef chanced to lie in the river's path, and being harder than the adjacent rocks, it formed an obstruction that made rapids, known as the Falls of the Ohio.

Mississippian formations contain fewer types of corals and, in general, less numerous specimens than the Devonian, but several kinds are restricted to this part of the geologic column.

Pennsylvanian corals are about as common as Mississippian, but the species and most of the genera are different, horn corals being

Fig. 12.11 Reconstruction of Silurian corals and associated invertebrates. The model represents part of the Niagaran shallow sea bottom in Michigan. It shows especially large colonial corals (*A, Favosites; B, Halysites; C, Synaptophyllum*) and other typical forms of marine life: camerate crinoids (*D*), nautiloid cephalopods (*E, Phragmoceras; F,* close-coiled form), trilobites (*G, Illaenus; H, Arctinurus*), and brachiopods (*I, Pentamerus*). (*Courtesy of Chicago Museum of Natural History; prepared by George Marchand under direction of I. G. Reimann.*)

more numerous and widely distributed than the colonial kinds. One of the most common horn corals (*Lophophyllidium*) had a prominent central axis, which forms a spikelike projection in the center of the calyx. A colonial form (*Chaetetes*), which is distinguished by the very minute size of the closely packed tubes and by the massive growth of the colonies (to 3 feet in diameter), is an important guide fossil of Lower and Middle Pennsylvanian rocks (Fig. 10.22).

The Permian is noteworthy because of several new kinds of fossil corals, which resemble Paleozoic much more than Mesozoic types (Fig. 11.19).

Bryozoans

Few classes of marine invertebrates have a record of highly varied and long-sustained evolution that exceeds that of the bryozoans, yet, because of the minute size of the individuals and of many of the colonies, their importance is easily overlooked.

The oldest known bryozoans occur in Cambrian limestones of western Canada and central Texas, but only a few specimens have been found. In some Middle and Upper Ordovician deposits, especially certain limy shales, they are extraordinarily abundant, in both individuals and species (Fig. 12.13). America has yielded at least 74 genera and 392 species of Ordovician bryozoans. As compared with later bryozoan faunas, those of this time are characterized by the preponderance of massive colonial growths ("stony bryozoans"). This was the time of maximum development of bryozoans characterized by long tubes divided by numerous diaphragms.

Fig. 12.12 Restoration of Devonian corals and associated invertebrates from Michigan. Solitary corals (*A–E*) and colonial corals (*F–L*) predominate; other animals are crinoids (*M, N*), lacy bryozoan (*O*), nautiloid cephalopods (*P, Q*), trilobites (*R, S*), gastropod (*T*), and brachiopods (*U–W*). A few individually identified genera are (*A*) *Heliophyllum*, (*C*) *Siphonophrentis*, (*L*) *Hexagonaria*, (*R*) *Terataspis*, (*U*) *Stropheodonta*, (*V*) *Leptaena*, (*W*) *Atrypa*. (*Courtesy of Rochester Museum of Arts and Sciences; model prepared by George Marchand under direction of I. G. Reimann.*)

Some Silurian formations, especially those belonging to the lower and middle parts of the system, contain very abundant bryozoans, but large massive types are less common. There are numerous delicate branching colonies and the first important development of lacelike fronds. The American Silurian bryozoans number some 95 genera and 336 species.

The bryozoans of Devonian and later Paleozoic time are characterized by the dominance of delicate lacy and slender branching types. The variety is exceedingly great. Though the bryozoans are less conspicuous than most other invertebrate groups, they are by no means the least interesting or valuable in correlation of the rock formations. Some delicate twiglike growths had apertures arranged all around the branches, and some on one side only. A branching form with triangular cross section (*Prismopora*) is an important index

fossil in the Upper Mississippian and Lower and Middle Pennsylvanian rocks of the United States.

The lacelike types of bryozoans had the tiny cells of the individual animals arranged in rows along slender branches, which are connected at regular intervals by slender crossbars. Some genera carry two rows of cells to the branch, and others a larger number. The cell apertures all open on the same side of the colony, the opposite side being nonporiferous (Figs. 9.18, 9.19, 11.19, 12.13).

A peculiarity of some of the late Paleozoic bryozoans (chiefly Mississippian) was the development of special types of solid calcareous supports. The most important one of these is seen in *Archimedes*, which looks very much like a coarsely threaded screw. This screwlike axis supported a spirally arranged lacy bryozoan frond (Figs. 9.18, 9.19, 12.14).

Brachiopods

Brachiopods are particularly characteristic of Paleozoic rocks, for they were most abundant and varied during this era, whereas in Mesozoic and Cenozoic time, they were represented by only a few surviving stocks of rather simple type. More than 3,500 species are already known from Paleozoic rocks of North America. The evolution of the brachiopods along various lines is shown by (1) composition and structure of the shell, (2) articulation of the valves, (3) nature of the pedicle opening and method of attachment, (4) form and surface ornamentation of the shell, and (5) development of various internal structures.

The Cambrian brachiopods are generally small, mostly less than ½ inch in length and width. The simplest, most primitive shells pre-

dominate, for the unhinged shells, composed partly or wholly of lime phosphate, are much more numerous than those with hinged, calcareous valves. Some shells had nearly equal valves with an opening for the pedicle shared by both valves, a feature repeated in the earliest stage of various later brachiopods (Fig. 5.21). Described species of Cambrian brachiopods number at least 59 genera and 536 species, of which 45 genera and 346 species occur in North America.

The succeeding Paleozoic Systems also hold a good representation of these simple, unhinged brachiopods. The fact that they occur almost exclusively in the dark shaly formations indicates that they are specially adapted to this type of environment. They are "facies fossils" and may be expected to occur whenever the proper environment or facies of sedimentation occurs. The insignificant changes

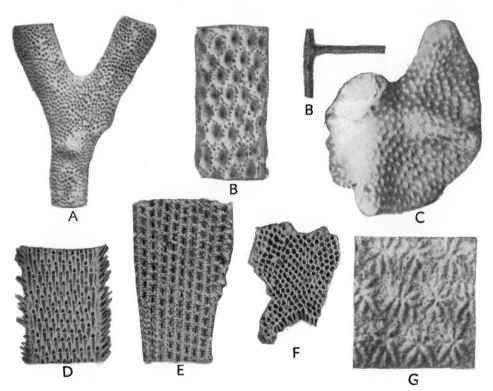

Fig. 12.13 Paleozoic bryozoans. Ordovician forms include *A* (*Hallopora*), *C* (*Monticuliporella*), and *G* (*Constellaria*); of Mississippian age are *D* (*Worthenopora*), *E* (*Fenestrellina*), and *F* (*Cyclopora*); and Pennsylvanian, *B* (*Rhombopora*). Enlarged, except *C* and one view of *B*, which are natural size.

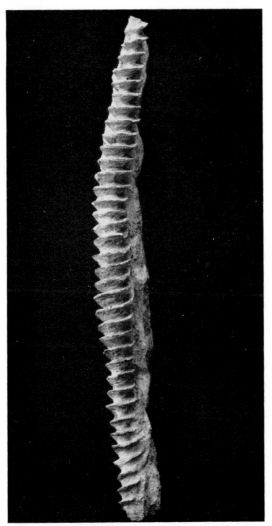

Fig. 12.14 Spiral support of the lacy bryozoan Archimedes. The lacy zoarial network originally attached to flanges of the spiral axis have been lost, for they are very fragile. Specimen from Warsaw Formation, Mississippian, at Warsaw, Illinois. Natural size. (*Courtesy of Chicago Natural History Museum.*)

shown by these shells, despite existence of the group for scores of millions of years, means that they have little value as indicators of any given geologic horizon. They furnish good examples of an animal stock that is very stable because unspecialized, yet adapted to an environment that always exists somewhere.

All main divisions of brachiopods are represented in Ordovician rocks. A marked advancement over Cambrian species is shown by (1) dominance of hinged calcareous over unhinged phosphatic shells; (2) increase in average size, variety, and numbers; (3) prevalence of strongly striated or plicated shells; (4) development of interlocking anterior margins, with fold and sinus; (5) abundance of concavo-convex shells; and (6) the appearance of specialized internal structures, such as spiral supports for the brachia. Several important groups, which are well represented throughout most of later Paleozoic time, make their appearance.

The group called *orthids* is characteristic of Ordovician rocks in which it reached its peak (Figs. 6.19, 12.15). The shells are generally wide-hinged and strongly plicated. Silurian and later Paleozoic strata contain many finely striated orthid shells of rounded outline.

Another very important group is that termed *strophomenids,* in which the shells are generally wide-hinged and flat, or concavo-convex. The most common Ordovician genera (*Rafinesquina, Leptaena,* and *Sowerbyella*) have a convex pedicle valve and concave brachial valve. This group was very abundant also in Silurian and later Paleozoic rocks (Figs. 6.19, 6.20, 10.22, 11.19).

Closely related *productids* are a dominant

Fig. 12.15 (Opposite page.) Representative Paleozoic brachiopods. Forms are all hinged, calcareous shells, natural size; some are figured in two or more views. Ordovician fossils include B (*Plaesiomys*), C (*Orthorhynchula*), and F (*Retrorsirostra*); Silurian, G (*Conchidium*) and H (*Pentamerus*); Devonian, D (*Platyrachella*) and E (*Gypidula*); Pennsylvanian, A (*Hustedia*).

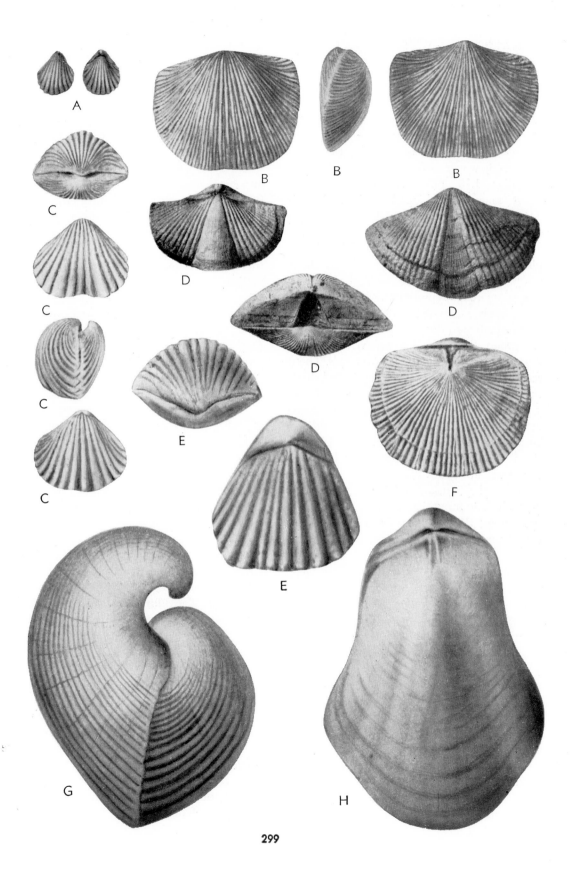

element in the Mississippian, Pennsylvanian, and Permian brachiopod faunas of the world. These shells have a very convex pedicle valve and concave brachial valve. Surface ornamentation typically consists of prominent radiating ribs, which may be crossed by concentric wrinkles, and there are commonly numerous long hollow spines, only the bases of which, however, usually appear on the fossils (Figs. 1.13, 10.22, 11.19J, 11.20). The largest known brachiopod (*Gigantella gigantea*), which attains a width of 12 inches or more, belongs to this group.

A third group (*rhynchonellids*), distinguished generally by strongly plicated shells with pointed beaks and no cardinal area, contains numerous representatives (especially *Rhynchotrema*), which are widespread in some formations (Fig. 12.15).

A group that includes several important Silurian index fossils is the *pentamerids*. These are mostly smooth, but some are plicated shells in which the interior is divided near the beaks by prominent converging partitions (most important genera, *Pentamerus, Stricklandinia, Conchidium, Gypidula*) (Figs. 7.22, 12.15).

The *spire-bearing brachiopods,* which appear first in Ordovician rocks, advanced greatly in the Silurian and in Devonian and later Paleozoic formations became a dominant type among the brachiopods. The most important genus (*Spirifer*) is a moderate- to very wide-hinged shell with plications radiating from the beaks and generally with a well-defined median depression (sinus) on the pedicle valve, and a corresponding elevation (fold) on the brachial valve. Internally, there are two spirally coiled brachial supports. The following evolutional changes are discerned: (1) plications in early forms (Silurian and most Devonian species) simple, undivided, absent on fold and sinus; (2) plications in intermediate forms (some Upper Devonian and most Mississippian species) simple, present on fold and sinus; (3) plications in late forms (Pennsylvanian, Permian), branching or arranged in bundles, present on fold and sinus; (4) modifications of shell structure and internal features that are made the basis of

separation into distinct genera. The great variety of shape and size in this group and its rapid evolution make many species very good index fossils (Figs. 8.19, 11.19, 12.15).

Two groups of highly specialized, peculiar-looking brachiopods lived in the Permian. One of them (*Prorichtofenia*) resembles a horn coral more than a brachiopod, for it has been strangely modified by its mode of attachment and by thickening of one of the valves. It is found in Texas, eastern and southern Asia, and southern Europe. The other (*Leptodus* and allied genera) has very prominent curving ridges and grooves on the inside of the shell, unlike any other brachiopod (Fig. 11.19). A reconstruction of a sea-bottom invertebrate assemblage adjacent to the western Texas Permian reefs shows numerous brachiopods and gives some idea of the variety of late Paleozoic representatives of the group (Fig. 12.16).

Pelecypods

The oldest known pelecypods occur in Middle Ordovician beds, where several genera suddenly make their appearance. These are rather archaic, generalized types that attained a climax in the later part of Ordovician time. They are characterized mainly by the presence of a large number of simple, similar teeth along the hinge line, which is a primitive type of dentition. Some of the characteristic types were prominently ribbed and had a large winglike expansion on one side of the beak. Others were much like the common living mussel. The Silurian contains fairly numerous fossil clams that differ mostly generically from those of the preceding period.

Pelecypods are abundant in many later Paleozoic formations, especially shales and sandstones. The species are somewhat different in each system, but the main types are very persistent and exhibit little real change. Several are smooth-shelled, rounded, subtriangular, or elongate in outline. Others have prominent concentric lines or plications radiating from the beak, and a few have a combination of these ornamental features. A primitive stage of development is indicated in the

Fig. 12.16 Reconstruction of Permian brachiopods and associated invertebrates. The model represents an area in western Texas. Brachiopods illustrated include spinose productids (*A*), richtofeniids (*B*), a *Neospirifer* (*C*), rhynchonellids (*D*), and terebratulids (*E*). (*Courtesy of L. B. Kellum and I. G. Reimann, University of Michigan; prepared by George Marchand with the guidance of G. A. Cooper.*)

majority of shells by unspecialized hinge structures, such as occur in the very youngest growth stages of many modern pelecypods.

Marine Devonian deposits of eastern North America, which are dominantly composed of shale and sandstone, contain a large pelecypod fauna, the description and illustration of which fill two large volumes of the *New York Geological Survey* (Fig. 12.17). Also, shaly, sandy, and oölitic beds of Mississippian, Pennsylvanian, and Permian age are characterized commonly by abundant clams (Fig. 11.19). The environment that produces oölite is evidently very congenial to the mollusks, as shown by many such limestones that contain especially numerous pelecypods and gastropods, whereas most limestones have more brachiopods, bryozoans, echinoderms, and corals than mollusks.

Gastropods

Gastropods are known from earliest Paleozoic time down to the present, their number and variety gradually increasing until they probably now enjoy their maximum vigor. More than 20,000 Recent species are known.

At the base of the Cambrian, the genera are small, archaic forms, that are mostly cap-shaped and exhibit only a slight tendency to coiling. Nevertheless, the gastropods are outranked only by trilobites and brachiopods in number of known Cambrian fossils. In some deposits of this period, straight-shelled pteropods were numerous. Coiled gastropods began to predominate in the later Cambrian, and in some formations they outnumber all other kinds of organisms.

During Ordovician time, there was a very great increase in the number, variety, and relative importance of the gastropods. In some of the Canadian strata, they afford the best index fossils available. Very prominent were the flat or low-spired shells, some with right-handed (*Ophileta*) and some with left-handed coils (*Maclurites, Lecanospira*). Moderately elevated, well-ornamented spiral shells (pleurotomariids) and some very high, screw-like spires (*Hormotoma*) are also present. The Mohawkian and Cincinnatian divisions also contain common representatives of this class, but they are by no means so important relatively. This is due largely to a tremendous increase in the number and variety of other invertebrates. The Ordovician was a time of considerable prominence of gastropods, however, as indicated by the occurrence of at least 700 American types (Fig. 6.19).

Silurian and later Paleozoic species are distinct from those of the Ordovician, but there is no very important change in type. The chief forms are coiled in a single plane (*Bellerophon* and allies) or an elevated spire (like *Pleurotomaria*), with a prominent notch or slit in the outer margin, and various coiled shells with entire margins (Figs. 7.22, 9.18, 10.22, 11.19, 12.18).

Fig. 12.17 Examples of Paleozoic fossil clams. Many Paleozoic pelecypods are much larger than those here illustrated. From the Devonian are *B* (*Phthonia*) and *E* (*Grammysia*); Pennsylvanian forms include *A* (*Leda*), *C* (*Pleurophorus*), *D* (*Aviculopecten*), and *F* (*Astartella*). Natural size.

Cephalopods

Two distinct groups of cephalopods are found in Paleozoic rocks, and they occur in nearly equal numbers. The first comprises the nautiloid shells, which predominate in older Paleozoic rocks. These are straight, curved, or coiled and are mainly distinguished by the simple, straight or gently curved sutures at the junctions of the inner chamber walls with the outer shell. The second group, known as ammonoids, have more complex sutures and develop a higher degree of ornamentation than is observed in the first. It probably had its beginning in Late Silurian time, advanced rapidly in the Pennsylvanian and Permian Periods, and achieved a remarkable culmination in the Mesozoic Era.

The evolutional advancement of the cephalopods is shown chiefly by (1) the form of the shell, (2) surface ornamentation, (3) shape of the aperture, and (4) nature of the sutures.

As regards the form of the shell, the perfectly straight, gently tapered type is most primitive, and the curved, loosely coiled, and tightly coiled types represent successively more advanced modes of growth. The tightly coiled shells may be divided into groups on the basis of the shape of their cross section or the extent to which the outer whorls are in contact with and cover the inner. The shape of the shell may range from very flatly discoidal to extremely thick and globular, the outer border or periphery being sharply pointed, rounded, flattened, or angulated. The cross section of a whorl similarly may vary from circular to quadrangular, polygonal, or crescentic. An abnormal shell form, seen in a few early Paleozoic and Mesozoic families, is a spiral, gastropod-like twisting or, more rarely, an erratic bending without definite plan.

Surface ornamentation consists of various sorts of ridges, nodes, or spines; of fine lines and granulation; and of color (which almost invariably is lost in fossilization). The majority of nautiloids are smooth, but the shells of many ammonoids are highly ornamented.

The aperture, not preserved in all fossils, is commonly simple and round but may be modified by shallow or deep indentations of the borders and by a beaklike projection of a part of the shell. The most highly modified apertures among the nautiloids are seen in Silurian and Devonian shells, which have the living chamber nearly closed by inbending edges of the aperture. Some Jurassic and Cretaceous ammonoids have very abnormal apertures.

The sutures are plain and smooth in the primitive nautiloids, and in modern *Nautilus;* they are only gently curved. A progressive change in the form of the sutures appears, especially among the ammonoids. From

Fig. 12.18 A few Paleozoic gastropods. A symmetrically coiled, frilled shell is shown in *A* (*Phragmolites,* Ordovician, ✕3); the others show common forms of conical spires, natural size (*B, Worthenia,* Pennsylvanian; *C, Gyroma,* Devonian; *D, Clathrospira,* Ordovician).

slightly curved they pass to distinctly wavy and in part angulated and then, by increasing crenulation, achieve a more and more complex pattern that is most extreme in some of the Mesozoic shells.

The sudden advent of a varied, well-advanced cephalopod fauna in basal Ordovician beds indicates the existence and gradual development of this important group in some region during earlier time. Small straight-shelled forms (*Volborthella, Salterella*), which occur in Lower Cambrian rocks, may be primitive cephalopods.

Nautiloids. Nautiloid cephalopods are numerous in some of the Ordovician formations, appearing commonly first in the Canadian Series. Straight (*Orthoceras, Endoceras*) and slightly curved (*Cyrtoceras*) shells greatly predominate, but there are several genera of loosely coiled and close-coiled shells. In one group (Lituitidae), there is evidence of the decadence of a former tightly coiled stock, for the shells are well coiled in the youthful stages but revert to the primitive straight form in the adult stage. In another (Plectoceratidae), the growth of the shell follows roughly the elevated spiral form of a gastropod, an even greater deviation from the typical cephalopod shell form. The Ordovician straight-shelled cephalopods are characterized by the large size of the tube (siphuncle), connecting the chambers by the filling of it in many genera with mineral deposits, and by the large size of some of the shells, estimated to have had a length up to 15 feet. The majority of these shells were smooth externally, but several bore transverse ribs, and in mid-Ordovician time some with longitudinal ridges also appeared. In none of the coiled cephalopods is there appreciable lateral overlapping of a whorl on the one next within, each part of the shell being therefore subcircular in cross section. There were upward of 350 species of cephalopods in the Ordovician of North America (Figs. 6.19, 12.19).

The culmination of nautiloid cephalopods was reached in Silurian time, when the greatest number and variety of these animals existed. On the average, they were not so large,

perhaps, as their predecessors. A peculiarity of several genera (*Trimeroceras, Phragmoceras,* Fig. 7.20) was the constriction of the aperture to an opening so narrow that movements of the animal must have been greatly hindered. Such specialization is a character indicating decline or abnormal deviation and presaging extinction of these branches of the nautiloid stock. The proportion of coiled shells was greatly increased in Silurian time, the number approximately equaling that of the straight and curved types. Before the close of the period, the first of the more complexly sutured cephalopods had appeared.

Among late Paleozoic nautiloids, we find the unprogressive, straight-shelled types almost as common as they had been in the Ordovician and Silurian. Some Mississippian shells from northern Arkansas and southern Oklahoma have a maximum diameter of nearly 8 inches and a complete length of more than 5 feet. The fact that these straight-shelled nautiloids persisted with so little change and survived almost all the more advanced forms reminds us again that the specialized products of evolution are in general the first to disappear whereas the unspecialized conservative types live longest. Coiled nautiloids were fairly common in each of the late Paleozoic Periods. There were several smooth-shelled species, but the ornamented types are most interesting and significant of evolutional change. Some of the Mississippian and Pennsylvanian shells have prominent nodes along the sides, and a few were of large size, attaining a diameter of nearly 18 inches.

Ammonoids. The first ammonoids have sutures that are nearly straight, classification with the ammonoids being indicated by other characters. The ammonoid stock is, of course, a derivative of the nautiloids, and features typical of the latter, such as relatively simple sutures, a small open space left by the first-formed whorl, and the structure of the tube (siphuncle) connecting the chambers, are found in the majority of Paleozoic ammonoids. All but a few are tightly coiled: some with whorls barely touching, others with outer

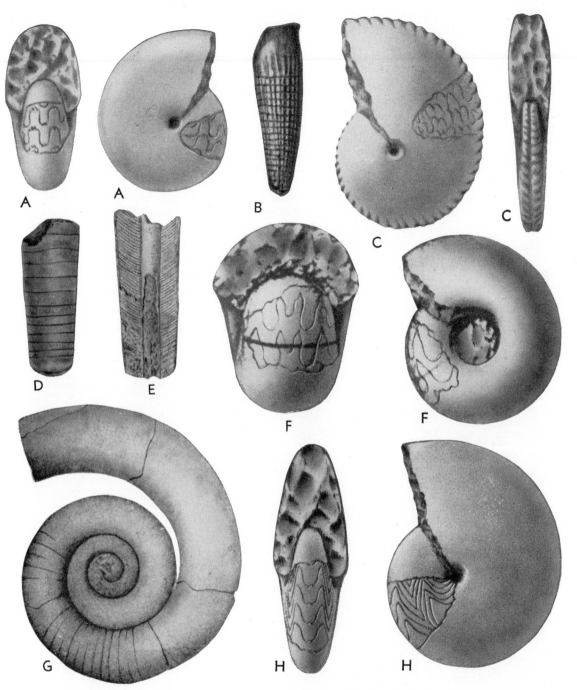

Fig. 12.19 Representative Paleozoic cephalopods. Simple-sutured shells include *B* (*Kionoceras*, Silurian), *D* (*Mooreoceras*, Pennsylvanian), and *E* (*Cameroceras*, Ordovician), all of which have straight shells; and *G* (*Tarphyceras*, Ordovician), a coiled form. Ammonoid cephalopods, characterized by moderately complex sutures, include three Pennsylvanian forms: *A* (*Eothalassoceras*), *F* (*Eoasianites*), and *H* (*Gonioloboceras*); and a Permian shell, *C* (*Artinskia*). Natural size.

whorls partly embracing the inner, and still others so highly involute that only the outermost whorl can be seen. Several Devonian and Mississippian genera (*Clymenia, Aganides, Gephyroceras*) have moderately curved and angulated sutures. Others (*Beloceras, Prolecanites*) show much more numerous wavy irregularities of the sutures. The sutures of some Pennsylvanian genera and of many Permian shells (*Medlicottia, Marathonites*) show division into subordinate crenulations. A few Permian ammonoids (*Cyclolobus, Waagenoceras*) have still more complicated sutures that foreshadow the remarkable types so abundant in Mesozoic rocks (Figs. 7.22, 7.23, 8.21, 10.22, 11.1, 11.21, 12.19).

Trilobites

As shown by studies of growth stages and by the order in geologic time of the develop-

ment of various adult characters, the features that chiefly mark evolution among trilobites are (1) position of sutures on the head shield, (2) nature and location of the eyes, (3) changes in the central lobe (glabella) of the head shield, (4) suppression or overdevelopment of various anatomical features, and (5) ornamentation.

Trilobites not only occur in the oldest known fossil-bearing beds but are the most abundant organisms of Cambrian age. Their complexity of structure and variety of form indicate clearly that the beginning of the trilobites must date far back into Precambrian time. Several hundred species have been described from the Cambrian, and it is estimated that over 1,000 undescribed species are contained in collections of the United States National Museum. As compared with later Paleozoic trilobites, Cambrian forms show

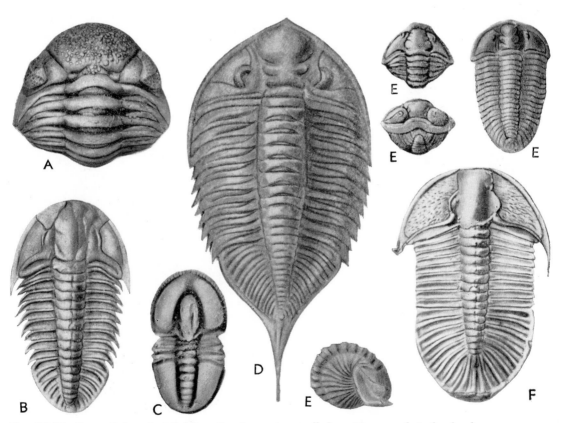

Fig. 12.20   Some Paleozoic trilobites. Specimens in enrolled position, so that the hard carapace protects the vulnerable underside: *A, Phacops,* Devonian; *E, Flexicalymene,* Ordovician. Cambrian genera: *B, Bathyuriscus; C, Eodiscus; F, Orria.* Silurian genus: *D, Dalmanites.* All natural size.

several distinguishing features: (1) Very small, larva-like genera, with subequal head and tail shields and only two or three thoracic segments, are common (agnostids, eodiscids, Fig. 12.20C). (2) A heterogenous group, characterized by a long body having numerous thoracic segments and a very small pygidium, is prominent (conocoryphids, olenellids, paradoxidids, olenids, Figs. 5.16, 5.21 to 5.23, 12.20B, F). (3) Species without eyes or with only simple eyes are numerous, and the majority of those with compound eyes have very small ones, set well away from the axial lobe. (4) The central head lobe commonly shows distinct transverse division, and the longitudinal three-lobed character of the carapace is always strongly defined. Some of the Lower Cambrian trilobites had very long spines, and several genera are distinguished by unusually large tail shields. In size, the trilobites of this period ranged from shells less than ¼ inch in length to more than 18 inches (*Paradoxides, Wanneria*).

Ordovician time marks the culmination of trilobites, for their remains are more abundant and varied in rocks of this period than in any others. Among noteworthy forms are small to medium-sized carapaces that have a relatively large head shield bearing a broad pitted brim and long backward-pointing spines (*Cryptolithus*). In one group (*Ampyx*), the head carries a prominent forward or upward projecting spine. Some types are long-bodied and fairly conservative (*Triarthrus*); others are specialized in the development of snoutlike anterior projections of the head (*Megalaspis, Hoplolichas*) or bizarre spinose ornamentation (*Acidaspis, Ceratocephala*) and decadent in the obsolescence or loss of typical features of the head and tail (*Illaenus, Bumastus*). In some genera, there is no trace of segmentation of the central head lobe, which may be indistinct. One form (*Cyclopyge*) shows a remarkable development of the eyes, which are expanded to cover the entire outer thirds of the head shield. Almost all the Ordovician trilobites were able to roll up, so as to conceal the ventral region, and many fossils in this position are found (Figs. 12.20, 12.21). The largest known trilobite (*Uralichas*) is from Ordovician strata in Portugal. It had a length of about 30 inches. Some American specimens (*Isotelus maximus*) attained a length of nearly 24 inches.

The Silurian history of the trilobites is marked mainly by the disappearance of earlier forms. There were only half as many families in the Silurian as in the Ordovician; the number of genera was reduced about one-half (99 to 47), and the number of species from about 390 to 180. One large group was conservative, another carried to an extreme the tendency to overdevelop certain features or to become spinose, and a third lost almost all trace of the fundamental trilobate plan of the shell (Fig. 12.22).

Among the Devonian and later trilobites, two groups may be differentiated. The general appearance in the one is that of a well-advanced but conservative trilobite, without frills, special ornamentation, or any unusual peculiarities and without marks of degeneration such as appear in several of the Silurian branches. *Dalmanites* and the abundant *Phacops* illustrate this group. The other is over-decorated and peculiarly specialized in various ways (Figs. 12.23, 12.24). Extreme development of spines is seen on head, body, and tail, and in one genus the central lobe of the head became very strongly bulbous. These abnormal types did not survive into the Mississippian, when only a few genera of the conservative group, all belonging to a single fam-

Fig. 12.21 Enlarged view of enrolled Flexicalymene, from the front. (*Courtesy of Chicago Natural History Museum.*)

Fig. 12.22 Silurian trilobites with nearly obsolete trilobation. The form farthest left, with pointed head and tail, is *Trimerus*, and the five specimens at the right with subequal large smooth head and tail pieces are *Bumastus*. Both genera illustrate an evolutionary trend toward simplification of the carapace form. (*Courtesy of Buffalo Museum of Science; prepared by George and Paul Marchand under the direction of I. G. Reimann.*)

ily, are found. The number is further reduced in the Pennsylvanian, and finally the last of the race is found in the Permian. The over-development in different ways and specialization that led to extinction are well illustrated by various branches of the trilobites, and the persistence of the conservative, unspecialized stock is seen in its survival to latest Paleozoic time (Figs. 8.20, 10.22, 12.20A).

Chelicerates

The chelicerates comprise two numerically unequal groups, both represented by living arthropods and both known as fossils in Paleozoic and younger rocks. The groups are named Merostomata and Arachnida. The merostomes have the longer paleontological record, for they make appearance in the Lower Cambrian and are known in each of the Paleozoic systems. They include extinct orders (Aglaspida, Eurypterida) and one to which the modern king crabs (*Limulus*) belong (Xiphosurida). The arachnids comprise the spiders and scorpions, which are vastly more numerous in kinds than the merostomes but, excepting scorpions and ticks, not known earlier than Pennsylvanian.

Peculiar arthropods known as sea spiders (Pycnogonida) have been classed with the chelicerates but now are considered to belong in a separate group. They occur in the Devonian but do not merit attention here other than notice that such animals exist.

Eurypterids. The eurypterids are an interesting group of extinct arthropods which include the largest animals of this phylum, measuring up to 9 feet in length. The body was elongate and provided with a thin chitinous segmented shell. The head region bore on its dorsal side an outer pair of large compound eyes and an inner pair of simple eyes; on the ventral side there were six pairs of appendages, some of which in certain forms were armed with pincers. The tail (*telson*) was long and pointed or flat. The presence of gills shows that the eurypterids were aquatic, and the structure of the appendages indicates that they were mostly mud crawlers, though some were probably good swimmers. Their antecedents, the aglaspids, are found associated with normal marine organisms in Cambrian and Ordovician rocks, and this group did not survive into the Silurian. Eurypterids, which are known from Ordovician to Permian, seem to have become adapted to a brackish-water environment, and their remains are found only exceptionally (probably by after-death displacement of skeletal parts from normal habitats) with marine fossils. Eurypterids in Pennsylvanian and Permian beds are fresh-water forms. A Silurian specimen and restoration of a Silurian eurypterid assemblage are illustrated (Figs. 12.25, 12.26).

Arachnids. The oldest known representatives of the arachnid group are Middle Silurian scorpions from Scotland, and only slightly younger are Upper Silurian scorpions from New York. These are almost identical in appearance with modern specimens, and scorpions from Devonian and Pennsylvanian rocks are little different (Fig. 10.23). The Silurian forms are found with marine invertebrates and probably were aquatic, whereas those of Pennsylvanian time evidently had become adapted to life on land, breathing air.

Arachnids other than scorpions comprise 15 orders, of which 4 are confined to Paleozoic time. Although all are very loosely designated as spiders, some (such as ticks and pseudoscorpions) are not much like the true spiders (Araneida), which are one of the 12 arachnid orders that are known as Paleozoic fossils. Thus, both broadly and

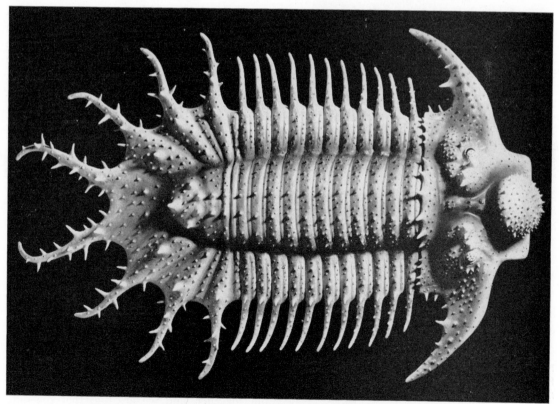

Fig. 12.23 Largest known Devonian trilobite. This species, *Terataspis grandis,* which attains a length of approximately 21 inches, is very bizarre in the shape of the head and tail, as well as the spikelike extensions of the thoracic segments. (*Courtesy of Buffalo Museum of Science; reconstruction prepared by Paul Marchand under direction of I. G. Reimann.*)

narrowly, spiders are an ancient stock (Fig. 12.27).

Crustaceans

Crustaceans are almost exclusively aquatic arthropods, most of which live in the sea. They are distinguished by various structural characters that are only suggested here by citing more or less familiar examples of the group—lobsters, crabs, crayfishes, shrimps, barnacles. Geologically most important, especially in Paleozoic rocks where some other common types of crustaceans are absent, are

Fig. 12.24 A Devonian trilobite with prominent faceted eyes. This fossil belongs to the genus *Odontochile;* it was collected from the Grand Tower Limestone of southern Illinois. The upper photograph, showing enlargement of the eye, is ×5; the lower figure is a view of the trilobite from the rear, ×1. (*Courtesy of Chicago Museum of Natural History.*)

abundant kinds of minute bivalved forms belonging to the subclass named Ostracoda.

Ostracodes. The average size of ostracodes is expressed in terms of length of the carapace; this is approximately 2 millimeters, the range in length of most species being from 0.5 to 4 millimeters. Mostly they are ovoid in outline, but sharp angles may be present. Some are smooth and gently rounded, others ornamented with granules, nodes, ridges, pits, or spines, and still others marked by prominent projecting frills. In Paleozoic formations, they range from Lower Ordovician to topmost fossiliferous beds of the Permian, and depending on how some Cambrian fossils are classified, ostracodes may be represented there also. Because the ostracodes are abundant in many strata and generally different from layer to layer, they are very useful for making correlations (Fig. 12.28).

Other crustaceans. Shrimplike fossils and some closely resembling crayfishes are well known in Pennsylvanian rocks, and these are classed with crustaceans, but some from the Cambrian now are thought to be closer to the trilobites than to crustaceans (Fig. 12.27). A great variety of bivalved crustaceans that differ from the ostracodes are distributed from Cambrian to Permian, and even general characters of these here must be overlooked, except for mention of a host of crustaceans known as estheriids that are world-wide in briny-water environments such as inland lagoons of Permian time. These are valuable fossils because others are lacking. Barnacles (Cirripedia) are very ancient crustaceans; fossils belonging to this group are distributed through the Paleozoic from Ordovician into the Mesozoic.

Insects

A development of Paleozoic life that attracts special attention is the first appearance of insects. This group has expanded in later earth history until at present there are more species of insects than of all other kinds of animals put together, and we are told that the only serious competitors of man are the insects. It is perhaps fortunate that the size of modern insects is not that of certain individuals of

Pennsylvanian time, when 4-inch cockroaches scurried over the ground and dragonflies with a 30-inch wing spread droned through the air (Figs. 2.10, 10.23, 12.27).

The most primitive and one of the most important orders of late Paleozoic insects (Palaeodictyoptera) is characterized by the very archaic structure of the wings, which have a type of venation matching almost exactly the hypothetical ancestral insect wing. To this group belong the first definitely known insects, which occur in rocks of Early Pennsylvanian age. Before the extinction of the primitive insects in Permian time, the order gave rise to several transitional stocks which in turn introduced existing orders.

The cockroaches (Blattoidea) were the most common type of insect in the Pennsylvanian Period (some 800 species) and were numerous in the Permian. The order did not die out at the close of Paleozoic time but, on the contrary, has persisted to the present day, taking rank as the oldest existing insect group that is represented by fossils. In view of his antiquity of ancestry and once large size and numbers, the despised modern cockroach is entitled to hold his head high among insect associates.

The Pennsylvanian dragonflies are assigned to a more primitive order than that to which the living representatives of this group belong, the difference being mainly in wing

Fig. 12.25 Fossil eurypterid from Upper Silurian rocks near Buffalo, New York. The outline of the body with its head region (cephalothorax) and segments back to the spikelike telson, as well as the appendages, is clearly shown; also there are traces of carbonaceous residue. The species is *Eurypterus remipes lacustris*. (*Courtesy of American Museum of Natural History.*)

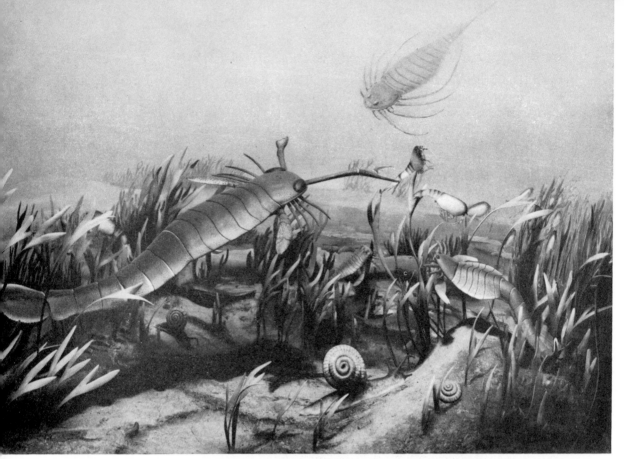

Fig. 12.26 Eurypterid group from the Late Silurian. This restoration shows different kinds of eurypterids moving about in and above clustered sea weeds. (*Courtesy of Chicago Natural History Museum; model prepared by George Marchand under direction of I. G. Reimann.*)

structure. About a dozen fossil species are known.

The most remarkable occurrence of Paleozoic insect fossils yet found in the world is in Lower Permian strata a few miles south of Abilene, Kansas. More than 12,000 specimens have been collected here, and very much has been learned from them concerning the early differentiation and evolution of the insects.

Worms

Generally speaking, no class of animals is less adapted to preservation in the fossil state than the worms, because their bodies as a rule lack hard parts. This is unfortunate, for the extreme variety of modern worms and the abundance of species dwelling in the sea suggest that the paleontologic record would be much richer if these organisms were well

represented. Fossils in this group include (1) pincer-like or variously shaped tooth-bearing jaw parts (scolecodonts) of annelid worms; (2) calcareous tubes secreted as a covering that is generally attached to some shell or other foreign substance; (3) borings or trails made in sediments on the sea floor; and possibly (4) the microscopic, generally spined objects (conodonts) that are variously interpreted as mouth parts of worms or dermal structures of fishes.

Scolecodonts and conodonts are surprisingly abundant fossils in some Ordovician and Silurian strata, and the fact that the various kinds discovered at different horizons are readily distinguishable makes this group of fossils useful as stratigraphic markers. Most of the specimens are less than 1 millimeter in length. Fossil worm tubes are known from Ordovician and Silurian rocks. Certain zones

Fig. 12.27 Pennsylvanian arthropods from Mazon Creek nodules in Illinois. These fossils come from a locality in northern Illinois about 50 miles southwest of Chicago that has yielded many hundreds like them. They are important in furnishing evidence of life on the lands, especially organisms that are not commonly found preserved. Here illustrated are crustaceans (*A, D, H, I*); myriapods, or "thousand legs" (*B, E*); insect wing (*C*); spider (*F*); primitive insect (*G*). (*Courtesy of Chicago Natural History Museum.*)

in the Cambrian are specially characterized by an abundance of vertical borings (*Skolithos*) of rather small diameter that generally occur in sandstone. Among guide fossils of the Lower Silurian sandstones of the Appalachian region are markings interpreted as the trails of marine worms (*Arthrophycus*).

One remarkable exception to the rule concerning preservation of these soft-bodied creatures is found in a large collection of fossils from the Middle Cambrian Burgess Shale in British Columbia. Among other fossils is a profusion of worms, flattened by pressure but

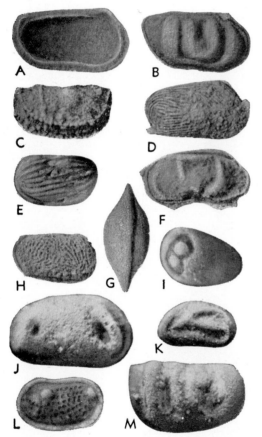

Fig. 12.28 Some representative Paleozoic ostracodes. Choice of the fossils illustrated is based on showing average nature of forms found together, *A–G* being from a Mississippian formation and *H–M* from a Devonian formation. All are side views of the carapace, except *G*, which is an edge view showing the hinge line and unequal valves; *A* shows the interior of a valve. Magnifications ×10 to ×15. (*After Geis, Morey, and Wilson.*)

showing body segments, legs, delicate hairlike appendages, and even internal structures. This amazing glimpse of a highly developed assemblage of soft-bodied marine organisms serves to emphasize the conclusion that a host of similar animals, including the worms, existed in early Paleozoic time.

Echinoderms

Varied sorts of echinoderms, which are exclusively marine invertebrates, are abundant in Paleozoic formations, especially from Lower Ordovician upward. The attached forms, which grew fixed by a stem, are the most common and useful as guide fossils (Fig. 12.29). Of the three classes of stemmed echinoderms, cystoids, which are the most primitive, occur in Cambrian rocks; the budlike blastoids and highly organized crinoids make their appearance in Ordovician formations.

Cystoids. The cystoids appeared first in the Cambrian and attained maximum numbers and variety in the Ordovician (21 genera, 59 species) and Silurian (28 genera, 113 species). Only a very few cystoids are known from beds younger than Silurian (Fig. 12.30A). They are therefore characteristic of the older Paleozoic strata.

Blastoids. Blastoids are distinguished by their five-sided, beautifully symmetrical, budlike form and their generally prominent, finely cross-striated, food grooves. The average size of the calyx is small. These echinoderms were unimportant in early Paleozoic times. They advanced during the Devonian and increased remarkably in numbers and variety in the Mississippian, but after this sudden climax they virtually disappeared. A few blastoids occur in the Early Pennsylvanian rocks of North America, and several species lingered on into the Permian.

One of the commonest Devonian blastoids (*Nucleocrinus*) has about the shape and size of a small hickory nut and is distinguished by very narrow food groove areas. The most important genus in the Mississippian beds (*Pentremites*) is broad at the base, and the sides slope upward toward the top (Figs. 9.18C, 12.30, 12.31G). Its maximum de-

Fig. 12.29 Crinoidal limestone from Middle Devonian of western Illinois. The fragments of crinoids that form a considerable part of this rock are nearly all parts of stems, some with segments still joined together and others consisting of individual segments. Several of these latter show the fine radial ridge-and-groove pattern of the articulating surfaces and the central opening, which characterizes all such stems. Fossils other than crinoids are bryozoans, marked for identification (*A–E*). Magnification ×4. (*Courtesy of C. W. Collinson, Illinois Geol. Survey.*)

velopment in both species and number of individuals is found in the Upper Mississippian rocks. Certain beds of this age in southeastern Missouri, southern Illinois, and western Kentucky contain almost perfect specimens of blastoids that may be collected by thousands.

Crinoids. The structural characters that are of chief importance in classification and in the evolution of the crinoids are (1) the plan of the plates in the dorsal part of the calyx

and (2) the number, method of branching, and structure of the arms.

The first definitely known crinoids occur in Lower Ordovician rocks and are common in some higher portions of the system (Fig. 6.19). Several are distinctive index fossils. Each of the main orders of crinoids, except the articulates, to which most modern crinoids belong, is present in Ordovician faunas, which contain about 125 described crinoid

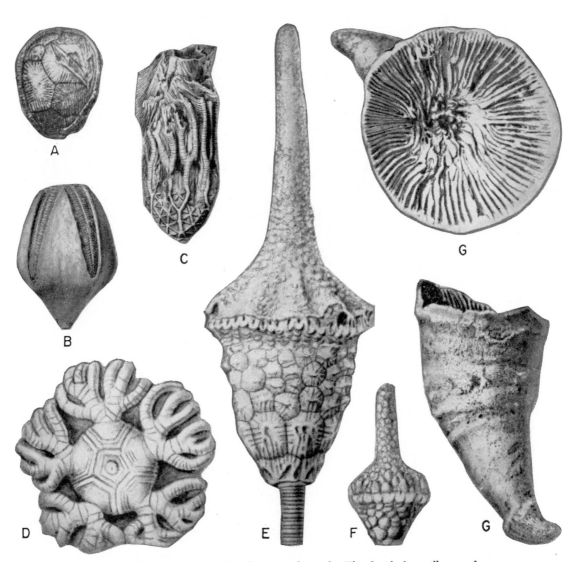

Fig. 12.30 Representative Paleozoic echinoderms and corals. The fossils here illustrated include a cystoid (*A, Pseudocrinites,* Devonian), a blastoid (*B, Pentremites,* Mississippian), camerate crinoids (*C, Glyptocrinus,* Ordovician; *D, Platycrinites,* Mississippian; *E, Teleiocrinus,* Mississippian; and *F, Batocrinus,* Mississippian), and a horn coral (*G, Zaphrentis,* Devonian). Natural size.

Fig. 12.31 Early Mississippian (Osagian) crinoids and other echinoderms. This restoration shows representatives of each main group of late Paleozoic crinoids: Flexibilia (*A, Forbesiocrinus*), with highly mobile arms incurved at tips; Inadunata (*B, Cyathocrinites; E, Barycrinus*), with base of arms not incorporated in calyx; and Camerata (*C, Uperocrinus; D, Dichocrinus; F, Gilbertsocrinus*), with arm bases included in calyx. Other echinoderms are blastoids (*G, Pentremites*) and ophiuroids or brittle stars (*H*). (*Courtesy of Chicago Natural History Museum; model prepared by George Marchand under direction of I. G. Reimann.*)

species. Silurian time witnessed a notable advance in the number and variety of crinoids (about 300 species), all of which differ from antecedent forms (Figs. 7.22, 7.23). Some were very peculiarly specialized. In one (*Eucalyptocrinites*), the arms fitted into partitioned spaces formed by solid calcareous walls raised above the calyx; in another (*Crotalocrinites*), the arms jointed laterally to form a broad flexible network; and in still another (*Petalocrinus*), the arm structures were developed into solid petal-like projections extending outward from the tiny calyx. All these types occur in the Silurian of the central United States and of northern Europe. In some of the Silurian deposits, there are numerous specimens of minute crinoids (*Pisocrinus*) having calices no larger than a pea.

The maximum development of the crinoids clearly belongs to the later part of Paleozoic time, especially the Mississippian Period (Figs. 9.18, 9.20, 12.30, 12.31).

The most specialized and abundant crinoid class in later Paleozoic time was the so-called camerate crinoid, distinguished by its proportionately large, solidly roofed calyx composed of many plates. In the Early Mississippian Epoch, an almost explosive expansion of the camerates made them the outstanding element in marine invertebrate life. At this time the shallow seas of the central Mississippi Valley were a vast "sea-lily" garden, the remains of crinoid skeletons serving to compose the larger part of limestone strata 200 to 500 feet thick and covering tens of thousands of square miles. More than 400 different species have been described from this region. Some had small, delicate plates and very slender, feathery arms; others had a large calyx composed of thick heavy plates and were variously ornamented with knobs and spines. A variety of specialized forms is seen. Advanced evolution is indicated in several types by reduction in the number of plates in the basal series, the normal number, five, being reduced to three or even two. Some types had elliptical stem segments and the stem was twisted.

From the standpoint of usefulness of these fossils in identification of the stratigraphic divisions in which they occur, it is interesting to observe that most of the species and even some genera are very short-lived. Thus, most of the earliest Mississippian crinoid species disappeared before the beginning of the succeeding stage, and in the latter there are successive zones in which less than 5 per cent of the species persist from one zone to the next. This short vertical range is characteristic of complexly organized, rapidly evolving organisms. The only difficulty in making largest use of the crinoids in correlation of beds is that the calices, which generally are necessary for identification of species, are commonly broken into separate plates and scattered. Except in a few localities, complete crinoid "heads" are uncommon.

North America furnishes some of the most famous crinoid-collecting places in the world. The best Devonian crinoids come from New York, Michigan, and along the Ohio River near Louisville, Kentucky. A slab of Lower Devonian limestone from eastern New York, in the Peabody Museum at Yale University, shows more than 300 complete crinoid calices. Most prolific of all are some Mississippian localities, especially near Burlington, Iowa, and Crawfordsville, Indiana. Many remarkable slabs have been collected in central Iowa, near the little town of Le Grand. Chief foreign areas are in England, Belgium, and the Rhineland and near Moscow, Russia.

Starfishes and echinoids. Starfishes are known as fossils in Paleozoic rocks beginning in Ordovician deposits. Their presence and comparatively high degree of development are interesting, but this group of echinoderms is not important in any of the fossil faunas (Fig. 12.31*H*).

The echinoids, or sea urchins, were represented in the Ordovician by a single genus (*Bothriocidaris*) having a small globular shell and in the Silurian by four known genera. The ancient echinoids are characterized chiefly by the large number of columns of plates in the shell. The time of great abundance and differentiation of the echinoids was in the Mesozoic Era.

Plates and spines of sea urchins are commonly found in many formations from Devonian to Permian in age, but complete specimens of the test are generally rare. Worthy of special mention are plates and spines from the Upper Devonian of Iowa, which are perhaps more highly and peculiarly specialized than in any other known echinoid. These plates overlapped one another like shingles on a roof, and the spines, shaped like inverted collar buttons with hexagonal bases, fitted together to form a secondary armor outside the real shell. Some of the Mississippian, Pennsylvanian, and Lower Permian strata contain numerous elongate echinoid spines, with a variety of ornamental spinelets on many of them. The polygonal plates commonly have a large rounded boss in the middle, marking the place of attachment of one of the large movable spines. Smaller spine bases occur on the outer borders of the plates. Occasionally a complete test is found, most frequently in some of the Mississippian formations. The St. Louis Limestone is particularly known for an echinoid that, as suggested by the name *Melonechinus,* strikingly resembles in form a small cantaloupe.

Graptolites

Graptolites are an interesting extinct group of organisms known only from Paleozoic rocks and almost entirely restricted to the Ordovician and Silurian. They have much importance for purposes of correlation and age determination of the rocks containing them.

Classification of the graptolites in main divisions of the animal kingdom long has been a subject of debate. At different times they have been grouped with the coelenterates, bryozoans, and still other divisions. Now, largely as the result of studies on exceptionally well-preserved specimens that are not distorted by compression, their affinity with some types of living hemichordates (close to the Chordata, which contains the vertebrates) has been reasonably established. Hence, the graptolites are placed much higher in evolutionary progression than the coelenterates.

Remains of graptolites are extraordinarily abundant in black shales that contain few other kinds of fossils. A few occur in limestone. Accurate correlation of graptolite-bearing deposits, even on opposite sides of the earth, as in England, United States, and Australia, is possible (1) because the animals, attached to seaweeds or supported by a float of their own construction, were transported widely by oceanic currents and (2) because there was comparatively rapid evolution of different species, so that beds only a few feet apart vertically may be characterized by entirely different graptolite assemblages (Fig. 6.23).

Evolutionary changes among the graptolites are seen in (1) the form of the colonies and (2) the shape and arrangement of the cups. The lower, and therefore older, graptolite zones show species in which numerous branchings are characteristic, while successively appearing later types have branches reduced to 16, 8, 4, 2, and finally 1. Primitively, also, the branches appear to have hung more or less directly downward; in later, more advanced genera, they grew horizontally outward, and, finally, turning upward, the rows of cups were established in a position back to back. There is, therefore, a tendency in colony form to pass from many branches to a single one and from downward-hanging branches, each with a single row of cups, to those with a double row of cups growing back to back. The simplest cups are short cylindrical tubes growing obliquely outward from the initial cup. In specialized types, these turn at right angles to the stem or even form an S-shaped bend, and part of the tube may be variously constricted.

The graptolites first appeared in the Middle Cambrian and are widespread in the uppermost Cambrian rocks. The Ordovician marks the heyday of graptolite abundance and differentiation, and in the shale deposits where they occur, they are much the most important among all fossils. There are 67 genera and more than 475 species of graptolites in Ordovician rocks of North America. By Silurian time, they had greatly declined in numbers but are still important. Here occur some of the most peculiar and highly specialized examples. In America, about 35 genera and 175 species of Silurian graptolites are recorded. A few stragglers, consisting of the most long-lived, primitive stocks, lived on into Early Mississippian time.

VERTEBRATES

Fishes

The earliest known fish remains, representing the very primitive group called *ostracoderms*, occur in Ordovician sandstone (Harding) of eastern Colorado and Wyoming. The fossils consist of bony fragments that reveal little of the nature of the fishes themselves, but in later Paleozoic strata, both marine and fresh-water species are represented by fairly complete skeletons. The Silurian rocks contain scattered bony spines that were borne by some of the early sharklike fishes.

The Devonian Period is often termed the Age of Fishes. This does not mean that fishes reached the peak of their career at this time or that they exceeded in number and variety other kinds of life. Rather, for the first time fishes became well represented in the fossil record, and because of their great advancement in the evolutionary scale over any of the invertebrates, they may properly be termed the dominant animals of the period. The fishes are the first animals provided with cartilaginous or bony internal structures, a central nervous system, and other specialized characters that distinguish the vertebrates. For this reason and because the higher vertebrates were undoubtedly derived from them, the Paleozoic fishes are of special importance. Neither pale-ontologic nor embryologic evidence, however, indicates the exact mode of transition from invertebrate ancestral stock to fish, and we are left to infer relationships from similarities of structure and the geologic order of appearance of the successively higher types of life.

Ostracoderms. The oldest fairly complete remains of fishes come from beds (Downton-ian) that are variously classed as uppermost Silurian or lowermost Devonian. Since almost all occur in nonmarine or estuarine deposits, it is reasonable to conclude that the first verte-brates began their existence in waters of the land and only later entered the seas. The best fossils have been found in the British Isles, Norway, Spitsbergen, and eastern Greenland. They all belong to the bony-plated group of primitive jawless fishes called *ostracoderms*, the largest of which was about 12 inches long. Several types have been discovered, but the most common forms were distinguished by

the well-armored head region, behind which was a fishlike trunk and tail covered by bony plates and scales. Formerly, it was supposed that fishes initially had only cartilaginous skeletal parts and acquired bony structures gradually in the course of their evolution. The fact that the most primitive fishes have abundant bone does not agree well with this idea, and modern judgment is that fishes pro-vided with cartilaginous skeletons, like the sharks, have evolved in the direction of los-ing their inheritance of bony hard parts. The advanced nature of sharks is shown by well-developed jaw structure and other features.

Placoderms. Next, we may give attention to the so-called *placoderm* fishes, which had a strong bony armor in the head region but differ from ostracoderms in the well-devel-oped articulation of their jaws (Figs. 8.23, 12.32). Also, some of this group attained large size, total length being as much as 30 feet. A few possessed very stout bony spines at the

Fig. 12.32 Devonian placoderm (above) and modern air-breathing actinopterygian fish. The placoderm, shown as a restoration, is *Dinichthys*, with heavily armored head region (jointed at the neck) that reached a length of 10 feet, the whole fish having an estimated length up to 30 feet. The modern air-breathing fish is a ganoid type (*Polypterus*) from Africa, which ranges in length to 3 feet. (*Courtesy of American Museum of Natural History.*)

Fig. 12.33 Restoration of primitive ray-finned (actinopterygian) fish from Devonian rocks. This is *Cheirolepis*, which lived in fresh waters. One-half natural size. (*Courtesy of American Museum of Natural History.*)

front edge of the fins, strengthening them and causing them to project rigidly from the body. The tail was asymmetrical, like that of living sharks. The most peculiarly specialized placoderms were a group of jointed-neck fishes called *arthrodires,* in which the front part of the armored head was united by a ball-and-socket joint with the back part; thus the head was freely movable up and down on the trunk. Most of the placoderms evidently inhabited fresh waters, but some were adapted to a brackish-water environment, and a few are found in marine deposits. All but one group (Acanthodii) became extinct before Mississippian time, and the last of the assemblage disappeared in Permian time.

Sharks. True sharks and their close relatives the rays first appear in Jurassic deposits, but several kinds of sharklike fishes loosely classifiable as sharks are recognized in Devonian-to-Permian marine deposits (Fig. 8.22). Mostly they are represented by teeth, from which it is inferred that the remainder of the skeleton had largely lost its primitive bony structure.

Bony Fishes. The *bony fishes* (Osteichthyes), which comprise all higher types having advanced jaw structure, bony skeleton, lungs or air bladder, well-developed fins, and a body covering of scales, are important elements of late Paleozoic fish faunas. They include two main groups: (1) the lobe-finned fishes, or crossopterygians, of which the lung fishes are an offshoot, and (2) the ray-finned fishes, or actinopterygians.

The lobe-finned group is distinguished chiefly by the limblike appearance of the pectoral and pelvic fins, which have a fleshy middle portion supported by bones resembling those of the limbs of land vertebrates (Fig. 2.5). The body is covered by scales, which have a bony lower layer and a superficial layer of shiny enamel (cosmoid type). The teeth are conical in shape and commonly show the peculiar complexly folded "labyrinthine" internal structure seen in the Paleozoic amphibians. It is very probable that these fishes, which appeared in Early Devonian

time, possessed lungs like those of the modern lung fishes, and the firm conclusion is reached that this type of fish is the ancestral stock of the amphibians and higher vertebrates.

The ray-finned fishes are distinguished by structure of the fins, which lack bony supports. Their scales differ from those of lobe-finned fishes in having a proportionally much thicker enamel layer (ganoid type), although the scales of modern forms (including all game fishes) are thin and flexible. Some (*Polypterus*) have air sacs suited for air-breathing but these are not classified as true lung fishes (Dipnoi), which are crossopterygians. The extremely varied assemblage of living bony fishes (teleosts), which comprise more than 90 per cent of all existing species of fishes, are the most highly organized, and they are equally adapted for life in the seas and waters on land. They are descendants of the Paleozoic ray-finned fishes, which first appear in Devonian rocks (Figs. 12.32, 12.33).

Amphibians

The first known land vertebrates appeared in late Paleozoic time, the most ancient fossil indication of this class being footprints of a three-toed animal, doubtless an amphibian, in Upper Devonian rocks of Pennsylvania and skeletons in Devonian deposits of northeastern Greenland. The amphibians belong next above fishes in the evolutional scale. Modern amphibians include animals that live in water a good deal or all of the time (salamanders, newts) and also animals that are exclusively air breathers in adult life (frogs, toads).

The Paleozoic amphibians differ especially from those of the present day in the presence of a covering of plates on the head, which in the larger forms was a heavy bony armor. Accordingly, they are commonly called *stegocephalians,* the name meaning "roofed head." All these amphibians had relatively flat, generally broad heads with eyes directed upward and the mouth very wide. A well-developed tail is invariably present, although it is relatively short in a few forms (as *Cacops*).

The early, more primitive types were

animals having short, weak legs and laterally flattened tails that functioned as an aid in swimming. Some of the Paleozoic amphibians were only 1 or 2 inches long, but some forms were as large as a crocodile. There was a considerable variety of these animals in Pennsylvanian and Permian times. Some were ponderous and evidently very sluggish, waddling about in a slow, lumbering fashion; others were active, lizard-like creatures with lighter bodies and well-developed limbs; some were probably very capable swimmers; and a few were entirely legless, snakelike forms. The stegocephalians lived in the fresh waters and on the lands. Probably most of them were carnivorous, judging by the nature of the teeth, feeding on invertebrates, small fishes, and other amphibians (Fig. 12.34).

One of the most prominent groups of stegocephalians, called *labyrinthodonts*, show intricately infolded structure of the enamel of the teeth, a peculiarity that is noted in Devonian lobe-finned fishes. The labyrinthodonts attained the maximum known size among amphibians, some having a broad, bony head 4 feet long and a total length of about 15 feet. The skull in these animals was unusually heavy and solid, and the breast was covered by three large, thick bony plates.

An interesting feature that is shown very clearly in Paleozoic amphibians is an opening on the top of the skull behind and midway between the eye orbits. This marks the position of a third eye (so-called pineal eye). The aperture occurs also in primitive fishes, many fossil reptiles, and one living reptile. As a vestigial organ, this eye is present in all higher vertebrates, including man.

The stegocephalians probably originated in Devonian time. Skeletal remains are known in rocks of Mississippian age in Europe, but in America they have not yet been found in beds older than Pennsylvanian, which have yielded some 90 species of these animals. They continued as an important element in the land fauna of Early Permian time, but rapid increase in the number of reptiles pushed them into a subordinate place. Stegocephalians were rare in the later Permian, and they disappeared in the Triassic Period.

Reptiles

The most highly developed animals of later Paleozoic time are the reptiles. Reptiles, like amphibians and fishes, are cold-blooded, and in skeletal structure the more primitive reptiles can hardly be differentiated from certain stegocephalians. From an evolutional standpoint, however, the advancement of reptiles over amphibians is almost comparable to that of fishes over invertebrates. This improvement is seen mainly in the nature and mode of development of the egg. In amphibians and fishes, the eggs are necessarily laid in water.

Fig. 12.34 Restoration of a small Pennsylvanian amphibian (Diplovertebron). (*Courtesy of Chicago Natural History Museum.*)

There is virtually no stored food material, and the almost embryonic newly hatched young are required to fend for themselves. Among reptiles, structures are introduced in the egg which, for the first time, make the animal independent of water as a surrounding medium during at least the early stages of development. This is accomplished by the presence in the egg of an outer protective covering or shell but mostly by the development of two membranes within the shell. One of these membranes (*amnion*) serves as a sort of water bag over the delicate embryo, preventing its drying up, and the other (*allantois*) is a sac, well supplied with blood vessels, which functions as a respiratory organ, the air passing readily through the porous outer shell. Food during embryonic growth is supplied by yolk substance within the egg. The significance of these structures is exceedingly great as regards conquest of the lands by vertebrate life, for the reptiles and their descendants (birds and mammals) were liberated from dependence on aquatic surroundings for growth in the egg and first life stages after birth. A few reptiles give birth to fully formed young.

The primitive, first-known reptiles, in rocks of Pennsylvanian age, were much like amphibians, for the limbs were short, hardly lifting the squat, plump body above ground. The head was armor-plated like that of the stegocephalians. The tail was generally long, the hand and foot five-fingered, and the body probably scale-covered but not armored. The teeth were mostly large, sharply pointed, and in some species distinctly curved backward, of use in catching and holding flesh. Such characters certainly were not universal, however, for some well-known Pennsylvanian reptiles (Fig. 10.23) were light-limbed lizard-like animals that probably were quite agile. Most of the late Paleozoic reptiles were certainly carnivorous, but a few had rounded, blunt teeth that were not adapted for flesh-eating.

An interesting Permian fossil that so combines structural characters of amphibians and reptiles as to make its classification very doubtful is *Seymouria* (Fig. 11.17). This animal is not actually a connecting link that is ancestral to true reptiles because undoubted reptiles of Pennsylvanian age are known.

The amphibian-like Pennsylvanian and Early Permian reptiles (cotylosaurs) are the stem from which, at about the beginning of Permian time, branched other reptilian types with higher, more lightly built skulls; longer legs; and variously different skeletal characters.

Many of the Early Permian reptiles were evidently sluggish creatures, but others were moderately active (Fig. 12.35). Judging from general form and especially from characters of limbs and teeth, some waddled about in the shallow streams or swampy places, probably feeding on invertebrates and grubbing succulent roots and stems. Others suggest the

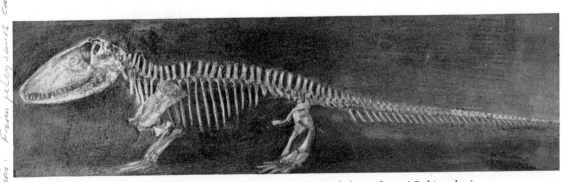

Fig. 12.35 Skeleton of a Permian reptile from Texas. The animal shown here (*Ophiacodon*) is a near relative of the fin-backed pelycosaur reptiles, but it has normal dorsal processes on the vertebrae. Reptiles of this type attained a length of nearly 12 feet. (*Courtesy of American Museum of Natural History.*)

later insectivores. At least one type, with a form much like the modern lizard, had well-formed slender limbs adapted for swift running, the leg bones being light and hollow as in birds. This creature may have been partly arboreal.

A few reptiles returned to the open waters to compete with and probably prey upon fishes, perhaps including types like those from which they themselves had descended a few million years before. Unlike the fishes and amphibians, however, the aquatic reptiles were exclusively air breathers, for no reversion from a higher type of respiratory structure, such as the lungs, to a lower, such as gills, is known in any animals that have once fully attained the air-breathing habit.

Pelycosaurs. The most peculiarly specialized of the ancient Paleozoic reptiles were finbacked forms (pelycosaurs), some of which attained a length of at least eight feet (Fig. 11.18). Along the back was a very high fin, supported by bony spines of the vertebrae, the longer fin spines being as much as 3 feet high. Most of these animals were carnivorous, and they lived exclusively on land. It is not apparent that the dorsal fin was advantageous for either offensive or defensive purposes. These reptiles first appeared in Late Pennsylvanian time and became extinct before the end of the Permian Period.

Therapsids. Another interesting group (therapsids), which is important from an evolutional standpoint, had teeth that are differentiated into types almost exactly corresponding to the incisors, canines, and molars of mammals. The skull has a distinctly mammalian appearance, which contrasts strongly to that of the ordinary reptile having jaws armed with teeth that are all of the same kind. The first mammals, of which the oldest known occur in Triassic rocks, are believed to have sprung from this stock.

READINGS

BULMAN, O. M. B., 1957, Graptolites: in *Treatise on marine ecology*, H. S. Ladd, ed., Geol. Soc. America Mem. 67, vol. 2, pp. 987–991.

CLINE, L. M., and BEAVER, HAROLD, 1957, Blastoids: in *Treatise on marine ecology*, H. S. Ladd, ed., Geol. Soc. America Mem. 67, vol. 2, pp. 955–960.

COOPER, B. N., 1953, Trilobites from the lower Champlainian formations of the Appalachian Valley: *Geol. Soc. America Mem.* 55 (69 pp., illus.).
Good illustrations of trilobite assemblage (see pp. 1–6 for general discussion).

COOPER, G. A., 1957, Brachiopods: in *Treatise on marine ecology*, H. S. Ladd, ed., Geol. Soc. America Mem. 67, vol. 2, pp. 801–804.

DUNCAN, HELEN, 1957, Bryozoans: in *Treatise on marine ecology*, H. S. Ladd, ed., Geol. Soc. America Mem. 67, vol. 2, pp. 783–799.

ELLISON, S. P., JR., 1957, Conodonts: in *Treatise on marine ecology*, H. S. Ladd, ed., Geol. Soc. America Mem. 67, vol., 2, pp. 993–994.

FLOWER, R. H., 1957, Nautiloids of the Paleozoic: in *Treatise on marine ecology*, H. S. Ladd, ed., Geol. Soc. America Mem. 67, vol., 2, pp. 829–852.

LAUDON, L. R., 1957, Crinoids: in *Treatise on marine ecology*, H. S. Ladd, ed., Geol. Soc. America Mem. 67, vol. 2, pp. 961–971.

MILLER, A. K., 1957, Ammonoids of the Paleozoic: in *Treatise on marine ecology*, H. S. Ladd, ed., Geol. Soc. America Mem. 67, vol. 2, pp. 853–859.

OKULITCH, V. J., and NELSON, S. J., 1957, Sponges of the Paleozoic: in *Treatise on marine ecology*, H. S. Ladd, ed., Geol. Soc. America Mem. 67, vol. 2, pp. 763–770.

RUEDEMANN, RUDOLF, 1942, Graptolites of North America: *Geol. Soc. America Mem.* 19 (652 pp., illus.).
Comprehensive systematic work with numerous illustrations. (Pages 1–51 give discussions of general morphology, ecology, classification, and evolution.)

STUMM, E. C., 1949, Revision of the families and genera of the Devonian tetracorals: *Geol. Soc. America Mem.* 40 (92 pp., illus.).
Illustrates a rich coral assemblage.

WANG, Y., 1949, Maquoketa Brachiopoda of Iowa: *Geol. Soc. America Mem.* 42 (55 pp., illus.).

A representative group of Late Ordovician brachiopods.

WELLS, J. W., 1957, Corals: in *Treatise on marine ecology*, H. S. Ladd, ed., Geol. Soc. America Mem. 67, vol. 2, pp. 773–778.

WHITTINGTON, H. B., and EVITT, W. R., II, 1953, Silicified Middle Ordovician trilobites: *Geol. Soc. America Mem.* 59 (137 pp., illus.).

Shows exceptionally ornamented and well-preserved fossils (see pp. 3–33 for general description, morphology, and occurrence).

WILLIAMS, ALWYN, 1953, North American and European stropheodontids; their morphology and systematics: *Geol. Soc. America Mem.* 56 (67 pp., illus.).

QUESTIONS

1. Why is much more information available concerning the nature of land plants in post-Devonian deposits than those of earlier age?

2. What are the distinguishing characters of the main plant groups represented by Pennsylvanian fossils, including ferns, seed ferns, lycopods, cordaites, horsetail rushes, and conifers (Figs. 12.2 to 12.5)?

3. Why are some sponges better adapted to fossilization than others? What are the characters found to be most useful for classification of fossil sponges? Describe some representative types of Paleozoic sponges (Figs. 12.6 to 12.10).

4. What are the most noteworthy similarities and differences observable in comparing the restorations of bottom-dwelling invertebrates of Cambrian, Silurian, and Devonian shallow seas illustrated in Figs. 12.10 to 12.12? Note particularly the representation of each invertebrate phylum.

5. How are bryozoan colonies most readily distinguishable from colonial corals (Figs. 12.13, 12.14)? What Paleozoic systems contain abundant fossil bryozoans, and how are average bryozoan assemblages from older Paleozoic rocks different from those found in Mississippian-to-Permian deposits?

6. What specialized structures or adaptations of brachiopods can be recognized in fossils illustrated in Figs. 12.15 and 12.16?

7. What are the distinguishing features of the three main groups of mollusks (pelecypods, gastropods, cephalopods) that are common Paleozoic fossils (Figs. 12.17 to 12.19)? How are nautiloid cephalopods distinguished from ammonoids, and what difference in their distribution in Paleozoic systems is observed?

8. What trends in the evolution of the trilobites are discernible (Figs. 12.20 to 12.24)? In what Paleozoic system are the trilobites most varied as indicated by the number of observed genera and species? In what system are they proportionally most numerous, outnumbering other kinds of invertebrates?

9. Why are the eurypterids inferred to have lived in a brackish-water environment and not in normal seas (Figs. 12.25, 12.26)? What morphological characters set the eurypterids well apart from trilobites, allying them rather with scorpions and spiders?

10. What are the features that mainly distinguish ostracodes from other crustaceans (Fig. 12.28)? In what kinds of environment do these arthropods thrive? Why are they very useful guide fossils?

11. What dominant kinds of echinoderms occur as fossils in Paleozoic strata (Figs. 12.29 to 12.31)? Which ones are most important as rock builders?

12. What are ostracoderms and in what Paleozoic rocks are they found? What are the distinguishing characters of the placoderms (Fig. 12.33)?

13. What is the nature of evidence indicating that amphibians evolved from crossopterygian fish ancestors?

14. How do reptiles differ from amphibians, and in what Paleozoic system do they first appear?

13.

MESOZOIC ERA:

TRIASSIC PERIOD

Vividly colored Triassic badlands in the Painted Desert of northern Arizona.

Courtesy of U.S. Geol. Survey

Beginning of Mesozoic time. The Mesozoic Era, which begins with the Triassic Period, is so named to indicate the intermediate nature of its organisms between ancient life of the Paleozoic and the modern types of the Cenozoic. Mesozoic time is well designated as the Age of Reptiles, because this group of animals dominated the land, sea, and air. Paleo- zoic reptiles were merely forerunners and modern reptiles only a remnant of the Mesozoic hosts, which include the largest of all land animals, having lengths up to 87 feet and estimated weight of 50 tons. Such giant reptiles are exceeded only by whales, which are marine mammals that may exceed 100 feet in length and 70 tons in weight.

Type region. The name Triassic signifies threefold and was adopted for the early Mesozoic deposits because they consist of three well-marked divisions in the part of Europe where first detailed studies of them were made. The type Triassic region is central Germany (Fig. 13.1). The lower part of the section there is made up of continental redbeds, the middle is composed of marine shale and limestone, and the upper division comprises redbeds. Although this tripartite succession of strata is not at all characteristic of Triassic deposits in general, the name has been adopted throughout the world.

The standard for correlation of marine Triassic deposits is the section of the Mediterranean region in Europe, where Lower, Middle, and Upper Triassic are represented by highly fossiliferous limestone and other deposits.

Triassic Formations of North America

Recognition of Triassic in North America. Occurrence of Triassic deposits in North America is established partly from their position above known Permian and below Early

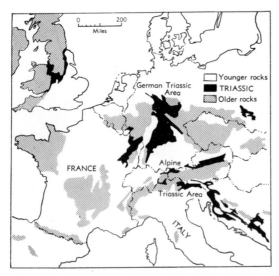

Fig. 13.1 Distribution of Triassic outcrops in west-central Europe. The Triassic rocks were named from outcrops in Germany, but the region most important for correlation of Triassic deposits in other parts of the world is that of the Alps region, which contains abundant marine fossils.

Jurassic strata in some regions but mainly on the basis of organic remains preserved in them as fossils. Among such fossils are both marine and nonmarine animals and a variety of land plants. Inasmuch as marine Triassic deposits are confined to the western part of the continent and deposits of this age in other areas are wholly nonmarine, age determinations depend on different groups of fossils.

Character and distribution of deposits. Marine Triassic deposits, consisting mostly of dark shale and limestone, are found lying disconformably (or in places paraconformably or conformably) on Permian and older rocks throughout most of the western part of the continent from Mexico to Alaska. Outcrops almost everywhere occur in narrow belts along the edges of structural uplifts, as, for example, on flanks of the Black Hills, Rockies, Big Horns, Wind Rivers, and other mountain ranges (Fig. 13.2). Other outcrops are broader and very irregular in shape, reflecting generally a near-horizontal attitude of the Triassic strata and effects of local erosion.

In states east of the Mississippi River, Triassic outcrops are found only in north- or northeast-trending belts close to the Atlantic. These are mapped in North Carolina, Virginia, Maryland, Pennsylvania, New Jersey, New York, Connecticut, Massachusetts, and Nova Scotia (Fig. 13.2).

Subsurface distribution of Triassic formations extends nearly continuously in the Western States between mountain uplifts, but rocks of the system are known to be absent throughout a large area extending northward from the Panhandle of Texas; this territory of no Triassic includes most of western Kansas, Nebraska, and South Dakota as well as considerable parts of Colorado and North Dakota. Similarly, much of Montana, Saskatchewan, and Alberta lack Triassic beneath the surface. Of course, these features of distribution call for explanation either by nondeposition or by post-Triassic removal as result of erosion, and in studying the historical geology of the region, it is important to discover, if possible, how the determined present conditions were produced.

Concealed Triassic rocks in the eastern United States comprise small areas beneath the Atlantic and eastern Gulf Coastal Plains. They consist of sedimentary deposits resembling those of outcrop belts in North Carolina and northward and also of igneous rocks less definitely identifiable as Triassic. The existence of subsurface Triassic now mapped (Fig. 13.3) has been ascertained by drilling, except that a patch of Triassic shown in the Gulf of Maine was discovered by dredging.

As preliminary survey of the character of Triassic deposits in North America, attention may be directed to (1) marine, (2) nonmarine, and (3) igneous rocks. As far as known, marine Triassic is confined to the West, where in many places beds are highly fossiliferous, although generally neither the rock successions nor their fossils have yet been studied in detail. The thickest known section, amounting to more than 25,000 feet, occurs in central Nevada. Marine Triassic rocks are about 4,000 feet thick in California, and several hundred feet of beds of this age occur in Oregon, Washington, and Idaho. Much-disturbed Triassic formations in British Columbia are distinguished by abundance of associated volcanic rocks; the section attains a thickness of 15,000 feet.

Continental deposits of Triassic age are widely exposed in the Rocky Mountains States, where they consist mostly of rather evenly bedded, brilliantly colored sandstone and shale (Fig. 13.3). Also, the Triassic sedimentary rocks seen in the eastern outcrop belts are nonmarine red sandstone and shale associated with local dark-colored shale and some coal beds. The average thickness of Triassic rocks in this region is approximately 10,000 feet, but it may exceed 20,000 feet.

Igneous rocks include andesitic and basaltic extrusives in western areas, especially as rock and mineral fragments incorporated in sediments. In the eastern Triassic belts, dark-colored igneous rock occurs commonly as extrusive sheets and also in the form of sills and dikes, the latter extending beyond the areas of Triassic sedimentary formations so as to intersect pre-Triassic rocks.

Divisions. Triassic rocks in North America are conveniently classed in three main parts, respectively designated as the Lower, Middle, and Upper Triassic Series (Fig. 13.4). These do not correspond precisely to the threefold division of Triassic in Germany, correlation being based, instead, on the marine section of the Mediterranean area. The Early Triassic corresponds closely to the time represented in making the lower redbeds deposits of the German Triassic section, but the line between Middle and Late Triassic belongs above the uppermost marine deposits of central Germany. Placement of continental Triassic formations in the geologic column requires correlation based on plant or animal remains of the land and depends on knowledge of age equivalence of nonmarine and marine formations in reference sections of Europe.

Features of Triassic History in North America

Marine submergence of the Pacific Border. The distribution and nature of formations exposed in the western United States support inference that during Early Triassic time a shallow extension of the Pacific invaded California and Nevada, reaching eastward as far as Arizona and Idaho. This sea was confined to the old Cordilleran geosyncline, which had been occupied repeatedly by Paleozoic marine waters, and as Triassic sedimentation progressed, the trough subsided slowly. The marine deposits diminish in thickness eastward and interfinger with continental formations that are widely distributed in the Rocky Mountains States. It is clear that the eastern margin of this Early Triassic sea shifted in position as time elapsed.

In the middle part of the period, the area submerged by the sea was mainly restricted to the Nevada-California region and western British Columbia. Abundant volcanic activity during this epoch, especially in the north, is shown by the common occurrence of extrusive igneous rocks interbedded with marine sediments, which also are largely composed of volcanic fragmental materials. Active volcanoes probably were numerous. The volcanic activity continued throughout Late Triassic

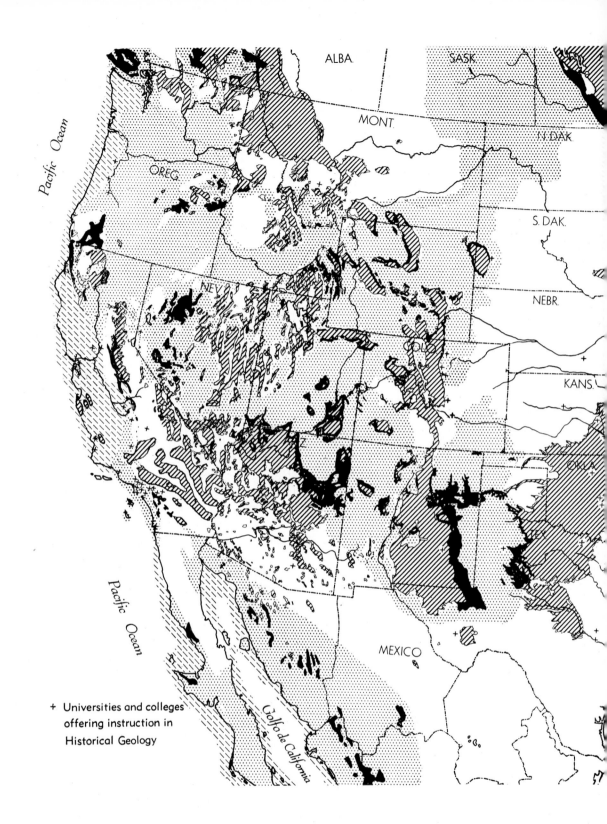

+ Universities and colleges
  offering instruction in
  Historical Geology

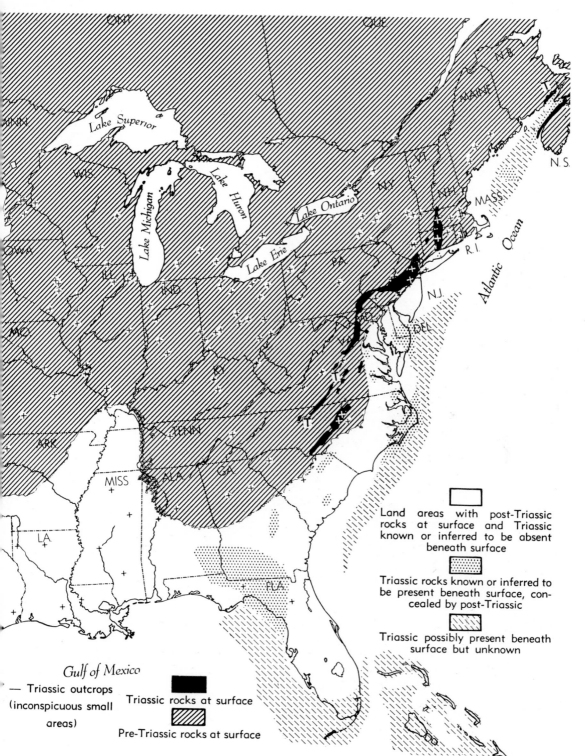

Legend (on map):

Land areas with post-Triassic rocks at surface and Triassic known or inferred to be absent beneath surface

Triassic rocks known or inferred to be present beneath surface, concealed by post-Triassic

Triassic possibly present beneath surface but unknown

— Triassic outcrops (inconspicuous small areas)

Triassic rocks at surface

Pre-Triassic rocks at surface

Fig. 13.2 Distribution of Triassic rocks in the United States, southern Canada, and northern Mexico. The outcrops and subsurface occurrences shown indicate the original distribution of the system, modified by aggregate effects of removal of deposits by post-Triassic erosion or locally by displacement resulting from post-Triassic bathylithic igneous intrusions.

Fig. 13.3 Red sandstone beds of Triassic age in western Wyoming. These evenly layered rocks (Chugwater) were evidently deposited in shallow lakes or spread by sluggish streams over a flat plain. They lack marine fossils. (*N. H. Darton, courtesy of U.S. Geol. Survey.*)

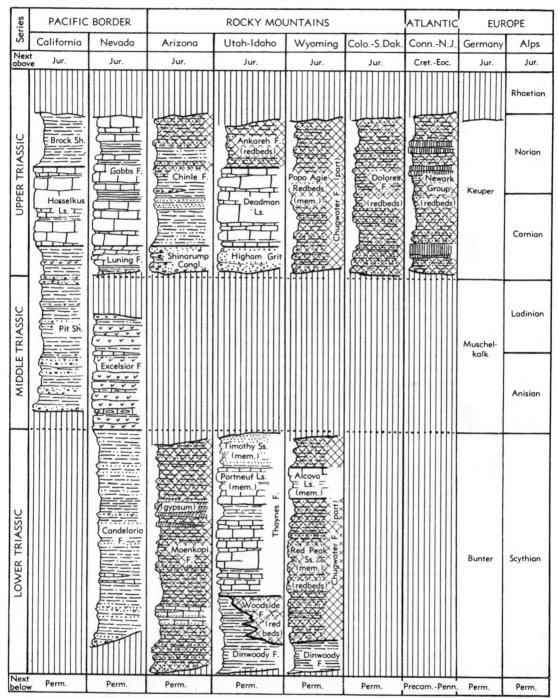

Fig. 13.4 **Time-rock divisions of the Triassic System and rock units assigned to them in representative important Triassic sections of North America.** The vertical scale does not represent time duration or thickness of rocks but is determined by suitability for plotting the various recognized rock units, placement of which indicates correlation in age. Lithologic character is represented graphically (explanation of symbols in Appendix B). Necessarily, the plotted thickness is not to scale, although it approximates proportional values in many sections. Vertically ruled areas denote absence of deposits.

time in British Columbia but abated farther south, where deposits belonging to this part of the Triassic consist mainly of shale and limestone.

Plains deposits of West Central States. Somewhat evenly bedded, bright-colored fine sandstone, siltstone, and shale, which are interpreted to represent alluvial deposits laid down in a plains environment, are widespread in the West Central States (Figs. 13.5, 13.6). The country now comprising the Colorado Plateau in Arizona and Utah, the Rockies from New Mexico to Montana, and the western border of the Great Plains from Texas to the Dakotas seems to have been a nearly featureless vast lowland plain throughout the Triassic Period. At least the western part, and perhaps all of it, sloped gently westward to the shores of the sea that occupied the Cordilleran geosyncline. During the early part of the period, this plain was the site of very widespread but only moderately thick sedimentation. Sand and mud washed from the interior of the continent were spread out by the sluggish overloaded streams so as to form coalescent alluvial deposits, which, through

alternate wetting and drying, were thoroughly oxidized. A prevailing red color is derived from the iron oxides distributed through the sediments. The even bedding and lateral uniformity of parts of the Early Triassic deposits suggest deposition in standing water, such as the temporary lakes now formed during times of rainfall in intermontane basins of the West.

Periodic and oft-repeated exposure of the sediments to the atmosphere is very unfavorable for preservation of plants or animals in a plains region, even though remains are buried here and there. Accordingly, the Triassic deposits of this region are mostly unfossiliferous. Exceptionally, the deposits yield identifiable impressions of land plants and bones of animals. Among the latter are fairly numerous skulls and some nearly complete skeletons of reptiles, especially crocodile-like forms that lived mostly in the water. Also, there are remarkably clear footprints of reptiles which, when carefully studied, have allowed fairly reliable inferences about the animals that made them. On the whole, the western United States does not seem to have been a semi-desert region, as inferred by some geologists

Fig. 13.5 Upper Triassic shaly deposits overlain by Lower Jurassic cliff-making sandstone. The Triassic beds (Chinle) of the outcrop in southern Utah shown here are less brilliantly colored than in the Painted Desert country, but they also contain petrified trees and rare bones of alligator-like aquatic reptiles. The paraconformity at the top of the Triassic beds is a very even surface. (*R. C. Moore, courtesy of U.S. Geol. Survey.*)

Fig. 13.6 Very evenly stratified Lower Triassic deposits along the Arizona-Utah boundary near Kanab. Shaly strata of the lower slopes and lower part of the cliff that weather in buttresses are unfossiliferous, dark red-brown beds that commonly bear ripple marks. They were evidently laid down in brackish water near the shore of a shallow inland sea; beds into which they grade westward contain marine invertebrates. The capping rock of the cliffs is a green-gray conglomeratic sandstone deposited by streams. It rests unconformably on the red-brown beds. (*J. K. Hillers, courtesy of U.S. Geol. Survey.*)

on the basis of the red color and generally unfossiliferous nature of the beds. On the contrary, both physical and organic evidence points to a prevailingly moist condition.

The transition from plains sedimentation of the sort described to marine sedimentation that was proceeding concurrently farther west in Triassic time is an important subject for investigation. Redbeds deposits of eastern areas should grade laterally into nonred marine deposits in western areas, or if lateral changes in lithology are abrupt, one group of deposits should interfinger with the other. Both of these suppositions are found in different places and in varying degree to accord with facts (Fig. 13.7), for lowermost Triassic deposits in the Wyoming-Idaho region show gradation from east to west whereas succeeding deposits interfinger with one another (Fig. 13.8). Correlated with these conditions that express sedimentary facies is a marked thickening of Triassic rocks westward, for in this area we travel from a platform into a geosyncline in proceeding from central Wyoming into southern Idaho. The fossiliferous marine beds in the West allow reliable determinations of relative age in the very sparsely fossiliferous or unfossiliferous redbeds, and equivalence in age of marine organisms (such as ammonoid cephalopods) with animals and plants of the land can be established. Without dovetailing of the two kinds of deposits, such correlation would not be possible. Finally, attention may be directed to a great hiatus in the sedimentary record of this region, as now understood, for no Middle Triassic deposits are recognized (see Fig. 13.4). Fossiliferous marine Upper Triassic rests disconformably

on fossiliferous marine Lower Triassic in Idaho, but redbeds of the continental succession in Wyoming (Ankareh Formation) include equivalents of both, which must mean that the disconformity is not recognizable in the redbeds.

Early and Middle Triassic erosion in eastern North America. Coincident with the crustal deformation that raised the Appalachian Mountains system, presumably somewhere near the end of Paleozoic time, erosion began to attack the upraised folds, cutting downward through successively older Paleozoic rocks. The rock materials thus excavated must have been carried from the mountains area by both eastward- and westward-flowing streams, and they came to rest temporarily or permanently along the lower stream courses and in the sea. During Early Triassic time, the mountains belt was doubtless still rugged and erosion vigorous. No geologic record of these conditions is preserved, however, and we can pic-

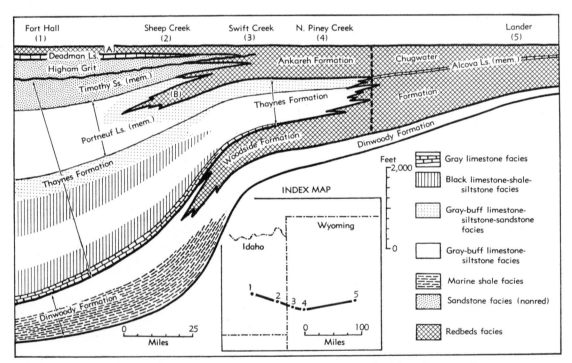

Fig. 13.7 Sedimentary facies of Triassic deposits in Wyoming and Idaho. Continental deposits consisting of redbeds prevail in eastern parts of this region, whereas very much thicker marine deposits of equivalent age occur in the west. These relationships and the manner in which different facies interfinger have much importance in deciphering features of geologic history. (*Data from Bernhard Kummel.*)

ture them only by inference. We do know that by late Middle Triassic time much of this country had been worn down to a plain, which cut across complex rock structures. In many places, however, the erosion surface preserved beneath Triassic continental deposits shows considerable relief, with valleys filled by Triassic sediments.

The products of erosion in eastern North America during Early and Middle Triassic times undoubtedly were very extensive, but all those carried eastward now lie concealed beneath younger Mesozoic and Cenozoic deposits, mostly beyond the present Atlantic shore line, and those carried westward have been entirely removed by subsequent erosion except in distant areas beyond the Mississippi. Although the area of Early Triassic continental sedimentation in the Rocky Mountains region was far from the Appalachians, it is very possible, if not probable, that some of these western deposits are products of mountain erosion in eastern North America. Such a suggestion has not been considered seriously by geologists, for they are generally prone to conclude that sedimentation in any given geologic period was limited to little more than territory in which the deposits now remain. That very large areas of deposits once present have been entirely denuded calls for unwarranted stretch of the imagination, they think. Conservatism of this sort is open to challenge whenever conditions (such as the nature and volume of sedimentary deposits in relation to source areas for them) suggest former wide distribution of sediments that now are missing.

Late Triassic valley deposits in the Atlantic Border region. In the late part of Triassic time, parts of the Appalachian region that had been eroded to a lowland began to be covered by stream-borne deposits derived from near-by uplands. These uplands were either parts of Appalachian folded and elevated rocks (deformed by the Appalachian mountain building) that had not yet been worn down or tracts raised by renewed uplift. The latter suggestion is the more probable explanation of active local erosion that supplied large quantities of sediment for deposits

Fig. 13.8   Ripple-marked Triassic sandstone near Salt Lake City, Utah. Ankareh Formation in Parley's Canyon, Wasatch Mountains. (*J. C. Anderson, courtesy of U.S. Geol. Survey.*)

in neighboring territory, especially in view of finding that the accumulating deposits periodically suffered displacement by faulting. The areas of sedimentation sank as clastic detritus was spread over them, until in some of the subsiding basins as much as 20,000 feet of deposits were laid down.

Remnants of the Triassic deposits, consisting of gray and reddish shale, silt, and sand-

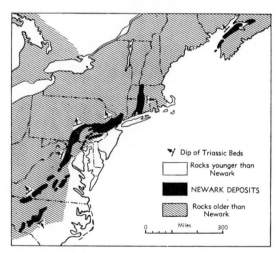

Fig. 13.9   Distribution of Triassic outcrops in eastern North America. The Triassic rocks occupy structurally depressed belts distributed from North Carolina to Nova Scotia. The dip of the Triassic beds in each individual belt is uniform in direction.

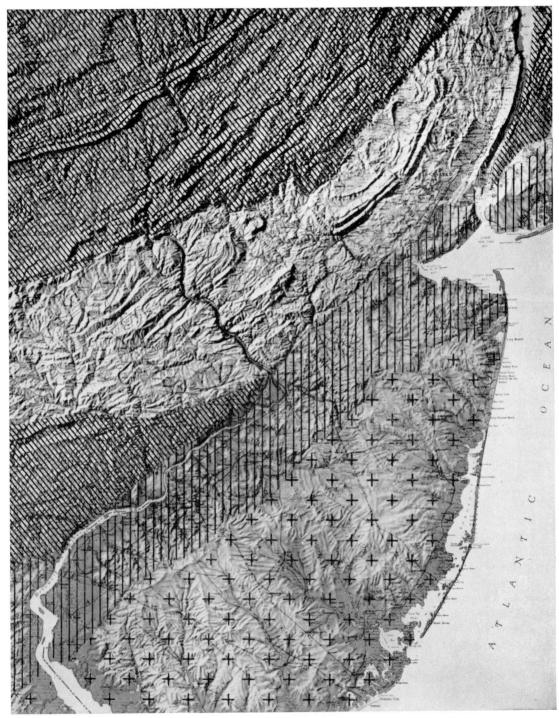

Fig. 13.10 Triassic outcrop area in eastern Pennsylvania, New Jersey, and New York.
The oblique-ruled area shows the distribution of pre-Triassic rocks; vertical-ruled, Cretaceous
rocks; pattern of crosses, post-Cretaceous. The area without pattern is Triassic lowland, except
for curved ridges in New Jersey bordering the Hudson (Palisades) and farther west
(Watchung Mountains). (*Relief map by courtesy of Aero Service Corporation.*)

Fig. 13.11 Thin sandstone layers of Triassic age on Connecticut River at Turners Falls, Mass. The Triassic sandstone of this area has yielded numerous well-defined footprints of dinosaurs. The track-bearing sand and silt were presumably spread out on flat-floored valleys by streams. (*Courtesy of W. E. Corbin, Florence, Massachusetts.*)

stone, are distributed for 1,000 miles northward and northeastward from North Carolina (Fig. 13.9). The basins of sedimentation, which may be compared with the Great Valley of central California and with partly enclosed basins between mountain ranges in Nevada, were downfaulted on one or both sides. Movement along the fault planes did not consist of a single displacement of great magnitude, but rather of many successive small movements. Thus, sedimentary filling of the valleys approximately kept pace with the subsidence of their floors. Proof that the movements occurred in this way is found in the presence of successively younger local deposits of coarse conglomerate, found at the borders of the valleys where streams built alluvial fans, one above another (Figs. 13.10 to 13.12).

The chief areas of Triassic continental deposits adjacent to the Atlantic are shown in Figs. 13.9 and 13.10. One of the largest continuous areas of outcrop extends from north-

ern Virginia across parts of Pennsylvania and New Jersey to southeastern New York, and another is found along the Connecticut Valley in Connecticut and western Massachusetts. These are fertile lowlands in which there are many fine farms, as, for example, in the country around Gettysburg, Pennsylvania.

The rocks of all the Triassic areas are similar in character, consisting mostly of reddish-brown sandy shale and sandstone. Some of the sandstones are thick and show cross-bedding, whereas others are very thin and grade laterally into shale. The common presence of feldspar grains in the sandy layers indicates dominance of mechanical over chemical weathering in the areas that supplied the sediments. These source areas presumably consisted of adjacent uplands of the Appalachian Mountains, but the absence of granite pebbles or other kinds of crystalline rocks in Triassic conglomerates bordering the basins is a puzzling feature, because it signifies that the sedimentary rocks of the folded Appalachian geosyncline had not been stripped away so as to expose underlying crystallines.

Some of the Late Triassic beds in the Atlantic States are evenly stratified, suggesting deposition in shallow temporary lakes, such as occur in intermontane basins of Nevada and the Great Valley of California. Locally there are clearly marked footprints of land reptiles. The red color of the rocks and general absence of fossil remains are indicative of thorough oxidation of the sediments before, during, or shortly after deposition. These features do not signify dry desert conditions, but rather they may be interpreted to denote temperate climate with alternate wetting and drying of the deposits.

The occurrence of black shale and coal beds in some of the Virginia and North Carolina areas indicates the existence of lakes and swamps, in or adjacent to which there was an abundance of plants. The nature of this vegetation is shown by many well-preserved plant fossils. It is recorded that the first coal mined for fuel in North America was obtained from some of the Triassic coal deposits of Virginia.

Igneous activity in the eastern Triassic basins. Recurrence of widespread volcanic activity during the time of Late Triassic sedimentation in eastern North America is shown by the presence of dark extrusive and intrusive igneous rock, which is associated with all the Triassic sedimentary basins. For the most part, this igneous rock, called *trap*, occurs in the form of sheets lying roughly parallel to the sedimentary strata. Most of the sheets represent lava flows, as proved by restriction of contact metamorphic effects to the lower side of the sheets, by the vesicular nature of the top of parts of the sheets, and by the presence of lava fragments incorporated in the base of overlying sedimentary layers. Some sheets, such as that which makes the Palisades along the Hudson opposite New York City, are sills. There are also dikes that not only intersect the Triassic sediments but, in places, run long distances through adjoining areas of pre-Triassic rock. That the lava was very liquid and that extrusion was of the nonexplosive type are indicated by the evenness and enormous extent of some of the flows; originally these must have had an almost perfectly horizontal attitude. The igneous rocks are now tilted and broken by post-Triassic crustal movements, and because most of them are much harder than the adjoining sedimentary rocks, they form ridges.

Fig. 13.12 Conglomeratic Triassic rock consisting mainly of limestone fragments. This polished specimen of so-called "Potomac Marble" from the vicinity of Reading, Pennsylvania, is largely made up of limestone fragments derived from Paleozoic formations. The source of the limestone is judged to have been not far distant, because limestone wears away rapidly during transportation. (*B. L. Miller, courtesy of Pennsylvania Geol. Survey.*)

Triassic Life

Conditions of preservation. Life of the lands in Triassic time is much less completely known than that of various other periods of past earth history. This is because well-preserved fossil remains are relatively scanty and local in distribution. There is no good reason, however, to think that land plants and animals were much less abundant or varied in the Triassic than later in the Mesozoic Era. Probably the real reason for relative paucity of Triassic organic remains in continental deposits is the unfavorable conditions for preservation. Most of these strata show signs of periodic aeration and oxidation during accumulation, and such conditions lead almost inevitably to destruction of plants or hard parts of animals that chance to be buried. Many thousand vertebrate footprints are known from sandstone layers in parts of the Connecticut Valley, yet skeletal remains of the animals that made these tracks are almost wholly lacking.

Plants. Among plants of Late Triassic time, coal-swamp floras are known from well-preserved fossils in the coal basins of North Carolina and Virginia. Some of these plants resemble their antecedents of Pennsylvanian time, but a number of distinctive and important new forms also occur. Continental Triassic deposits in the Western States, especially in the area of the Petrified Forest at Adamana, Arizona, contain the silicified trunks of great trees that attained a height of more than 100 feet and a diameter of as much as 7 feet. These trees are related to modern members of the pine family growing on the western slopes of the Andes in South America. The palmlike cycadeoids and their relatives are a characteristic component of Mesozoic floras, and they appear among Triassic plants. An unusual one, known from straight-edged leaves up to 13 inches across and more than 3 feet in length, is *Macrotaeniopteris,* found in the Triassic of eastern Pennsylvania. Excellently preserved leaves of ferns, conifers, and ginkgos occur also.

Invertebrates. Marine strata of Triassic age in western North America and other parts of the world contain a large assemblage of invertebrates, among which coiled cephalopods with complex sutures are the most diagnostic (Fig. 13.13). Distinctive clams are common. Although brachiopods are not an important

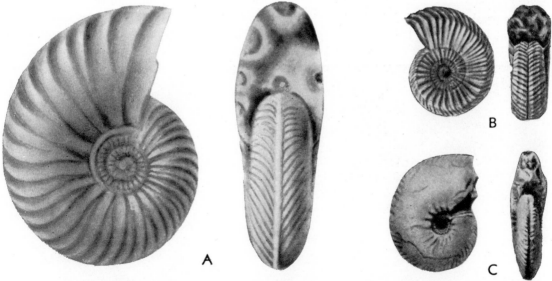

Fig. 13.13 Typical Triassic ammonites. Fossils of this cephalopod group are extremely numerous and varied, occurring throughout the world in Triassic marine deposits. They are the chief index and guide fossils for zonation and correlation. Types shown are *A, Ceratites,* Middle Triassic; *B, Clionites,* Upper Triassic; *C, Arpadites,* Middle and Upper Triassic. Natural size.

constituent of the faunas, some kinds are almost identical with Permian types. A remnant of the abundant and characteristic group of Paleozoic crinoids also occurs, especially in Middle Triassic rocks of Germany. On the whole, however, the Triassic marine faunas are strikingly different in constituents from those found in older strata.

Vertebrates. The most important Triassic animals are the vertebrates, which include a variety of fresh-water fishes and the beginning of the great Mesozoic expansion of the reptiles. Dinosaurs, mainly identified by their three-toed tracks in the Triassic deposits of the Atlantic Border, were abundant and considerably varied in size range (Fig. 13.14). Among reptiles from the western Triassic, one of the most noteworthy is a crocodile-like aquatic reptile distinguished by a very long narrow snout; these animals, called *phytosaurs,* must have inhabited the sluggish streams and shallow ponds in considerable numbers.

Amphibians attained their maximum known size in Triassic time. They belong to the thick-skulled group known as *stegocephalians* (Fig. 13.15).

Climate

The prevalence of red deposits in Triassic continental formations has been interpreted

as meaning widespread arid or semiarid climate during much of the period. Opposed to this are the nature of plant and animal life of the time, in so far as known, and the indication in the rocks themselves of the existence of many sluggish streams and shallow-water bodies. The red color, derived from thorough oxidation of iron minerals, is most favored by alternate wetting and drying rather than prolonged occurrence of desert conditions. Signs point neither to cold climate nor to widespread tropical conditions; probably both in eastern and western North America, subtropical savanna climates, characterized by alternating wet and dry seasons, prevailed.

Mountain Building

Palisades disturbance. During and after the epoch of Late Triassic valley deposition near the Atlantic, faulting and tilting of crustal blocks produced mountainous topography in a belt lying east of the present Appalachians. Probably this deformation, which was not accompanied by folding of strata, occurred near the close of Triassic time. Deposition in the valley basins was interrupted, and the strata, including interbedded volcanics, were tilted so that they now dip mostly at angles of 15 to 30 degrees (Fig. 13.17). The inclination is uniformly eastward in some outcrop areas,

Fig. 13.14 Footprints of a two-legged dinosaur on a slab of Triassic sandstone. Just before burial by overlying sand, the smoothed part of the slab was under water whereas the rough rain-pitted part was above water. (*Courtesy of W. E. Corbin, Florence, Massachusetts.*)

Fig. 13.15   Restoration of Triassic amphibian. This creature, from the Upper Triassic of Germany, is a stegocephalian that marks the peak of size attained by amphibians from their first appearance to the present. Its length of 3.5 feet is gigantic for amphibians, and thus it is named *Mastodonsaurus giganteus*. (*Courtesy of J. Augusta and Z. Burian, Praha; published by permission.*)

Fig. 13.16   An armored lizard from Triassic rocks near Cameron, Arizona. This reptile (*Palaeosuchus*) is represented by an unusually complete, well-preserved skeleton. The animal is characterized by a double row of rectangular bony plates along the back. (*Courtesy of American Museum of Natural History.*)

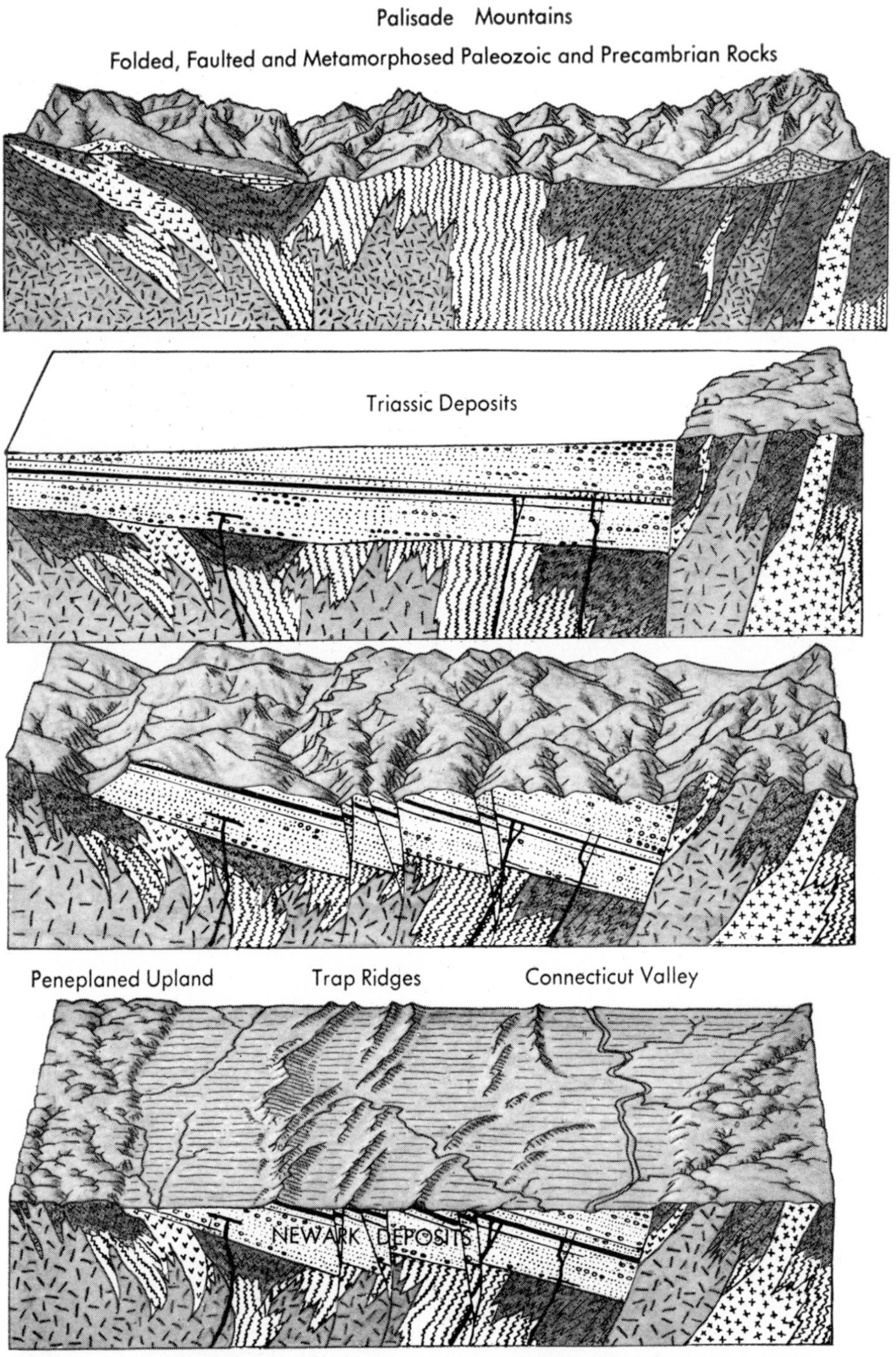

Palisade Mountains

Folded, Faulted and Metamorphosed Paleozoic and Precambrian Rocks

Triassic Deposits

Peneplaned Upland   Trap Ridges   Connecticut Valley

NEWARK DEPOSITS

Fig. 13.17 Geologic evolution of the Triassic deposits in the Connecticut River Valley. The diagrams, reading from top to bottom, represent pre-Triassic rugged topography; depression and covering by Triassic deposits of part of the peneplaned old-rock surface; erosion of tilted and faulted Triassic strata surface in Early Jurassic time; and the present landscape, which shows evidence of recent peneplanation followed by moderate uplift. (*Modified from Joseph Barrell.*)

such as the Connecticut Valley, and westward in others, as in New Jersey and Pennsylvania. The structural pattern as a whole suggests that the observed belts of eastward- and westward-dipping Triassic are remnants of a broad faulted anticlinal structure, the central part of which has been entirely eroded. This deformation is known as the Palisades disturbance, named from the Palisades of the Hudson opposite New York.

Close of the Period

The end of the Triassic Period is marked by the interruption of sedimentation and probably also by the Palisades disturbance. Marine waters that had occupied areas in the western United States during Late Triassic time retreated, and this country was not again submerged until the middle part of the Jurassic. An unconformity separates continental Late Triassic deposits from those belonging to the early part of the Jurassic, indicating uplift that changed conditions of deposition to those of erosion. In some areas, however, the boundary between the Triassic and Jurassic Systems is not well defined, and continental sedimentation may have been more or less continuous. Important crustal deformations near the close of the Triassic are recognized in parts of western North America.

Economic Resources

Triassic mineral resources are decidedly minor as compared with other geologic systems in North America, but this is less true when account is taken of the whole world. The chief materials from these rocks are coal, salt, manganese, zinc, and stone products.

Coal. Beds of coal occur in Triassic basins of Virginia and North Carolina. From this source came the first coal mined in North America, but it has never been quantitatively very important, even though annual production has been reported to be 10 million tons. Japan produces about the same amount from southwestern Honshu, which is the only place on any continent where Triassic coal is good anthracite. China obtains approximately 40 million tons and South Africa 5 million tons of Triassic coal annually.

Other resources. Salt deposits of Triassic age occur in the British Isles and in continental Europe, about 5 million tons yearly being produced in England. Manganese in the amount of slightly less than 30,000 tons annually comes from Triassic formations in Italy. Zinc of Triassic age occurs in West Germany, the Alps, and Silesia (now included in Poland). The Silesian area is one of the world's chief zinc-producing areas.

READINGS

COLBERT, E. H., 1947, Little dinosaurs of Ghost Ranch: *Natural History*, vol. 56, pp. 392–399, 427–428 (illus.).
Describes important discoveries of Triassic reptiles.
———, 1951, *The dinosaur book*, McGraw-Hill Book Company, Inc., New York (156 pp., illus.).
Includes descriptions of Triassic fossils.
———, 1955, *Evolution of the vertebrates*, John Wiley & Sons, Inc., New York (479 pp., illus.). Early ruling reptiles, pp. 146–157.
Describes first crocodilians and dinosaurs.
DAUGHERTY, L. H., 1941, Upper Triassic flora of Arizona: *Carnegie Inst. Wash. Publ.* 526 (108 pp., illus.).
Good illustrations, including trees of petrified forests.
KUMMEL, BERNHARD, 1957, Paleoecology of Lower Triassic formations of southeastern Idaho and adjacent areas: in *Treatise on marine ecology*, H. S. Ladd, ed., Geol. Soc. America Mem. 67, vol. 2, pp. 437–467 (illus.).
LONGWELL, C. R., and DANA, E. S., 1932, *Walks and rides in central Connecticut and Massachusetts*, New Haven (229 pp.).
Describes Triassic exposures in a classic region of New England.

McKee, E. D., 1954, Stratigraphy and history of the Moenkopi Formation of Triassic age: *Geol. Soc. America Mem.* 61 (133 pp., illus.).

Good description of stratigraphy, environments of sedimentation, and fossils representing Early Triassic time in the Southwest (especially pp. 1–81).

Muller, S. W., 1949, Sedimentary facies and geologic structures in the Basin-and-Range Province: *Geol. Soc. America Mem.* 39, C. R. Longwell, ed., pp. 49–54 (illus.).

Describes typical Triassic deposits in Nevada.

Reeside, J. B., Jr., et al., 1957, Correlation of the Triassic formations of North America, exclusive of Canada: *Geol. Soc. America Bull.*, vol. 68, pp. 1451–1514 (illus.).

Most comprehensive and authoritative discussion of classification and correlation of Triassic deposits in North America.

QUESTIONS

1. From study of the map showing distribution of Triassic rocks in the United States and adjacent parts of Canada and Mexico (Fig. 13.2) what conclusions, if any, can be drawn concerning the structure of Triassic formations adjacent to the Atlantic seaboard, exposed in elongate disconnected patches from Nova Scotia to North Carolina? Concerning thickness of Triassic deposits in these areas? Concerning the general topographic expression of Triassic outcrops? Would knowledge that thickness of Triassic here is mostly measured in thousands of feet help in making deductions as to probable structure and topographic expression? How is Triassic known to underlie large areas in western United States and yet to be lacking in much of the Great Plains country, for example?

2. How is the contemporaneity of thick marine Triassic deposits in western parts of the Idaho-Wyoming region (Fig. 13.7) and comparatively thin nonmarine redbeds in eastern parts of this area ascertained? What evidence shows that the sea margin shifted considerably back and forth with lapse of time?

3. Referring to the relief map of Triassic and associated rocks in Pennsylvania, New Jersey, and New York (Fig. 13.10), why is most of the Triassic outcrop area a lowland? What is the nature of the rocks that form the Palisades and the Watchung Mountains? What is the direction of regional dip in the Triassic area?

4. What feature of the "Potomac Marble" illustrated in Fig. 13.12 other than prominence of limestone constituents indicates nearby sources of the pebbles?

5. What are features that, if discovered in the field, serve reliably to identify a sheetlike body of igneous rock as a sill? As an extrusive flow? As a dike?

6. Supposing that the four footprints shown in Fig. 13.14 form part of a trail consisting of 20 or more prints approximately identical in size and spacing with these, can it be proved that the tracks were made by a bipedal animal rather than quadrupedal? Why are these tracks identified as having been made by a dinosaur? Why not by a bird or unknown type of three-toed mammal?

7. How can a fossil amphibian (Fig. 13.15) found in water-laid sedimentary deposits be distinguished from an aquatic reptile of similar shape discovered in the same deposits (see Appendix A)?

8. Why is topography of mountainous type presumed to have characterized southern New England during geologic intervals that preceded and followed Triassic sedimentation in parts of this region (Fig. 13.17)? What is the evidence for recognizing at least two peneplanations that differ widely in age? What geologic conditions are responsible for the discontinuous hogbacks that are prominent features of the Connecticut Valley? Why are these ridges arranged *en echelon*, partly paralleling one another (Fig. 13.17, *bottom*)?

14.

MESOZOIC ERA:

JURASSIC PERIOD

Jurassic sandstone cliff in Zion National Park, Utah.   *Courtesy of Union Pacific Railroad*

Jurassic rocks and the time they represent are named from the Jura Mountains, along the borders of France and Switzerland (Fig. 14.1). There, as in southern Germany and in England, deposits of this age consist mostly of shallow-water marine deposits that contain an extraordinary variety and abundance of well-preserved fossils. These are the fossiliferous

beds that led William Smith, the Englishman who is called "father of stratigraphic geology," to the discovery, shortly before 1800, that various sorts of fossils were consistently restricted to certain beds and, accordingly, that successive rock layers could be distinguished on the basis of their contained fossil remains. It was Smith who first made this fundamental observation, which serves as prime basis for correlating fossil-bearing strata and which has guided correct classification of deposits according to geologic age. Study of European Jurassic formations has been particularly important in developing other essential principles of historical geology. Also, interest in its fossiliferous outcrops has led many able young men to become paleontologists.

The Jurassic deposits in Europe are clearly set apart as a natural geologic division of major rank, for they represent extensive marine transgression, after emergent condition of the continent at the close of Triassic time and before similar emergence at the end of Jurassic time. As a whole, also, the host of Jurassic organisms comprises an assemblage that differs notably from life of the adjoining periods, even though all Jurassic plants and animals are descendants of Triassic ancestors and though Cretaceous forms of life developed out of Jurassic progenitors. The standard Jurassic section, which is based partly on outcrops in the Jura Mountains and adjacent country and partly on deposits in England, contains a dozen divisions that are classed as stages. These are divided in turn into zones that can be recognized very widely.

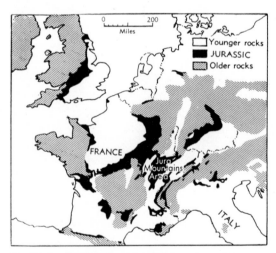

Fig. 14.1 Distribution of Jurassic outcrops in west-central Europe. The Jura Mountains, from which the Jurassic System is named, extend along the border of France, Germany, and Switzerland. Other classic regions for study of Jurassic deposits are in northeastern France and England.

Occurrence of Jurassic Rocks in North America

Basis for recognition. Occurrence of marine deposits of Jurassic age in western North America and the Gulf of Mexico region is established by the presence of distinctive sorts of invertebrates, including especially various complex-sutured cephalopods; belemnites, which are primitive antecedents of the squids; oysters and clams; and distinctive fragments of characteristic Jurassic crinoids. Continental deposits of Jurassic age in North America also have yielded a variety of vertebrate, invertebrate, and plant remains, which are identical or closely allied to corresponding organisms of the European Jurassic. Many of these fossils serve to identify a particular narrow zone within the succession of Jurassic deposits to which they belong. In general, however, the Jurassic formations of North America are much less fossiliferous than those of Europe and some other parts of the world.

Character and distribution of deposits. The most complete succession of Jurassic marine deposits in North America occurs along the Pacific Border in California and Oregon (Figs. 14.2, 14.3). The section of these rocks, 15,000 to 25,000 feet thick, consists mainly of dark silty to sandy shale and sandstone, associated with much volcanic material. The rocks have been profoundly disturbed by subsequent deformation, which has partly metamorphosed them, broken them along large thrust faults, and brought them into such position that a large fraction of the original deposits has been eroded away. Outcrops occur in isolated patches. Fossils are not numerous or very well preserved. Accordingly, details of geologic history in this region are not well known.

Marine shale and sandstone, locally associated with calcareous deposits, are widely distributed in the Rocky Mountains region and extend northeastward as far as the Black Hills in South Dakota. Contained fossils indicate the Middle and Late Jurassic age of these deposits, which are mostly less than 1,000 feet thick, although in Idaho they attain a thickness of about 5,000 feet.

Marine Jurassic strata, representing a seaway entirely distinct from those in western North America, are known in Mexico; western Texas near El Paso; beneath the surface of northern Louisiana, southwestern Arkansas, and northeastern and southern Texas; in Cuba; and in some other parts of the West Indies. The deposits include shale, sandstone, and limestone and, in the Louisiana-Arkansas area, anhydrite and salt.

Continental Jurassic deposits are widely distributed in parts of the West that contain also continental Triassic beds, but, unlike the Triassic, no strata of Jurassic age are exposed east of the Mississippi (Figs. 14.4 to 14.8). Cross-bedded sandstone, which in places attains a thickness of 2,000 or 3,000 feet, is the main type of continental Jurassic deposit found in the West. Outcrops are distributed from Arizona and southern Nevada to Idaho and Montana. Some of the most prominent cliffs and mesas of the Colorado Plateau country are made by these Jurassic sandstones; Zion National Park in southwestern Utah contains especially fine exposures of them (Fig. 14.6).

Divisions. In western Europe, the Jurassic contains three main parts, which in upward order are frequently termed the Black, Brown, and White Jurassic, the first being predominantly composed of dark-colored shale, the second having prominent brown sandstone, and the third being composed mostly of light-colored limestone. Although these lithologic divisions have only regional significance, they are associated with differences of the faunas, and on the basis of faunal distinctions, we may recognize Lower, Middle, and Upper Jurassic in North America. Each of these is divided into time-rock units called *stages,* having names derived from European localities, and these are employed in more detailed age classification of the Jurassic deposits wherever possible (Fig. 14.3).

Features of Jurassic History

Submergence of the Pacific Border. The chief feature of Jurassic history in the Pacific Border region, extending from California to Alaska, is marine submergence that began early in the period and, with only minor in-

terruption, persisted to near its close. We may note also that deposits laid down in this sea contain very little limestone; most of the sediments are fine to coarse products of erosion of nearby land, admixed in places with abundant volcanic materials.

During Early Jurassic time, lands adjoining this western sea were relatively low, for almost all the Lower Jurassic deposits are fine-textured.

The Middle Jurassic was an epoch of special explosive volcanic activity, as judged by prevalence of lava and tuff interbedded with the marine sediments and by the volcanic origin of many constituents of the sediments.

Late Jurassic deposits were mostly dark muds, but in places these also are associated with much volcanic material.

Throughout the period, the Pacific Border sea was separated by a land area from territory in the Rocky Mountain province, which temporarily was invaded by a shallow sea and which during other parts of Jurassic time was the site of extensive continental sedimentation. This intervening land area contains no Jurassic deposits but was undergoing erosion, and sediment from it was carried both westward and eastward.

Continental sedimentation in the Rocky Mountains region. During Jurassic time, there were no mountains where the Rockies now stand. This great area was then a featureless plains country, as shown by the extent and nature of widespread continental deposits, but the sea covered much of the plain in part of the Middle and Late Jurassic.

The continental deposits consist of red clay, fine silt, and fine- to medium-grained sandstone. The redbeds are closely comparable to those of Triassic age in the same region and doubtless denote continuation of the same conditions of deposition. These were interpreted in the preceding chapter as the work of sluggish streams in a plains country of very gentle slope and deposition in shallow fresh-water ponds of temporary existence. The effect of alternate wetting and drying in producing thorough oxidation of iron minerals is seen in these Lower Jurassic

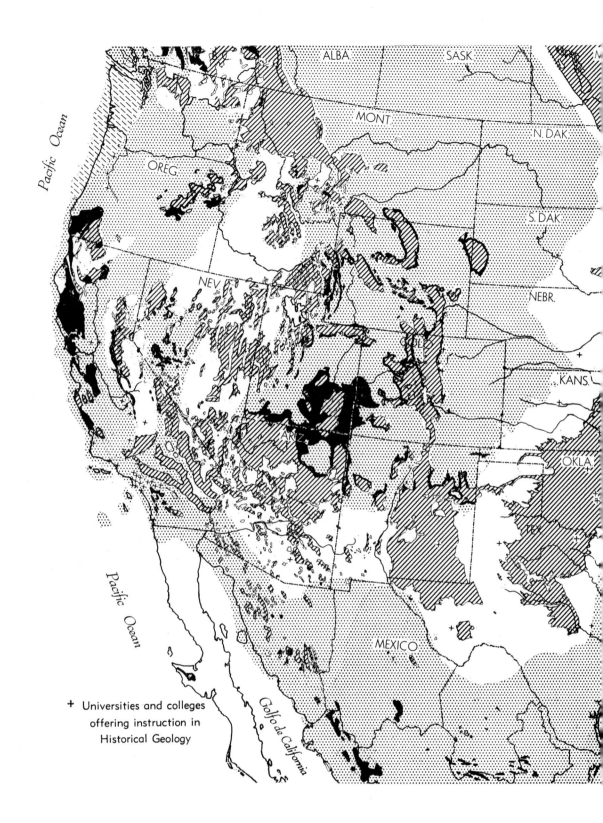

+ Universities and colleges
  offering instruction in
  Historical Geology

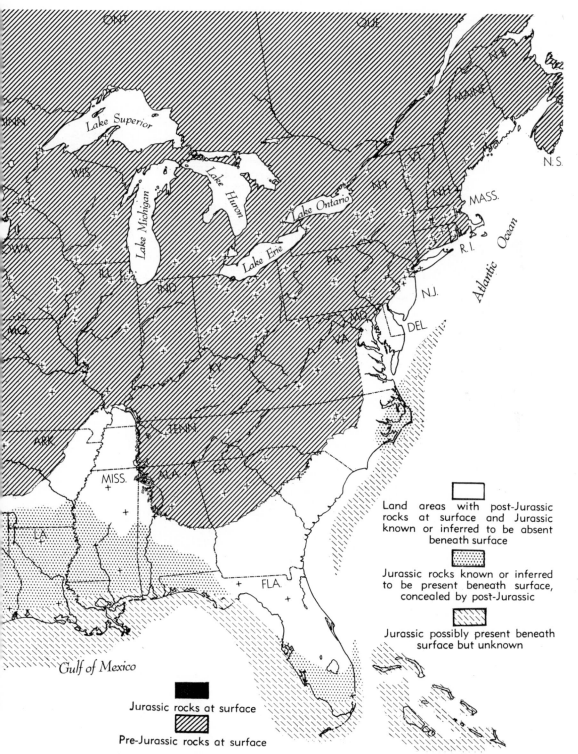

Land areas with post-Jurassic rocks at surface and Jurassic known or inferred to be absent beneath surface

Jurassic rocks known or inferred to be present beneath surface, concealed by post-Jurassic

Jurassic possibly present beneath surface but unknown

Jurassic rocks at surface

Pre-Jurassic rocks at surface

Fig. 14.2 Distribution of Jurassic rocks in the United States, southern Canada, and northern Mexico. The outcrops and subsurface occurrence shown indicate the original distribution of the system, modified by aggregate effects of removal of deposits by erosion and by displacement resulting from post-Jurassic bathylithic igneous intrusions.

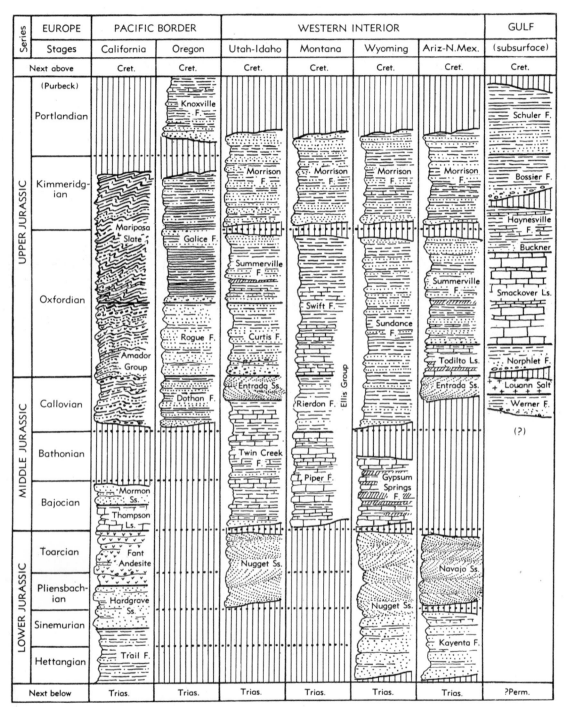

Fig. 14.3 Time-rock divisions of the Jurassic System and rock units assigned to them in representative important Jurassic sections of North America. The vertical scale does not represent time duration or thickness of rocks but is determined by suitability for plotting the various recognized rock units, placement of which indicates correlation in age. Lithologic character is represented graphically (explanation of symbols in Appendix B). Necessarily, the plotted thickness is not to scale, although it approximates proportional values in some sections. Vertically ruled areas denote absence of deposits.

Fig. 14.4 Hogback of Jurassic sandstone in southern Utah. This northward-looking air view, from a point on the San Juan River west of Blanding, shows at left a monoclinal valley carved in Triassic shale and in the middle part of the view light-colored Jurassic sandstone that makes an escarpment known as "Comb Ridge." In the right background are Cretaceous strata, and along the skyline are intrusive igneous rocks that form the Abajo Mountains. (*Courtesy of Spence Air Photos.*)

deposits, as in similar sediments of Triassic and Permian age.

Scarcity of organic remains is a natural accompaniment of conditions of deposition that we have inferred. Nevertheless, there are local deposits containing abundant teeth and bones belonging to reptiles that roamed the plains. From such places in Upper Jurassic deposits many complete skeletons have been collected. Some of the fossil-bearing spots seem to indicate quicksands formed in backwater or eddy pools along the Jurassic streams, and some may represent water holes where the animals congregated.

Most of the Jurassic sandstone deposits, especially as seen in the Colorado Plateau country, are very uniform in texture and strongly cross-bedded. The grains are well rounded and sorted, like sand in the dunes of the Sahara or other deserts, and some wind-faceted pebbles have been found. These features show that the sand was carried into the plateau country by winds and that the sandstone was made by compaction and cementing of loose dune sand. The lithified sand-dune area marks an extensive Jurassic desert, which spread over territory in Nevada, Arizona, New Mexico, Colorado, Utah, Idaho, and possibly other states. Thin horizontal sheets of mud-cracked clay, a few yards in lateral extent, are found locally in the midst of the sandstone; such deposits call to mind the shallow evanescent ponds that may form between dunes after a rain—places where fine wind-blown sediment may be trapped until the water disappears.

Middle and Late Jurassic marine invasion of the Western Interior. Continental sedimentation in states of the Rocky Mountains area was interrupted late in Middle and Jurassic time by lowering of the plains surface or elevation of sea level to such extent that a shallow

Fig. 14.5 Jurassic sandstone in southeastern Utah. This view shows natural bridges eroded in the massive sandstone; Arches National Monument. (*Courtesy of D. L. Hopwood, Denver, Colorado.*)

sea reached southward from the Arctic to the borders of Arizona and into Colorado and South Dakota (Fig. 14.3). In Montana several hundred feet and in Idaho at least 3,000 feet of limestone were laid down in this seaway, but in most of the submerged area the sediments consist of mud and sand. These deposits are recognized as marine in origin by the common occurrence of marine fossils in them. Concentration of sea water in lagoons at the

Fig. 14.6 Lower Jurassic sandstone in Zion National Park, Utah. The impressive magnitude of these massive sand deposits, light-colored in the upper part and increasingly reddish below, is well shown. East wall of Zion Canyon, with the Great White Throne in center of view. (*Courtesy of Union Pacific Railroad.*)

margin of the shallow sea, both when it was most extensive and during its retreat, is recorded by deposits of gypsum. No salt beds are known, however. This sea vanished before the close of Jurassic time.

Late Jurassic continental sedimentation in the Western States. From Colorado westward to Nevada and in states to the north and south in this region are persistent shaly and fine sandy deposits containing some beds of nodular limestone. These are fresh-water deposits that in most places are called Morrison (Fig. 14.3). They are a few hundred feet thick and originally must have been a continuous sheet of strata made by sluggish streams and accumulated in shallow ponds.

Some of the best-preserved skeletons of dinosaurs come from Morrison beds in Utah (Dinosaur National Park, near Vernal) and Colorado near Denver (Fig. 14.8).

Jurassic seas in the Gulf region. Marine Jurassic deposits, which evidently represent the invasion of shallow seas from the Gulf of Mexico, are found in extreme western Texas and adjacent parts of Mexico. There are no outcrops of Jurassic strata farther east in the Gulf region.

Deep drilling in southwestern Arkansas, northern Louisiana, northeastern and southern Texas, and northeastern Mexico has demonstrated the existence in that area of a thick succession of marine Jurassic deposits lying unconformably below oldest Cretaceous strata. The Jurassic age of the buried formations is proved by many fossils obtained from well samples. Salt and anhydrite have been penetrated by some wells in this region. These minerals indicate the former existence of basins or lagoons containing concentrated brines, but there are also extensive limestone and marine shale deposits that denote normal marine conditions.

The total extent of Jurassic seas in the Gulf coastal region is not yet known, but it is probable that part of the coastal plain east of the Mississippi River is underlain by marine Jurassic sediments. If so, they are deeply buried, for a 10,000-foot well drilled in central Florida ended in the lower part of the Cretaceous.

Erosion in eastern North America. Absence of exposed Jurassic formations in any part of eastern North America and the fact that no well borings along the Atlantic Coastal Plain have anywhere penetrated known Jurassic deposits support the inference that during the Jurassic Period this entire region was undergoing erosion. We may conclude that the margin of the Jurassic sea lay somewhere east of the present coast line.

Even though erosion seems to have prevailed on land, alluvium must have been spread out along the lower courses of stream valleys, and it is likely that in some places sediment accumulated in lakes and was spread out by wind. Such deposits, however, either have been removed subsequently or, if buried by Cretaceous strata, have not been identified except in easternmost North Carolina, where beds in the bottom part of a deep well are judged to be Jurassic (Fig. 14.2). There is no known evidence that the Appalachians or adjacent belts were sufficiently elevated to have mountainous relief, but the average elevation and slope of the land surface favored erosion rather than sedimentation.

Jurassic Life

Plants. Conifers and the palmlike plants called *cycadeoids* were main types of vegetation, as indicated by plant remains found in continental Jurassic deposits (Fig. 14.10). Modern types of flowering plants, including

Fig. 14.7 Cross-bedded Lower Jurassic sandstone. This view shows part of the Navajo Sandstone in southern Utah a few miles east of Kanab. (*R. C. Moore.*)

trees like the oak, elm, maple, and poplar, had not yet made an appearance, although very scanty angiosperm remains are known. As in Pennsylvanian time, the land floras of the Jurassic seem to have been remarkably uniform throughout the world. It is true even that Jurassic plant assemblages from the Arctic and Antarctic regions differ little from those found in temperate and subtropical areas.

Land animals. Land areas of Jurassic time, we may be sure, were abundantly populated by a varied assemblage of vertebrate and invertebrate animals. In the streams and other fresh-water bodies were many kinds of fishes, amphibians, reptiles, mussels, snails, crustaceans, worms, and water bugs; on dry land there were hordes of reptiles, diminutive archaic mammals, ants, and other crawling insects; in the air were flying reptiles, the

Fig. 14.8 Varicolored shaly continental deposits of Late Jurassic age in central Wyoming. These deposits (Morrison) were laid by streams and in shallow lakes. They have yielded numerous fine skeletal remains of dinosaurs and fresh-water crustaceans (ostracodes) almost identical with fossils found in uppermost continental Jurassic beds of England.

earliest known birds, and a variety of winged insects, including moths and butterflies. This range is comparable to the animal life of modern time, even though only a small part of all the kinds of Jurassic creatures that actually lived are yet known.

The dominant kinds of Jurassic life were very different from those of the present day, for the earth was then ruled by reptiles. Among these reptiles, the dinosaurs were chief, and among Jurassic dinosaurs are the most ponderous land animals of all earth history. A majority of them were herbivorous, but some were flesh-eaters; some walked on four legs, and others, holding the body semi-erect, used the front limbs as arms; some were aquatic or semiaquatic, whereas others were adapted for running swiftly on land. A few were armed with grotesque bony plates and spines (Fig. 14.9). The main types of Jurassic dinosaurs and associated reptiles of other types are treated in Chap. 16, on evolution of life in the Mesozoic Era.

The oldest known birds, provided with teeth and having a lizard-like tail with many vertebrae, are reptilian creatures, which are classified as birds because they have feathers (Fig. 14.10).

The appearance of first-known mammals in Middle and Late Jurassic deposits is a specially noteworthy feature of the life record belonging to this period. They were small animals, the largest having the size of a house cat, but as forerunners of vertebrates that became dominant in Cenozoic time, including the present, they are interesting and important. Mostly described from fragmentary remains, numerous kinds have been recognized on the basis of fossils collected in southern England and Wyoming.

Marine life. Marine deposits of the Jurassic Period contain fossil remains of plants and animals, which in many places are unsurpassed in variety, abundance, and perfection of preservation. The plants are represented especially by calcareous algae that built large reefs

Fig. 14.9 Restoration of the plated dinosaur *Stegosaurus*. One of the most bizarre reptiles of all time is this small-brained, ponderous Jurassic dinosaur, some 20 feet long and 11 feet high at the hips. It was a herbivore that inhabited the western United States. (*Courtesy of U.S. National Museum.*)

Archaeopteryx
evolution of
feather

Fig. 14.10 A Jurassic landscape. This restoration shows several flying reptiles (pterosaurs); the earliest known birds (*Archaeopteryx*), which had teeth and a long lizard-like tail; tiny dinosaurs; and the characteristic palmlike Mesozoic plants called *cycadeoids*. (*C. R. Knight, courtesy of Chicago Natural History Museum.*)

locally. Among animals, vertebrate types include fishes and reptiles, and shelled invertebrates represent all main phyla.

The Jurassic marine reptiles comprise four groups: the remarkably streamlined, fishlike ichthyosaurs; squat-bodied, long- and short-necked types called *plesiosaurs;* sea lizards known as *mosasaurs*, which attained great size;

turtles; and the only crocodiles that ever took to the sea and became adapted to marine life. The limbs of all these reptiles are modified into flippers or paddles that are entirely unsuited for locomotion on land, but despite their adaptation for life in the sea, they were air breathers.

The varied assemblage of marine inverte-

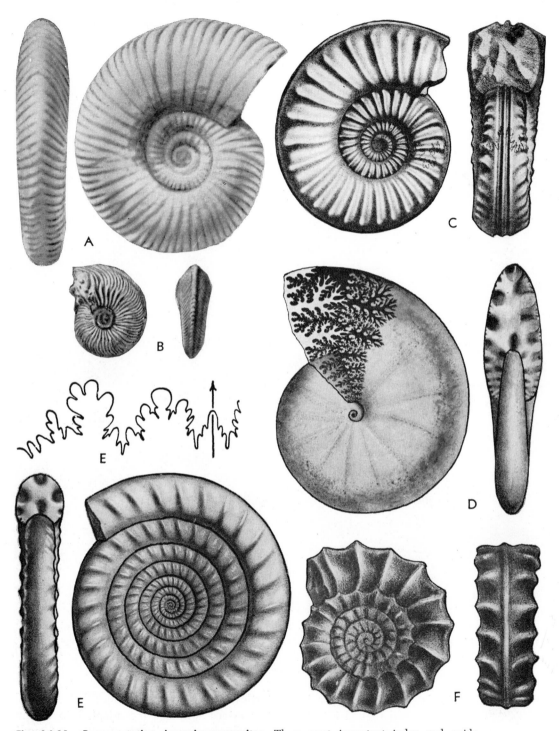

Fig. 14.11 Representative Jurassic ammonites. These most important index and guide fossils are distinguished by shell shape and suture pattern. Forms here illustrated are *A, Idoceras,* ×1; *B, Cardioceras,* ×1; *C, Megarietites,* ×0.4; *D, Zetoceras,* ×0.5; *E, Caloceras,* with drawing of suture, ×0.75; *F, Echioceras,* ×1.5; *A, B,* Upper Jurassic; *C–F,* Lower Jurassic. (*C–F, from Treatise on Invertebrate Paleontology, courtesy of Geological Society of America and University of Kansas Press.*)

brates has chief value for correlation of Jurassic deposits laid down in shallow seas, and dominant among these are the complex-sutured coiled cephalopods called *ammonites* (Fig. 14.11). The ammonites were able to swim freely in the open ocean as well as in shallow seas of continental areas. Also, after the death of the cephalopod, the gas-filled chambered shell could float and thus be carried long distances by marine currents, just as the modern pearly nautilus is commonly transported after the death of the animal. In these ways, identical kinds of Jurassic ammonites are found in widely separated regions of the world. They exhibit a remarkable variety of external ornamentation and pattern of the internal sutures. Their rate of evolutionary change was rapid, so that forms

from different horizons are readily differentiated. Some Late Jurassic ammonites attained gigantic size, rivaling the largest coiled cephalopod shells known, which occur in Cretaceous rocks (Fig. 14.12).

Another type of widespread Jurassic cephalopods is found in the ancestral relatives of the squids, called *belemnites*, characterized by a dense cigar-shaped internal skeleton of calcite.

Jurassic echinoderms are especially represented by sea urchins and crinoids. The most common type of crinoids had a pentagonal, or star-shaped, stem that in some specimens had a length greater than 50 feet.

Foraminifers, sponges, corals, bryozoans, brachiopods, clams, snails, arthropods, and some types of worms include a host of species,

Fig. 14.12 Giant Late Jurassic ammonite in the Canadian Rockies. Two views of a virtually uncollectable fossil found in basal Kootenay (Upper Portlandian) beds near Fernie, British Columbia. The specimen, identified as *Titanites occidentalis*, is 4.5 feet (137 centimeters) in diameter. (*Courtesy of Hans Frebold, Geol. Survey Canada.*)

which are distinguished from older and younger representatives of these groups.

Marine sedimentary deposits of various sorts that are distributed throughout northwestern Europe are exceptionally rich at many places in well-preserved invertebrate fossils. These permit recognition of many faunal zones and are the basis for dividing the rock succession into widely recognized stages and lesser stratigraphic units.

One of the best known sedimentary rocks in Europe is the Solnhofen Limestone of southern Germany. This Jurassic rock has an exceptionally fine grain and has long been the commercial standard for lithographic limestone. In addition, it contains a variety of exceptionally well-preserved fossils including many shelled invertebrates and some impressions of soft-bodied organisms such as jellyfishes. From this rock also come the famous specimens of oldest known birds, which bore teeth, and flying reptiles. Very similar limestone of Early Jurassic age (Holzmaden) in southern Germany has yielded many remarkable specimens of marine reptiles (ichthyosaurs, plesiosaurs, and others) and exceptionally well-preserved crinoids.

Climate

The uniformity of land floras in widely separated parts of the world, including high and low latitudes, and associated cosmopolitan aspects of continental and marine faunas, all point to a prevailing mild equable climate during the Jurassic Period. In some areas, such as the southwestern United States, part of Jurassic time was evidently marked by such aridity as to produce truly desert conditions. In general, however, there seem to have been no strongly marked climatic belts, and no evidence of glacial climate is known anywhere.

Mountain Building

In western Nevada mountain-building crustal movements of Early Jurassic age have been identified by the discovery of marine Middle Jurassic strata lying unconformably on strongly folded and thrust-faulted Lower Jurassic and older rocks.

The Sierra Nevada and Coast Ranges of California, mountainous parts of southwestern Oregon, and the Cascade Mountains of Washington and British Columbia contain highly disturbed Jurassic and older formations that generally have been thought to indicate the occurrence of a major epoch of mountain building late in the Jurassic Period (in terms of stage divisions defined in Europe, post-Kimmeridgian and pre-Portlandian, as measured by age determinations of strata assigned to some parts of these units). The name "Nevadan orogeny" has been applied to this important mountain building. Studies made in recent years serve to cast grave doubts as to the occurrence of Late Jurassic mountain-building deformations in the Pacific Border region, for neither in the Sierra Nevada nor California Coast Ranges are significant unconformities found in the upper part of the Jurassic succession. Furthermore, in the northern Cascades of Washington an unbroken sequence of deposits extending from lower Upper Jurassic (Oxfordian) well up into the Lower Cretaceous (Valanginian) has been demonstrated. The most important folding, faulting, and metamorphism of rocks in these areas is pre-Upper Jurassic—almost surely pre-Middle Jurassic and post-Triassic—thus possibly corresponding to the Early Jurassic movements mentioned in western Nevada.

Accompanying or following the Jurassic mountain building in western parts of North America, bathylithic igneous intrusions invaded the deformed sedimentary rocks on a huge scale. Granitic rocks (mostly granodiorite) were introduced in upper parts of the earth's crust and today, after prolonged erosion in Cenozoic time, are exposed in large areas, such as high parts of the Sierra Nevada (Fig. 14.13) and many other places northward into Canada. Generally, the granites have been classed as Jurassic in age, as indicated on the most recent geologic map of the United States published by the U.S. Geological Survey. In this book they are assigned to the Cretaceous (Fig. 15.2) on the basis of radioactive age measurements that indicate less antiquity than Jurassic, although some bathyliths of the Klamath Mountains region actually are Jurassic.

Fig. 14.13 Great cliff of bathylithic intrusive rock of ?Jurassic age in the Sierra Nevada of California. This view in Yosemite National Park affords a good exposure of part of the enormously extensive igneous masses (*granodiorite*) that were intruded into sedimentary rocks of the Cordilleran geosyncline at the time of the Nevadan mountain building.

Close of the Period

In many parts of the world that were inundated by Jurassic shallow seas, marine waters were withdrawn into nearest ocean basins before the close of the period. This is demon-strated by the occurrence of nonmarine deposits adjacent to the Jurassic-Cretaceous boundary or by an unconformity between rocks of the two systems. Some areas, however, furnish record of uninterrupted sedimentation extending from Late Jurassic into

Early Cretaceous time, with a conformable sequence of marine deposits (for example, in California, Washington, and southern France). In such places, the boundary between the systems is fixed by correlations with youngest Jurassic and oldest Cretaceous as identified where distinction can be recognized. Actually, because of readily observed differences in the characters of marine faunas, especially in the nature of successive kinds of ammonoid cephalopods, there is little difficulty in determining what strata should be classified as Jurassic and what as Cretaceous.

Economic Resources

Jurassic rocks and mineral deposits associated with them or classed as Jurassic in age have great aggregate importance. These resources include especially iron, coal, gold, petroleum, salt, bauxite, and stone, but of this list only gold and salt are Jurassic resources in North America, and question is raised if the gold and the salt really are Jurassic.

Iron. The Jurassic System is a leading source of the world's iron, ranking next to the Precambrian in supplying needs of the steel industry. The deposits, which are of sedimentary origin, occur in England and Alsace-Lorraine. The ores have been worked for many decades and have served as a mainstay of European economy and, as regards the Alsace-Lorraine deposits, an origin of war-causing friction between the French and Germans. Current annual production of Jurassic iron ores is in the neighborhood of 60 million tons.

Coal. The Jurassic is also an important coal producing system, especially in the Siberian part of U.S.S.R., where extensive areas are underlain by Jurassic coal of commercial quality and thickness, in Australia and Tasmania, locally in various parts of Europe, in China

and Japan, and finally, in eastern Greenland and Spitsbergen.

Gold. The leading area of gold production based on ores presumed to be of Jurassic age is the western slope part of the Sierra Nevadas in California, where rich gold-bearing veins intersect folded sedimentary rocks. The deep-seated origin of these veins is igneous intrusive rock emplaced during or subsequent to the Nevadan orogeny. The area includes the famous Mother Lode, which is one of the richest gold deposits ever discovered in North America. Counting placer deposits derived from the Mother Lode belt and gold mined from veins, the district has produced nearly $2,000 million in gold values.

Petroleum. Considerable amounts of oil have been found in buried Jurassic formations of the Gulf region in southern Arkansas, northern Louisiana, and eastern Texas; also there is some Jurassic oil production from Wyoming. Greatest yield of petroleum from this system is from fields of the Middle East.

Salt. Salt underlies Jurassic strata in the Gulf region, the stratified deposits being named Louann (Fig. 14.3). This may be the same as the widely distributed salt found in hundreds of Gulf region salt domes, where intrusive plugs of salt a mile or more in diameter penetrate Cretaceous and younger deposits (Chap. 17), and if so, commercially large production of rock salt is obtained from this source. Possibly the salt is Jurassic.

Other resources. Bauxite, a chief source of aluminum, is mined in southeastern Europe from Jurassic formations. In various parts of Europe, Jurassic limestones are much used for construction of buildings; for example, Oxford University and various cathedrals are built with cut stone from the Jurassic. One of the largest brick plants in the world, in central England, uses Jurassic clay.

READINGS

Berry, E. W., 1918, The Jurassic lagoons of Solenhofen: *Sci. Monthly*, October, pp. 361–378 (illus.).
   Interesting nontechnical account of one of the most famous fossil localities in the world.
Colbert, E. H., 1951, *The dinosaur book*, McGraw-Hill Book Company, Inc., New York (156 pp., illus.).
   One of the best relatively brief books on these fossils.

COLBERT, E. H., 1955, *Evolution of the vertebrates,* John Wiley & Sons, Inc., New York (479 pp., illus.). [1] Marine reptiles, pp. 158–169. [2] Flying reptiles and birds, pp. 170–182. [3] Triumph of the dinosaurs, pp. 183–203. [4] Years of the dinosaurs, pp. 204–214. [5] Beginning of the mammals, pp. 227–238.

Includes exceptionally well-written accounts of Jurassic vertebrate animals.

IMLAY, R. W., 1957, Paleoecology of Jurassic seas in the Western Interior of the United States: in *Treatise on marine ecology,* H. S. Ladd, ed., Geol. Soc. America Mem. 67, vol. 2, pp. 469–504.

Valuable description and interpretation of Jurassic sedimentation in western United States.

PETERSON, J. A., 1954, Marine Upper Jurassic, eastern Wyoming: *Am. Assoc. Petroleum Geologists Bull.,* vol. 38, pp. 463–507.

SCHUCHERT, CHARLES, and LeVENE, C. M., 1940, *O. C. Marsh, pioneer in paleontology,* Yale University Press, New Haven, Conn. (541 pp., illus.).

Contains (chap. 7) description of finding of Jurassic dinosaurs.

SIMPSON, G. G., 1926, The age of the Morrison Formation: *Am. Jour. Sci.,* ser. 5, vol. 12, pp. 198–216.

STOKES, W. L., 1944, Morrison Formation and related deposits in and adjacent to the Colorado Plateau: *Geol. Soc. America Bull.,* vol. 55, pp. 951–992.

The Morrison beds contain specially interesting sedimentary characters throughout a very large region.

QUESTIONS

1. Jurassic sandstone deposits, 1,000 to 3,000 feet or more thick in southern Utah (Chap. 14, frontispiece), are inferred to have accumulated in a Sahara-like desert environment. Can you point out reasons for accepting this interpretation, or can evidence opposing it be suggested?

2. Referring to the Jurassic distribution map (Fig. 14.2), what explanation can be offered for the entire absence of Jurassic outcrops in the eastern United States? Although concealed Jurassic formations have been penetrated by wells in Mississippi, Arkansas, northern Louisiana, and many parts of western United States, they have not been reached near the Gulf Coast and various other places (as throughout much of northern Mexico, the Great Valley of California, and beneath the very thick Cenozoic lavas of Oregon and Washington). What are reasons for mapping concealed Jurassic in areas where its presence is not demonstrated by obtaining samples (for example, on the continental shelf beneath the Gulf of Mexico)?

3. What was the prevailing direction of sand transportation when the cross-bedded sandstone illustrated in Fig. 14.7 (view looking north) was deposited? Give reasons for your answer. Why are most of the laminae truncated at their upper extremities? What significance as to the environment of sedimentation can be ascribed to (a) general uniformity of grain size of the sand, (b) well-rounded shape of the grains, (c) similarity of cross-bedding pattern throughout the rock?

4. What are the most important distinctions in lithology, stratification, and organic content between the Morrison Formation (Fig. 14.8) and subjacent Jurassic sandstones such as the Navajo, Entrada, Nugget, and other like formations? Why is the Morrison interpreted to have been formed mostly by sedimentation in fresh-water bodies (ponds, shallow lakes, sluggish streams) rather than formed by wind transportation and deposition? What evidence denies its origin in a widespread but very shallow inland sea, possibly bordered by extensive mud flats?

5. What are the reasons for classifying pterosaurs as flying reptiles unrelated to birds (Fig. 14.10, Appendix A)? Why are the earliest known birds recognized as undoubted descendants of reptilian ancestors?

6. What are several inescapable deductions concerning geologic history of the Canadian Rocky Mountains country adjacent to Fernie, British Columbia, based solely on observation of features seen in Fig. 14.12?

7. Can you suggest reasons for lack of certainty concerning the geologic age of the bathylithic core of the Sierra Nevada in California, despite sureness of excluding it from Precambrian, Paleozoic, and Cenozoic origin?

15.

MESOZOIC ERA:

CRETACEOUS PERIOD

Rocky Mountains front southwest of Denver, Colorado, showing upturned Cretaceous strata.

T. S. Lovering, courtesy of U.S. Geol. Survey

The third and last division of the Mesozoic Era is known as the Cretaceous Period. The name, introduced in 1822, is derived from the Latin word *creta* (chalk), which is prominently exposed in the White Cliffs of Dover, southeastern England, and along the north coast of France, across the English Channel (Fig. 15.1). This is the classic area where the Cretaceous deposits were first differentiated from the underlying Jurassic and overlying beds long known as Cenozoic (Paleogene, Neogene). The subdivisions comprising the standard section for comparison and correlation with Cretaceous deposits in other parts of the world have been defined from outcrops in France, England, western Germany, Belgium, Holland, and Denmark.

The Cretaceous System is well set apart

as a major division of the geologic column, because important unconformities occur at both the base and summit in most areas. This statement should not be understood to mean that almost everywhere there are unconformities marked by obvious physical characters, for this is untrue. In the Gulf Coast region of the United States, for example, the upper limit of the Cretaceous System is an obscure disconformity or paraconformity, yet the boundary is definite and serves to mark the limit of deposits respectively assigned to different eras, Mesozoic below and Cenozoic above. Cretaceous rocks throughout the world are distinguished by the nature of their fossils, for these include many genera and species unknown in older or younger strata and they lack diagnostic fossils of the Jurassic and early Cenozoic.

Chalk or chalky limestone is by no means the only type of deposit occurring in the Cretaceous System; as a matter of fact, the chalk is far outranked quantitatively by shale and sandstone. There is much hard non-chalky limestone, and in places coal beds are prominent. Nevertheless, no other geologic system contains widespread chalk deposits, and the term *Cretaceous* is accepted as an appropriate designation for late Mesozoic rocks throughout the world.

Recognition of Cretaceous in North America

Index and guide fossils. Distinctive plants, invertebrates, and vertebrate remains that characterize Cretaceous deposits in northwestern Europe are found to be widely distributed in deposits of corresponding age in North America. These fossils not only serve to establish the Cretaceous age of the deposits containing them but, despite some differences due to regional variation, permit close correlation with subdivisions of the European standard section.

For purposes of such correlation, the ammonites are the chief guide fossils, because they show considerable evolutionary change from zone to zone and because, as swimmers, they could intermigrate freely between areas occupied by the sea. Some index fossils of

European Cretaceous zones (name-givers to the zones) occur also west of the Atlantic; naturally, these are very helpful as indicators of age equivalence, but not necessarily more so than other fossils. Echinoids are also useful guide fossils in some Cretaceous zones, and certain sorts of Cretaceous clams have nearly world-wide distribution. The microscopic shells of foraminifers of a type provided with calcareous globular chambers are characteristic of Cretaceous marine deposits throughout the world and form a large part of the substance of chalk beds. Although characteristic of the Cretaceous, these fossils are relatively long ranging within the system.

The appearance of many true flowering plants, the angiosperms, in Cretaceous deposits is an especially important feature of the fossil record, and it serves to distinguish Cretaceous from Jurassic.

Dominance of reptiles in the vertebrate faunas of Cretaceous time links the system with Mesozoic and separates it from Cenozoic. Also, kinds of reptiles found in Cretaceous rocks of widely distant parts of the world are found to be similar or identical.

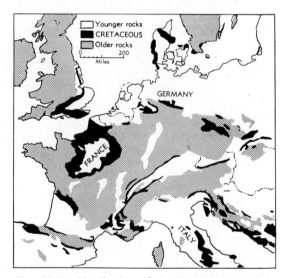

Fig. 15.1 Distribution of Cretaceous outcrops in west-central Europe. The classic region in which rocks belonging to the Cretaceous System were first studied closely is in France and western Germany. Main divisions now recognized throughout most of the world were defined there. The outcrops in England and Denmark also are important.

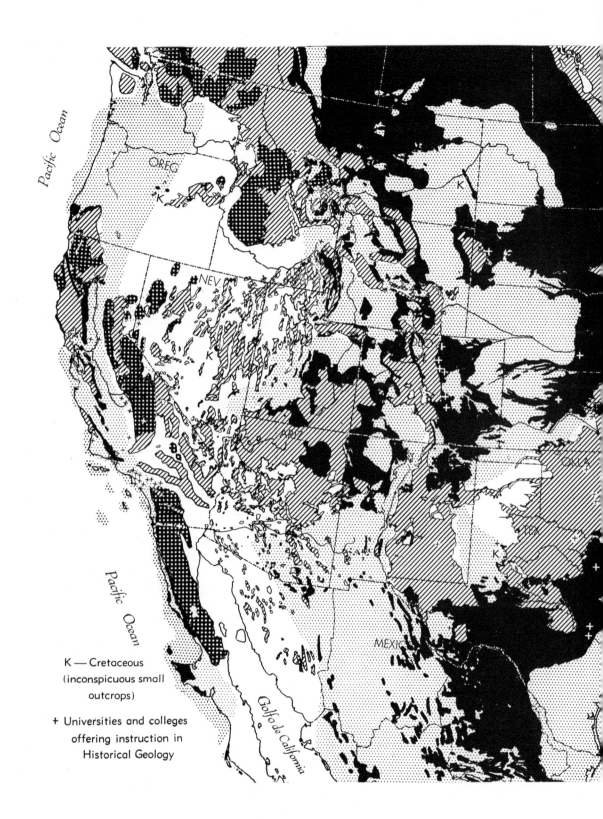

K — Cretaceous
(inconspicuous small
outcrops)

+ Universities and colleges
offering instruction in
Historical Geology

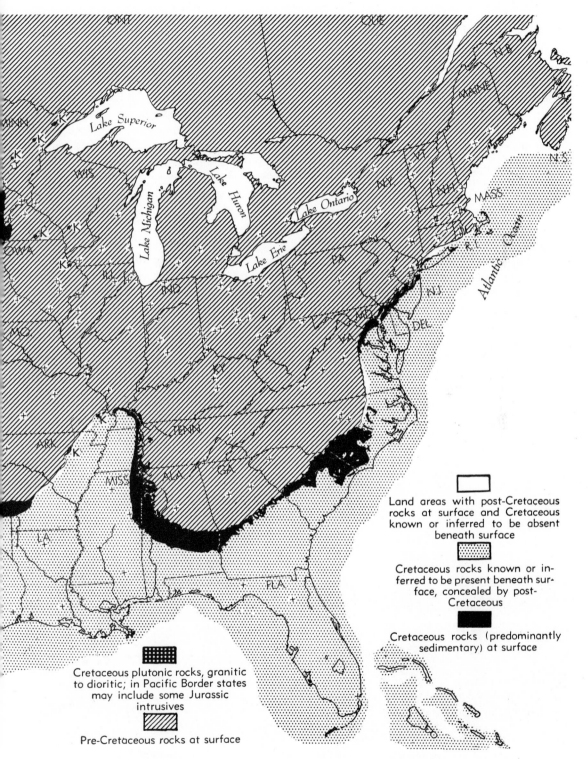

Land areas with post-Cretaceous rocks at surface and Cretaceous known or inferred to be absent beneath surface

Cretaceous rocks known or inferred to be present beneath surface, concealed by post-Cretaceous

Cretaceous rocks (predominantly sedimentary) at surface

Cretaceous plutonic rocks, granitic to dioritic; in Pacific Border states may include some Jurassic intrusives

Pre-Cretaceous rocks at surface

Fig. 15.2 Distribution of Cretaceous rocks in the United States, southern Canada, and northern Mexico. The outcrops and subsurface occurrences shown indicate the original distribution of the system, modified by aggregate effects of removal of deposits by erosion.

Character and Distribution of Deposits

Cretaceous formations of North America are conveniently treated in four parts according to their distribution: (1) along the Atlantic Border, (2) the plains country adjacent to the Gulf of Mexico, (3) the Rocky Mountains and adjoining plains to the east, and (4) the Pacific Border region (Fig. 15.2). Although similar in some respects, the Cretaceous of each of these divisions shows differences from the others.

Atlantic Border. A narrow belt of Cretaceous outcrops extends almost uninterruptedly along the inner border of the Atlantic Coastal Plain from Long Island, New York, to Georgia (Fig. 15.3). The landward margin of the Cretaceous coincides with the physiographic feature known as the Fall Line, which marks the head of navigation on most rivers flowing into the Atlantic. Falls or rapids occur where streams pass from the hard rocks of the Appalachian Piedmont Plateau onto weak stratified rocks of the coastal plain, and the availability of water power at points accessible by marine shipping was the chief factor determining the location of many cities in the eighteenth and nineteenth centuries. Thus Trenton, Philadelphia, Wilmington, Baltimore, Washington, Richmond, Columbia, Augusta, and other large settlements are located along the inner margin of the Cretaceous outcrop.

At the base of the Cretaceous is a profound unconformity, inasmuch as the subjacent rocks in most places are resistant, strongly deformed, metamorphosed Precambrian rocks or Paleozoic granite. Elsewhere, the Cretaceous rests on the beveled edges of tilted Triassic strata or on truncated strongly folded Paleozoic rocks.

Cretaceous formations of the Atlantic Border include both continental and marine deposits. The attitude of the beds is nearly horizontal, but there is a uniform gentle dip toward the sea, reflecting in part the original position in which the beds were deposited and in part a gentle seaward tilting that is interpreted to represent slight crustal warping. Overlying Cenozoic beds are nearly parallel to the Cretaceous and also dip seaward. The basal Cretaceous deposits consist of prevailingly unconsolidated gravel or sand, mostly

Fig. 15.3 Typical country formed by Cretaceous deposits in the Atlantic Coastal Plain. Most of the outcrop area is well covered by soil and vegetation, but the nature of the deposits may be studied along many gulleys and artificial exposures such as highway cuts.

of fluviatile origin, and these are followed in varying manner by clay, sand, and calcareous beds called marl that in part contain marine fossils. Aggregate thickness in most places does not exceed 1,000 feet.

Subsurface distribution of Cretaceous deposits along the Atlantic Border is continuous beneath all of the Coastal Plain seaward from the Cretaceous outcrop belt and beneath nearly all of this plain where no Cretaceous is exposed along the edge of the Piedmont crystalline rocks (as throughout eastern Virginia and northeastern North Carolina) (Fig. 15.2). In addition, Cretaceous deposits surely are present beneath younger sediments east of the coast line, probably extending with attenuated thickness far beyond the continental slope. On the map showing distribution given in this chapter, no Cretaceous is indicated beyond the edge of the continental shelf, that is, approximately along the depth contour of 600 feet.

Gulf region. Cretaceous outcrops extend westward from Georgia in a belt that crosses central Alabama and swings northward east of the Mississippi to the southern tip of Illinois. West of the Mississippi, Cretaceous rocks appear in southwestern Arkansas and in a widening belt are traced thence southwestward into Mexico. The Cretaceous of the Gulf region resembles that of the Atlantic Border in its gentle seaward inclination and in having a profound unconformity at its base. In most places, the rocks beneath the Cretaceous are Paleozoics, strongly folded in Georgia, Alabama, Arkansas, and Oklahoma but nearly horizontal elsewhere. The folded Paleozoic rocks were smoothly truncated by erosion prior to deposition of earliest Cretaceous sediments. In part of the country west of the Mississippi River, buried Jurassic strata immediately underlie the Cretaceous.

The lowermost Cretaceous deposits commonly consist of coarse sandstone or conglomerate, and this is followed by 1,000 to 3,000 feet of shale, sandstone, chalk, and chalky limestone. Most of the deposits yield marine fossils. The outcrops of successive formations are arranged in parallel belts, weak rocks forming lowlands and harder formations forming uplands or landward-facing escarpments, commonly tree-covered.

Beneath the surface, Cretaceous beds have a very wide distribution, for as in the Atlantic Coastal Plain, the Cretaceous dips seaward and is mapped as extending to the outer edge of the continental shelf. Thus, the subsurface area of distribution considerably exceeds the outcrop area, and it is continuous from Florida to eastern Mexico south of the Rio Grande. Along most of the northwest margin of the Mississippi Embayment (broad northward extension of the coastal plain in the Mississippi Valley), Cretaceous rocks are exposed only in a couple of isolated patches, and elsewhere along this margin buried Cretaceous is overlapped by younger deposits that rest directly on pre-Cretaceous rocks (Fig. 15.2).

Rocky Mountains region. From Mexico to far northwestern Canada and Alaska, sedimentary deposits of Cretaceous age are distributed through a broad belt that in places exceeds 700 miles from east to west. The Rocky Mountains chain approximately marks the axis of this belt, which extends eastward into the High Plains country and westward across plateau and canyon country to borders of the Great Basin. The area marks the site of a geosyncline, in parts of which Cretaceous deposits attain a thickness of more than 15,000 feet.

Both nonmarine and marine deposits are very extensive. Among the former are conglomerate, sandstone, shale, and thick coal beds, laid down by streams and formed in shallow lakes and swamps (Fig. 15.4). Fossil land plants and remains of land animals are found in these continental formations. Strata of marine origin include chalk, chalky limestone, shale, and sandstone which in places contain numerous shells of oysters and other invertebrates (Figs. 15.4, 15.5). Dark-colored shale deposits are especially prominent, and they are very uniform in character for hundreds of miles along the outcrop.

A noteworthy feature of Cretaceous de-

Fig. 15.4 Cretaceous shale and sandstone near Grand Junction, Colorado. This air view of the Little Book Cliffs shows marine dark-colored Mancos Shale of uniform texture, several hundred feet thick, capped by Mesaverde Sandstone of continental origin. The flat-topped plateau in the background is Grand Mesa, which is covered by lava. (*Courtesy of Spence Air Photos.*)

posits in this province is the lateral change of sedimentary facies, reflecting variations in conditions of contemporary sedimentation on land, in lagoonal areas along the coast, in shallow marine waters near shore, and in somewhat deeper offshore environments. Sedimentary deposits representing each of these habitats grade laterally into one another and

interfinger, thus proving their equivalence in age.

Pacific Border. Embayments of the Pacific spread inland across parts of California, Oregon, Washington, and British Columbia during Cretaceous time, occupying downwarped and downfaulted blocks throughout the belt that had suffered strong deformation in the

Fig. 15.5 Thin-bedded Cretaceous chalky limestone resting on dark Cretaceous shale. This outcrop in southwestern South Dakota shows Greenhorn and Graneros beds which are representative of marine deposits that are extremely widespread in the Great Plains and the Gulf and Atlantic Coastal borders. (*N. H. Darton, courtesy of U.S. Geol. Survey.*)

Nevadan orogeny. The deposits are rather local and somewhat variable, but some of them are exceptionally thick, in places exceeding 40,000 feet. The deposits comprise mostly shale and sandstone, which represent rock materials eroded from adjacent mountainous areas formed in pre-Cretaceous orogeny.

Divisions

Cretaceous formations in North America are divisible into two main parts known as Lower Cretaceous and Upper Cretaceous (Fig. 15.6). These parts are separated in places by an unconformity and by well-marked differences in the fossils representing both marine and nonmarine habitats. In the Gulf region, the Lower Cretaceous is commonly known as the Comanchean Series and the Upper Cretaceous as the Gulfian Series. Several stages and substages are recognized that are judged to correspond closely to similar time-rock divisions of the European section.

In Europe and other parts of the world outside North America, deposits of Cretaceous age also show a twofold division. Sedimenta-

tion during the period seems to have been fairly continuous, and on the basis of differences in fossils, the column is divided into a number of stages defined from localities in western Europe.

Features of Cretaceous History in North America

Submergence of the Atlantic Border. The outstanding feature of Cretaceous history in eastern North America was gradual depression of the continental border. This downwarping brought to a close the erosion that during Jurassic time had peneplaned a large part of the coastal region. The shore line shifted inland. Early in the Cretaceous, the shore line moved from a position well east of the present coast line to points approximating the modern sea border, and on the landward side of this Early Cretaceous shore, sluggish streams built a coastal plain of sand and mud in the Chesapeake Bay region. These fluviatile sediments comprise the exposed Lower Cretaceous formations of the Atlantic region.

Stratigraphic correlation chart of Cretaceous formations across Interior, Gulf, Pacific, and Rocky Mountains regions.

Series	Stages (Europe)	INTERIOR (Standard)	GULF (Standard)	PACIFIC Calif.	ROCKY MOUNTAINS Utah	SW. Wyo.	C. Wyo	C. Mont
Next above				Eoc.	Paleoc.	Eoc.	Paleoc.	Paleoc.
UPPER CRETACEOUS — Senonian	Maastrichtian	Hell Creek F.; Fox Hills Ss. (Montana Group)	Navarro Gr. (Gulf Series)		North Horn F. (part); Price River F.		Lance F.	Hell Creek F.; Fox Hills Ss.; Bearpaw Sh.
	Campanian	Pierre Sh.; Eagle Ss. (Montana Group)	Taylor Marl (Gulf Series)				Lewis Sh.; Mesaverde F.	Judith River F.; Claggett Sh.; Eagle Ss.
	Santonian	Telegraph Cr F. (Colorado Group)						Telegraph Cr F.
	Coniacian	Niobrara F. (Colorado Group)	Austin Chalk (Gulf Series)			Adaville F.; Hilliard Sh.	Cody Sh.	
	Turonian	Carlile Sh.; Greenhorn Ls. (Colorado Group)	Eagle Ford Sh.	Chico F.	Indianola F.	Frontier F.	Frontier F.	Colorado Sh.
	Cenomanian	Belle Fourche Sh. (Colorado Group)	Woodbine F.					
LOWER CRETACEOUS — Albian	Albian	Mowry Sh.; Newcastle-Fall Riv Ss.; Red Sh. (Gannett Group; Comanche Series)	Washita Gr.; Fredericksburg Gr.	(Horsetown Group; Shasta Series)	Aspen Sh.; Bear River F.	Mowry Sh.; Thermopolis Sh.		Kootenai F.
	Aptian	Draney Ls.; Bechler Congl.; Peterson Ls. (Gannett Group)	Trinity Gr.; Nuevo Leon Gr. (Coahuila Series)				Cloverly F.	
	Neocomian — Barremian	Ephraim Congl. (Gannett Group)			Gannett F.			
	Hauterivian		Durango Gr. (Coahuila Series)	(Paskenta Grt)				
	Valanginian							
	Berriasian							
Next below				Jur.	Jur.	Jur.	Jur.	Jur.

374

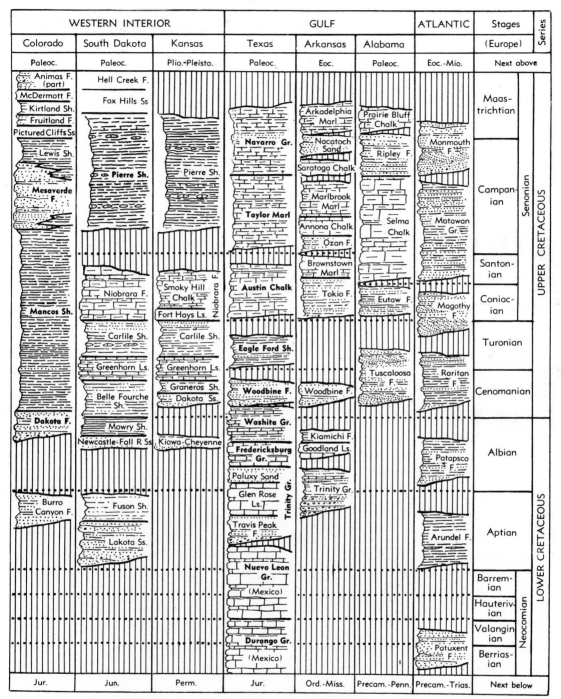

Fig. 15.6 Time-rock divisions of the Cretaceous System and rock units assigned to them in representative important Cretaceous sections of North America. The vertical scale does not represent time duration or thickness of rocks but is determined by suitability for plotting the various recognized rock units, placement of which indicates correlation in age. Lithologic character is represented graphically (explanation of symbols in Appendix B). Necessarily, the plotted thickness is not to scale, although it approximates proportional values in many sections. Vertically ruled areas denote absence of deposits.

In the later part of Cretaceous time, the Atlantic sea moved farther inland. Marine sediments buried virtually all of the Early Cretaceous coastal plain and in most places came to rest on areas that had received no Lower Cretaceous sediments. Thus, marine Upper Cretaceous beds are seen resting directly on erosion-beveled Precambrian crystalline rocks. Nonmarine coastal plain sediments were doubtless spread over a considerable area in Late Cretaceous time, but subsequent erosion has removed most of this material.

Marine oscillations in the Gulf region. Cretaceous history in the region bordering the Gulf of Mexico is interpreted to have begun with landward shift of shallow seas, but the advance was not uniform along all parts of the coast, nor was submergence steadily progressive. East of the Mississippi, no Lower Cretaceous rocks are exposed, and throughout a large area well borings show that Upper Cretaceous strata rest directly on Paleozoic or older rocks. Evidently, the sea did not occupy this region in Early Cretaceous time, and the attitude of the land surface was not changed so as to cause appreciable deposition of fluviatile coastal plains deposits.

West of the Mississippi, on the other hand, there was a considerable Early Cretaceous marine inundation (Fig. 15.7). That the sea advanced gradually and steadily in the early part of the period is shown by the regularly greater landward extent of successive higher divisions of the Lower Cretaceous marine deposits. Higher rock units overlap lower ones and, along their landward margins, are found resting directly on pre-Cretaceous rocks. Most of the observed Lower Cretaceous rocks are marine, but marginal nonmarine deposits are also found preserved beneath sediments of the advancing sea. Eventually marine waters covered most of Texas, reached into Arkansas

Fig. 15.7 High bridge across the lower Pecos River in western Texas. The canyon valley of the Pecos near its confluence with the Rio Grande is carved in hard Lower Cretaceous limestone. These rocks cover a very large territory in central and western Texas.

and central Kansas, and advanced to Montana.

Then came a great retreat of the Cretaceous sea. Large areas of recently formed marine deposits were uncovered and began to be eroded. In central Texas, beach sands at the margin of the restricted sea came to be deposited directly on limestone representing far offshore conditions in the immediately preceding epoch of transgressive seas. This major marine oscillation in the Gulf region serves to separate Early Cretaceous from Late Cretaceous time.

Renewed advance of the sea occurred in the latter part of the Cretaceous Period. This time, transgression was rapid, and the area of submergence vastly exceeded the farthest reach of Early Cretaceous marine waters. The Gulf States east of the Mississippi were covered (Figs. 15.2, 15.8). The Mississippi Valley was flooded approximately to St. Louis, which, if it had existed in Cretaceous time, might have

been a Gulf port; westward and northwestward, the sea gained access to the Rocky Mountains geosyncline, making a vast inland waterway that reached to the Arctic without interruption (Fig. 15.9). During Late Cretaceous time, accordingly, no natural boundary separated the Gulf and Rocky Mountains provinces. Marine animals were able to intermigrate freely, and although chalk is more prominent in the south and in the Kansas region, the nature of deposits is much the same (Fig. 15.10).

Sedimentation in the Rocky Mountains geosyncline. The sediment-filled trough known as the Rocky Mountains geosyncline is a very broad, not very sharply delimited segment of the earth's crust that roughly coincides in location with the Rocky Mountains chain from northern Mexico into Canada (Fig. 15.9). Maximum thickness of Cretaceous rocks is found in the Utah-Wyoming-Colorado portion

Fig. 15.8 Upper Cretaceous marine clay and sand in southwestern Georgia. The exposure, in a highway cut near Cusseta, shows by its gullied surface the little-consolidated nature of the deposits. (*D. H. Eargle, courtesy of U.S. Geol. Survey.*)

of the geosyncline, where the system locally attains a thickness of more than 30,000 feet; another area of unusually thick deposits occurs near the southeastern corner of Arizona, where nearly 25,000 feet of Cretaceous rocks have been measured. The subsidence of the geosyncline evidently proceeded at a rate that closely matched the progressive infilling of sediment, because all the marine strata are shallow-water types of deposits and there are thick subaerially formed conglomerates, sandstones, shales, and coal beds. The Lower Cretaceous and upper part of the Upper Cretaceous are especially characterized by nonmarine formations. That development of the Rocky Mountains geosyncline is essentially a feature of Cretaceous history is indicated by lack of noteworthy thickening in this region of Jurassic, Triassic, and Paleozoic strata, although generally these are widely distributed in the Rocky Mountains area.

Eastward, the predominantly clastic deposits of the geosyncline are thinner and parts of the rock succession become increasingly calcareous. In eastern Colorado, western Kansas, and Great Plains States farther north, there are extremely uniform, evenly bedded limestone (Fig. 15.11), chalk (Fig. 15.10), and chalky shale. At the base of the Upper Cretaceous section is an unusually widespread deposit of well-sorted, commonly cross-bedded sandstone called Dakota (Fig. 15.12); because this formation is very pervious, it readily takes up large quantities of ground water at various outcrops and yields this water to innumerable wells in the plains country, many of the wells being artesian and thus flowing under hydrostatic head. The sandstone is not quite the same in age everywhere, as is shown by differences in its fossils from place to place and by the fossil content of conformably overlying strata (Fig. 15.6). We conclude that the sea occupied some parts of the geosyncline earlier than others.

The thickest and most widespread deposit laid down in the trough consists of dark silty shale of very uniform texture (Figs. 15.4, 15.13). Especially in the western half of the geosyncline, the shale is interbedded with sandstone, and there is a general increase in the thickness and prominence of sandstone going westward (Figs. 15.14, 15.15). Increasing prominence of coarse sediments to the west, including the presence of nonmarine river-laid deposits, indicates that much detritus came from uplands (called Manhattan geanticline, from a locality in Nevada) that separated the Rocky Mountains geosyncline from the Pacific Border region.

No such lateral transition in the Cretaceous sediments is found along the east margin of the geosyncline, and thus we may infer that lands near the sea in this direction were low. Inasmuch as the volume of Cretaceous clastic sediments in the geosyncline totals many hundred cubic miles, the amount of erosion demanded to supply these sediments is correspondingly great, and the chief area of erosion is inferred to have bordered the geosyncline on the west.

Infilling of the geosyncline resulted in grad-

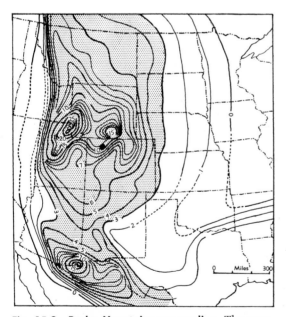

Fig. 15.9 Rocky Mountains geosyncline. The numbered contours indicate thickness of the Cretaceous System in thousands of feet, the geosynclinal area being marked by shading that is arbitrarily bounded by the 3,000-foot thickness contour. Maximum thickness of more than 30,000 feet is recorded in northeastern Utah. (*Data from J. B. Reeside, Jr., courtesy of U.S. Geol. Survey.*)

Fig. 15.10 Cretaceous chalk in western Kansas. This erosion remnant, called "The Sphynx," is part of the pure calcareous Cretaceous deposits that have a total thickness of about 700 feet in Kansas. The beds yield numerous remains of marine invertebrates and some well-preserved skeletons of large fishes, swimming reptiles, toothed diving birds, and flying reptiles that fell into the water and were drowned many miles from nearest land. (*Courtesy of Kansas Geol. Survey.*)

ual encroachment of land areas on the inland sea until, near the close of the period, marine waters almost disappeared. The last remnant of the interior sea is represented by marine deposits, classed as earliest Cenozoic, in western North Dakota.

Sea invasions along the Pacific Border. Relatively narrow seaways along the Pacific Border were the site of very thick sedimentation in Cretaceous time. The deposits consist mostly of gravel, sand, and silt derived from the upland that separated the Pacific Border from the Rocky Mountains geosyncline. As shown by features of bedding and by contained fossils, the sediments were laid down in shallow water, despite the fact that in parts of California the total thickness of sedimentary materials is 8 miles. This signifies that the basins sank slowly as sediment was poured into them. Admixture of volcanic fragmental materials with the sediments shows that there

were active volcanoes, but the extent of volcanism was much less than in the Jurassic.

Cretaceous Life

Beginning of modern floras. The Cretaceous Period was a time of great advancement among land plants, for it was in this part of earth history that deciduous trees like the elm, oak, maple, poplar, and a host of other flowering plants that dominate the modern world became fairly common. Conifers, cycadeoids, and ferns persisted in reduced numbers, but it is the covered-seed plants, called *angiosperms*, that are the most noteworthy Cretaceous plants. The new forms of vegetation include a large variety of flowering shrubs and herbs, as well as the trees growing along streams, scattered in groves on the plains, and crowded thickly in forests. They clearly reflect the influence of seasons in which alternation in conditions of warmth and moisture, or both,

Fig. 15.11 Evenly bedded thin limestones and chalky shale of Late Cretaceous age. The exposure shows typical appearance of the Greenhorn Limestone as seen near Pueblo, Colorado. Farther east, in Kansas, this formation is more largely limestone, one of its layers being the "fence-post bed," so called because it is much used for making fence posts. (*G. K. Gilbert, courtesy of U.S. Geol. Survey.*)

Fig. 15.12 Basal Upper Cretaceous sandstone in Nebraska. This exposure of Dakota Sandstone shows evenly cross-bedded structure, with laminae of coarse-grained, well-sorted sand all sloping in the same direction. It is a water-laid deposit, and at least during accumulation of the beds here seen, currents moved uniformly from left to right, truncating tops of previously formed cross beds and covering them with new layers. (*N. H. Darton, courtesy of U.S. Geol. Survey.*)

was the main control of plant growth and probably a main factor in origin of the angiosperms. Inasmuch as the plants are the primary source of food for animals, the advent of modern floras in Cretaceous time may reasonably be interpreted as an antecedent to the great expansion of mammals and birds during the Cenozoic Era.

Continued dominance of reptiles. Among vertebrates living on land, reptiles were the most numerous, largest, and most varied. Chief were the dinosaurs, which included both flesh-eating and herbivorous types. A group of dinosaurs especially characteristic of the latest Cretaceous are the large-skulled, horned ceratopsians, which persisted to the very close of the period and then abruptly disappeared (Fig. 15.16). None of the known Cretaceous dinosaurs equal in bulk some of those from the Jurassic, but flying reptiles and some of those living in the seas represent the peak of development of these creatures during the Mesozoic Era (Fig. 15.17).

Remains of birds have been found in Cretaceous marine deposits, one type representing a tireless flier like the sea gull and another a large wingless diving bird. These birds had teeth but otherwise were more like the petrel and loon than their reptilian ancestors.

Lastly, among the Cretaceous land vertebrates are the mammals. These hairy, warm-blooded creatures were still small, relatively insignificant animals that doubtless scurried to cover out of the pathway of the dinosaurs or other reptilian lords that they chanced to meet. Their multicuspid teeth suggest that they fed on insects, nuts, grains, and not improbably they learned to prey on the eggs of reptiles, which had been laid in the warm sand to hatch. In mental development and physical activity, they so excelled the sluggish reptiles that they became swiftly adapted to changed conditions of environment at the close of the Mesozoic Era, assuming dominance as the reptiles proved unable to cope with these changes.

Invertebrate life. Shallow seas of Cretaceous time swarmed with foraminifers to such extent that their microscopic shells form a large part of the chalk deposits; they are also very abundant in many shale and some sand deposits. All main groups of larger marine invertebrates, including those dwelling on the bottom of shallow seas and some that were able to swim freely in the open ocean, are well represented in Cretaceous marine deposits. Dominant among these animals are the mollusks, including especially a variety of clams and complexly sutured cephalopods. Characteristic Cretaceous pelecypods include thick-shelled oysters (Fig. 15.19E), large concentrically ribbed clams (Fig. 15.19A), and reef

Fig. 15.13 Upper Cretaceous shale badlands near Grand Junction, Colorado. The air photograph shows a typical area of Mancos Shale, intricately dissected and bare of vegetation, on slopes below the Little Book Cliffs. (*Courtesy of Hal Shelton, Golden, Colorado.*)

Fig. 15.14 North face of the Mesa Verde Plateau in southwestern Colorado. The plateau is formed of Cretaceous shale and sandstone that dip very gently southward. The shale (Mancos) is marine, but the overlying sandstone (Mesaverde) is mainly nonmarine, and in part of this region it is coal-bearing. (*Courtesy of Spence Air Photos.*)

builders of peculiarly coral-like form (rudistids) having steeply conical thick walls (Fig. 15.19B–D). Many types of tightly coiled cephalopods and some loosely coiled and straight forms occur in the Cretaceous rocks (Figs. 15.18, 15.20). These bear highly complex sutures, and many of them had external ribs, nodes, and spines. The largest coiled ammonites attained a diameter of more than 5 feet. In addition, there are internal-shelled belemnoids (Fig. 15.20B). Among echinoderms, there are free-swimming crinoids and extremely numerous sea urchins. Many of these fossils preserved in the chalk have extraordinary delicacy and beauty. As a whole, the Cretaceous marine invertebrates show approach to modern conditions in the rise of mollusks and prominence of echinoids, but they differ in prominence of ammonites, which are entirely lacking in Cenozoic marine deposits.

Climate

Study of Cretaceous sedimentary deposits and fossils calls attention to many indications of climatic diversity. The presence of angiosperms in vegetation of the lands points to temperate climate, yet relative warmth and humidity are indicated by the widespread distribution of such plants as the fig and breadfruit, which now are restricted to subtropical or warm temperate climates; along with cycadeoids, these plants occur in Cretaceous rocks of Alaska and Greenland. On the other hand, evidence of Cretaceous glaciation is reported from eastern Australia, and among Cretaceous deposits are evaporites that indicate at least local aridity.

Variation in climate seems to be associated with the size, placement, and amount of relief of land areas of the globe. Times of lowlands and very extensive seas are marked by wide-

Fig. 15.15 Overhanging cliff of Cretaceous sandstone in Mesa Verde National Park. Cave shelters in canyon walls of the sandstone (Mesaverde) were used by cliff dwellers for construction of their homes, built of stone masonry. (*Courtesy of D. L. Hopwood, Denver, Colorado.*)

Fig. 15.16 *Triceratops*, largest of the horned dinosaurs. These dinosaurs, which lived in the latest part of Cretaceous time, had no teeth at the front of the jaws but a turtle-like beak instead. The skull of some specimens is 8 feet long. (*Courtesy of U.S. National Museum.*)

383

Fig. 15.17 Aquatic and flying reptiles of Late Cretaceous age. Skeletal remains of these animals are found in chalk beds of western Kansas and elsewhere. The large swimming lizard (mosasaur named *Tylosaurus*) attained a length of 50 feet or more. The hammer-headed flying reptile (*Pteranodon*) is the largest known representative of this group, with wing spread as great as 26 feet; it must have been able to soar in effortless manner hundreds of miles from nearest land. (*Courtesy of J. Augusta and Z. Burian, Praha; published by permission.*)

spread warm, humid climate, whereas uplifted lands and prominent mountain ranges are associated with climatic diversity, which includes cold and dry climate in various places along with heat and humidity in others. Thus, we might expect that after the building of the prominent mountains formed by pre-Cretaceous orogeny in the Pacific Border region, climatic diversity might especially characterize Early Cretaceous time in parts of North America. Subsequently, when seas spread very widely over North America and other continents, we may anticipate existence of equable climates, with warm temperatures extending to high latitudes. Persistence of uplands and even of mountains is indicated, however, by the nature and quantity of sediments derived from these areas.

Mountain Building and Close of the Period

Laramian revolution. Toward the close of Cretaceous time, one of the major mountain-building epochs of world history affected North and South America and produced strong crustal deformation in Europe and Asia (Figs. 15.21, 15.22). This is known as the Laramian revolution, the name being derived from the Laramie Range in the Rockies of Wyoming. This was a time of folding, faulting, and considerable crustal elevation throughout the length of the Rockies, from Alaska to Mexico, and throughout some 5,000 miles of the Andean belt, from Colombia to Cape Horn. Compression seems to have been exerted chiefly from the west—that is, from the Pacific Ocean segment of the globe—against the American continent. Folding and metamorphism of rocks in the Andes, which are close to the Pacific, are very complex, but in the Rockies, which are many hundred miles from the Pacific Border, rigidity of the compressed rocks was sufficient to prevent intricate deformation. Cretaceous and older rock strata are found turned up very steeply and locally overturned. Also, there are large thrust faults along which crustal blocks were pushed eastward several miles, but as a whole, the structure of the Rocky Mountains is much less complex than that of the Coast Ranges or Sierra Nevada country.

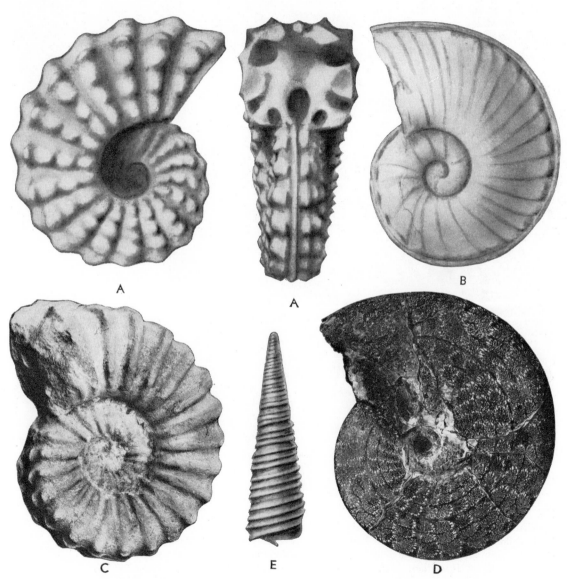

Fig. 15.18 Cretaceous ammonites and a gastropod. Characteristic invertebrates of Cretaceous time are the last of the complexly sutured cephalopods called ammonites: *A. Mortoniceras; B, Prionocyclus; C, Acanthoceras; D, Placenticeras,* with outer shell exfoliated, thus showing the extremely complex suture pattern. A high-spired gastropod (*E, Turritella*) also is illustrated. All approximately natural size. (*C, D, courtesy of Chicago Natural History Museum.*)

Fig. 15.19 Cretaceous pelecypods. The concentrically wrinkled shells of *Inoceramus* (*A*) are characteristic Upper Cretaceous fossils throughout the world, different species being useful in defining various zones. So-called rudistid clams, distinguished by strongly inequivalved coral-like form and growth commonly in colonies especially adapted to a warm-water habitat, are illustrated by *Hippurites*, from Upper Cretaceous beds in France (*B*, side view; *C*, summit, with lidlike small valve in place; *D*, interior of large valve). An exceptionally thick-shelled representative of the oyster family is the species of *Exogyra* (*E*) illustrated. The zone is marked in Upper Cretaceous deposits of the Gulf Coast region. (*B–D, courtesy of Chicago Natural History Museum.*)

Fig. 15.20 Restoration of Late Cretaceous shallow-sea bottom. The invertebrates shown crawling about and swimming among the seaweeds are various kinds of mollusks, which strongly dominate the marine fauna of this period. Cephalopods include ammonites of straight-shelled type (*A, Baculites*), planispirally coiled type (*C, Placenticeras*), and loose-spiral type (*D, Helicoceras*), as well as belemnoids (*B, Belemnitella*) resembling modern squids externally but having a stout internal shell. Several kinds of gastropods (*E, Volutoderma; F,* others) and pelecypods (*G*) are shown. (*Courtesy of L. B. Kellum and I. G. Reimann, University of Michigan, Museum of Paleontology; model prepared by George Marchand.*)

The geologic date of the Laramian revolution is indicated by study of the strata that, respectively, are affected or relatively undisturbed by the deformation. Thus, along the Front Range of the Rockies in Colorado, very late Cretaceous rocks are found steeply upturned and overthrust in places by faults, which proves that in this area the disturbance was initiated some time later than the time of formation of these beds (Fig. 15.23). Near by, there are nonfolded Paleogene (Eocene) deposits in which reworked sediments derived from the uplifted Rockies can be identified. The deformation is dated as belonging between a time late in the Cretaceous and early in the Paleogene. Similar observations made in other areas (Fig. 15.24) prove that

the movements involved in the Laramian revolution were not all at precisely the same date —some are a little earlier, others a little later, and precise dating in several places is not determinable. As a whole, the mountain building is definitely associated with the close of Cretaceous time and the beginning of the Paleogene Period. Associated with geographic and organic changes, particularly as marked by the abrupt disappearance of the dinosaurs and rapid rise of mammals, we recognize the end of the Mesozoic Era and beginning of the Cenozoic.

Economic Resources

Cretaceous rocks are rich in the variety and quantity of substances useful to man. First in

Fig. 15.21 Folded Cretaceous strata in central northern Wyoming. This air view from a point north of Greybull, Wyoming, shows Sheep Mountain and girdling hogback ridges and shallow valleys eroded in Upper Cretaceous strata. The beds, chiefly marine, were folded during the Laramian revolution near the close of Cretaceous time. (*Courtesy of Barnum Brown, American Museum of Natural History.*)

importance come petroleum and natural gas, then coal, and following these fuels are high-grade clays, cement materials, bauxite (source of aluminum), vanadium, antimony, diamonds, gold, silver, copper, zinc, glauconite (useful as fertilizer), chalk, building stone, glass sand, and several others. In addition, ground water deserves mention, because pervious Cretaceous sandstones, such as Dakota in the northern Great Plains country and Trinity sands in the Texas region, are extremely important sources of water supplies, including both municipal and rural domestic.

Petroleum and natural gas. In the world as a whole, the Cretaceous System ranks next to Neogene (Miocene-Pleistocene) as a producer of oil and gas, the total cumulative yield of oil amounting to approximately 12,000 million barrels and additional proved reserves being estimated at about 10,000 million barrels. In the United States, some 750

oil and gas fields produce from Cretaceous rocks, their past production and proved reserves of oil amounting to more than 10,000 million barrels and gas totaling several trillion cubic feet.

The East Texas field, near Henderson and Kilgore, is the largest single oil-producing area in the Western Hemisphere, with a rated capacity of approximately 5,000 million barrels. Its oil comes from sandy deposits (Woodbine) at the base of the Upper Cretaceous section in an area extending 35 miles from north to south and ranging in width from 4 to 7 miles in east-west direction. The field was discovered in 1930 and is still a major contributor to the leadership of Texas as an oil-producing state. Several other Cretaceous fields are located in Texas, Louisiana, and Mississippi, an unusual one that may be mentioned being the Lytton Springs field in central Texas (Caldwell County), for the oil here is obtained from igneous rock (serpentine) that penetrates Upper Cretaceous beds. The oil undoubtedly is an accumulation derived from the Cretaceous sedimentary rocks, but wells yield as much as 5,000 barrels a day from the igneous-rock reservoir. Most of the large oil fields of Wyoming, Colorado, and Montana produce from Cretaceous formations, and recently very large reserves of oil and gas have been discovered in northwestern Alberta.

Some of the outstanding Cretaceous oil fields of the world are located in eastern Mexico north and south of Tampico. In one of these (Huasteca) a porous Lower Cretaceous limestone reef mass (named El Abra) is productive in an area 50 miles long and nearly a mile wide, past yield amounting to more than 1,000 million barrels; one well, rated as the largest single producer in the world, flowed for a time at the rate of 260,000 barrels a day. Another field (Poza Rica) now being developed in this area obtains oil from Upper Cretaceous limestone; its reserve is computed

Fig. 15.22 Folded Mesozoic strata in southwestern Utah. An anticline near Hurricane, Utah, exposing Triassic rocks deformed by Laramian folding. (*Courtesy of Hal Shelton, Golden, Colorado.*)

Fig. 15.23 Wall of nearly vertical Cretaceous sandstone at the margin of the Rocky Mountains Front Range in Colorado. The upturning of this rock unit and associated strata occurred during the Laramian revolution. (*N. H. Darton, courtesy of U.S. Geol. Survey.*)

to be approximately as large as that of Huasteca.

A considerable part of the large oil production of Venezuela comes from Cretaceous formations.

An example of a major Cretaceous gas-producing area is the Carthage field, which covers nearly all of Panola County in eastern Texas. The productive area contains more than 375 square miles, and its reserve is computed to be 5 trillion cubic feet. The gas comes from Lower Cretaceous limestone (Glen Rose).

Coal. Rocks of Cretaceous age rank next to the Pennsylvanian in quantity of their contained coal of commercial grade. The Cretaceous deposits are chiefly found in the Rocky Mountains region, extending from Arizona and New Mexico in the south far into Alberta in the north. Many individual beds exceed 10 feet in thickness, and in general they are easily mined. Most of the coal is lower in grade than Pennsylvanian coal, being classed as subbituminous to bituminous. In central Colorado (Crested Butte district), where the coal has been changed to anthracite by the metamorphic effects of igneous intrusive rocks, and in the Crowsnest Pass area of southwestern Alberta, where the Cretaceous formations have been strongly folded, high-grade coal is mined. The coal varies in age from place to place, in some areas being mainly Lower Cretaceous but elsewhere occurring in the lower, middle, or upper part of the Upper Cretaceous. The most widespread and most important coals are found in continental formations of the Montana Group (Fig. 15.6), near the top of the Cretaceous section.

Other resources. Even brief review of each kind of mineral resources obtained from Cretaceous rocks would require more than allowable space. Therefore, notice is restricted here to the widely disparate items of clay and diamonds.

Fig. 15.24 Angular unconformity between tilted late Upper Cretaceous and horizontal Paleogene (early Eocene) strata. The deformation of the rocks below the unconformity belongs to the Laramian revolution, which here can be fairly well dated, since beveling of the Cretaceous occurred before deposition of the Eocene (Wasatch) beds. Oldest Paleogene (Paleocene) deposits are lacking. These outcrops occur near Meteetse, Wyoming. (*C. A. Fisher, courtesy of U.S. Geol. Survey.*)

Cretaceous clays deserve attention because deposits in several places possess qualities that fit them for making porcelain, chinaware, and pottery. Consequently, industries devoted to manufacture of such products, as near Denver, Colorado, in Kansas, and around Raritan Bay, New Jersey, are located adjacent to these deposits. Although some selective sorting of the raw clay commonly is required, resources are inexhaustible. Of course, lower-grade clay products in large quantity—brick, tile, and the like—also are made at many places using Cretaceous clays or shales.

Diamonds are obtained from placers in Brazil, India, and elsewhere, all of these being secondary deposits. As primary minerals, diamonds occur in basic igneous intrusive rocks classed as peridotites, and one of these that penetrates Cretaceous sedimentary rocks near Murfreesboro, in southwestern Arkansas, is thought to be of Cretaceous age; it contains diamonds of good quality and has been worked commercially, although not in recent years. The world's chief source of diamonds since 1871 has been the Kimberley district in South Africa, where the mode of occurrence is like that near Murfreesboro. The weathered igneous rock in the Kimberley mine has been excavated to a depth of more than 2,000 feet, with annual production of diamonds ranging from 1 to 3 million carats, valued at an average of about $10 per carat as rough stone. Other mines also report large production. Present yield of the district is approximately 1.6 million carats a year.

READINGS

COBBAN, W. A., 1951, Colorado Shale of central and northeastern Montana and equivalent rocks of Black Hills: *Am. Assoc. Petroleum Geologists Bull.*, vol. 35, pp. 2170–2198.

DUNBAR, C. O., 1949, *Historical geology*, John Wiley & Sons, Inc., New York (567 pp.), Cretaceous time and end of an era, pp. 359–394.

EARDLEY, A. J., 1944, Geology of the north-central Wasatch Mountains, Utah: *Geol. Soc. America Bull.*, vol. 55, pp. 819–894.
Describes eight pulsations of Laramian mountain making in a critical region.

———, 1951, *Structural geology of North America*, Harper & Brothers, New York (624 pp.). [1] Atlantic Coastal Plain, pp. 129–141. [2] Gulf Coastal Plain, pp. 541–561. [3] Mesozoic Rocky Mountains systems, pp. 273–283. [4] Canadian and Montana Rockies, pp. 291–307, 340–346. [5] Central Rockies, pp. 315–339, 347–392.
Excellent, well-illustrated account of Cretaceous and associated rocks in Coastal Plains and Interior regions.

GREGORY, H. E., and MOORE, R. C., 1931, The Kaiparowits region [Utah]: *U.S. Geol. Survey Prof. Paper* 164, pp. 94–113.
Typical area of Colorado Plateau Cretaceous deposits.

MULLER, S. W., and SCHENCK, H. G., 1943, Standard of the Cretaceous System: *Am. Assoc. Petroleum Geologists Bull.*, vol. 27, pp. 262–278.
Discusses time-rock classification.

PIKE, W. S., JR., 1947, Intertonguing marine and nonmarine Upper Cretaceous deposits of New Mexico, Arizona, and southwestern Colorado: *Geol. Soc. America Mem.* 41 (103 pp.).
Excellent for study of Cretaceous sea-margin sedimentation.

REESIDE, J. B., JR., 1944, The thickness and general character of the Cretaceous deposits in the Western Interior of the United States: *U.S. Geol. Survey*, Oil and gas investigations, Prelim. Map 10 (with text).
Valuable summary.

RUBEY, W. W., 1929, Origin of the siliceous Mowry Shale of the Black Hills region: *U.S. Geol. Survey Prof. Paper* 154, pp. 153–170.
Important paper on sedimentation.

SPIEKER, E. M., 1946, Late Mesozoic and early Tertiary history of central Utah: *U.S. Geol. Survey Prof. Paper* 205-D, pp. 117–161.
Reviews principles of orogenic dating with application to Laramian deformations in Utah.

Stephenson, L. W., 1937, Stratigraphic relations of the Austin, Taylor, and equivalent formations in Texas: *U.S. Geol. Survey Prof. Paper* 186, pp. 133–146.
Upper Cretaceous sedimentation in Gulf Coast region.
———, 1939, Cretaceous System: in *Geology of North America, Geologie der Erde*, Gebrüder Bornträger, Berlin, pp. 519–549 (illus.).
Useful summary of Cretaceous rocks in Atlantic and Gulf regions.
———, and Reeside, J. B., Jr., 1938, Comparison of Upper Cretaceous deposits of Gulf region and Western Interior region: *Am. Assoc. Petroleum Geologists Bull.*, vol. 22, pp. 1629–1638.

QUESTIONS

1. Referring to the map showing distribution of Cretaceous rocks in the United States and parts of adjoining countries (Fig. 15.2),
(a) How may discontinuity of Cretaceous outcrops between New York City and southwestern Arkansas be explained?
(b) How are Cretaceous rocks known or inferred to be present throughout the Atlantic and Gulf Coastal Plains, including Florida, and beneath the continental shelf seaward from the present coast?
(c) What is the regional structure of the Coastal Plains, and how is this demonstrable from the map?
(d) In a geologic section extending from northeastern Mississippi to southwestern Arkansas, what should be the structural attitude of Cretaceous rocks? Why?
(e) What information supplied by the map supports the indicated absence of Cretaceous deposits other than in the northwestern corner of the Panhandle region of northern Texas?
(f) What reasons can be suggested for the much greater breadth of Cretaceous outcrops in northeastern Mexico, Texas, and northward from Kansas than of those east of the Mississippi River?
(g) Does the map furnish evidence that Cretaceous rocks originally were far more extensive than now in the Rocky Mountains region? If so, specify all such indications you can find. If not, explain why the map fails to aid in answering this question.
(h) How can the prevailing absence of Cretaceous rocks in territory extending southward from eastern Washington to the Golfo de California be explained?
(i) With knowledge that marine Cretaceous deposits exist in southwestern Arkansas, western Texas, Kansas, and California, which areas would you expect to contain most similar invertebrate faunas and which the most dissimilar? Why?
(j) Why is it reasonable to infer that Cretaceous deposits formerly were present in western Ontario north of Lake Superior? If so, why should one conclude that they rested nonconformably or with angular unconformity on Precambrian rocks?
2. Referring to the chart showing Cretaceous time-rock divisions and rock units (Fig. 15.6),
(a) What state furnishes the most complete record of marine sedimentation? Most complete record of nonmarine sedimentation? In what regional divisions indicated at the top of the chart do these states respectively occur?
(b) Account for the prevailing absence of early Lower Cretaceous (Neocomian) deposits in the United States.
(c) Although breaks in sedimentation in various sections coincide in position with boundaries of stages, as indicated by paleontological correlations, others do not; also, continuity of sedimentation rather commonly is recorded across interstage boundaries. What is the significance of these observations?
(d) Note the separation of Atlantic Coast Cretaceous formations, some marine and some nonmarine, by hiatuses. What does this mean in terms of geologic history? If a Cretaceous section were available from a deep offshore well in this region, how would you expect it to differ from that shown in the chart? Why?
(e) Explain interfingering of Mesaverde and associated shaly strata in the central Wyoming and Colorado columns.
(f) In Western Interior columns, how can Mesaverde rocks (nonmarine) be determined as age equivalents of Pierre Shale strata (marine)?
3. Near Grand Junction, Colorado, Cretaceous strata of the Little Book Cliffs are gently inclined (Fig. 15.4) whereas the basalt-capped Grand Mesa has an essentially horizontal sur-

face. What features of local geologic history are indicated by this difference? Is there evidence that the valley of Colorado River here began to be carved before extrusion of the Grand Mesa lava, being influenced by Cretaceous-rock structure, or does valley carving appear to be post-lava?

4. Referring to the map showing original thickness and distribution of sediments in the Rocky Mountains geosyncline (Fig. 15.9),

(a) Account for the relatively abrupt thinning of deposits on the western and southwestern sides of the geosyncline as compared with very gradual eastward thinning.

(b) What is the significance of observation that largest proportion of clastic sediments and coarse gravelly deposits is in areas of maximum thickness, especially toward the west?

(c) Since thickness closely approximates aggregate subsidence of the geosynclinal floor during Cretaceous time, can average subsidence rates be computed for any area using 70 million years as duration of the period? If so, what are these rates in northeastern Utah (30,000 feet), central southern Wyoming (19,750 feet), southwestern New Mexico (24,500 feet)?

(d) Taking account of separate measurements for Lower Cretaceous (LK) and Upper Cretaceous (UK), allowing LK 30 million years and UK 40 million years, recompute previous answers for northeastern Utah (LK = 11,000 feet, UK = 19,000 feet), central southern Wyoming (LK = 250 feet, UK = 19,500 feet), and southwestern New Mexico (LK = 19,000 feet, UK = 5,500 feet). Conclusion derived from this recomputation?

5. If the cross-bedded sandstone illustrated in Fig. 15.12 were folded so as to stand vertical, as in Fig. 15.23, what features of the cross-bedding could be used for reliable identification of the top of successive sandstone layers?

6. Referring to Figs. 15.21 and 15.22, what topographic features reveal the direction and steepness of inclination of rock strata? Locate places on each photograph where the beds dip most steeply and where they are most nearly horizontal. What is the relation of each to regional structure seen?

7. Remains of more than 600 flying reptiles (*Pteranodon*, Fig. 15.17) have been found in marine Cretaceous beds of western Kansas and adjacent states. Some consist of more or less complete skeletons, but more commonly only wing bones are observed, sometimes a pair of them close together. Can you suggest a plausible explanation of the occurrence of numerous isolated wings or parts of wings?

8. Referring to the fossils illustrated in Fig. 15.18A and D, in what parts of these shells was the main body of the animal located? What illustrated features confirm your answer?

9. Referring to Fig. 4.23 (p. 93) and Fig. 8.17 (p. 202), why are the deformed Beltian and Paleozoic rocks in the Canadian Rockies considered to furnish part of the record of the Laramian deformation? Can this be confirmed by geologic features shown in the photographs? If not, how is Laramian dating of the deformation determined?

16.

NATURE AND EVOLUTION
OF MESOZOIC LIFE

Tyrannosaurus, of Late Cretaceous age, greatest
of the flesh-eating dinosaurs.

C. R. Knight, courtesy of
Chicago Natural History Museum

No part of earth history offers record of such strange and varied life as that of the so-called medieval era of life development. The culmination of reptiles in size, numbers, and differentiation of kinds was accompanied by a very remarkable adaptation of members of this class to almost every type of environment and mode of life. Dinosaurs, the "terrible lizards," were the rulers of the land, attaining a ponderous bulk unequaled in history of land animals. Few, if any, predaceous creatures can rival the carnivorous dinosaurs in ferocious dagger-like teeth and claws, and possibly excepting common turtles, no armored, vertebrate animals of other type or time are more bizarre than some of the armored dinosaurs

(Fig. 16.1). Land reptiles of this time included true lizards, and in the waters of the land there were turtles and crocodiles. One group of reptiles developed a batlike form, becoming suited for flight in the air. From reptiles, also, the birds were derived. Several reptilian stocks became specially modified for life in the sea, some acquiring a fishlike form that made them entirely unable to travel on land. The Mesozoic is well named the Age of Reptiles.

Among invertebrates, there are many interesting organisms. The complexly sutured, tight-coiled, and externally ornamented cephalopods, known as ammonites, are undoubtedly the most distinctive and important. An almost incredible variety of these shells is represented by Mesozoic fossils, but none are known from younger rocks. As regards evolution of invertebrate stocks, therefore, the era may be designated appropriately as the Age of Ammonites. The appearance of very abundant cephalopods of the squid type is evidenced by innumerable cigar-shaped "guards," which form part of the internal shell structure. Pelecypods and gastropods increased greatly in importance and in similarity of form to modern types. Sea urchins were much more common and varied than at any earlier time.

Also, the Mesozoic Era may be called the Age of Cycadeoids, because these extinct palm-like plants, related to the comparatively unimportant cycads of modern floras, dominated the flora of the earth's medieval time.

CONTRASTING FEATURES OF MESOZOIC AND PALEOZOIC LIFE

A general characteristic of Mesozoic organisms, which may be emphasized, is the contrast to Paleozoic life. So great is the change that early geologists were convinced that a worldwide catastrophe must have wiped out existing forms of life at the close of the Paleozoic Era and that a new creation at the beginning of Mesozoic time repopulated the earth with different kinds of plants and animals. Difference in the complexion of Mesozoic life is shown by (1) disappearance of such animals as the trilobites, blastoids, and archaic types of crinoids, bryozoans, and corals; (2) the great decline of such an abundant and characteristic Paleozoic group as the brachiopods; (3) the rapid development and differentiation of such groups as the ammonites among invertebrates and the reptiles among vertebrates; and (4) the introduction of new types of plants and animals. Most of the Mesozoic classes of organisms flourished for a time and then died, without seeing the beginning of Cenozoic time.

The changes in life at the close of the Paleozoic Era, great as they are, should not lead us to overlook the fact that all phyla, many orders, and not a few families and genera survived from Permian into Triassic or later times. The Triassic invertebrate faunas include several forms that differ only in minor ways from Permian predecessors. Among vertebrates, also, there are Triassic reptiles in both Europe and South Africa that are almost identical with Permian species. The later faunas are descendants of the earlier ones, and present knowledge indicates plainly that the two are not so sharply differentiated at the boundary of the eras as was once supposed.

Dominance of Reptiles

The outstanding character of life on the earth during the Mesozoic Era is prominence of reptiles. The progress of these animals, as of any kind of life, may be measured (1) by their numbers, variety, size, and similar physical characters; (2) by their success in getting food, in avoiding or conquering enemies, and in adapting themselves effectively to environment; and (3) by the extent to which they became fitted to all possible modes of life. In the Triassic, Jurassic, and Cretaceous Periods, reptiles achieved extraordinary abundance and variety of form and stature (Fig. 16.2). They learned to feed on many kinds of plants, fresh-water and marine invertebrates, fishes, amphibians, other reptiles, and doubtless some of the primitive mammals. Their only real competitors were members of their

Fig. 16.1   Restoration of a Cretaceous armored dinosaur. Skeletons of these animals (*Paleoscincus*), collected in western Canada, show that the back and sides were covered by thick bones. (*E. M. Fulda, courtesy of American Museum of Natural History.*)

own class. They became remarkably specialized for life on the lands, in the seas, and in the air.

The first reptiles were sluggish animals, which in form and general habits probably resembled their amphibian ancestors. As the reptiles developed, however, some branches became increasingly fitted for life on the lands. Others returned to the waters and became thoroughly at home there. Still other branches took to the air and underwent radical changes of form. The plasticity and virility of the reptile group during its Mesozoic history are well shown by this rapid conquest of practically all possible habitats. The tendency to expand remarkably, which is seen also in the career of the mammals in Cenozoic time, is a sign of racial adolescence, just as inadaptability to changing environment and exaggeration of some characters seem to be marks of racial senescence.

Land Reptiles

Among land reptiles, an important line of development appears in changes of the limbs that make for ease in carrying the weight of the body and for speed. Primitive reptiles, like their amphibian ancestors, carried the body close to the ground, their short, rather weak legs extending outward from the sides and then downward. The legs moved in a lateral arc, and in walking, the gait was a slow, awkward waddle. The first improvement, as regards locomotion on land, is seen in a change of the attitude of the lower part of the limbs, bending downward so that the body of the reptile is somewhat elevated. This is the plan of the limbs in modern lizards and very many Mesozoic land reptiles. A next very important advance consists in swinging the entire length of the legs beneath the body, so that they move forward and backward in

Fig. 16.2 *Diplodocus,* **a Jurassic herbivorous dinosaur.** This reptile is distinguished by its very long neck and tail, total length of the animal ranging to 100 feet. (*Courtesy of J. Augusta and Z. Burian, Praha; published by permission.*)

a vertical plane and considerably increase the length of the stride. Some of the Mesozoic reptiles, especially among the dinosaurs, show this development, but they do not carry it to the extreme seen in many of the mammals, where the length of limbs is increased by walking on the tips of the fingers and toes (Fig. 16.3).

Aquatic Reptiles

Special adaptation to their environment is shown by aquatic reptiles in form and structure of the limbs and shape of the body. The limbs tend to become paddle- or finlike, the bones above the wrist and ankle becoming short and broad, while the phalanges are lengthened by additional joints. Such an appendage is admirably fitted to serve in swimming but is quite useless for walking. Some of the aquatic reptiles developed a remarkably streamlined fishlike form, which is really the best design for swift movement in water. They propelled themselves mainly or entirely by the tail, which bore a good-sized fin, and there was also a dorsal fin (Fig. 16.4).

Flying Reptiles

The flying reptiles (and likewise the birds) probably learned first to glide and only later to fly. Adaptation to flight through the air is seen in a general lightening of the bones of the skeleton, but especially in a very remarkable modification of the structure of the fore limbs, among true flying reptiles for support of a membranous wing and among birds for a wing clothed with feathers (Fig. 16.5).

This progressive modification of the reptile group into divergent branches, with different modes of life and the consequent effects on body form and structure, is an outstanding feature in the Mesozoic history of life.

PLANTS

General Character of Mesozoic Floras

Notwithstanding the fact that the plants of Mesozoic time are the direct descendants of late Paleozoic species and that several of the latter lived essentially unchanged into the

Fig. 16.3 An outdoor bathtub formed by a dinosaur footprint. This track, in a Lower Cretaceous formation of Texas, holds 18 gallons of water. (*Courtesy of Roland T. Bird and American Museum of Natural History.*)

Fig. 16.4 Mesozoic aquatic reptiles. Two leading types of Jurassic marine reptiles shown here competing for a catch of fish are plesiosaurs (at left) and ichthyosaurs (at right). The plesiosaurs are distinguished by their relatively long neck and powerful flippers, whereas ichthyosaurs have no neck and rely mainly on their large tail fin for swimming. (*C. R. Knight, courtesy of Chicago Natural History Museum.*)

"snake thru strung turtle"

Triassic Period, the floras of Mesozoic age are distinctively new and different. The dominant plant group was that of the cycad-like Bennettitales, but ferns and conifers were nearly equal in number of species. Most of these were short or only moderately tall, so that one of the main contrasts to the Pennsylvanian floras consists in the absence of gigantic scale trees and cordaites. The horsetails (Sphenopsida) had several generic representatives. The ferns were relatively small, quite unlike the Paleozoic vine- and treelike ferns and seed ferns. A general exception to the small average size of Mesozoic plants is seen in some of the conifers, which grew to a height of more than 100 feet. In late Mesozoic time, the highest type of seed-bearing plants (angiosperms), which are dominant today, made their appearance and became the most important element in the vegetation of all lands.

Cycadeoids

This interesting plant group (Bennettitales), which is characteristic of the Mesozoic Era, is closely related to the modern cycads, which are represented by many living species in tropical and subtropical regions (Fig. 16.6). Cycads have a woody trunk with a large central pith cavity; the outer part is cloaked by a mat of hanging dead leaves or bears closely spaced scars that mark the former attachments of leaves. The trunk is very short and bulbous in some species, about as wide as high, but in others it attains a height of more than 50 feet. At the top is a graceful crown of long, palmlike leaves which have a strong stem axis and very numerous narrow elongate leaflets at the two sides. A large cone at the crest of the cycad in most living species contains the reproductive elements.

Fossil Bennettitales had very interesting flower-like structures, in which a circle of male spore-bearing stamens surrounded a pear-shaped female organ provided with numerous seed ovules (Fig. 16.9). Some fossils show separate male and female "flowers," though both may have been borne by the same plant. At least 40 different species have been rec-

Fig. 16.5 A late Jurassic flying reptile, *Rhamphorhynchus*. This type of pterosaur, known from Germany and central Africa, is characterized by its relatively large head with strong, obliquely set teeth and by its long tail with rudder-like tip. Its wing attained a length of 32 inches. (*Courtesy of J. Augusta and Z. Burian, Praha; published by permission.*)

light
skeletal structure
4th finger elongate

earliest
known flying
reptile
32 long

ognized in Triassic coal-bearing deposits near Richmond, Virginia. One of the most abundant kinds (*Sphenozamites*) had leaves up to 4 feet in length, with lateral leaflets 8 to 10 inches long and as much as 4 inches wide. Another type (*Macrotaeniopteris*, Fig. 13.17) had simple, undivided leaves approximately 1 foot in width and 3 feet in length.

During the Jurassic Period, the cycad-like plants were dominant in the land vegetation, for approximately two-fifths of all the known plant fossils are of this type (Fig. 16.7). If cycad species were relatively as numerous today, we should have some 40,000 different kinds. The Jurassic forms were very widely distributed and fairly uniform in character, for practically the same kinds of leaves occur in rocks of this age in England, northern Greenland, Alaska, Oregon, Australia, and Antarctica.

Cretaceous cycadeoids are also abundant but mostly quite different from earlier types. Trunks, flowers, fruits, and seeds are common (Figs. 16.8, 16.9). The trunks were mostly less than 4 feet in height and diameter, their sides being covered by pits that mark the attachment of leaf fronds and fruits. Following Early Cretaceous time, the chief types declined and disappeared.

Conifers

This plant group, to which the pines, cedars, and other cone-bearing evergreens belong, was an important element in the Mesozoic floras, but the fossil record is fragmentary. Triassic conifers are best known from the southwestern United States, where in the Painted Desert of Arizona and in parts of adjacent states are widely scattered fossilized trees and several "fossil forests." The most famous tree locality is an area of about 40 square miles near Adamana, Arizona, which has been set aside as the Petrified Forest National Monument. There lie thousands of fossilized logs, many of them broken up into short segments, others complete and unbroken (Fig. 16.10). The enclosing sediments have been so removed from one that it forms a natural bridge over a ravine some 20 feet

Fig. 16.6 A type of living cycad. The palmlike leaves and nature of the trunk of this plant (*Dioon edule*) correspond closely to those of common Mesozoic Cycadinae. (*Courtesy of G. R. Wieland, Yale University.*)

deep and 30 feet across, probably the only bridge of this sort in the world. The average diameter of the logs is 3 to 4 feet, and the length 60 to 80 feet. Some logs 7 feet in greatest diameter and 125 feet long have been observed. None are standing in position of

Fig. 16.7 Leaf of a Jurassic cycad-like plant. *Ctenophyllum*, showing part of median leaf stem and leaflets, natural size.

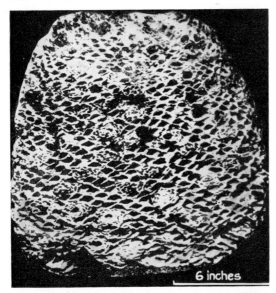

Fig. 16.8 Trunk of a Cretaceous *Cycadeoidea* from Maryland. The lozenge-shaped dark pits are leaf bases, marking places of attachment of the long leaves. Scattered among them are several "flower" buds. (*Courtesy of E. W. Berry, Johns Hopkins University.*)

distant. The cell structure and fibers have been almost perfectly preserved by molecular replacement of silica, much of it in the form of chalcedony and agate that is beautiful and varied in coloring of rich yellows, reds, and purples.

Jurassic and Cretaceous rocks in North America also contain many kinds of conifers, the remains consisting of impressions of leafy twigs, cones, and branches.

Ferns

These plants comprise approximately one-third of the known floras of Mesozoic age, excepting Late Cretaceous when the rise of the higher plants reduced the relative importance of fern species. Triassic ferns are best known in America from North Carolina, Virginia, and Pennsylvania, where coal-bearing beds show persistence of swampy conditions. In this environment, ferns were the dominant kind of plant, and many were of large size. The Jurassic and Cretaceous fossil ferns were all of moderate size, but locally, they were unusually abundant.

Horsetails and Ginkgos

Both in swampy coal basins of the Atlantic Border and in southwestern interior river plains, Triassic descendants of the Paleozoic

growth but, with branches stripped, lie scattered about as though floated by running water until stranded and subsequently buried in the places where they are now found. The original forests may have been scores of miles

Fig. 16.9 Restoration of a Cretaceous fossil *Cycadeoidea* "flower." (*Courtesy of G. R. Wieland, Yale University.*)

horsetails are found. The ribbed stems were 4 to 5 inches in diameter and 20 to 30 feet long. This stock is also known in smaller species from the Cretaceous.

From a botanical standpoint, one of the most interesting Mesozoic plant fossils is the maidenhair tree (*Ginkgo*), which was one of the most abundant and widely distributed trees during Jurassic time and which is represented today by a single species, native in China and Japan but introduced in parts of the United States and Europe. The ginkgo attains a height of 80 feet or more, has a relatively smooth trunk that in fully grown specimens may be 3 feet in diameter, and bears broad subtriangular leaves with veins radiating from the pointed base. In its peculiarly specialized method of seed fertilization and details of structure, the ginkgo stands apart from all other plants. It enjoys the distinction of being probably the oldest living kind of tree. It has come down so little changed that it is difficult or impossible to discover differences between fossils and present leaves. In Oregon there are beds containing beautifully preserved ginkgo leaves by the hundred. Jurassic deposits in Alaska, Greenland, northern Europe, and Siberia also contain them. Naturally this plant occurs in later Mesozoic and

in Cenozoic floras, but it does not stand out so prominently as in the Jurassic, when the host of modern-type leafy trees had not appeared. It became extinct in North America during the Neogene Period, but when reintroduced by man from its native habitat in China, it was found to grow luxuriantly.

Flowering Plants

The highest type of plants, dominant in modern floras, are the flowering plants (Angiospermae), in which the seeds are inclosed in a protecting case or fruit. Two classes are recognized: (1) monocotyledons, which start with a single leaflet, lack a differentiation of the stem into pith, wood, and bark, and have parallel-veined leaves, and (2) dicotyledons, which start with two leaflets, show division into pith, wood, and bark, and have leaves with a network of veins. The first group includes the grasses, cereals, palms, lilies, and the like, while the second contains most of the forest trees, such as maples, oaks, and elms, and a great variety of shrubs and herbs.

The oldest plant remains accepted as definitely belonging to angiosperms are pollen grains from a Jurassic coal bed in Scotland, but otherwise this plant group makes its earliest appearance in the Lower Cretaceous, where

Fig. 16.10 Large silicified conifer of Triassic age. These sections of a tree trunk were exposed by weathering of continental deposits (Chinle) in the area of the petrified forest at Adamana, Arizona. There are many such trees ranging up to 7 feet in diameter and 125 feet in length. (*Courtesy of Chicago Natural History Museum.*)

leaves referred to 16 modern families of flowering plants are found. These include the willows, poplars, beeches, oaks, elms, laurels, sassafras, figs, grapes, and other familiar living groups. The species are all different from those of today. The Upper Cretaceous floras, represented by very abundant well-preserved leaves, show a strongly dominant angiosperm content with many modern-looking elements. In Greenland and Alaska, there are Upper Cretaceous plant-bearing beds containing conifers and hardwoods that include many of the same species found in the central and southern part of the United States. Among them are extinct representatives of the dogwood, persimmon, fig, tulip tree, eucalyptus, sycamore, breadfruit tree, and many others that today mainly inhabit moderately warm climates. The breadfruit tree is limited at present to within 20 degrees of the equator.

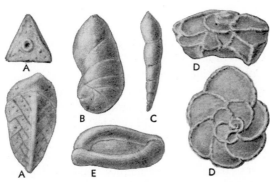

Fig. 16.11 Mesozoic foraminifers. A. *Tritaxia*, Cretaceous, ×15.—B. *Marginulina*, Jurassic, ×50.—C. *Dentalina*, Triassic, ×45.—D. *Globotruncana*, Cretaceous, ×50.—E. *Triloculina*, Triassic, ×40.

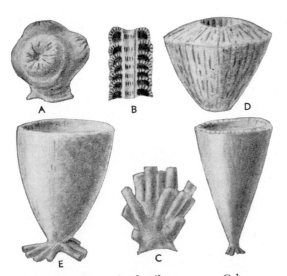

Fig. 16.12 Mesozoic fossil sponges. Calcareous sponges include A, *Stellispongia*, Jurassic, ×0.7; and B, C, *Barroisia*, Cretaceous (B, longitudinal section, ×2; C, colony, ×0.7). Others are siliceous sponges: D, *Pachyteichisma*, Jurassic, ×0.35; E, *Coscinopora*, Cretaceous, ×0.35; (F) *Ventriculites*, Cretaceous, ×0.35.

PROTISTA

Protozoans

The important fact about fossil protozoans during Mesozoic time is their abundance and great variety in the Cretaceous rocks. The chalk and chalky limestone of this age, which are practically world-wide in occurrence, contain multitudes of the minute shells of foraminifers. The geologic formations penetrated by drilling in the oil-field regions of Louisiana, Texas, and northeastern Mexico are successfully identified by study of shells of this type washed from the well cuttings. In this connection may be noted the discovery, at shallow depth in certain Gulf Coast oil wells, of abundant Cretaceous species of foraminifers mingled with Paleogene species, the age of the rocks being evidently Paleogene. The fact that the Cretaceous types are all slightly worn whereas the others are fresh and unmutilated supports the conclusion that the older shells were weathered and transported from some Cretaceous outcrops and redeposited with shells of much younger species that were living at the time.

Although foraminifers were extremely abundant in late Paleozoic time, when some of them were important rock builders, little is known of protozoans during the Triassic Period. They were fairly abundant in Jurassic time, the majority of species resembling Cretaceous forms (Fig. 16.11)

INVERTEBRATES

Sponges

Both siliceous and calcareous sponges are abundant in some Mesozoic rocks (Fig. 16.12).

The former occur in limestones, but the latter only in sandy or muddy sediments deposited in shallow near-shore waters. This accords with conditions in living species, for the siliceous sponges inhabit moderately deep water while the calcareous types predominate in shallow water. The chief development of siliceous sponges is seen in thick beds of these fossils, highly varied in kinds, in Jurassic limestones of central Europe and again in Upper Cretaceous rocks of western, central, and southeastern Europe. The common occurrence of flint in many of the Mesozoic formations, especially in Cretaceous chalk, indicates that siliceous sponges of the more primitive sorts were also abundant, for the separated skeletal elements (spicules) of these largely supply the silica. Many kinds of calcareous sponges appear in the Triassic rocks of the Alps region, in parts of the European Jurassic, and in the Cretaceous.

Coelenterates

Corals. The corals of Mesozoic time are similar to those living in the warm shallow seas of the present day, and both of these differ from the ancient Paleozoic corals in having a basic sixfold symmetry (Fig. 16.13). The structural plan is very clearly seen in many genera, which show six main radial walls (septa) and more or less numerous subordinate ones. Both solitary corals and compound, colonial types occur, but the latter greatly predominate. Most types are long-lived, persisting through two or more of the Mesozoic periods, and some have lived from the Triassic to the present.

In North America, most Mesozoic rocks contain few corals, partly because marine deposits are restricted, except in the Cretaceous. In Europe, however, there are large numbers of reef-building corals in some of the Triassic formations of the Alps region. The Jurassic is especially rich in corals at very many places, and they occur in high latitudes as well as in the equatorial belts, indicating widespread warm waters. The Cretaceous beds locally contain many corals.

Hydrozoans. Two types of hydrozoans are represented among Mesozoic fossils. One consists of colonial polyps that secrete dense calcareous layers at the base, forming a deposit very much like that of the Paleozoic stromatoporoids. Some of these lime-secreting hydrozoan colonies were especially abundant in the Mediterranean region in Jurassic time. The other consists of jellyfishes, which, though they contain no hard parts, are known from

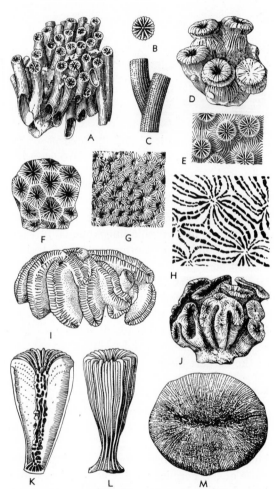

Fig. 16.13 Mesozoic corals. Both solitary and colonial forms occur, all distinguished by sixfold symmetry in arrangement of the septa.——*A–C. Stylosmilia*, Jur.; *A*, ×0.7; *B*, ×1.3.——*D. Margarosmilia*, Trias., ×10.——*E. Stylina*, Jur., ×0.7.——*G, H. Thamnasteria*, Trias.; *G*, ×0.7; *H*, ×3.5.——*I. Rhipidogyra*, Jur., ×0.25.—— *J. Gyrodendron*, Jur., ×0.7.——*K, L. Parasmilia*, Cret., ×1.3 (*K* showing specimen split longitudinally). ——*M. Leptophyllaraea*, Cret., ×0.7. (*Treatise on Invertebrate Paleontology*, courtesy of *Geological Society of America and University of Kansas Press*.)

Fig. 16.14 **A Jurassic jellyfish.** *Rhizostomites,* from Solnhofen, Germany, ×0.5. (*From von Ammon.*)

remarkably perfect impressions in the very fine-grained lithographic limestone of Jurassic age at Solnhofen, Germany (Fig. 16.14), and in some flinty concretions of Late Cretaceous age. The Solnhofen beds are famous for the variety and perfection of their fossils, which include, in addition to common marine invertebrates, several kinds of insects, marine reptiles, and the two only known specimens of the earliest birds.

Echinoderms

Crinoids. The Mesozoic crinoids are more like those of the present than any that lived in Paleozoic time. Virtually all the Paleozoic kinds of crinoids had disappeared before the close of the Permian, and a new order, which includes the Mesozoic and modern crinoids, appeared in the Triassic.

The most interesting fossils of this class in the Jurassic rocks are specimens (*Pentacrinus*) that show the complete calyx with attached arms, measuring as much as 3 feet in height and width. The entire length of stem in some individuals may have been more than 50 feet, exceeding any other known crinoid. The separated stem segments, like small five-pointed stars, are common in some American Jurassic marine strata, but well-preserved crowns that are exhibited in many of our museums come from Europe.

An equally striking but very different form (*Uintacrinus*) of Cretaceous age was a free-swimming stemless crinoid, having slender arms as much as 4 feet long, outstretched from its globular calyx (Fig. 16.15). This crinoid is known in England, Germany, France, Australia, and western America, especially in Kansas, from which the most remarkable specimens come. They are found on thin sheets of limestone, the surface of which is crowded as closely as possible with beautifully preserved individuals with arms attached.

Echinoids. During Mesozoic time, the sea urchins, or echinoids, began the climb toward their present position of prominence. Fossil remains of the group are very abundant and widespread, especially in the Jurassic and Cretaceous rocks (Fig. 16.18F). Chief features of their history in the era are (1) rapid increase in numbers and variety and (2) progressive specialization of (*a*) the regular echinoids toward increased spinose ornamentation and (*b*) the irregular echinoids toward increased eccentricity of position of mouth and anus, and a marked bilateral instead of radial symmetry. Many echinoid species are important guide fossils.

Asterozoans. Starfishes and brittle stars are long-ranging echinoderms, known from early Paleozoic to the present, but they are not common fossils. Numerous kinds, however, are known from Mesozoic strata, and locally they are exceptionally abundant (Fig. 16.16).

Bryozoans

The abundant Paleozoic bryozoans belong chiefly to two orders, which are restricted to that era. Those of the Mesozoic, and also of later time, belong almost wholly to two other orders (cyclostomes, cheilostomes), of which the first has very simple cylindrical tubes and rounded apertures but the second has a complex organization (Fig. 16.17). In many of them is a mechanism that serves to extend the animal from its little cell and to close the aperture by a movable lid when it withdraws into its tube. The bryozoans expanded astonishingly during Cretaceous time and have been important ever since.

Brachiopods

This class of shelled animals, which had been so abundant and varied in the seas of Paleozoic times, is relatively reduced in the

Fig. 16.15 Portion of a slab covered with specimens of a free-swimming crinoid. These crinoids (*Uintacrinus*) were found on a thin limestone interbedded with chalk of Cretaceous age in western Kansas. About one-half natural size. (*Courtesy of University of Kansas Natural History Museum.*)

Mesozoic Era, although locally there were numerous individuals belonging to a few species. The most important persisting types were smooth-shelled and more or less simple in outline. They are characterized especially by the internal calcareous support for the brachia, which is in the form of a loop. Angularly plicated shells with pointed beaks and no calcified brachial supports occur locally. The spire-bearing brachiopods were represented by a few forms that lasted until Early Jurassic time. Lastly, there were the very simple, thin-shelled calcium phosphate types (like *Lingula*), which have persisted practically unchanged from very early Paleozoic time down to the present day. The brachiopods of the Mesozoic are a declining race, but it is interesting to observe that the kinds that survived the changes of closing Paleozoic time are, in the main, the simple and conservative in structure, neither highly specialized nor degenerate, and some of these have been able to survive to modern time.

Pelecypods

The bivalved, bottom-dwelling mollusks, called *pelecypods*, assumed greater prominence in Mesozoic faunas than in those of Pale-

Fig. 16.16 Fossil starfishes of Cretaceous age. This slab of Austin Chalk from Austin, Texas, contains an unusual number of beautifully preserved starfishes (*Austinaster mccarteri*). (*Courtesy Texas Memorial Museum, University of Texas.*)

ozoic time. Before the Triassic, they had been common locally and varied in form, but altogether a conservative, relatively simple class of animals, which was distinctly secondary in importance to others. A gradual but marked change is seen among clams of the Mesozoic Era. Many of the ancient types lived on, but the majority of species acquired a higher type of structure, as indicated in the more complexly specialized hinge teeth and other features, and their actual and relative numbers gave them a much more prominent place in the life assemblage. Some were beautifully ornamented, some developed a more peculiar and strangely specialized form than any other known pelecypods, and some attained a huge size that probably exceeds all others of this class.

One of the most important groups was that of the oyster (*Ostrea*) and its allies. The first oysters had appeared in Pennsylvanian time, but during the Mesozoic they expanded remarkably and were much more important than today. Distinguishing features of the oyster family are the distorted form and unequal size of the two valves that result from the cementation of the shell to foreign objects during part or all of the life of the animal, the presence of only one instead of two muscles to hold the valves together, and the absence of distinct hinge teeth. The larger, deeper valve is beneath, and the smaller, flatter opposite valve is above, fitting over the other like a lid. Some of the Mesozoic oysters were not unlike modern kinds, but several had radiating ribs or plications. Two members of the oyster family that were especially abundant and important horizon markers in the Jurassic and Cretaceous rocks are *Gryphaea* and *Exogyra* (Figs. 15.19*E*, 16.18*B*). Some specimens of these had a shell nearly 2 inches thick. In places, fossils of these types are so numerous that rock layers several feet thick are mainly composed of them, and when the strata disintegrate, the ground may be literally blanketed with shells. One of the most common and widely distributed pelecypods in some of the Cretaceous formations is called *Inoceramus*

(Figs. 15.19*A*, 16.19). The shell is rounded in outline and marked by prominent concentric grooves and ridges. A few species attained gigantic size, measuring 4 feet across.

The subtriangular shells of *Trigonia*, distinguished commonly by ornamentation of nodes or ribs that differ in the anterior and posterior portions of the shell, are characteristic of Mesozoic formations (Fig. 16.18*A*). They are rel-

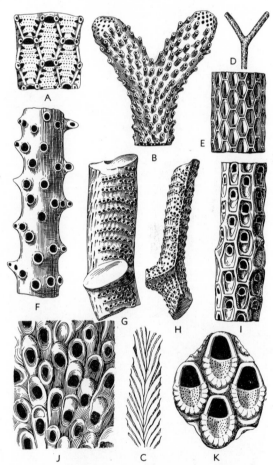

Fig. 16.17 Cretaceous bryozoans. Cyclostome types are illustrated in *B–H* and cheilostomes in *A, I–K.*—*A. Reptescharipora,* ×20.—*B, C. Cardioecia,* exterior and longitudinal section, ×7.5.—*D, E. Filicea,* ×1, ×7.5.—*F. Filisparsa,* ×7.5.—*G, H. Bicrisina,* side and edge views, ×7.5.—*I. Dimorphocellaria,* ×20.—*J. Euritina,* ×20.—*K. Costula,* ×20. (*Treatise on Invertebrate Paleontology, courtesy of Geological Society of America and University of Kansas Press.*)

Fig. 16.18 Representative Mesozoic invertebrate fossils. All the figured forms except *E* (Jurassic) are from Cretaceous rocks. Pelecypods include *A* (*Trigonia*), *B* (*Gryphaea*), *C* (*Crassatellites*), and *D* (*Pecten*); *F* is one of the irregular sea urchins (*Hemiaster*); a gastropod of modern aspect is shown in *G* (*Lirosoma*); cephalopods include the internal shell of a squidlike form, *E* (*Belemnitella*), and complexly sutured coiled shells, *H* (*Pseudoschloenbachia*) and *I* (*Pervinquieria*). Approximately natural size.

atively more prominent in the Jurassic System than in other rocks of the era.

In the middle and especially the late part of Mesozoic time, peculiarly specialized pelecypods known as *rudistids* developed a shell having the form of a horn coral, covered at the top by a nearly flat lid (Fig. 15.19*B*–*D*). The shell walls may be excessively thick, and the height of the coral-like lower valve more than 2 feet. The abnormal features of these pelecypods are evidently the result of a sedentary, fixed mode of growth on the sea bottom,

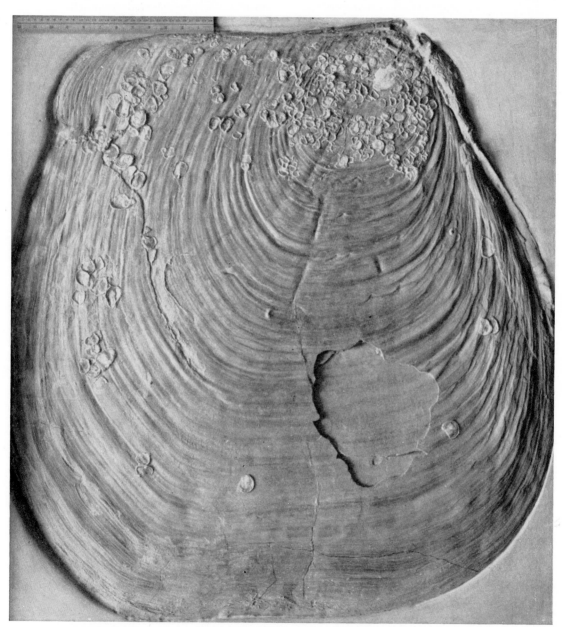

Fig. 16.19 Large pelecypod shell from the Cretaceous chalk of western Kansas. This nearly complete specimen of *Inoceramus* is 3 feet in length and nearly the same in width; it is not the largest known, for some individuals attain a length of nearly 5 feet, but this fossil is exceptionally well preserved. Many small oysters are attached to the *Inoceramus* shell. (*Courtesy of G. F. Sternberg, Fort Hays State College Museum, Kansas.*)

where they generally lived in closely crowded colonies, the remains of which may form thick beds of limestone. These pelecypods abound in the warmer-water deposits of Cretaceous time.

Fresh-water mussels are common in some of the Mesozoic continental formations.

Gastropods

Gastropods are a common but not a dominant element in the invertebrate life of the Mesozoic (Figs. 15.18E, 16.18G). Many of the species belong to well-established families that date back to early Paleozoic times, but a very large number of new ones, representing more advanced biological orders, were introduced during the era. The latter are characterized externally by various ornamental features, but especially by the presence of a tubelike elongation of the shell in front of the aperture, that is, at the end of the shell opposite the spire, for accommodation of a siphon. Species of gastropods belonging to the air-breathing group are known in some Mesozoic continental deposits.

Cephalopods

The most interesting of the marine invertebrates of Mesozoic time are the cephalopods. They are also one of the most abundant, widespread, and stratigraphically important classes. The four-gilled, external-shelled types are dominant and include both nautiloids, characterized by simple sutures, and ammonites, which have complex sutures. The two-gilled cephalopods (belemnoids, sepioids), with internal shell, also occur and in some strata are abundant (Figs. 15.20, 16.20).

Nautiloids. The nautiloids, although common in Mesozoic seas, were greatly overshadowed by the host of ammonites. Most of them were tightly coiled and highly involute, like the modern nautilus, and some attained a diameter of more than 12 inches. There is a tendency toward complication of the sutures, such as marked the ammonoid (ammonite-like) branch, but this did not proceed farther than development of a few rounded inflections.

Ammonoids. The beginning of specialization of external-shelled cephalopods, which culminated in the exceedingly complex Mesozoic ammonites, dates back to the Devonian Period. Their development is chiefly manifested (1) in increasing complication of the sutures, (2) in external ornamentation, but also (3) in the form of the shell, (4) in modifications of the aperture, and (5) in increase in size.

The sutures (junction of the shell partitions with the inner wall of the shell) are only moderately curved or angulated in the simplest ammonoids. This type was characteristic of the later Paleozoic rocks, but some of the ammonites of the Triassic are little, if any, more advanced. An increased number of bends and angles in the suture line, accompanied by a progressive complication in pattern, marks the development of most Mesozoic ammonites (Figs. 13.15, 14.12, 15.18, 16.21). The diversity is amazing, but each type of suture is constant, according to genus and species. Because even slight changes in the sutures are readily determinable, and with other characters permit definite recognition of specific differences, these shells are well fitted to serve as markers of stratigraphic zones and of geologic time. They lived in enormous numbers, were distributed all over the world, and underwent comparatively rapid change.

External ornamentation of the ammonite shells consists of lines, ridges, nodes, or spines, and the variety of form and arrangement of these is very great. Some shells are smooth, but the vast majority carry some sort of surface decoration. Around the outer margin of many coiled shells is a ridge or keel; in others there is a groovelike depression; in still others this part of the shell is not differentiated.

The form of ammonite shells shows much variation. All but a few are coiled in a plane, but among these are evolute types in which all the whorls are completely visible from the sides, whereas others are involute, the outer whorls partly or entirely concealing the inner ones. The cross section of the shell ranges from very narrow and laterally compressed to very broad and vertically flattened. Several genera have an elevated spiral shell, which is typical of most gastropods but is abnormal among the cephalopods. A few specialized, degenerate types have shells with very erratic twists and bends. Others show reversion toward an ancestral primitive state in the tendency to uncoil and become straight. These peculiar forms are a mark of approaching extinction, for they appear toward the close of the career of some branches of ammonites.

The aperture of most ammonites, where known, is unconstricted, and the edges of the shell mouth are smooth or gently curved. In some, however, the lateral margins are extended very prominently forward, or the ventral portion of the shell projects like a beak. A few exhibit very narrow, abnormal apertures, which is an overspecialized character presaging disappearance of these evolutional branches.

Average Mesozoic ammonites have shells that measure a few inches in diameter. Some genera are characterized by robust size, having shells more than a foot in diameter, and a few attained gigantic proportions, measuring 5 feet or more across. If one of these mammoth forms could be uncoiled, the shell would measure not less than 20 feet in length.

Fig. 16.20 Jurassic belemnoids from the Black Hills region, South Dakota. The numerous cigar-shaped fossils are the solid internal hard parts of *Pachyteuthis densus,* approximately one-third natural size. (*Courtesy of American Museum of Natural History.*)

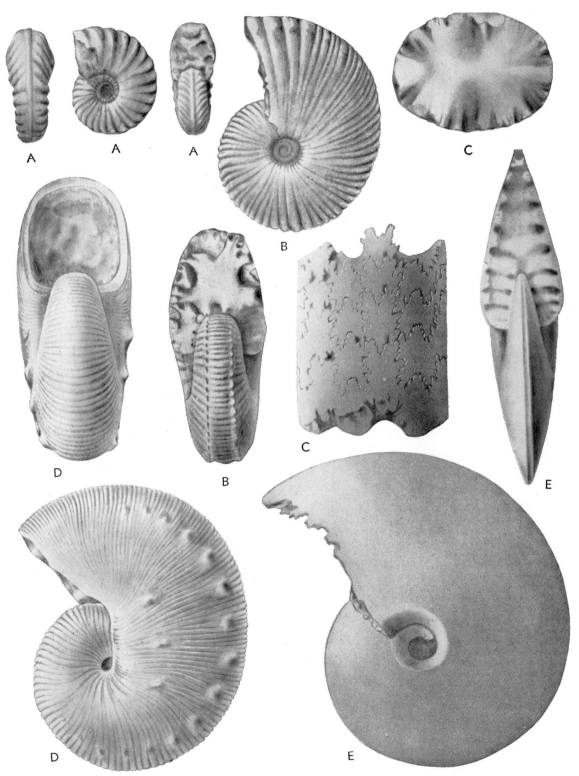

Fig. 16.21 Typical Mesozoic cephalopods belonging to the group of ammonites. *A* (*Ceratites*) is a Triassic shell; the others (*B, Discoscaphites; C, Baculites; D, Acanthoscaphites; E, Placenticeras*) come from Cretaceous rocks. Approximately natural size.

Fig. 16.22 **Restoration of Jurassic belemnoids swimming above an oyster bank.** (*Courtesy of Chicago Natural History Museum.*)

Study of the distribution of ammonite species in the Mesozoic rocks shows not only that a large proportion are restricted to a narrow vertical range, making them valuable as index fossils, but that in a broad way the genera and families of the Triassic are almost wholly distinct from those of the Jurassic. In turn Jurassic forms differ from those of the Cretaceous.

The abundance, variety, and complexity of evolutionary modifications among ammonites during their heyday in Mesozoic time, followed by their rapid decline and utter extinction, constitute a remarkable chapter in the record of life on the earth. It is paralleled, however, by the history of various other classes of animals and plants, which more or less slowly advanced to a certain point, then expanded rapidly to a peak, only to decline to a small remnant of their former greatness or to vanish entirely. This seems to be a lesson of life—adolescence, adult virility, senility, death.

Belemnoids. The two-gilled cephalopods, to which the modern squids, cuttlefishes, and octopuses belong, are interesting creatures that first appear in Mississippian rocks, but the importance of their geological record is much less than that of their cousins, the ammonoids and nautiloids.

The body of the extinct cephalopods called belemnoids was elongated, cylindrical, and pointed at the posterior end. The head bore a circlet of powerful muscular tentacles armed with rows of little hooks on the inner sides. The abdomen contained a rather large ink bag, filled by an extremely opaque brownish-black fluid that could be ejected by the animal so as to form a dense cloud in the water and conceal retreat. This ink bag may be represented in fossils by a dark-colored carbonaceous residue.

The shell of the belemnoids was internal and consisted of three parts: (1) a chambered cone, somewhat resembling a simple, straight-shelled nautiloid, (2) a delicate shoehorn-like projection extending forward from the mouth of the cone, and (3) a solid cigar-shaped piece that fits around the pointed end of the cone and extends some distance beyond it. It is this last, called the *guard* or *sheath*, that is most commonly found as a fossil. It shows a fine prismatic, radiating structure around the long axis (Figs. 16.18*E*, 16.20).

More than 350 species of belemnoids are known from Jurassic and Cretaceous rocks. In some strata, shells of this type occur by the millions and are found all over the world (Fig. 16.22). Their name, first used nearly 400 years ago, means thunderbolt and refers to the fancied resemblance of these fossils to the weapons of the gods.

Crustaceans

Crustaceans are arthropods somewhat resembling the trilobites, which disappeared at the close of the Paleozoic Era. A great number and variety of crustaceans, some of them sur-

prisingly like modern species, occur as fossils in Mesozoic rocks.

Ostracodes are very numerous in many of the Mesozoic strata, but they belong almost wholly to types unknown in Paleozoic rocks. On the other hand, a majority of the Mesozoic ostracode genera have persisted to the present day. These fossils are a valuable aid in identifying formations and zones encountered in wells that penetrate the Cretaceous rocks.

Cirripeds, the barnacles, are fairly well known in Cretaceous beds, although not common. Some are much like living species.

Higher crustaceans of many sorts, including the lobsters, crayfishes, crabs, and other kinds, made their appearance during the Mesozoic (Fig. 16.23). Remarkably preserved specimens, in which all the appendages are complete, occur in some deposits, especially the famous Solnhofen Limestone, of Jurassic age, in Germany. An interesting group that is well represented in Jurassic and Cretaceous rocks is that of the decapods.

Insects

As now known from a series of wonderful fossil insect collections of Pennsylvanian and Permian age, many important insect orders had been established before the beginning of Mesozoic time. The best record of insects in the Mesozoic comes from Jurassic rocks in Europe. Besides cockroaches, dragonflies, and other "first families" among the insects, the Mesozoic rocks contain representatives of the true bugs (Hemiptera), both terrestrial and aquatic; the flies (Diptera), with some 30 Jurassic species; butterflies and moths; the ants, wasps, and bees; beetles; locusts and crickets; plant lice; caddis flies; scorpion flies; lacewing flies; and May flies.

VERTEBRATES

Fishes

Practically all groups of modern fishes are represented by fossils found in Mesozoic rocks. The appearance of the majority is distinctly more like that of modern types, and the structural character of the skeleton, scales,

Fig. 16.23 An Upper Jurassic crustacean of slightly lobster-like form. The fossil is *Eryon arctiformis*, from the Solnhofen Limestone of Germany. Natural size. (*Courtesy of Chicago Natural History Museum.*)

and fins trends strongly toward those dominant today. Especially important is the introduction of the teleosts, or true bony fishes, which include approximately 90 per cent of living kinds.

The Triassic strata of the Atlantic Coast region have yielded an interesting assortment of well-preserved fish fossils, which show the regularly arranged rhombic scales of the body, the fins, and the plates of the head but reveal little of the partly ossified skeleton. They lie on their side and are flattened to paper thinness on bedding planes of the rock. Jurassic fishes are rare in North America but are common in Europe.

The Cretaceous marine deposits of the United States contain fairly abundant fish remains. Shark teeth of various sorts, some sharply pointed like those of modern sharks and others broadly flattened for crunching and grinding, have been collected from many outcrops of shale and chalk. Fish scales occur abundantly in many Cretaceous beds and are especially characteristic of some. A few types are as much as 1 inch in diameter. The long bony fish spines, vertebrae, and fossils showing the complete bony skeleton with associated scales and fins are found. Some of these fishes attained a length of 15 feet and, as indicated by numerous large pointed teeth, were fiercely predaceous in habit (Fig. 16.24).

Main features in the Mesozoic history of the fishes are (1) the dominance in fresh waters of the "ray-finned" bony fishes (actinopterygians), which are types leading to the teleosts; (2) the invasion of the sea by this group, which in Paleozoic time was mainly restricted to fresh water; and (3) a revival of sharks, skates, and rays, which had nearly disappeared at the close of the Paleozoic Era.

Amphibians

The beginning and rise of amphibians, the lowest type of land vertebrates, are part of the Paleozoic record. Mesozoic types of these animals are most common in Triassic rocks. The early Mesozoic amphibians belong chiefly to the broad- and heavy-skulled stegocephalians called *labyrinthodonts*, some of which were 15 feet long (Fig. 13.18). Their bodies were bulky, the tails short and stumpy, and the legs so short that it seems they could hardly have carried the body without dragging it on the ground. It is probable that the weight of the body was buoyed up in the water most of the time. These large amphibians did not persist beyond the Triassic. The first of the batrachians (frogs, toads) appeared in the Jurassic Period, and the first urodeles ("salamanders") in the Early Cretaceous.

Land Reptiles

Age of Dinosaurs. The Mesozoic Era frequently is called the Age of Dinosaurs, because these creatures were the most striking animals of the time and were world-wide in

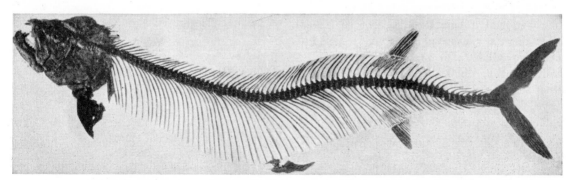

Fig. 16.24 Skeleton of a large Cretaceous marine fish from the chalk of western Kansas. Some specimens of this fish (*Portheus*) attain a length of 15 feet. Many other kinds of marine and fresh-water fishes of Mesozoic age are represented by fossils. (*Courtesy of University of Kansas Natural History Museum.*)

Fig. 16.25 Three types of late Mesozoic dinosaurs. In the left foreground are two aquatic dinosaurs, the duck-billed *Trachodon*, commonly 40 feet long; it belongs to the group of ornithischians. Ready to attack them is the great carnivorous *Tyrannosaurus*, which attained a length of 50 feet. In the right background birdlike "ostrich dinosaurs," *Struthiomimus*, are light-limbed swift-running forms that lack teeth. The tyrannosaur and *Struthiomimus* are saurischians. This dinosaur group belongs to Late Cretaceous in western United States. (*Courtesy of J. Augusta and Z. Burian, Praha; published by permission.*)

distribution. They dominated the lands for some 140 million years, from Early Triassic until the close of the Cretaceous Period.

Some dinosaurs were small, little larger than a hen, but others attained the greatest size of any land-living vertebrates, reaching a weight of perhaps 50 tons, a length of nearly 100 feet, and a height of 20 feet or more. Most dinosaurs were plant-eaters, but some were fierce beasts of prey that fed on the flesh of other dinosaurs and doubtless any other sort of animal they could capture. Some were slow-moving ponderous beasts of the plains and forests, a few were evidently lithe swift-running forms, and others were aquatic or semiaquatic types that lived in lakes, rivers, and swamps. All had a body covering of horny scales, somewhat like those of modern lizards, but this was supplemented in some by development of thick bony plates that made a strong defensive armor. As a whole, therefore, the dinosaurs were a highly varied assemblage that became adapted to a wide variety of environments (Fig. 16.25). Although they were cold-blooded creatures and were characterized by amazingly small brain size in comparison with the bulk of the body, they were certainly successful forms of organic growth. They held place at the head of the procession of life for a very long time.

The name "dinosaur," meaning terrible lizard, is familiar to almost everyone, whether he knows about other fossils or not. Skeletal remains and restorations are well displayed in several of our great museums. Also, dinosaurs have been publicized by cartoonists and in commercial art. Yet it is very difficult to visualize these reptiles as living, breathing animals that roamed the lands in numbers where we now live. It is an interesting task in our study to become acquainted with at least the main types of dinosaurs and to construct as accurate a picture as we can of life on the earth during the age of dinosaurs.

Skeletal study of the dinosaurs, especially of the skull, shows that, among modern reptiles, they are most closely related to the lizards, snakes, and crocodiles. Among fossil forms, they show kinship with the flying reptiles (pterosaurs) and an important group of Triassic reptiles known as *thecodonts*, which are judged to be the ancestral stock that gave rise to the dinosaurs. Diagnostic similarities of thecodonts and dinosaurs include structure of the skull and a special type of hip girdle, in which bones of the pelvis were strengthened and modified in order to support the body when carried mainly or wholly by the hind legs. The thecodonts were an early group of reptiles that show adaptation for two-footed locomotion. The front limbs were reduced in size and became handlike, useful for grasping. The strong hip bones, stoutly joined to the backbone, became a sort of fulcrum on which movements of the body were pivoted, a long tail acting as counterbalance to the fore part of the body. Similar features broadly distinguish the dinosaurs, even though a majority of them reverted to a four-footed mode of locomotion.

Dinosaurs are divisible into two main groups, one of which—the lizard-hip (saurischian) dinosaurs—has a thecodont type of pelvic girdle, whereas the second—the bird-hip (ornithischian) dinosaurs—shows modification of pelvic structure toward that of the birds.

Saurischian dinosaurs. The lizard-hip dinosaurs are first recognized in Triassic rocks; nevertheless, they are far more abundant and widely known from Jurassic deposits; some persisted to the very close of the Cretaceous Period. They include divergent stocks having different form, food habits, and general mode of life. One group, mostly flesh-eaters, maintained a bipedal mode of walking and gradually lost the functional use of the fore limbs, which became greatly diminished in size.

A good example of these dinosaurs is the Cretaceous *Tyrannosaurus*, which attained a

length of about 50 feet and stood some 20 feet in height (Fig. 16.25). Its hind limbs were long, strong, and powerful, and the great claws at the tips of its outspread toes indicate that the feet were used not only for walking but for holding prey. The much smaller front limbs were also armed with large sharp talons and were doubtless used for grasping and tearing flesh. The skull of *Tyrannosaurus* is large, relatively narrow, and deep, and edges of the wide gaping mouth were armed with long, dagger-like teeth (Fig. 16.26). Heavy jaws, sharp teeth, and claw-armed limbs are equipment of a beast of prey. The large size of this dinosaur indicates that no contemporary animal of Cretaceous time was safe from his attack. Indeed, fossil bones of the largest known dinosaurs, which belong to the plant-eating group, have been found that show the marks of the tyrannosaur's teeth.

Other saurischian dinosaurs collectively known as *brontosaurs* walked on four legs, had relatively small heads, and show by the nature of their teeth that they fed exclusively on various sorts of plants. They were herbivores. A typical example of them is *Apatosaurus*, which inhabited western United States in Jurassic time (Fig. 16.27). It was one of the most ponderous of all known dinosaurs.

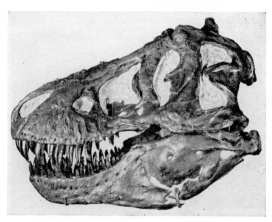

Fig. 16.26 Skull of a tyrannosaur showing dagger-like teeth. This skull is 43 inches long, 40 inches high, and 35 inches wide; the teeth are 3 to 6 inches long. (*Courtesy of American Museum of Natural History.*)

Fig. 16.27 **Ponderous Jurassic plant-eating "brontosaurs" named Apatosaurus.** These dinosaurs which attained a length of about 65 feet, probably were semiaquatic in habit, like the still larger *Brachiosaurus*. (*C. R. Knight, courtesy of Chicago Natural History Museum.*)

The hind limbs were notably larger and more massive than the fore limbs, but all four feet were short and broad, somewhat like those of an elephant; the neck and tail were long. It is judged that the brontosaurs lived mostly in shallow ponds, lakes, and streams, where the water would help support their enormous bulk (Fig. 16.28). One reason for thinking that these animals lived at least partly in the water is the location of the nostrils at the very top of the skull, as is common in some other aquatic air breathers (Fig. 16.29). Several dinosaurs are known to have had webbed feet and to have been able not only to wade but to swim. Presumably, these animals fed on the lush vegetation of marshy areas, as well as plants on land. The brontosaur's head was no bigger around than the neck, and even if this dinosaur spent most of its time eating, one can hardly understand how the needs of body metabolism could be supplied, unless all movements were very sluggish and food demands of such a cold-blooded reptile were very much lower than in a mammal of like bulk.

Ornithischian dinosaurs. In general, the bird-hip dinosaurs, which were plant-eaters, show more variation and specialization than are seen among the saurischians. Four main types are readily differentiated among the ornithischians: duck-billed, plated, armored, and horned dinosaurs.

1. Among several genera of the duck-billed dinosaurs known from Jurassic and Cretaceous rocks of Europe and North America, we may select *Trachodon* as representative (Fig. 16.25). The duckbills, similar to their thecodont ancestors, walked on the hind legs and carried the body in a relatively upright position, using the long ponderous tail as counterbalance. *Trachodon*, which attained a height of 15 feet, was a relatively large duckbill that lived in Late Cretaceous time. The skull was broadened and flattened. The jaws were paved with closely packed peglike teeth, as many as 2,000 in all, making a surface admirably suited for crushing and grinding. Several specialized kinds of trachodonts are known, some with prominent crests and one (Fig. 16.30) with excessive thickness of bone in the top part of the skull.

2. The plated dinosaur, called *Stegosaurus*, is one of the most bizarre animals of the Mesozoic Era (Fig. 16.31). It lived in western North America during Jurassic time. When full grown, it was about 20 feet long and 11 feet high over the hips. This dinosaur had

Fig. 16.28 Largest known quadrupedal dinosaurs, *Brachiosaurus*. These animals were as much as 85 feet in length, and their weight is estimated to have been about 50 tons. They are represented here in their presumed habitat, wading about in water that helped support their enormous bulk. *Brachiosaurus* is known from Late Jurassic and Early Cretaceous deposits, occurring in Colorado and central Africa. (*Courtesy of J. Augusta and Z. Burian, Praha; published by permission.*)

Fig. 16.29 Adaptation of *Brachiosaurus* for aquatic habitat. The elevated location of the nostrils on the skull seems to be correlated with living much of the time in not-too-deep water bodies, even though ability to be almost completely submerged could hardly have been greatly advantageous to animals able to reach the height of a three-story building. (*Modified from E. H. Colbert.*)

stout pillar-like legs, and although it walked on all four feet, the front limbs were barely half as large as those behind. The skull was small, narrow, and pointed in front. Chief characteristic of the stegosaurs is the presence along the back of a great bony frill, formed by pointed plates standing in a double row. The largest of these plates, located over the hips, measures more than 2 feet across. On the tail were four long, curved, horny spikes. What use or benefit this decidedly unwieldy dorsal crest may have had for the stegosaur is not at all clear. The bony plates along the back and the spines on the tail could hardly have served very effectively as a defense mechanism. We may suppose that, unless the carnivorous dinosaurs of the time lacked sense enough to make a flank attack, the stegosaurs must have furnished their share of meals to the flesh-eaters. *Stegosaurus* itself surely possessed a very low order of intelligence, judg-

Fig. 16.30 Portrait of the "bone-headed dinosaur." This is *Pachycephalosaurus* (name meaning thick-headed reptile), of Late Cretaceous age, which had a length of more than 30 feet. The top of its head, above the diminutive brain case, was heavy, solid bone. How this could have been useful to the animal is a puzzle. (*Courtesy of American Museum of Natural History.*)

ing from the minute size of its brain (Fig. 16.32).

3. Cretaceous rocks have yielded the skeletons of truly armored dinosaurs known as *ankylosaurs,* and one of these, which resembles a giant armadillo, is *Palaeoscincus* (Fig. 16.1). The skull and the whole area of the arched back were strongly protected by bony masses that fitted closely together but permitted movement between them. At the sides and along the club-shaped tail were laterally directed large spines. Squatted low on its short legs, the ankylosaur should have been well able to protect itself from carnivorous enemies such as the tyrannosaurs.

4. Among the last and most highly specialized of the dinosaur group are the horned dinosaurs, or ceratopsians (Fig. 16.33). They appeared on the scene in Late Cretaceous time and persisted until the close of the period. Although they walked on all four feet, the hind limbs were notably larger than those in front. The body and tail were relatively short. Their outstanding character was the very large bony head that bore a prominent horn or horns and carried a backward-projecting shield over the short neck. The jaws were toothless at the front, being produced as a strong parrot-like beak. The earliest known horned dinosaurs, found in Cretaceous rocks of Mongolia, resembled later ones, except in having only the rudiments of a horn and in attaining maximum size of only 5 or 6 feet (Fig. 16.34). Nests of fossilized eggs belonging to this dinosaur have been discovered, and in some of the eggs, bones of unhatched embryo horned dinosaurs have been found (Fig. 16.35).

Greatest of the horned dinosaurs is *Triceratops,* which lived near the close of Cretaceous time (Fig. 16.36). This animal attained a length of 20 or 30 feet and had a skull some 8 feet long from the tip of its beak to the back of the neck shield. Above each eye was a strong horn, and between these, farther front, was a shorter one. *Triceratops* was seemingly an inoffensive plant-eater. When attacked, it should have been fairly safe as long as it

Fig. 16.31 A Jurassic landscape in the western United States showing two stegosaurs. Characterized by their huge bony plates along the back and spines on the tail, these small-headed, four-footed dinosaurs are one of the strangest known reptiles. (*C. R. Knight, courtesy of Chicago Natural History Museum.*)

±20 feet long jin only

faced the enemy. That some of them had arguments among themselves and settled matters by combat is indicated by discovery of fossil skulls that show healed grooves and fractures, representing injuries seemingly made by another horned dinosaur.

Disappearance of the dinosaurs. A major question concerning the dinosaurs, which is very unsatisfactorily answered, is the reason for their abrupt and utter extinction at the close of Mesozoic time. These animals had been rulers of the land on all continents of

the globe during more than 100 million years. They were still numerous and varied in the closing part of Cretaceous time. Yet not one of the dinosaurs, as far as known, persisted in the Cenozoic Era. Suggested explanations of this disappearance include (1) climatic and other great physical changes associated with post-Cretaceous mountain building, which altered environment in such manner as to prevent adaptation of the dinosaurs to the new conditions; (2) the rise of much more intelligent animals belonging to the mammals,

Fig. 16.32 Brain and spinal cord of *Stegosaurus*. Enlargements of the spinal cord in the pelvic (*C*) and shoulder (*B*) regions for controlling movements of the limbs and tail were as much as 20 times greater than total volume of the brain (*A*) in the small skull. Nervous reactions were very dominantly of simple reflex nature. (*Modified from E. H. Colbert.*)

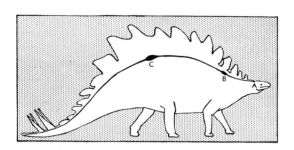

which may have furnished too keen competition, especially if some of the small mammals preyed on the eggs of dinosaurs; (3) a spreading disease of some unknown sort, which may have wiped the dinosaurs out; and (4) effects of a conjectured epoch of excessive bombardment of the earth by cosmic rays.

Marine Reptiles

All reptiles are air breathers, and this suits them for life on land. During the age of reptile dominance in the Mesozoic Era, however, different groups of these animals found it advantageous to seek their food supply in the sea. As time elapsed, they became increasingly at home in this wholly different sort of environment. The body outline was streamlined to permit easier and faster swimming, and limbs, which had been adapted to walking or running on land, slowly changed in the direction of appendages for swimming, serving either as oarlike paddles or as fins that aided in orientation of the body (Fig. 16.4). This modification of limbs resulted in notable shortening of the bones of the upper leg and arm and in elongation and flattening of the fingers

Fig. 16.33 One-horned ceratopsian dinosaur from western Canada. This form was about 18 feet long when fully grown, with a skull measuring 3 feet or a little more from front to back. Its bones have been found in late Upper Cretaceous rocks of the Red Deer River Valley in Alberta. (*Courtesy of J. Augusta and Z. Burian, Praha; published by permission.*)

and toes, which were joined together laterally by flesh and skin. Ultimately, these adaptations made the aquatic reptiles entirely unsuited for getting around on shore. Fossil remains of unborn young within the body of the mother have been observed, proving that some of these animals did not return to the beach even for laying eggs. Four main groups of Mesozoic marine reptiles are recognized: ichthyosaurs, mosasaurs, plesiosaurs, and turtles.

Ichthyosaurs. Fishlike reptiles, called *ichthyosaurs* (fish lizards), attained a very remarkable external similarity to the fishes. The head was extremely long and pointed, the jaws being armed with sharp teeth adapted for catching prey. The head joined the body without a distinct neck, and the streamlined rear part of the body tapered gracefully to the strong, large tail fin, which, as in fishes, was the main organ of propulsion. The limbs were shortened and flattened to a paddle shape, and there was even a dorsal fin that served as a keel (Fig. 16.37). These animals lived from Triassic to Late Cretaceous time. They were not large, like most dinosaurs, averaging only about 7 feet in length, but one Lower Jurassic ichthyosaur (*Leptopterygius*, from Europe) had a skull 7 feet long, which indicates a total length of approximately 43 feet.

Mosasaurs. Marine lizards, which structurally are related to modern living lizards but show adaptation of the limbs into flippers, are known as *mosasaurs*. These animals had a pointed head, a very long slender body, and a tail flattened for use as a swimming organ. The largest known specimens attained a length of 50 feet and were veritable sea serpents (Fig. 15.17). A peculiar feature of the lower jaws is a double-jointed arrangement, which enabled these animals to swallow prey larger than the normal gape of the mouth. Sharp recurved teeth not only line the jaws but occur in the roof of the mouth. These marine lizards lived in the Cretaceous seas; some of the best skeletons have been found in the chalk of western Kansas.

Plesiosaurs. Another group of aquatic reptiles that appeared in Triassic time and per-

*±6' met
length
basic form
from which
others evolved*

Fig. 16.34 **Skeletons of an early ceratopsian dinosaur which was hornless.** The fossils (*Protoceratops*) shown here were collected from Late Cretaceous deposits in Mongolia. (*Courtesy of American Museum of Natural History.*)

8"-6"

Fig. 16.35 **Nest of six dinosaur eggs, from Cretaceous sandstone in Mongolia.** Some of these eggs, nearly as large as those of an ostrich but more slender, contain bones of unhatched dinosaurs (*Protoceratops*). (*Courtesy of American Museum of Natural History.*)

Fig. 16.36 Three-horned dinosaurs named *Triceratops*. When a pair of horn points belonging to these reptiles first were found in Colorado in 1887, the well-known paleontologist O. C. Marsh misinterpreted them as horns of a fossil bison. Now, complete skeletons of *Triceratops* supply detailed information of their dinosaur nature. (*Courtesy of J. Augusta and Z. Burian, Praha; published by permission.*)

Fig. 16.37 Skeleton and carbonized impression showing body outline of an ichthyosaur. This fossil from Jurassic marine shale in western Germany clearly shows the adaptation of ichthyosaurs for aquatic life. (*Courtesy of American Museum of Natural History.*)

sisted into the Late Cretaceous comprises the plesiosaurs. Their chief characteristics generally were a small head, long neck, short broad body, and large powerful flippers that furnished the means of locomotion. A plesiosaur has been described as "a snake strung through the body of a turtle." Some relatively short-necked, long-headed plesiosaurs are known. The largest known plesiosaurs had a length of 50 feet. These reptiles were probably much slower, more cumbersome swimmers than the ichthyosaurs or most fishes, for paddles are poorer propelling organs than a tail, but the supple neck probably aided the plesiosaurs in catching fish. The occurrence of a number of rounded and polished gizzard stones, in association with plesiosaur skeletons, indicates that these reptiles did not depend on teeth to grind up food.

Turtles. During Mesozoic time, as at the present day, there were turtles that lived in the sea. Their rounded body is flattened above and below and encased in a bony or horny sheath. Flippers furnished the means of swimming. One of the marine turtles from the Cretaceous had a length of 11 feet and a width across the front flippers of 12 feet.

Flying Reptiles

Some of the Mesozoic reptiles, collectively known as *pterosaurs* (winged reptiles), learned to fly and eventually became highly modified for life in the air. The specialization of their skeleton is seen particularly in the modification of the arms to form supports for wide membranous wings and in the general lightening of the bones of the skeleton. The limb bones are hollow and air-filled, as in birds. The wing structure of the pterosaurs, however, differs from that of birds, in which finger bones are fused together as support for strong feathers that grow from the skin. It differs also from the wing of the bat, which uses several elongated fingers to support the wing membrane. The pterosaur wing was supported by a very elongated fourth finger; the other fingers were short and could be used by the animal to hang from rocks or trees (Fig. 16.38). Probably these reptiles could glide and

soar better than they could fly by fluttering their poorly designed wings (Fig. 16.39).

Pterosaurs range in size from creatures smaller than a sparrow to the great *Pteranodon*, found in the chalk beds of western Kansas, which attained a wingspread of more than 26 feet (Fig. 15.17). The head of this huge flying reptile bore a long, sharp-pointed beak and also a nearly equally long bony crest, which gives a most peculiar pickax-like appearance. The entire skeleton of *Pteranodon*, even in its mineralized state as a fossil, weighs hardly 5 pounds. Some pterosaurs had long tails, whereas others seem to have been tailless. The flying reptiles first appeared in Late Triassic time and persisted until near the close of the Cretaceous.

It is a curious fact that nearly all discovered remains of flying reptiles are preserved in marine deposits. The pterosaurs could soar through the air above land undoubtedly, and probably they did so. If they died on land, their bones happened not to be buried in stream or lake deposits where they might be preserved. The characteristic association of

Fig. 16.38 Skeleton of a Late Jurassic flying reptile. This exceptionally well-preserved fossil (*Pterodactylus*) from Solnhofen, Germany, shows all the bones in articulated position. Note the three short fingers at lower left and much-elongated "little finger" that supports the wing. Three-fourths natural size. (*Courtesy of American Museum of Natural History.*)

fossil flying reptiles with salt-water deposits, commonly also in places that must have been many scores of miles from nearest land, has been interpreted to mean that these animals lived on fishes, like several sorts of modern sea birds. They may have been able to glide almost tirelessly above the waters, but, as already noted, there is no reason to think that they were skillful, swift flyers. Presumably they could alight on the sea surface and rise again, else the supposition that their diet consisted largely of fishes must be discarded. That the flying reptiles were themselves captured and eaten by marine animals, such as the mosasaurs, perhaps, is suggested by observations of fossil hunters working in Cretaceous marine shale deposits of the Dakotas. Barnum Brown, of the American Museum of Natural History, recently spent part of a field season searching for pterosaur remains in the strata just mentioned, and he was successful in finding some skeletons. Mostly, however, he discovered here and there only wing bones—nothing else. He concluded that the meaty part of the animals had been devoured by some marine beast of prey which had cast aside the leathery wings because they were entirely lacking in food value.

How pterosaurs could have got about when they were not flying is hard to understand. Surely they could not walk on their hind legs in bipedal manner, like a bird, nor does it seem that they could have waddled awkwardly on all fours, with wings folded back and using their three small front toes on the ground. These front toes obviously were useful for clutching a tree limb or rock ledge, and it is possible that the flying reptiles may have hung upside down like a bat.

Birds

Among fossil remains of Mesozoic backboned animals are skeletons of birds. They comprise the most ancient known representation of the feathered clan, but if it were not for preservation of feathers associated with their skeletons, the Jurassic birds, at least, surely would be classified as reptiles. They would be judged to represent a divergent stock of reptiles, because they resemble the pterosaurs in having light hollow bones and very strong hip and breast girdles, yet differ greatly from pterosaurs in arm structure. They are clearly allied to the same group of reptiles that gave rise to the dinosaurs.

Unlike all modern birds, those of Mesozoic

Fig. 16.39 Restoration of an Early Jurassic pterosaur, *Dimorphodon*. This reptile has a relatively long tail, like *Rhamphorhynchus*, thus differing from *Pterodactylus* and various other short-tailed forms. (*Courtesy of American Museum of Natural History.*)

Fig. 16.40   Oldest known birds, *Archaeopteryx*, and diminutive dinosaur, *Compsognathus*.
The beautifully preserved complete skeleton of *Archaeopteryx*, associated with imprints of its
feathers, was found at Eichstatt, Germany, in 1877 and sold to the Berlin museum for 20,000
marks, at present exchange rate equivalent to about $5,000. (*Courtesy of J. Augusta and
Z. Burian, Praha; published by permission.*)

age had jaws lined with short, sharp teeth.
Wing structure, on the other hand, corresponds
to that of modern birds in that stiff, hard
feathers, which are highly modified scales,
are attached to the skin covering the fingers
and lower arms, so as to make a flying surface
that is very unlike that of the pterosaurs.
Moreover, the development of feathers furnished a means of insulation that permitted
evolution of a warm-blooded body, as in the
mammals. Warm-blooded animals are adapted
to a more active life than sluggish cold-
blooded creatures.

The oldest known fossil birds (*Archaeopteryx, Archaeornis*) are represented by
practically complete skeletons from Upper Jurassic rocks in Germany (Fig. 16.40). They
were pigeon-sized flying creatures that had a
long lizard-like tail, extended laterally on each
side by a row of feathers. The bones of the

fore limb that form a wing are like those of
a lizard in having the same number of joints,
but the hand has only three separate fingers,
terminating in claws.

Marine Cretaceous rocks, representing
former sea bottom that was many miles distant
from the nearest land, have yielded the remains of a strong-winged archaic sea gull
(*Ichthyornis*) that also had teeth. This bird
must have been able to fly long distances over
the Mesozoic seaways, now and then diving
downward for fish.

Largest and most specialized of the known
birds of Mesozoic age is a large swimming
and diving bird (*Hesperornis*) that somewhat
resembles the modern loon. It eventually attained an over-all length of 6 feet, as shown
by well-preserved skeletons found in the Cretaceous chalk of western Kansas. The long
strong legs indicate a powerful swimmer, but

the joints at the pelvis show that the limbs could be moved only sideward and outward, not forward or backward, like those of modern birds in walking and swimming. *Hesperornis* would have had much trouble trying to get about on land. Although primitive in having many sharp teeth at edges of the jaws, this bird was specialized in having lost all functional use of its wings, which indeed were so rudimentary that they could not be used for paddles like those of a penguin.

Mammals

Remains doubtfully classed as mammalian, the stock to which man and the higher animals of the present belong, are found in the Triassic, but definitely recognizable primitive mammals occur in the Jurassic and Cretaceous rocks. The fossils consist of teeth, lower jaws, and fragmentary parts of the skeleton, all of which show that these animals were diminutive, rather insignificant creatures. Two groups are distinguished: (1) herbivorous forms, having teeth provided with several tubercles (multituberculates), and (2) four orders of probably insectivorous mammals, smaller than the first group and having sharp-cusped teeth.

Among characters that distinguish true mammals from mammal-like reptiles, the nature of the teeth probably is most diagnostic. In mammals, the teeth are clearly differentiated into incisors, canines, premolars, and molars, whereas in the mammal-like reptiles (which have teeth corresponding to incisors and canines), the so-called cheek teeth behind the canines are all similar or at most marked by a gradual increase in complexity from front to back. Reptiles lack premolars and molars.

The multituberculates appeared in the Late Triassic and persisted to Eocene time. They are the most abundant and successful type of Mesozoic mammals. Probably they were egg-layers, but of this there is no proof.

The sharp-cusp-toothed mammals of probable insectivorous habits were small shrewlike creatures, which are judged to include the ancestors of the mammals of Cenozoic time. Most important are the trituberculates, which are known from Late Jurassic rocks of England and Wyoming, and from Late Cretaceous beds. Several primitive tiny opossums occur in Cretaceous deposits of North America.

The brain cavity in the skulls of Mesozoic mammals indicates that the intelligence of these animals was low as compared with later mammals, but it was higher than that of any of the reptiles. The mammals did not offer serious competition to the reptilian rulers of the Mesozoic world, but their line persisted, and with the decline of the dinosaurs, they began to expand sharply and to branch out in many directions. The rise of the mammals to rulership of the lands is the main theme of the Cenozoic history of life.

READINGS

ANDREWS, H. N., JR., 1947, *Ancient plants and the world they lived in,* Comstock Publishing Associates, Inc., Ithaca, N.Y. [1] Cycads, plants of the dinosaur age, pp. 137–156. [2] Ginkgo, pp. 157–167.

ARKELL, W. J., 1957, Introduction to Mesozoic Ammonoidea, *Treatise on invertebrate paleontology,* Part L, Mollusca 4, pp. L81–L129. Geological Society of America and University of Kansas Press, Lawrence (490 pp.).
Highly authoritative and readable account of the characters and evolution of Mesozoic ammonites.

COLBERT, E. H., 1951, *The dinosaur book,* McGraw-Hill Book Company, Inc., New York (156 pp.).
Well-illustrated, essentially nontechnical description, not only of dinosaurs, but of other Mesozoic reptiles and birds.

————, 1955, *Evolution of the vertebrates,* John Wiley & Sons, Inc., New York (479 pp.). [1] Early ruling reptiles [Mesozoic], pp. 146–157. [2] Marine reptiles [Mesozoic], pp. 158–169. [3] Flying reptiles and birds, pp. 170–182. [4] Dinosaurs, pp. 183–214. [5] Beginning of mammals, pp. 227–238.
Excellent account of these various groups.

MOORE, R. C., LALICKER, C. G., and FISCHER, A. G., 1952, *Invertebrate fossils*, McGraw-Hill Book Company, Inc., New York (766 pp.). [1] Geologic history of ammonoids, pp. 376–386. [2] Echinoids, pp. 675–714.
Also illustrates and discusses other Mesozoic invertebrates.

QUESTIONS

1. What groups of Paleozoic organisms are unknown as fossils in Mesozoic rocks? What new groups, if any, are introduced in phyla represented by organisms that seemingly become extinct at end of Paleozoic time?

2. How do gymnospermous plants differ from ferns, sphenopsids (like *Calamites* and *Annularia*), and lycopsids (like *Lepidodendron* and *Sigillaria*)?

3. What type of sedimentary deposits and in what geologic system are foraminifers important as rock builders? How does the Mesozoic foraminiferal assemblage differ from that of late Paleozoic time, particularly in the absence of a great world-wide assemblage that characterizes successive zones of Pennsylvanian and Permian rocks?

4. How are Mesozoic corals distinguished as a group from those of earlier age? What sort of environment favors development of coral reefs?

5. In what respects are the paleontological records of Paleozoic and Mesozoic echinoderms chiefly dissimilar? What groups, common in some Paleozoic systems, are lacking in post-Permian deposits, and what new groups, if any, make appearance in Mesozoic rocks?

6. Give distinguishing characteristics of major bryozoan groups (a) confined to Paleozoic rocks, (b) common to Paleozoic and Mesozoic, and (c) first known in Mesozoic strata.

7. What are some kinds of brachiopods that do not persist into post-Permian beds, and what general features characterize Mesozoic brachiopod assemblages? Why are brachiopods lacking in pre-Cretaceous Mesozoic rocks of eastern United States?

8. Describe distinguishing features of the following important types of Mesozoic pelecypods: (a) rudistids, (b) *Trigonia*, (c) *Exogyra*, (d) *Inoceramus*, (e) *Gryphaea*.

9. What groups of cephalopods occur abundantly in many Mesozoic formations, and what are identifying characters of each? In what ways do cephalopod assemblages of Triassic, Jurassic, and Cretaceous age resemble one another, and on what basis is each readily distinguished from the others?

10. How can equivalence in age of specified marine invertebrates (for example, associated species of *Ostrea* and *Exogyra*) and land plants (such as specimens of the cycadeoid *Bennettites*) or land animals (such as remains of certain kinds of dinosaurs) be determined?

11. What are the distinguishing characters of saurischian dinosaurs? What main groups do they include? In what Mesozoic systems are they known as fossils, and in which do they attain culmination in size? What were the food habits of the most ponderous saurischians?

12. What are four kinds of ornithischian dinosaurs? What distinctive group of dinosaurs is found in the youngest Cretaceous rocks?

13. How is mode of locomotion (quadrupedal, bipedal) correlated with classification of the dinosaurs? Food habits (herbivorous, carnivorous)? Habitat (terrestrial, semiaquatic)? Development of protective armor?

14. What are four kinds of Mesozoic marine reptiles, and what are the distinguishing characters of each? Which of the four persists today? What adaptation of the limbs is developed by the marine reptiles?

15. In what respects do skeletal structures of flying reptiles resemble those of birds, and how do they differ? What distinctly reptilian attributes are exhibited by *Archaeopteryx*, and what features prove beyond doubt the propriety of classifying this creature as a bird?

16. How do Mesozoic mammals differ from contemporaneous reptilian types of life? What characters denote their primitive nature as compared with modern mammals?

17.

CENOZOIC ERA:

PALEOGENE PERIOD

Middle Paleogene lake deposits (Wasatch) at Bryce Canyon, Utah.

Courtesy of Chicago and North Western Railway

The Paleogene Period comprises the early part of post-Cretaceous geologic time, extending from the close of the Mesozoic Era to about midway in the Cenozoic Era. Defined in Europe and recognized there by most geologists, it embraces the smaller time divisions named Paleocene, Eocene, and Oligocene Epochs. These epochs and deposits corresponding to them, classed as series, are well recognized in North America, but grouping of them as a separate period (and system) has not yet gained general currency on this side of the Atlantic, as seems desirable. The alternative name Nummulitic, which has been used for this division (based on common occurrence of the discoid foraminifers known as *Nummulites* in marine deposits), is not suitable, because so very many early Cenozoic formations lack these fossils—naturally including all nonmarine deposits—and because nomenclature derived from paleontology is nowhere else used for main divisions of the eras. The Paleogene is followed by the Neogene Period, which contains approximately the later half of Cenozoic time, extending to the present.

Another classification of post-Cretaceous time and rocks employs the terms Tertiary and Quaternary for divisions of extremely unlike duration, since Tertiary represents more than 98 per cent of the Cenozoic Era and Quaternary the insignificant remainder. Tertiary, as a designation applied to rocks (and hence to a part of geologic time), dates from 1759, when an Italian geologist (Arduino) published names that he thought were appropriate for main rock divisions in a local mountain area being studied by him. Massive crystalline rocks in the core of the mountains he called Primary, well-indurated and folded fossil-bearing strata above the Primary he named Secondary, and semiconsolidated sedimentary deposits found unconformably overlying the Secondary he classified as Tertiary. This was a natural procedure entirely suited to the area in which Arduino used it. However, his simple threefold division of rocks soon was extended to many other parts of Europe where it did not fit or where, at least, the names were applied differently. Thus, Primary was used variously for rocks now identified as Precambrian, for Precambrian combined with Paleozoic, or for Paleozoic alone; Secondary was used for strata now defined as Mesozoic or Mesozoic and Paleozoic together; Tertiary was more consistently recognized as applicable to most deposits now known as Cenozoic. The name Quaternary represents a sort of afterthought (1830); it was added to take care of such surficial materials as the alluvium of river valleys, wind-blown sand of dune areas, glacial deposits, and the like, all obviously very young geologically and by their nature considered to be post-Tertiary. The use of Primary and Secondary now is almost universally abandoned but handed down by custom; Tertiary (for all pre-Pleistocene Cenozoic deposits) and Quaternary (for Pleistocene and Recent deposits) persist. All should be discarded. That Tertiary is not third and Quaternary not fourth can be overlooked; it is because these terms are so very ill suited for delineation of Cenozoic historical geology that they are rejected.

The first detailed study of Paleogene formations was made in the broad structural basin in northern France that incloses Paris, known, therefore, as the Paris Basin. Accordingly, this has come to be considered as the classic region for differentiation of most standard subdivisions, classed as stages, in the geologic succession (Fig. 17.1). In particular, this area provides the type sections for study of Eocene deposits. The series named Paleocene and Oligocene, which were not separately recognized when Eocene was defined, are based mainly on deposits in Belgium, southeastern England, and western Germany, not far distant from the Paris Basin. A better standard of reference for Eocene rocks could hardly have been found anywhere, because the strata exposed at many places near Paris offer a nearly unbroken succession of highly fossiliferous deposits, in which marine formations alternate with continental beds. The Paleogene marine fossils are mostly preserved in remarkable perfection, and they may be collected in abundance at many outcrops. The nonmarine deposits have yielded numerous vertebrates and other organic remains of the land. The study of the fossil vertebrates led the famous anatomist Cuvier to the conclusion—new and important at the time of its publication in 1812—that bones found in the Eocene strata near Paris belonged to extinct species of animals having characters quite unlike any known living creatures.

Occurrence of Paleogene Deposits in North America

Recognition of Paleogene. Cretaceous rocks of the Atlantic and Gulf Coastal Plains and along the Pacific Border of North America

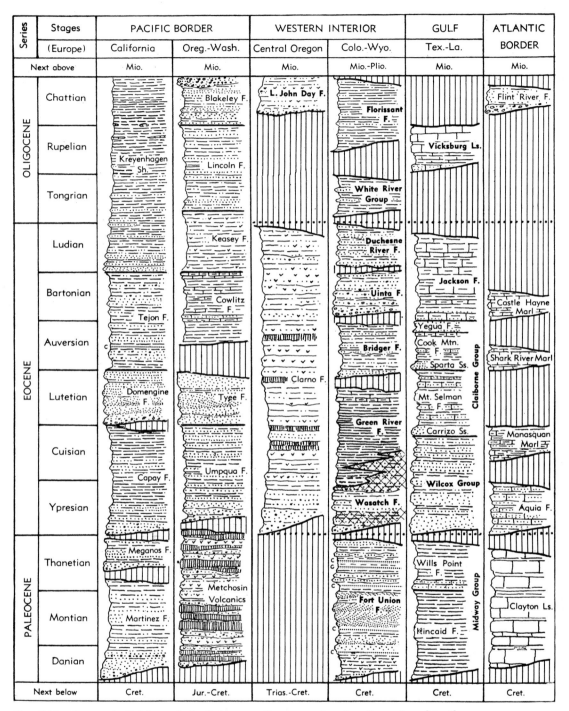

Fig. 17.1 Time-rock divisions of the Paleogene System and rock units assigned to them in representative important Paleogene sections of North America. The vertical scale does not represent time duration or thickness of rocks but is determined by suitability for plotting the various recognized rock units, placement of which indicates correlation in age. Lithologic character is represented graphically (explanation of symbols in Appendix B). Vertically ruled areas denote absence of deposits.

are overlain by marine and nonmarine deposits, largely unconsolidated, that obviously are geologically late in origin. This is shown by their position above the Cretaceous as uppermost parts of the stratified sedimentary materials at many localities, and it is strongly suggested, though not proved, by their general lack of induration. Many beds are abundantly fossiliferous. Assemblages of marine fossils collected from these beds in both eastern and western parts of North America, when compared with successive Paleogene faunas from northwestern Europe, abundantly demonstrate close correspondence, thus indicating approximate equivalence in age. Most genera are the same, and many species are almost identical. Some fossils from opposite sides of the Atlantic cannot be distinguished from one another, and for these the same names are employed. Accordingly, reasonably precise correlations of Paleogene deposits in Europe and North America are not difficult, despite some problems in definition of stratigraphic boundaries.

Paleogene marine deposits along the Pacific from California to Alaska resemble eastern Asiatic beds of equivalent age rather more closely than those of Europe, but there are enough cosmopolitan organisms in various groups (foraminifers, mollusks, and others) to permit fairly satisfactory correlation of sections in this region also. A puzzling problem that is not yet solved, however, relates to some discrepancy in correlations based on foraminifers and those derived from study of larger invertebrates.

Land-plant remains from Paleogene deposits of Europe and North America generally are similar, and with advancement of paleobotanical studies, these fossils are found to compare in usefulness with vertebrates and marine invertebrates.

The interior of North America, west of the Mississippi, contains very widespread continental deposits that are younger than Cretaceous. Most of these in the Rocky Mountains and northern Great Plains regions are of Paleogene age, as determined by rather precise correlation of their plant and vertebrate remains with fossils occurring in continental deposits interfingered with Paleogene marine formations of coastal regions. Also, correspondence in age with Paleogene fossil-bearing subaerial deposits in Europe can be established. Thus, we have good grounds for recognizing and correlating most of the Paleogene formations of the continent. Study of the nature and fossil content of these deposits permits us to interpret the historical geology of Paleogene time in some detail and to learn fascinating features of the early evolution of the mammals during this part of recent earth history.

Character and distribution of formations. The Paleogene deposits of North America logically are treated in three sections according to their geographic distribution (Fig. 17.2): (1) Atlantic and Gulf Coastal Plains, (2) Western Interior region, and (3) Pacific Border region. Marine strata form a large part of geologic sections in the first and third areas, but in the second area deposits are almost exclusively continental. Surprisingly enough, marine Paleogene beds are discovered in a small part of western North Dakota, 1,000 miles or so from the nearest known beds of similar age and sea-laid origin.

The subsurface occurrence of Paleogene rocks is extensive in the Atlantic and Gulf regions, moderate in territory adjacent to outcrops of early Cenozoic deposits near the Pacific, and small in the Western Interior (Fig. 17.2).

Description of chief lithologic and structural characters and thickness of the Paleogene deposits in various regions is given in connection with the outline of geologic history of the period. A generalization that deserves notice here is the relative unimportance of volcanic rocks in most Paleogene sections, in spite of their prominence locally, as in southwestern Colorado, central Oregon, and western Washington; by way of contrast, Neogene rocks are mostly abundantly volcanic west of the Mississippi River.

Divisions. In both Europe and North America, the Paleogene System is recognized to contain main divisions classed as series. In upward order, these are named Paleocene,

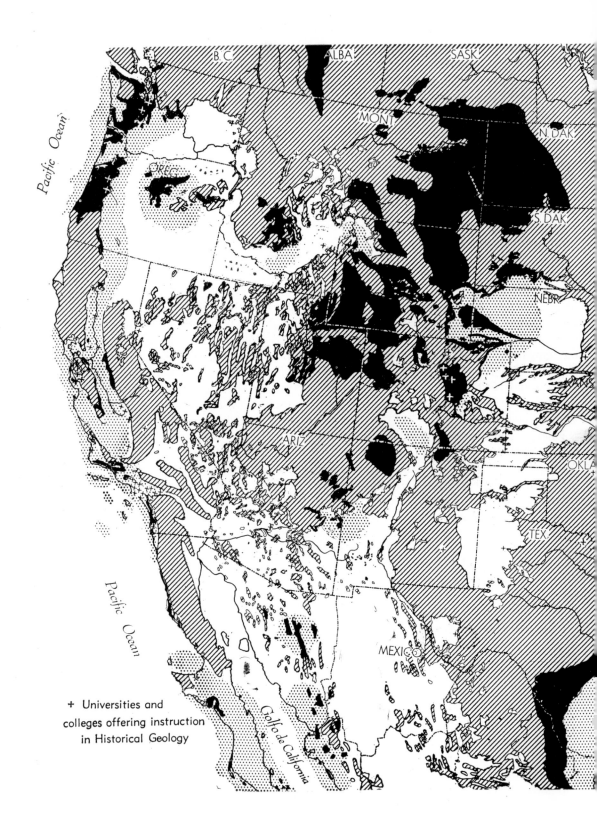

+ Universities and
colleges offering instruction
in Historical Geology

Pacific Ocean

Pacific Ocean

Golfo de California

B. C.

ALBA

SASK

MONT

N. DAK

S. DAK

NEBR

OREG

ARIZ

OKLA

TEX

MEXICO

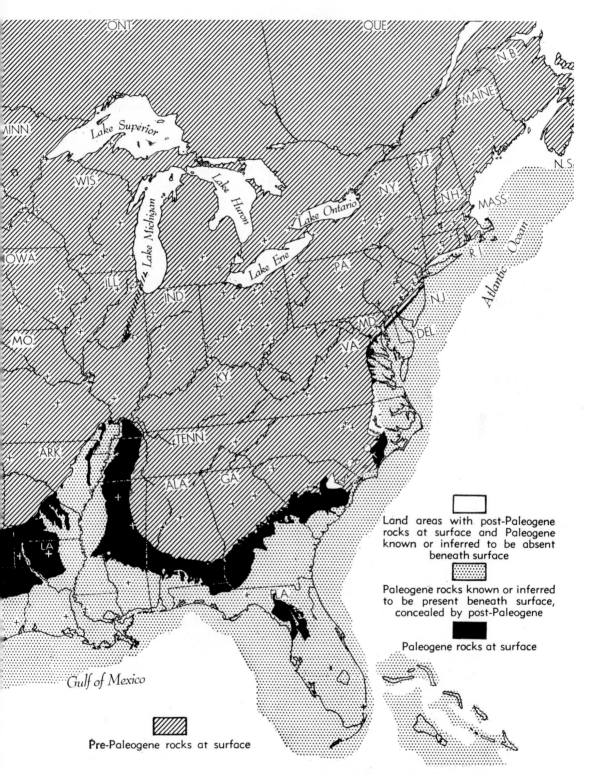

Land areas with post-Paleogene
rocks at surface and Paleogene
known or inferred to be absent
beneath surface

Paleogene rocks known or inferred
to be present beneath surface,
concealed by post-Paleogene

Paleogene rocks at surface

Pre-Paleogene rocks at surface

Fig. 17.2 Distribution of Paleogene rocks in the United States, southern Canada, and northern Mexico. The outcrops and subsurface occurrences shown indicate the original distribution of the system, modified by aggregate effects of removal of deposits by post-Paleogene erosion.

Eocene, and Oligocene. The names employing the ending "-cene" (from Greek, *kainos,* meaning recent) are based on approximate percentage of still-living species in the marine invertebrate faunas of the divisions, Paleocene (*palaios,* ancient) having virtually no modern species, Eocene (*eos,* dawn) having very few, and Oligocene (*oligos,* little, few) having a decided minority of living forms. Continuing through the Neogene, Miocene (*meion,* less) has faunas containing less than half of the species classed with living forms, Pliocene (*pleion,* more) more than half of the modern species, and Pleistocene (*pleistos,* majority, most) a preponderant part of the fauna identical with still-living species. Actually this nomenclature lacks significance, because identification of the series on proportion of living to extinct forms is impracticable, since close study demonstrates that even among Pleistocene invertebrates species seemingly the same as modern actually may be distinguishably different. Also, comparisons of marine organisms yield data quite unlike those obtained from study of land vertebrates and plants. Nevertheless, the series are considered to constitute valid divisions that in part reflect important changes of sea and land relationships, being recognizable mainly by distinctions in the nature of their contained fossils.

Paleogene Deposits and History of Coastal Plains Regions

Atlantic Coastal Plain. The coastal plain along the Atlantic, from Long Island to Florida, contains Paleogene deposits, but they are not exposed continuously (Fig. 17.2). This is because the landward margin of Paleogene beds in parts of Virginia, North Carolina, and South Carolina lies closer to the present coast line than the edge of Neogene deposits. Therefore, these younger Cenozoic sediments locally overlap and conceal the Paleogene formations. From eastern Virginia northward, the outcrop belt of Paleogene beds is very narrow, owing mainly to thinness of the system in this region (nearly everywhere less than 200 feet); only Eocene deposits of marine origin, mostly glauconitic and partly calcareous sands, are

recognized. They rest disconformably on Cretaceous formations, which in some places (as New Jersey) are lithologically so similar to the Paleogene that only well-marked differences in the fossils serve for definite identification. The existence of a hiatus between outcropping Upper Cretaceous and Paleogene strata is demonstrated by the absence of Paleocene deposits at the surface, although these have been identified in wells near the coast. After Cretaceous time the sea retreated in the northern Atlantic Coastal Plain area, but how much of the present continental shelf became land and for how long are unknown. At some distance offshore, probably not so far as the edge of the continental slope, sedimentation presumably was continuous from Mesozoic into Cenozoic time, and the deposits thus laid down should furnish an unbroken record of bottom-dwelling shallow-sea organisms. Because of great changes in marine faunas that occurred at or near the close of Mesozoic time (for example, disappearance of the host of ammonites), it would be interesting indeed to have an opportunity for study of uninterrupted fossil-bearing beds intermediate between Cretaceous and Paleogene.

In the southern part of the Atlantic Coastal Plain, from North Carolina to Georgia, Paleogene outcrops generally are broad, although discontinuous in the Carolinas. Deposits of this age are thicker than in the North, ranging to approximately 1,000 feet, and they contain a larger proportion of calcium carbonate in the form of marls and limestones. Prevailingly, the formations are marine, and each of the three series, Paleocene, Eocene, and Oligocene, are represented, although fluctuations of the sea are indicated by disconformities found at various horizons (Fig. 17.1). In the states north of Florida, Paleogene strata slope seaward at a rate of 20 to 30 feet to the mile, the oldest beds having their outcrops farthest inland and the youngest occurring nearest to the sea. Most of the formations yield readily to erosion. The topography of Paleogene outcrop areas generally is featureless, except for low hills or landward-facing low escarpments made by a few harder beds (Fig. 17.3).

Fig. 17.3 Atlantic Coastal Plain area underlain by Paleogene deposits. The flat topography and forest cover, as illustrated here in part of north-central Florida, characterize large parts of the Coastal Plains country.

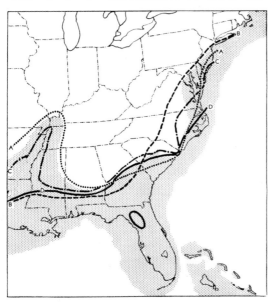

Fig. 17.4   Strand lines of Paleogene time in the Atlantic Border and eastern Gulf regions. Inferred location of the Paleocene shore during maximum submergence in this epoch is shown by the dotted line marked *A.* Successively later strand lines are indicated by the lines *B* for early Eocene (Wilcox), *C* for late Eocene (Jackson), and *D* for Oligocene. Distribution of Paleogene deposits, surface and subsurface, is shown by the shaded pattern. (*Data mainly from H. G. Richards.*)

The area in southernmost North Carolina and easternmost South Carolina where Paleogene outcrops are absent contains an important structural axis commonly known as the Great Carolina Ridge. It crosses the general strike of Cretaceous and Cenozoic formations, trending eastward under the Atlantic. Whether or not Paleogene deposits were laid down across this ridge landward from the present coast line is doubtful, but if so, they were stripped away before Neogene beds were spread over this area.

How much of the coastal plain country along the Atlantic was submerged during some part of Paleogene time? Clearly, it is erroneous to think that the present limits of marine deposits belonging to the successive Paleogene Series define the shore lines of Paleocene, Eocene, and Oligocene time, not considering fluctuations of the sea margin that doubtless occurred during each of these

epochs. Both intra-Paleogene and post-Paleogene erosion have obliterated once-present deposits, and inferred distribution of these must be taken into account in trying to reconstruct the paleogeography of the period. A map showing the presumed location of Paleogene strand lines in Paleocene, early Eocene, late Eocene, and Oligocene times in the Atlantic Border and Gulf regions is given in Fig. 17.4. This is based on both surface and subsurface information. Assuming that the position of successive shore lines is approximately correct, it is evident that maximum submergence characterizes no single Paleogene epoch, for the Paleocene inundation exceeded all others in the Mississippi Embayment, for example, whereas early Eocene or late Eocene extended farther inland than others in territory farther east. An island is inferred to have remained as unsubmerged land in north-central Florida in Oligocene time.

Gulf Coastal Plain. The coastal plain in states bordering the Gulf of Mexico is much wider than that along the Atlantic, and a broad inner belt of this plain is occupied by the outcrops of Paleogene formations (Fig. 17.2). South of the Rio Grande, the plain in Mexico is much narrowed.

The lowermost Paleogene deposits (Paleocene) seem everywhere to lie parallel on late Upper Cretaceous strata, suggesting that even if an important interruption in sedimentation separates Mesozoic from Cenozoic formations in the Gulf region, as indicated by paleontological evidence, no significant warping or other deformation of the crust was associated with the retreat of the Cretaceous sea. This may be true in a large part of the coastal plains area, but in several places rather pronounced uplifts did occur, sufficient to cause removal by erosion of many hundred feet of Cretaceous rocks and locally to expose pre-Cretaceous formations. In such localities the base of the Paleogene System is marked by an angular unconformity (Fig. 17.5). Abundant evidence of this sort obtained by deep drilling in Mississippi, Louisiana, southern Arkansas, and eastern Texas establishes the regional unconformity at the base of the Cenozoic deposits, even though it is mostly very obscure at the surface.

At outcrops of the Paleogene System, an alternating succession of marine and continental deposits is found, harder strata forming hilly uplands that commonly are well timbered and weak beds forming flat farm land. The outcrops occur in bands running approximately parallel to the coast, except in the neighborhood of the Mississippi River, where they curve northward; here continuity of the belts, especially in the northwest, is interrupted by late Neogene alluvial deposits forming part of the Mississippi River flood plain. As along the Atlantic, the oldest Paleogene formations are exposed farthest inland and the youngest occur nearest the coast. Greatest penetration of the shallow seas was in the Mississippi Valley, where in Paleocene time the southern tip of Illinois was submerged (Figs. 17.2, 17.4). The deep embayment in this area occupied nearly all of northern Mississippi, western Tennessee, parts of Kentucky and Missouri, and most of eastern Arkansas.

The Paleogene beds dip seaward at 30 to 40 feet per mile and thicken in this direction, as shown by well borings. In southern Louisiana and eastern Texas the total thickness of the system reaches 10,000 feet or more. Since physical characters of the deposits and the nature of their contained fossils denote origin in shallow water or (for some of them) above

sea level, the crust must have subsided approximately at the rate and in the amount of sedimentation. Actually, this sinking continued through Neogene time, for near the coast both on- and offshore where deep wells have been drilled, Neogene deposits 10,000 to 15,000 feet thick overlie the Paleogene. The margin of the Gulf is a geosynclinal belt.

During Paleogene time the Gulf margin fluctuated in position more or less, just as the strand line along the Atlantic moved back and forth. For example, after the Mississippi Embayment of the sea was formed in Paleocene time, the shore of early Eocene (Wilcox) time was located far to the south, crossing southern Mississippi and central Louisiana in a nearly straight west-trending line; the Mississippi Embayment had disappeared (Fig. 17.4). Subsequently, in late Eocene (Jackson) time, the central part of the embayment was reoccupied by marine waters, and toward the close of the Paleogene, in Oligocene (Vicksburg) time, the shore retreated approximately to its position in the early Eocene. These oscillations are demonstrated both by the geographic distribution of marine deposits belonging to successive divisions of the Paleogene strata and by occurrence of nonmarine beds that interfinger or grade laterally in seaward directions with the marine sediments. Throughout the central part of the Mississippi Embayment where early Eocene (Wilcox)

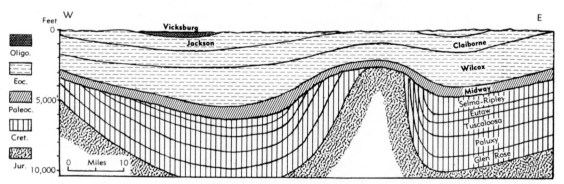

Fig. 17.5 Section of Paleogene and older formations in central Mississippi. This section, based on information obtained from numerous deep wells, extends from west to east across the Jackson Uplift, an important gas-producing area adjoining Jackson, Mississippi. Other structural uplifts in this region show similar relationships, especially the pronounced unconformity at the base of Paleogene deposits. (*Data mainly from Tom McGlothlin.*)

nonmarine deposits overlie Paleocene (Midway) marine deposits, retreat of the sea is demonstrated, and in the same region where late Eocene (Jackson) marine sediments rest on early Eocene (Wilcox) nonmarine beds, readvance of the sea likewise is proved.

Salt domes. A distinctive feature of Cenozoic geology in the Gulf Coastal Plains country is the occurrence of very numerous and widely distributed salt plugs that penetrate the Paleogene and younger beds from below. The plugs are subcylindrical masses of rock salt with vertical or even slightly overhanging walls; they are circular to elliptical in transverse section and commonly 1 or 2 miles in diameter. On their flanks the Cenozoic strata are bent steeply upward against them, and an arched cover of these strata (Paleogene over most deeply buried salt plugs, Neogene over shallower ones) extends over their summits. Accordingly, these structures are known as *salt domes* (Fig. 17.6). In upturned porous strata surrounding the salt masses and in so-called cap rock above the salt, large accumulations of oil and gas have been formed around many of the domes. The cap rock, which may contain commercially important deposits of sulfur, consists mainly of a jumbled mass of limestone, dolostone, and anhydrite that seemingly is a residual concentrate of relatively insoluble materials left behind as part of the rising salt was dissolved by ground water.

The salt is not of Cenozoic age, for none is known in Paleogene deposits and at least some of the salt plugs penetrate Cretaceous strata. Probably the source of the salt is a very widespread deposit or succession of deposits of Jurassic age, corresponding to bedded salt that has been penetrated by deep wells in northern Louisiana (Fig. 14.3). Because the salt is light and relatively mobile, the weight of overlying sediments has forced it upward, like grease in a grease gun, wherever it can find escape. As shown by wells and observations in mines (for example, on Avery Island in southern Louisiana), the salt of the plugs is highly contorted as a result of its upward thrusting through the Paleogene and younger deposits.

Erosion and Deposition in the Western Interior

Rocky Mountains region. The crustal deformation in the Rocky Mountains region, which brought the Mesozoic Era to a close, provided conditions that favored rapid erosion of some areas and accelerated deposition of erosion products in others. These conditions prevailed throughout a large part of the western interior of the continent. The wearing away of the mountains supplied large quantities of gravel, sand, silt, and clay, which were carried by streams to adjoining plains and intermontane basins. In places, there were extensive lakes that became gradually filled by even-layered, fine sediments, mostly shale but including some fresh-water limestone.

The Paleogene deposits of the Western Interior region differ from those of the continental borders in that they are almost exclusively nonmarine. Also most of them are highly variable in thickness and lithologic character, inasmuch as they strongly reflect local conditions of topography and the nature of rocks undergoing erosion in nearby source areas of the sediment.

West of the Rocky Mountains front, Paleogene deposits are chiefly associated with structural basins within the mountain area. These depressions between uplifted parts of the range began to receive the products of erosion from the mountain areas early in Paleocene time; some of them are now found filled with stream-borne gravel, sand, silt, and clay to depths of 20,000 feet or more (Fig. 17.7). Lake deposits occur in some of them; the most noteworthy are those of the Green River Basin in southwestern Wyoming and northwestern Colorado (Fig. 17.8). Here, finely laminated oil shale, 2,000 feet thick, contains fresh-water organic remains from which more than 100 billion barrels of oil could be distilled. Beautifully preserved leaves and skeletons of fishes come from these lake deposits in Wyoming.

Plains region east of the Rockies. The plains country east of the Rocky Mountains, from Colorado northward far into Canada, is blanketed by Paleogene continental forma-

Fig. 17.6 Geologic section of the Spindletop salt dome in eastern Texas. This typical salt dome, located at the south edge of Beaumont, Texas, has a cylindrical core of salt about a mile in diameter. Its nearly flat top is covered by hard cap rock, mainly composed of dolostone and anhydrite, that is encountered in wells at a depth of slightly more than 1,000 feet. The Cenozoic formations surrounding the salt plug have been turned upward around it by vertical thrust of the rising salt mass. More than 130 million barrels of petroleum have been produced from the flanks and cap rock of this dome. (*Courtesy of Humble Oil & Refining Company and Texas Memorial Museum.*)

Fig. 17.7 Early Eocene continental deposits in northern Wyoming. The little-consolidated nature of these clayey to silty, pink and gray color-banded strata is shown by the intricately eroded badlands topography seen in this exposure. It is located in the valley of Powder River, east of Sheridan, Wyoming. (*W. T. Lee, courtesy of U.S. Geol. Survey.*)

Fig. 17.8 Evenly bedded deposits of a great Eocene lake in northeastern Utah. This formation (Green River), more than 2,000 feet thick, covers an area of 50,000 square miles in Utah, Colorado, and Wyoming. It is rich in oil, which may be obtained from the shaly beds by distillation. (*D. E. Winchester, courtesy of U.S. Geol. Survey.*)

Fig. 17.9 Oligocene continental deposits in the Badlands of South Dakota. These river-laid silty deposits have been intricately carved by rain wash and stream erosion into gulleys, buttes, and ridges. In places, many well-preserved bones of mammals of the plains have been collected from these strata. (*N. H. Darton, courtesy of U.S. Geol. Survey.*)

tions, especially of Paleocene (Fort Union) and Oligocene (White River) age. The deposits were laid down by streams, which, by lateral shifting of their courses, built coalescent sheets and lenses of alluvial detritus so as to form very gently sloping aggradational plains of vast extent. This depositional process was not a continuous or uniform one throughout all of the plains region, however. The earliest deposits, for example, are confined to territory near the mountains in eastern Colorado, Wyoming, Montana, and Alberta. In western Kansas and northwestern Texas there are no Paleogene strata, and here late Neogene alluvial deposits rest directly on eroded Mesozoic and Paleozoic beds.

Divisions of the Paleogene, representing successively younger parts of the system, are identified by their fossil remains, chiefly many kinds of mammal bones but including also the leaves of trees and shrubs. Thus the changing nature and areas of sedimentation in the plains can be determined, and times of temporary interruption, accompanied by erosion, may be identified. Coal swamps existed in Paleocene time in much of the Wyoming, North Dakota, Montana, and Alberta portions of the plains country.

Marine deposits in North Dakota. A single area of marine strata, which are classed as belonging to the Paleocene Epoch, occurs in western North Dakota, where 200 to 300 feet of dark shaly beds containing oysters, foraminifers, and other marine organisms overlie uppermost Cretaceous dinosaur-bearing beds and interfinger laterally with basal Paleogene

Fig. 17.10 Mammal-bearing clay deposits of Oligocene age in South Dakota. These strata are part of the White River Group as exposed in the Badlands National Monument southeast of Rapid City. Equivalent beds occur also in western Nebraska. (*Courtesy of South Dakota State Highway Department.*)

plant-bearing continental deposits. This interesting, isolated occurrence of marine strata gives a record of the last remnant of the great interior sea, which in Cretaceous time had stretched from the Gulf of Mexico to the Arctic. Some of the fossils are most like forms occurring in marine deposits (Midway) at the base of the Paleogene in the Gulf region, but there is no physical evidence of any salt-water connection between North Dakota and the Gulf at this time.

Colorado Plateau region. The high plateau country of Utah is capped by Paleogene sedimentary formations and extrusive igneous rocks, mostly basaltic lavas. The brilliant color and fantastic sculpture of some of these rocks, as seen in such places as Bryce Canyon, attract the interest of the tourist, but such attraction is superficial compared with that offered by this region to students of Paleogene geologic history (Figs. 17.11, 17.12). In early Neogene time the plateau country was broken along several long north-south faults. The ruggedness of this region at the present day is partly an expression of these structural movements but mainly the work of tremendous erosion accomplished during Cenozoic time. This erosion has stripped away Paleogene and older rocks from many thousand square miles of the plateau country, causing retreat of the cliff margins of the plateaus and mesas and carving an intricate network of impassable canyons. Although the main drainage pattern and much of the denudation of the plateau region, as now seen, had been accomplished at the close of Paleogene time, the carving of the Grand Canyon and the deepening of innumerable tributary canyons

Fig. 17.11 Intricately carved Eocene beds in southern Utah. This view in Bryce Canyon National Park shows Wasatch Beds at the edge of the High Plateau country north of the Grand Canyon of the Colorado River. The deposits are calcareous sediments containing shells of aquatic snails, and their even stratification indicates origin in a lake. (*Courtesy of Union Pacific Railroad.*)

of the Colorado River are mainly the work of Neogene erosion.

Great Basin and Columbia Plateau region. To the west and north of the Colorado Plateau are the Great Basin and Columbia Plateau, which comprise semidesert country extending westward to the front of the Sierra Nevada and Cascade Range. Cenozoic continental deposits and igneous rocks are very widespread in this region, but almost all belong to the Neogene. In Nevada no Paleogene rocks are recognized, and the same generally is true of the Columbia Plateau country farther north. In eastern Oregon, however, moderately thick sedimentary and volcanic rocks (Clarno) furnish a record of a part of Paleogene time. Remains of land animals are poor, but recently found plants are exceptionally well preserved, showing not only external form but cell structures. When studies have been completed, these fossils should add materially to knowledge of early Cenozoic floras and their usefulness in correlations.

Pacific Border

Cenozoic history of the Pacific Border of North America is distinguished by the considerable erosion of uplifted crustal blocks in the Sierra Nevada and Coast Ranges, accompanied by thick sedimentation in depressed adjacent blocks, the largest of which comprises the Great Valley of California. The blocks are bounded by faults along which movements have occurred repeatedly, and associated compressive stresses have folded the post-Cretaceous strata with varying intensity at different times. Angular unconformities are found between the Paleogene and Neogene

Fig. 17.12 Rain-sculptured cliffs of early Eocene (Wasatch) beds in Bryce Canyon. This view shows characteristic regular bedding of the deposits, which lie unconformably on Upper Cretaceous strata. (*Courtesy of Union Pacific Railroad.*)

and between various divisions of each; also there is great inequality in thickness of the deposits from place to place. Marine formations predominate, but there are also continental sediments.

The Sierra Nevada, which border the California Valley on the east, are composed mainly of late Mesozoic granitic rocks that were exposed and peneplaned by pre-Paleogene erosion. The peneplaned surface is tilted toward the west and disappears beneath Paleogene and younger sediments of the Great Valley. Along the east front of the mountains is a major fault, along which rocks of the range have been moved upward, and those of the Great Basin dropped greatly, at some points (as in Death Valley) below sea level. The upward movements that have produced the modern Sierra Nevada began near the end of Paleogene time, and many deep valleys, such as Yosemite and Feather River Canyon, have been carved by erosion during Neogene time.

In western Oregon and Washington, the Cascade Mountains are essentially a northward continuation of the Sierra Nevada, and they also were pushed upward by Neogene movements. Parts of this range contain thick Paleogene sedimentary and igneous rocks, now tilted and faulted, and above these occur Neogene volcanics. Folded Paleogene deposits are found in the Willamette and Puget Valleys, west of the Cascades. The Coast Range, which forms mountainous uplands between these valleys and the sea, is composed of strongly folded and faulted Paleogene marine and nonmarine deposits, the latter containing many coal beds (Fig. 17.13).

Paleogene Life

Both on land and in the sea, noteworthy differences are recorded by fossils known from Paleogene strata and those of late Mesozoic age. Among vertebrates of the land, the outstanding changes are the disappearance of dinosaurs, flying reptiles, and toothed birds, and with the vanishing of these forms, there is a rise to dominant position of early types of mammals and advent of modern types of toothless birds. From the sea, the specialized aquatic reptiles, such as plesiosaurs, ichthyosaurs, and mosasaurs, were gone, and there were no longer any ammonites among marine invertebrates. These are remarkable changes, and they are seemingly greater in view of their abruptness.

Paleogene mammals were no longer exclusively diminutive creatures, like ancestors of these animals in Mesozoic strata (Figs. 17.14 to 17.16). Small mammals persisted, but along with them were some that equaled the elephant in size and weight. One of the evolutionary trends was average increase in size, and another the specialization of teeth and limbs. The mammals multiplied greatly in variety and numbers and became adapted to all sorts of habitats on land, in the air, and in fresh and salt water. The main types of Paleogene mammals, together with other organisms, are described in Chap. 19. We may note here only the facts that mammalian fossils are chief in importance among organic remains of continental Cenozoic deposits and that the bones found at many horizons have great value for correlating the strata laid down in different basins.

Marine invertebrate faunas of Paleogene time are especially characterized by abundance of relatively large disk-shaped foraminifers having very numerous internal chambers. These fossils, collectively called *nummulites* (little coin), are so abundant in Eocene strata of the Mediterranean and Himalayan regions that they are important rock builders. They occur also in equivalent deposits of the Gulf and Caribbean region of the Western Hemisphere. Other types of foraminifers are abundant in Neogene deposits and are much used for correlating beds penetrated in deep wells.

On the whole, marine invertebrates of Paleogene age show great similarity to faunas living on the shallow sea bottom today, and as already noted, this resemblance increases upward from the Paleocene. Gastropods and pelecypods are dominant types of shelled animals, but most of the phyla are well represented.

Many well-preserved leaves of land plants

Fig. 17.13 Deformed Paleogene (Eocene) strata on the Oregon coast covered unconformably by Pleistocene deposits. This natural bridge in Shore Acres State Park, southwest of Coos Bay in southwestern Oregon, is built of tilted Umpqua beds, a sedimentary and volcanic Eocene formation, beveled by Neogene erosion and thinly veneered by Pleistocene deposits. (*Courtesy of Oregon State Highway Department.*)

occur in some continental Paleogene beds. They represent living genera of trees and shrubs for the most part. They furnish valuable evidence concerning climatic environments, and many of these fossils are very useful for correlation of zones.

Climate

Throughout most of Paleogene time, the United States, Europe, and various other lands now belonging in cool, temperate zones had a warmer, wetter, and more equable climate than now. This is indicated by the occurrence of subtropical types of trees, including palms, as far north as southern Alaska, Saskatchewan and Alberta, and by common occurrence of large alligators, such as now roam the bayous of Louisiana and swamps of Florida. In far northerly latitudes of Alaska, Greenland, and Siberia were forests of large redwood, elm,

oak, walnut, and other trees that denote a moderately warm, moist, temperate climate. Fossil leaves of the magnolia and fig trees have been found in Paleogene deposits of Alaska.

In contrast to this widespread evidence of warm, moist climate, glacial deposits of Eocene age have been reported in southwestern Colorado. Cold climate seems to be associated with formation of mountains, which modify atmospheric circulation, induce precipitation, and make for local climatic variation. The glacial deposits in Colorado possibly are related in origin to mountains of the Laramian revolution. As these mountains were worn down and as sediments derived from them were poured into adjacent basins, a lowland type of warm uniform climate prevailed in this region during the Paleogene Period.

Fig. 17.14 A Paleocene primitive hoofed mammal. This restoration shows *Ectoconus,* which is one of the earliest known ungulates, belonging to an assemblage having very generalized skeletal features (condylarths). (*Courtesy of American Museum of Natural History.*)

Fig. 17.15 Large six-horned mammals (uintatheres) from late Eocene. These primitive hoofed mammals, belonging to a group that appeared in late Paleocene time and persisted through the Eocene Epoch, attained the size of a modern rhinoceros. Their skull, as much as 2.5 feet long, contained an extremely small brain case, indicating a low order of intelligence. (*Courtesy of J. Augusta and Z. Burian, Praha; published by permission.*)

Mountain Building

The Cenozoic Era embraces part of earth history when mountain building, unusual in magnitude and world-wide in extent, deformed the earth crust. The folding and faulting associated with this mountain building were not concentrated in time, nor do they seem to have been going on steadily. There were epochs, as during the Eocene, when seas were comparatively expanded over parts of the continents, and both the type of sedimentation in various basins and the regularity of sequence of deposits bear witness to the absence of noteworthy mountains near the areas of deposition. Such evidence points to at least temporary crustal stability.

Some strong mountain-making movements can be dated as belonging within the Paleogene Period, and in so far as the geologic date of deformation can be determined precisely, the times of crustal unrest in different places seem mainly to coincide with changes that define boundaries of the epochs: Paleocene, Eocene, Oligocene. Thus, the chief folding and faulting of rocks witnessed in the structurally complex Pyrenees Mountains, between France and Spain, can be shown to belong at or near the close of Eocene time, because Eocene and older rocks are greatly disturbed whereas Oligocene and younger strata on the flanks of the uplift are not affected.

The Alps Mountains are the result of several distinct deformations. Parts of this region were involved in late Paleozoic folding, but uplifted rocks of such ancient date were worn down long before the modern Alps were made. Evidence of considerable displacement of Alpine formations, indicating uplift of mountains in the Mediterranean area, is identified as approximately coincident with the Laramian revolution at the close of the Mesozoic Era. Other crustal movements occurred in different parts of the Alps, Carpathians, Apennines, and related ranges of the great Alpine chain, near the close of the Eocene, at the end of the Oligocene, and during Neogene time. The topographic elevation and ruggedness of the modern Alps are attributed mainly to geologically recent vertical upwarping of the highly disturbed strata that had been folded and faulted during the orogenies mentioned.

The Himalayas, Andes, and Coast Ranges of the Pacific Border of North America also were made chiefly during Cenozoic time, although all had undergone earlier deformation. In the Himalayas, Paleogene marine strata occur at 20,000 feet or more above sea level.

Economic Resources

Sedimentary deposits and igneous rocks of Paleogene age are enormously important as sources of both nonmetallic and metallic materials useful to man. These include almost the entire list of mineral resources, although by no means all contribute to the prominence of early Cenozoic formations in economic considerations. Especially, it is necessary to qualify conclusions as to the age of metallic resources such as copper, gold, silver, tin, zinc, and others having very great value (including several chief producing districts in the world), because the time of mineral deposition cannot be fixed precisely enough. Even so, reasonable guesses indicate probable Paleogene origin of many deposits, with aggregate value measured in $1,000 million.

Among economic resources known definitely to be derived from Paleogene rocks, attention here will be confined to three: petroleum, coal, and bauxite.

Petroleum. Under this heading may be included not only liquid petroleum but natural gas and the disseminated solid hydrocarbon substance named *kerogen,* which yields oil and gas when so-called oil shale is heated in a retort. Eocene deposits of oil shale in the Rocky Mountains region are much larger than any others known in the world.

Cenozoic formations contain approximately 60 per cent of the world's oil, and nearly half of these resources (vastly more than half if we count potential oil derivable from oil shale) belongs to the Paleogene. A large part

Fig. 17.16 Oligocene titanotheres from South Dakota. These animals are an extinct group known from Eocene and early Oligocene deposits. They are relatives of the horses, in spite of their dissimilar appearance. The largest attained a height of 8 feet at the shoulders. (*Courtesy of Chicago Natural History Museum.*)

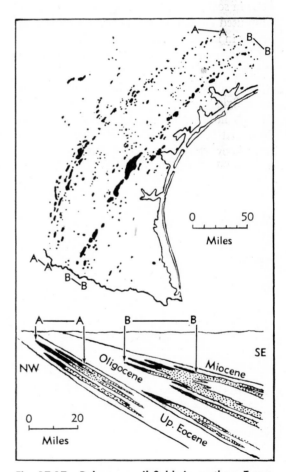

Fig. 17.17 Paleogene oil fields in southern Texas. The map shows two distinct trends (*A–A, B–B*) of fields parallel to strike of the beds, and the accompanying cross section indicates how the oil is trapped updip where pervious sand bodies wedge out between impervious clayey beds.

of the oil and gas produced along the Gulf Coast comes from Eocene and Oligocene sands (Fig. 17.17), and some of the important California fields also obtain production from Paleogene formations (Fig. 18.21). Most of the huge oil accumulations of the Middle East are in Neogene rocks, but important quantities are obtained also from beds identified as Oligocene.

The Eocene oil shale deposits in Colorado, Wyoming, and Utah extend over an area of 16,500 square miles and range in thickness from a few hundred to 3,000 feet. Their content of oil-yielding kerogen varies considerably from one division of beds to another, but using average values of determined quantities in sections measured in many places, the computed amount of total oil reserves is staggering in its magnitude. Even with allowances for inadequate information (for example, assigning only 3,000 million barrels to 9,200 square miles of oil shale in Wyoming), the gross figure obtained for the three states is 346,000 million barrels. All liquid petroleum produced in the world up to 1957 added to total known reserves as of that date is approximately 130,000 million barrels.

Coal. Continental deposits of Paleogene age contain very widespread coal deposits in the western United States and Canada as well as in eastern Asia. They occur in the Paleocene (Fort Union) of the northern Great Plains country, especially Wyoming, North Dakota, and Montana, and in Eocene formations of western Oregon and Washington. Lignite beds are found also throughout much of the Eocene outcrop area in the Gulf region, from Texas to Alabama. In all these areas the coal is worked for local uses, but mostly the deposits are little developed commercially. Nevertheless, the Paleogene coal resources of North America probably exceed 300,000 million tons.

In Japan, nearly the whole of the nation's coal supply comes from Paleogene deposits in the southern island of Kyushu and the northern island of Hokkaido. The coal is of good quality, mostly of bituminous grade, for the coal-bearing formations have been rather strongly folded and the coal beds thus partly metamorphosed by pressure. Natural anthracite occurs where some of the coal beds have been affected by igneous intrusions.

Bauxite. The chief domestic sources of bauxite, mined as aluminum ore, are in Paleogene rocks of the Gulf Coastal Plain extending from Arkansas eastward to Georgia. The deposits occur chiefly near the contact between Paleocene and Eocene strata. Bauxite deposits found in Virginia and Tennessee also are thought to have been formed in Paleogene time.

READINGS

Barton, D. C., 1933, Mechanics of formation of salt domes, with special reference to Gulf Coast salt domes of Texas and Louisiana: *Am. Assoc. Petroleum Geologists Bull.*, vol. 17, pp. 1025–1083.
    Important descriptive account of salt-dome structures and their origin.
———, Ritz, C. H., and Hickey, Maude, 1933, Gulf Coast geosyncline: *Am. Assoc. Petroleum Geologists Bull.*, vol. 17, pp. 1446–1558.
Carsey, J. B., 1950, Geology of Gulf coastal area and continental shelf: *Am. Assoc. Petroleum Geologists Bull.*, vol. 34, pp. 361–384.
Fenneman, N. M., 1931, *Physiography of western United States*, McGraw-Hill Book Company, Inc., New York (534 pp.). [1] Missouri Plateau, pp. 61–79. [2] Wyoming Basin, pp. 133–149.
    Describes regions associated with Paleogene deposits.
King, P. B., 1951, *The tectonics of Middle North America*, Princeton University Press, Princeton, N.J. (203 pp.). The Coastal Plains, pp. 160–182.
    Good survey of Coastal Plains geology.
Lowman, S. W., 1949, Sedimentary facies in Gulf Coast: *Am. Assoc. Petroleum Geologists Bull.*, vol. 33, pp. 1939–1997.
    Describes variations in Paleogene and Neogene sedimentation, with tectonic implications.
Moody, C. L., 1931, Tertiary history of Sabine Uplift, Louisiana: *Am. Assoc. Petroleum Geologists Bull.*, vol. 15, pp. 531–551.

Cenozoic Era: Paleogene Period ⚊ ⚊ ⚊ 455

RICHARDS, H. G., 1953, *Record of the rocks*, The Ronald Press Company, New York (413 pp.).
The Eocene (including Paleocene) and Oligocene, pp. 305–327.
Historical geology with special reference to marine oscillations and Atlantic Coastal Plain.

SPANGLER, W. B., and PETERSON, J. J., 1950, Geology of Atlantic Coastal Plain in New Jersey, Delaware, Maryland, and Virginia: *Am. Assoc. Petroleum Geologists Bull.*, vol. 34, pp. 1–99.
Stratigraphy of Cenozoic formations with structure contours and thickness maps.

STEPHENSON, L. W., 1928, Structural features of the Atlantic and Gulf Coastal Plain: *Geol. Soc. America Bull.*, vol. 39, pp. 887–899.

———, 1928, Major marine transgressions and regressions and structural features of the Gulf Coastal Plain: *Am. Jour. Sci.*, ser. 5, vol. 16, pp. 281–298.

THOMAS, E. P., 1950, Mississippi structures and their relation to oil accumulation: *Am. Assoc. Petroleum Geologists Bull.*, vol. 34, pp. 1502–1516.

QUESTIONS

1. Referring to Fig. 17.1, what deductions concerning geologic history in the Colorado-Wyoming region can be drawn from the interfingering of Wasatch and Green River beds, as indicated? What formational units shown on the chart can be identified as nonmarine (at least in part), and on what basis are they so distinguished? What units possess lithologic characters pointing rather surely to their marine origin? In what provinces are each of these kinds of deposits recognized?

2. Referring to Fig. 17.2,

(a) Can you suggest reasons for the white areas shown on the map in North and South Carolina? Nebraska, Kansas, Oklahoma, and Texas?

(b) How can the isolated outcrop of Paleogene rocks in northern Florida be explained? Can you identify a place or places in northern Florida or southeastern Georgia where deepest drilling is needed to reach buried Paleogene strata?

(c) Why are Paleogene outcrops discontinuous in the western part of the Mississippi Embayment?

(d) What are possible reasons for the abrupt great expansion in width of Paleogene outcrops in northern Louisiana and eastern Texas?

(e) Does isolation of Paleogene outcrops in various Rocky Mountains States constitute proof that they belong to nonmarine deposits? Why? Does your answer apply equally to Paleogene exposures in eastern Oregon?

(f) Are Paleogene outcrop areas shown in western Washington and Oregon necessarily indicative of marine deposits?

(g) Does the map supply any information acceptable as an unquestioned basis for restoring Paleogene deposits removed by post-Paleogene erosion? Where? Why?

3. Referring to Fig. 17.4,

(a) Admitting conjecture in location of strand line *A* in states west of Georgia, what sort of evidence indicates its location elsewhere?

(b) What observations support the indicated southeastward deflections of *A*, *C*, and *D* strand lines in the position of the North Carolina-South Carolina boundary?

(c) Why is existence of an Oligocene island indicated in northern Florida?

(d) Why is the distribution of Paleogene beneath seas of the continental shelf so much wider west of Florida than east?

4. What evidence is given in the cross section of the Jackson Uplift in Mississippi (Fig. 17.5) that deformation of pre-Paleogene strata and truncation of them by erosion were later than late Upper Cretaceous (Selma-Ripley) time? Can you account for anticlinal structure shown by the Paleocene and Eocene beds?

5. Referring to Fig. 17.6, what is the significance of steeper upturning of Paleogene strata (Eocene, Oligocene) than that of younger rock divisions? Do you think that very large quantities of oil and gas produced from the cap rock of this salt dome originated in the cap rock, salt, or surrounding predominantly clastic sedimentary formations? Why?

6. What features observable in Fig. 17.8 support statements given in the text that Green River Beds are lake deposits?

7. Why should sand deposits, as shown in Fig. 17.17, be localized in the Gulf Coastal Plains deposits, pinching out updip and also (as indicated for some) downdip?

18.

CENOZOIC ERA:

NEOGENE PERIOD

Mt. Rainier, late Neogene volcano that rises high above summit levels of the Cascade Mountains.

Courtesy of Washington State Advertising Commission

The Neogene Period contains the later part of Cenozoic time, from the close of the epoch known as Oligocene down to the present. Thus defined, it includes the Miocene, Pliocene, and Pleistocene Epochs, which, added together, are estimated to have a duration of approximately 28 million years (Simpson).

In Europe, the main reasons for the recog-

nition of Paleogene and Neogene are paleogeographical and paleontological. Paleogene time was characterized by very restricted continental submergence at the beginning (Paleocene) and toward the close (Oligocene), with maximum marine inundation in the middle (Eocene); the Neogene Period introduced another extensive invasion of land by the sea, but mostly in quite different areas from those covered earlier, and then the seaways gradually diminished until conditions of Pleistocene time (essentially those of the present) were obtained. Paleontologically, the Paleogene was preeminently the period of archaic types of mammals, virtually all of which now are extinct, and the marine faunas were obviously unlike modern ones, even though generally the same in composition. In the Neogene, mammals of modern sorts appeared and reached their culmination, and marine forms of life are identical or barely distinguishable when compared with living kinds. Thus, the partition of Cenozoic time into two main parts, with the dividing line between Oligocene and Miocene, seems reasonable and natural. Distinctions can be made in the same way in North America and other parts of the world.

Now, however, we encounter a difficulty. Europeans who have discarded Tertiary persist in recognizing Quaternary, which, in accordance with custom, contains divisions called Pleistocene and Recent. The Neogene Period, therefore, includes only Miocene and Pliocene. In North America, preponderant opinion of geologists now rejects separation of the Pleistocene (with its arbitrarily and artificially segregated appendage termed Recent) as an independent period, because, in fact, there is only the distinguishing feature of widespread glaciation to warrant setting it apart. This is not sufficient, especially in view of evidence that from Oligocene time onward Cenozoic temperatures generally were moving from the prevailing warmth of Paleogene climate toward colder and colder conditions. These reached a peak during the successive Pleistocene glaciations. Outside of regions covered by continental ice sheets, it is difficult to find a boundary between deposits that are agreed to be Pliocene, below, and Pleistocene, above; this question has been resolved for practical purposes by an international agreement. Taking account of these matters, Neogene time is not defined as ending when youngest deposits classified as Pliocene had been formed but is extended to include all the Pleistocene Epoch. We are living today in the Neogene Period.

Occurrence of Neogene Deposits in North America

Recognition of Neogene. Identification of Neogene sedimentary deposits of various sorts and igneous rocks belonging to Neogene time (Figs. 18.1 to 18.4) rests directly or indirectly on different kinds of evidence, those of chief importance being (1) paleontological; (2) structural, including stratigraphic position above older rocks; (3) lithologic, particularly as applied to glacial deposits; (4) age as computed from carbon-14 measurements, useful only for late Pleistocene materials; and (5) physiographic.

The study of fossils has paramount value, both for differentiation of Neogene fossil-bearing strata from older rocks and for classification and correlation of deposits found in different regions. The mammals, because of their great variety and complexity of skeletal parts that make for precision in identifying genera and species, deserve highest place as guide fossils in studying Neogene deposits. The mammals evolved rapidly, which makes them useful as zone indicators, and many of them migrated from time to time when conditions allowed, thus facilitating interregional and even intercontinental correlations. However, land mammals rarely are found in other than subaerial deposits, such as those of rivers, lakes, and swamps; marine mammals are too few to have much value. The marine Neogene sedimentary units commonly contain a host of invertebrate remains, especially foraminifers, mollusks, echinoids, and others (including corals in warmer-water environments). Bottom-dwelling kinds of invertebrates may be very useful for age determinations and correlation, but where pelagic forms are found, as among foraminifers, these are likely to be especially valuable. Among plant remains, the leaves of angiosperms and various parts of other plants are helpful. In recent years much attention has been given to the collection and study of Neogene spores and pollen grains,

Fig. 18.1 Early Neogene fossil-bearing sedimentary deposits in north-central Oregon.
These beds belong to the upper part of the John Day Formation, abundant mammals from
which now are interpreted to indicate early Miocene age, whereas lowermost parts of the
deposit are doubtfully identified as Oligocene. (*Courtesy of Oregon State Highway Commission.*)

for these are found to be very widely disseminated as result of wind and water transportation, many are highly distinctive, and
they serve to identify deposits of differing
age. Finally, the interfingering of fossiliferous
nonmarine and marine deposits in various
places allows the translation of one set of
paleontological indicators into terms of another, and this has indispensable value.

The interpretation of structural evidence,
especially the order of superposition and relation of rock units to unconformities or of
igneous bodies to associated sedimentary formations, should be well understood by the
student. As applied to Neogene rocks, this
differs from consideration of older geologic

divisions only in the absence of anything de-
finable as post-Neogene. In many places igneous rocks presumed to be of Neogene age cannot be proved by structural or other evidence
to be post-Paleogene, yet with confidence that
varies with local circumstances, these are pro-
visionally accepted as late Cenozoic.

Lithologic resemblances ordinarily are not
reliable as a basis for identifying any time-
rock unit, and this is true for the Neogene
generally. The unusualness of glacial deposits
in the geologic column—indeed, the unique-
ness of unconsolidated materials of this sort,
whether till or fluvioglacial in nature—justifies
their identification as Neogene. A similar exception can be allowed locally for other rock

units, such as some pyroclastic bodies in the Western States marked by distinctive petrographic characters, if their Neogene age is firmly established at some locality.

Carbon-14 age determinations generally are trustworthy in the range extending upward to 40,000 years, and they have added a great deal to studies of very young Pleistocene deposits. This time span is small compared with the estimated duration of the Pleistocene Epoch (1 million years) and insignificant in terms of the Neogene Period (approximately 28 million years).

Fig. 18.3   Neogene lava flows on the north rim of the Grand Canyon. Air photograph of volcanic cones and congealed lava cascade covering part of the canyon wall. Geologic recency of the extrusion is shown by physiographic relationships of the lava, yet it is old enough to have allowed the Colorado River to erode away the temporary 300-foot dam made by the lava in the bottom of the canyon and remove all but remnants of a lava tongue stretching 75 miles downstream from the place of this invasion, Lava Rapids near Toroweap. (*J. R. Balsley, courtesy of U.S. Geol. Survey.*)

Fig. 18.2   Late Neogene alluvial deposits in intermontane valleys of Nevada and southern California. The upper view shows fans on the northern slope of the Avawatz Mountains in southern California; the lower view shows thick alluvial fill at edge of the Diamond Mountains in central Nevada. (*J. R. Balsley, courtesy of U.S. Geol. Survey.*)

Fig. 18.4   Geologically recent cinder cone and basaltic lava. The clearly defined crater and ungullied sides of this cone in Diamond Valley, southwestern Utah, as well as the little-altered nature of the lava flow prove that the igneous rocks here are very late Neogene in age. (*W. T. Lee, courtesy of U.S. Geol. Survey.*)

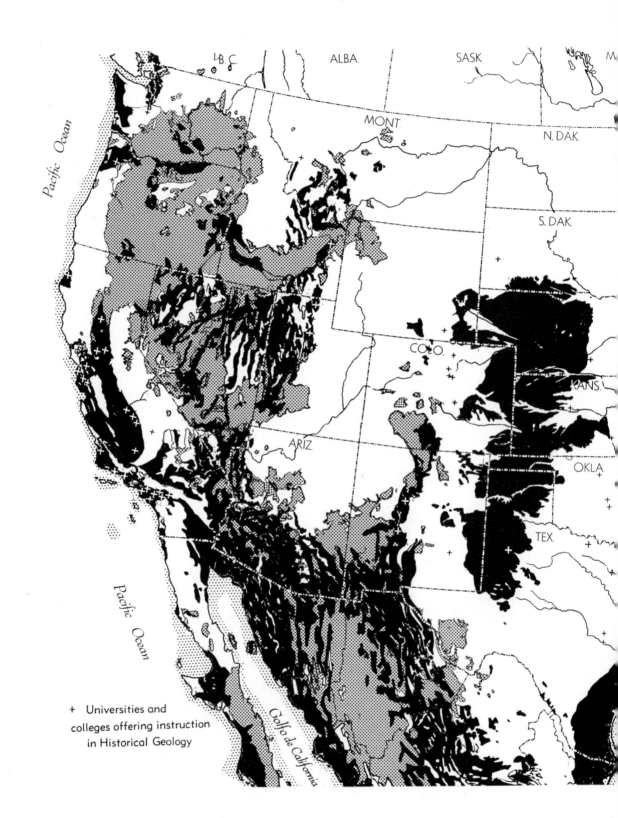

+ Universities and
colleges offering instruction
in Historical Geology

Fig. 18.5 Distribution of main areas of Neogene rocks (exclusive of glacial deposits) in the United States, southern Canada, and northern Mexico. The outcrops shown indicate the original distribution of the system, modified locally by effects of intra-Neogene erosion. Concealed Neogene deposits are confined to subsea areas of the continental shelves.

461

Physiographic evidence was mentioned as a basis of contributing (or even determining) value for recognition of Neogene deposits, because it is widely applicable to the youngest division of the rock column, whereas such evidence relating to older systems almost everywhere is obliterated or concealed from observation. Topographic features of glacial deposits, wind-blown sands in dune areas, alluvial fans, stream-terrace and flood-plain sediments, ridges of beach sand or gravel, volcanic cones, and the like, are examples of physiographic expression associated with some Neogene units.

Character and distribution of formations. Neogene rocks (including unconsolidated materials) of North America include marine deposits in coastal areas and extremely varied nomarine sediments distributed almost everywhere outside the coastal regions. The non-marine sediments include sheetlike stratified deposits in the Great Plains States and some areas farther west; widespread glacial till, fluvioglacial outwash, and loess; dune-sand deposits covering large and small areas in many places; alluvial sediments filling many valleys and distributed as flood-plain and terrace materials along thousands of stream courses; clastic, carbonate, evaporite, and peaty deposits in innumerable lakes, swamps, and playas; travertine, tufa, and sinter around hot and cold springs or along streams; cave deposits; talus and landslip debris; and others not specified. In addition, enormous quantities of extrusive igneous rocks and pyroclastic materials are spread widely in nearly all the Western States and Mexico, and intrusive igneous rocks of many sorts, shapes, and sizes occur throughout the West. This is a formidable array.

The map (Fig. 18.5) showing distribution of Neogene rocks omits the glacial deposits, alluvium of stream valleys (except the great fill in the Mississippi Embayment), and scattered minor late Neogene materials generally. Thus, attention may be directed to (1) the coastal belt of on- and offshore Neogene along the Atlantic and Gulf; (2) the nearly continuous sheet of Neogene sediments in the Great Plains region, reaching from South Dakota to northwestern Texas; (3) sedimentary and igneous rocks of the Cordilleran region, including in this the Rocky Mountains, Columbia Plateau, Cascade Mountains, Great Basin, and southwestern mountain-and-desert regions extending from southern California, Arizona, and New Mexico far into Mexico; (4) Neogene areas, mostly of sedimentary rocks, along the Pacific; and finally, (5) glacial deposits, to be studied at some length in Chap. 19.

Divisions. As stated in discussing the definition of the Neogene Period, sedimentary deposits and igneous rocks formed during this part of geologic time (and therefore classed as belonging to the Neogene System) comprise three series: in upward order, Miocene, Pliocene, and Pleistocene (Fig. 18.6). Subordinate time-rock divisions designated as stages are recognized. The standard succession of Miocene and Pliocene stages that is widely adopted for correlations throughout the world comes from Europe (column at left in the chart), but other stage units have been set up in some regions (as for Miocene deposits in California) for local use, chiefly because of uncertainty in recognizing the standard divisions. The Pleistocene Series in North America is divided into stages defined mainly on features of the glacial and interglacial succession of deposits in the Missouri and Mississippi valleys. Largely because the gradual expansion and later shrinking of a continental ice sheet lack agreed boundaries having uniformly applicable time significance, the Pleistocene stages do not now possess very much precision. They are the best we have, and they serve needs moderately well if their limitations are kept in mind.

Neogene Deposits and History of Coastal Plains Regions

Atlantic Coastal Plain. Neogene formations are geographically more extensive along the outcrops and generally more continuous in vertical succession than Paleogene deposits in the Atlantic Coastal Plain. Marine strata predominate, and at many places they abound

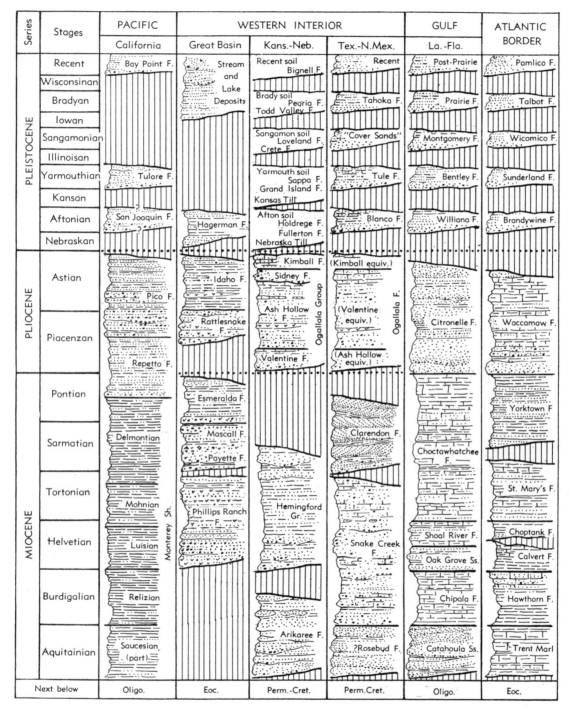

Fig. 18.6 Time-rock divisions of the Neogene System and rock units (including unconsolidated deposits) assigned to them in representative districts of North America. The vertical scale is not related to time duration or thickness of beds but is determined by suitability for plotting the various units, placement of which indicates correlation in age. Lithologic characters are represented graphically (explanation of symbols in Appendix B). Glacial deposits mostly are omitted from this chart, because areas of the columns lie outside the main glaciated territory of the continent.

in varied kinds of beautifully preserved invertebrates. Most widespread are fossiliferous Miocene beds, and these are distributed from Florida to Massachusetts (Fig. 18.7). Pliocene deposits, also locally rich in fossils, are restricted to the Carolinas, Georgia, and Florida. Marine marly beds of Pleistocene age occur in southern Florida, and for the collector of fossils, no outcrops can surpass exposures of these deposits in places along the Caloosahatchee River east of Fort Myers on the western Florida coast. This coast near Fort Myers, incidentally, is internationally known for the variety and beauty of its many Neogene shells that are not fossils—those found along the beaches and in shallow water of the Gulf.

The Miocene formations are approximately 500 feet thick in eastern and northern Florida and 400 to 600 feet in the Chesapeake Bay region, but from New Jersey eastward to Martha's Vineyard Island, about 200 feet is a maximum. The Pliocene, which includes nonmarine clay, sand, and pebble phosphate beds

Fig. 18.7   Miocene beds exposed along the Rappahannock River in eastern Virginia. The deposits here (Calvert) are massive but weak clay that contains well-preserved marine fossils. Most Neogene outcrops in the Atlantic Coastal Plain show only a few feet of beds and generally are not so good as this one. (*W. T. Lee, courtesy of U.S. Geol. Survey.*)

as well as marine strata, average less than 200 feet in thickness, and the Pleistocene deposits are even thinner, generally measured in tens of feet.

The shore lines of Neogene time advanced and retreated repeatedly along the Atlantic Border, sometimes being located scores of miles on the landward side of the present seacoast and sometimes probably not less distant on the seaward side. These fluctuations are recorded by the surface and subsurface distribution of the successive formations, especially those of Miocene and Pliocene age, and in the Pleistocene Epoch by actual traces (such as wave-cut cliffs and beaches) in many places at different heights above modern sea level and by evidence that, during times of glaciation, removal of oceanic water to form the ice sheets caused general lowering of sea level 300 to 450 feet. In early Miocene time, the southern part of the coastal plain was submerged while the northern part remained land; in middle Miocene, the north was more continuously and extensively sea-covered than the south; and in the late Miocene, central and southern parts of the coastal area were inundated while Maryland and New Jersey were above sea level. Early Pliocene shallow seas occupied all of eastern Florida and a narrow coastal plain belt northward to North Carolina, but in late Pliocene time, the strand line seems to have retreated to a position well out on the continental shelf. Past Neogene history amply supports the conclusion that the present-day shore line is a decidedly temporary geographic feature.

Gulf Coastal Plain. The Neogene deposits of the Gulf region generally resemble those of the Atlantic Border, but they have a wider outcrop belt (Fig. 18.5), are mostly very much thicker, and consist almost exclusively of clastic sediments. Predominantly, the exposed beds are nonmarine sands and clays, partly of deltaic origin near mouths of large streams and partly consisting of detritus spread by many small streams on a flat plain or carried into shallow lagoons. Down toward the Gulf, the continental deposits interfinger with marine beds or grade into them without clearly marked lithologic change. Sand bodies, of both subaerial and marine origin, tend to be lenticular in form, especially in areas of delta-building, and many of these sands now are found to be saturated with oil or gas; they are good reservoir rocks.

The greatest thickness of Neogene deposits, as indicated by innumerable deep wells, is in the southern Louisiana portion of the Gulf coastal belt where Miocene, Pliocene, and Pleistocene sediments aggregate 16,000 feet. This exceptional thickness is explained by the large volume of fine sand, silt, and clay transported by the Mississippi River, which during Neogene time built a succession of deltas outward into the Gulf. Subsidence of the deposits during sedimentation has served to retard greatly the rate of widening land at expense of the sea, because the sinking constantly gives room for more sediment. In this way the Gulf geosyncline, containing deposits estimated to be 40,000 feet thick in this area, has been developed.

Geological studies in the Gulf region are not confined to the coastal plains country, but they reach outward as far as possible under waters of the Gulf of Mexico, utilizing information of all sorts gained on shore and adding to this studies of sea-bottom sediments and organisms, submarine geophysical surveys, and detailed examination of well samples obtained in offshore drilling (Fig. 18.8). Wells now are being drilled at many locations, some in water more than 100 feet deep and some to depths of 15,000 feet; if desired, one of these wells might penetrate the shelf sediments to 22,000 feet or more, rivaling the present deepest well in the world located south of New Orleans. Important additions to knowledge of the Neogene deposits and structural features of the continental shelf are being made rapidly (Fig. 18.9).

The Neogene history of the lower Mississippi River, from Illinois southward, now is known in considerable detail. It is a complex record that contains some surprising features. For example, in late Pleistocene time the Ohio River was not a tributary of the Mississippi, with confluence, as now, near Cairo,

Fig. 18.8 Offshore well and drilling platform in the Gulf of Mexico south of Louisiana. This well is located in water 95 feet deep about 20 miles from the coast due south of New Orleans. The installation cost $1.5 million and is only one of many such wells exploring Neogene strata in the Gulf. (*Courtesy of Continental Oil Company.*)

Illinois. Instead, the Ohio flowed in an independent course in the Mississippi Embayment until it reached the Gulf shore. At this time, the Mississippi was located near the western border of the embayment, flowing southward through what is now eastern Arkansas and Louisiana until it also reached the Gulf. About 4,500 years ago these two rivers got together at a point near Natchez, Mississippi, and flowed thence about 100 miles to an entrance on the Gulf some 80 miles west of the present mouth of the Mississippi (Fig. 18.10). The junction of the Mississippi and Ohio at Cairo was established only 2,000 years ago. These dates are determined by carbon-14 measurements.

The history of erosion and sedimentation in the lower Mississippi Valley during late Neogene time has been shown to be one of alternate cutting and filling. Epochs of downward erosion are correlated with times of glaciation, when sea level was lowered by removal of water to make the many thousand cubic miles of continental ice sheets. Steepened gradients then caused the Mississippi and tributary streams to deepen their valleys by headward downcutting that began at the Gulf. When ice sheets melted, water in large volume was returned to the ocean basins, and the consequent rise in sea level caused the Mississippi and its tributaries to aggrade their valleys. Renewal of glaciation reversed these conditions, because lowering of sea level accelerated stream velocity. This caused erosion of previously deposited alluvium and renewal of downward cutting into bedrock. Deglaciation and rise of sea level again inaugurated another cycle of extensive alluviation, but at lower level than the first. In this man-

ner, successive alternating epochs of erosion and deposition have developed the present lower Mississippi Valley, broad flood plain, and great delta. The margins of the valley show the presence of terraces that are successive remnants of four main epochs of pre-Recent alluviation during Pleistocene time (Fig. 18.11). The highest of these terraces (Williana, Fig. 18.6) is about 350 feet above the present flood plain, and each of them has been traced upstream to the vicinity of Cairo.

At Houma, Louisiana, 50 miles southwest of New Orleans and about 40 miles from the Gulf, the base of Recent alluvial gravel is nearly 350 feet below sea level. Inasmuch

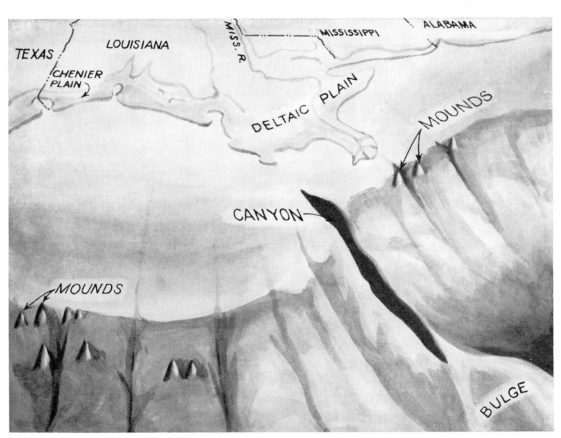

Fig. 18.9 Continental shelf and slope south of Louisiana with features reflecting late Neogene history. Most of the land area shown and all the offshore sea bottom illustrated are built of Neogene sedimentary deposits ranging in thickness to approximately 16,000 feet. The submarine canyon lies opposite the late Pleistocene mouth of the Mississippi River. The mounds probably mark locations of salt plugs being pushed upward, arching sediments above them; they appear oversteep because of vertical exaggeration. (*Courtesy of H. N. Fisk, Humble Oil & Refining Company.*)

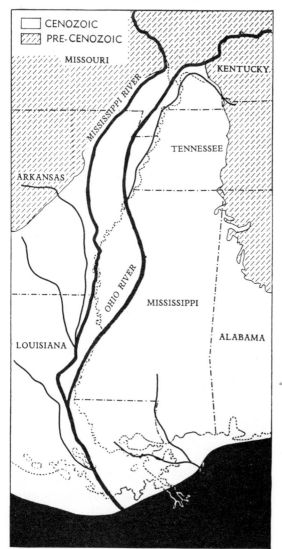

CENOZOIC

PRE-CENOZOIC

MISSOURI

KENTUCKY

ARKANSAS

TENNESSEE

LOUISIANA

MISSISSIPPI

ALABAMA

MISSISSIPPI RIVER

OHIO RIVER

Alluvium
PLEISTOCENE
Terrace deposits

PLIOCENE-
PALEOCENE

PRE-PALEOCENE

ARKANSAS

TENNESSEE

LOUISIANA

MISSISSIPPI

ALABAMA

Fig. 18.10   A late Pleistocene course of the Mississippi River and junction of the Ohio River with it in Louisiana. The drainage courses shown on this map represent conditions approximately 4,500 years ago, based on carbon-14 dating and data obtained from thousands of borings. (*Data from H. N. Fisk, Mississippi River Commission.*)

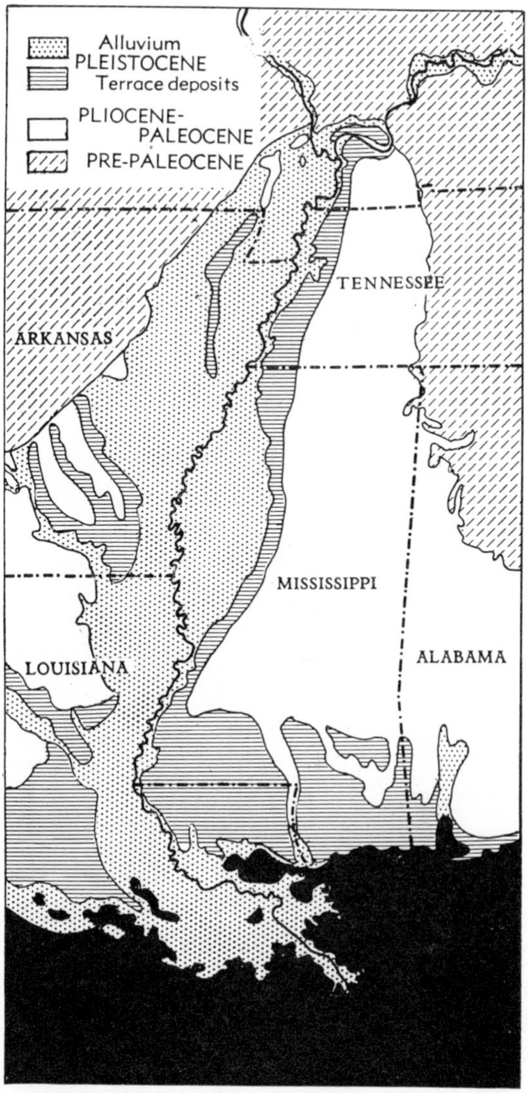

Fig. 18.11   Flood-plain and terrace deposits of the Mississippi River in the Mississippi Embayment. The flood plain and present course of the Mississippi River are of very late Pleistocene (post-Prairie) (Fig. 18.6) origin. Four sets of terrace deposits bordering the flood plain are earlier Pleistocene in age, representing alluviation in interglacial stages. (*Data from H. N. Fisk, Mississippi River Commission.*)

as no evidence of subsidence in late Pleistocene time is known in this part of Louisiana, the accumulation of this 350 feet of Recent alluvium is inferred to measure part of the rise of sea level produced by melting of the Wisconsinan ice sheet.

Salt domes. The occurrence and general nature of salt domes in the Gulf Coastal Plain were described in discussing the Paleogene formations, which the salt plugs penetrate. The plugs also are associated with Neogene deposits; indeed, a large majority of the scores of known domes, some in offshore locations, occur in the belt where Neogene beds are at the surface. In places where salt plugs pierce Miocene, Pliocene, or Pleistocene strata, the upward thrust of the salt is at least partly younger than the youngest rocks penetrated, but rise of the salt may have been going on for a very long time, beginning even in pre-Paleogene time. The progressive, possibly spasmodic instead of strictly continuous, intrusion of the salt can be demonstrated by structural relations of the surrounding sedimentary formations (Fig. 18.12).

Neogene History of the Great Plains Region

The plains country east of the Rocky Mountains is a vast, gently east-sloping area that in parts of eastern Colorado, western Kansas, and territory farther south seems as smoothly even and level as a seascape; the Staked Plains (Llano Estacado) of northern Texas

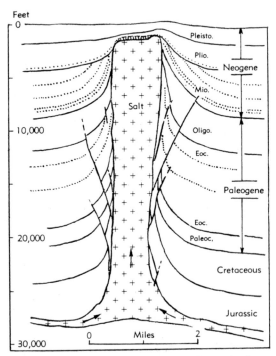

Fig. 18.12 Diagrammatic section of a salt dome in the Gulf region. The drawing represents in composite manner data obtained from several domes, for no wells have been drilled deeply enough to penetrate all the rock divisions shown. The base of the salt plug is hypothetical.

around Amarillo typically exhibit such a surface. Other parts of the region are less regular, having many shallow valleys or very irregularly distributed low hills, as in western Nebraska. This plains area is nearly all covered by Neogene deposits that are chiefly of fluviatile origin (Fig. 18.13); some sediments evidently were transported by winds, and locally there are beds laid in standing water such as small lakes and ponds. The maximum known thickness of these Neogene strata is approximately 600 feet; generally, they are less than 200 feet thick, thinning to a featheredge at the margins. They lie unconformably on Paleogene or Upper Cretaceous rocks at most places in the north but commonly on Permian redbeds in the south; locally they rest on Jurassic or Triassic. It is significant that nowhere south of western Nebraska and northeastern Colorado are Cenozoic deposits of Paleogene age found in the plains, which contrasts strikingly with the northern Great Plains where Paleogene deposits are spread very widely and Neogene sediments of sheetlike nature are absent.

The Neogene deposits of the region considered include Miocene, Pliocene, and Pleistocene in their northern part but only Pliocene and Pleistocene throughout the southern part.

During the early half of Cenozoic time, streams flowing eastward from the Rockies across the central and southern Great Plains functioned as degrading and transporting drainage ways, not aggrading ones, whereas in the Neogene Period deposition of streamborne sediments not only filled the previously carved valleys in this region but built a continuous sheet that covered the whole landscape. Former divides between valleys disappeared, and on the alluviated surface Neogene water courses shifted back and forth as aggradation proceeded. If we turn to present-day conditions in such places as the Imperial Valley or Great Valley of California and intermontane depressions of the Great Basin in Nevada (Fig. 18.2), we may find comparable stream-built plains, although on a much smaller scale and greater localization of thick deposits. Using such observation and information from physical geology concerning factors that control the work of running water, we may conclude that the Neogene deposits of the Great Plains furnish a record of increased aridity in this region during late Cenozoic time. Change from degradation to aggradation is explained by climatic change primarily and not by crustal warping that affected stream gradients.

Neogene History of the Cordilleran Region

Study of Neogene rocks and the history they denote in the mountains and valleys of western United States and Mexico takes us into a different world. Nothing corresponds seemingly to Neogene geology of the Atlantic and Gulf Coastal areas or that of the Great Plains. For convenience, we rather loosely designate this western country, prevailingly mountainous, as the Cordilleran region. Viewed as a whole, the prominence of igneous rocks and decidedly subordinate role of sedimentary deposits characterize the Neogene System in the Cordilleran region. The igneous rocks, especially of extrusive type, are enormously widespread, and in places they exhibit thicknesses measured in thousands of feet. In age they range from earliest Miocene to youngest Pleistocene, and hardly any subdivision of the region lacks representation of early, middle, and late Neogene igneous activity. This feature, in conjunction with the general nature of observed sedimentary bodies, strongly distinguishes the Neogene from Paleogene, and it is an important supporting reason for the division of Cenozoic rocks into these two systems.

Rocky Mountains. Thick extrusive igneous rocks that include both lava flows and pyroclastics, locally several thousands of feet thick, occur in the Rockies of central and southwestern Colorado and in northern New Mexico. Mainly these are early Neogene (Miocene), but Pliocene-Pleistocene extrusives are identified also. The roots of a Miocene volcano at Cripple Creek comprise rich gold-bearing intrusive rocks. In the San Luis Valley of south-central Colorado and southward along the Rio Grande Valley in New Mexico are

Fig. 18.13 Fluviatile middle Neogene deposits in western Nebraska. The gravelly, somewhat cross-bedded rock in the upper part of the view is Pliocene (Ogallala); it rests disconformably on Oligocene clay (Brule). The exposure is north of Ash Creek, Nebraska. (*N. H. Darton, courtesy of U.S. Geol. Survey.*)

thick fluviatile and lake deposits ranging in age from Miocene to Pleistocene; they have special importance locally as sources of ground water. Accordingly, Neogene time was marked in the Rocky Mountains region by volcanic activity and some sedimentation in basins but not on a scale comparable to the filling of Paleogene basins in Colorado, Wyoming, and Utah.

Columbia Plateau. The Columbia Plateau is a highland east of the Cascade Mountains occupying approximately 200,000 square miles in Washington, Oregon, Idaho, and northeastern California. It consist mainly of Neogene basaltic lavas that were extruded from various centers (some of the feeders, appearing as dikes, being clearly observable in canyon-wall outcrops of southwestern Idaho). They were built upward flow after flow (Fig. 18.14). Between many of the sheets are sedimentary deposits consisting of reworked volcanic debris, sand, and some clay, but the total volume of such materials is small in comparison with the volcanics. As shown by sections exposed along the Snake and Columbia Rivers and several other places, the lavas were poured out on country having considerable topographic relief, with hills and valleys carved in Precambrian, Paleozoic, strongly folded Mesozoic, and in places little-disturbed Paleogene rocks. The aggregate thickness of

the Columbia lavas has been estimated to be as much as 12,000 feet in some parts of the plateau; a recently drilled well near Yakima, Washington, proves that the lavas are more than 10,000 feet thick in this region. All of the Columbia rocks, including basalt sheets, unconsolidated ash and cinders, lithified pyroclastics (welded tuffs), and sediments, belong to the Miocene. The presence of some pillow lavas proves that under-water extrusions occurred locally. The age of the volcanic activity is indicated by bones of mammals and well-preserved leaves in some of the interbedded sedimentary layers.

Subsequent to the early Neogene volcanic activity, dissection of the lavas by work of streams began. If the area had attained plateau-like character as a result of the piling up of many flows, the cutting of deep canyons could proceed without crustal upwarp of the

Fig. 18.14 Miocene lava flows in central Washington. Two massive sheets of basaltic lava are seen in this view near the head of Deep Lake in Grand Coulee. Note the difference in the columnar jointing of the lower and upper flows. (*Courtesy of Washington State Advertising Commission.*)

Fig. 18.15 Cascade Mountains peneplain and volcanoes rising above it. In the foreground is Mt. Rainier, and southward in the background from left to right are Mts. Adams, Hood (approximately 110 miles distant), and St. Helens. Below them the level summits of Cascade Mountains ridges are peneplain remnants. (*Courtesy of Spence Air Photos.*)

region, but if the average elevation of the land surface was low (by sinking under weight of lavas), as is very possible, post-Miocene uplift must be inferred, for the Columbia River and other streams now flow in deep valleys cut in the lavas. The very youthful character of the valleys indicates that uplift of the region and associated downcutting by streams date from the late Neogene, probably not earlier than Pleistocene.

In many parts of the Columbia Plateau region volcanic activity of late Neogene age is recognized. At some places, like Craters of the Moon, northwest of Pocatello, Idaho, the surface of lava flows resembles that of modern lavas in Hawaii; obviously such flows are very late Pleistocene. Similar very young volcanic rocks are noteworthy in Oregon, as near McKenzie Pass, east of Eugene.

Cascade Mountains. The Cascade Mountains are a rugged range of considerably folded, partly metamorphosed Paleozoic, Mesozoic, and Paleogene rocks that, south of central Washington, are buried under early Neogene lavas continuous with those of the Columbia Plateau; these lavas, only weakly folded, form summit parts of the Cascades from central Washington to northeastern California. Chiefly interesting from the standpoint of Neogene history is the remarkable evenness of summit elevations, in both the lava and older rock portions of the range, which clearly denotes a post-Miocene peneplain that has been bowed upward to elevations of 6,000 to 8,500 feet along part of the axis of the range (Fig. 18.15). Deep erosion of the peneplain, mostly during Pleistocene time, has ensued. The Columbia River crosses the mountains in a transverse gorge cut down through thousands of feet of lava, which form a broad anticline with east- and west-dipping limbs. The arching of the lava sheets corresponds to the upwarping of the Cascades, and the Columbia is an antecedent stream that was able to maintain its course as the mountains rose across its path. As shown by its swift current, including rapids at The Dalles, the Columbia is still eroding actively.

Another feature of Neogene history in the Cascade Mountains is the building of numerous lofty volcanoes that rise high above the peneplain previously mentioned (Figs. 18.15

Fig. 18.16 Geologic relief map of Mt. Rainier and vicinity. This part of the Cascades contains folded Eocene sedimentary rocks (vertical ruling) west of Mt. Rainier and Miocene volcanics of the Columbia succession (crosshatched pattern) elsewhere, except for the volcano itself (crosses), composed of Pleistocene extrusives. (*Relief map courtesy of Aero Service Corporation.*)

to 18.17). Among these are Mt. Rainier, Mt. Hood, Mt. Shasta, and many other almost equally prominent peaks. The volcanoes were built mostly before uplift and dissection of the peneplain, but activity in erupting ash, cinders, and lavas has continued varyingly during the time of Pleistocene denudation. This is demonstrated by the appearance of some flows that seem barely to have cooled (Fig. 18.17) and by the actual explosive eruption of Mt. Lassen, in California, in 1914 and 1915. Crater Lake, in south-central Oregon, occupies the summit remnant of another great volcano (Mt. Mazama), decapitated by a huge explosion at some late Pleistocene date; the basin thus made is the best example of a caldera in North America (Fig. 18.18).

Great Basin. South and east of the Columbia Plateau is the Great Basin, distinguished by its lack of drainage outlets to the sea and by its many north-trending mountain ranges separated by dry flat-floored valleys. Western Utah, virtually all of Nevada, and parts of eastern and southern California are included in this province. The Neogene history of the region is characterized by abundant local volcanic activity, active denudation of mountains accompanied by alluvial filling of intermontane valleys, formation of evaporite deposits in salt lakes, and recurrence of faulting. In contrast to the absence of Paleogene rocks (Fig. 17.2), Neogene igneous and sedimentary accumulations extend throughout most of the Great Basin (Fig. 18.5).

During Pleistocene time, increase of precipitation associated with the advent of glacial conditions in other parts of North America greatly changed landscapes in the Great Basin. Local dry valleys gained lakes, and salt lakes were enlarged and freshened. Great Salt Lake in Utah, which early in Pleistocene time probably was about the same in location and size as now, was one of the water bodies that became expanded, and the enlarged lake was so different from the present one that it has been named Lake Bonneville. Modern Great Salt Lake covers 1,800 square miles and has a maximum depth of 50 feet, whereas Lake Bonneville had an area of 19,000 square miles

and was approximately 1,000 feet deep at the time of its greatest expansion. It was then a fresh-water lake, for an outlet was established northward into Snake River. Subsequently, with increase of evaporation over precipitation, the lake level sank lower and lower, size dwindled, and the water became increasingly salty. Great Salt Lake is the diminutive descendant of Lake Bonneville. Large quantities of salt have been deposited in parts of the

Fig. 18.17 Lava flows on the west side of Mt. Shasta, in northern California. The peak of Mt. Shasta is shown in the upper left corner of the view, and below it is the subsidiary crater of Shastina. Geologically recent lava flows are readily distinguished by their dark color and lobate margin. (*Courtesy of Hal Shelton, Golden, Colorado.*)

Bonneville Basin, and the existing lake is a brine containing more than 400 million tons of dissolved salt. Former lake levels are clearly marked by beaches and wave-cut cliffs and by large deltas of sand and gravel that were built out into the lake at the mouths of inflowing streams. These features and the flat topography of the old lake bottom are very striking characters of the landscape near Salt Lake City, Provo, and other cities of the Salt Lake Valley. A similar large Pleistocene lake in west-central Nevada is known as Lake Lahontan. An interesting deposit formed in parts of these lakes is large masses of calcareous tufa.

Neogene History of the Pacific Border Region

Along the Pacific Coast from British Columbia to Lower California (by no means continuously, however) are exposures of Ne-

Fig. 18.18 Crater Lake, in southwestern Oregon. This lake, which is 2,000 feet deep and about 6 miles in diameter, is more than 6,000 feet above sea level. The precipitous walls surrounding the lake rise 500 to 2,200 feet above the water. From this jagged rim the country slopes away in all directions. The mountain is a Pleistocene volcano. Wizard Island is a volcanic cone within the crater. (*Courtesy of Chicago and North Western Railway.*)

ogene formations, almost exclusively sedimentary and prevailingly marine. They extend inland only a few tens of miles at most, except that in California we may include the extensive Neogene deposits of the Great Valley (Fig. 18.5). On the west side of the Olympic Peninsula in Washington and farther south in northwestern Oregon, steeply folded Miocene marine shales and some sandy beds furnish a record of local sea invasions, but the deposits are poorly fossiliferous. By far the greatest development of Neogene formations on the western side of the continent is in California. Here, they are most varied in nature in different basins, thickest, generally most fossiliferous, richest in petroleum content, and best known. The region furnishes an unusual body of evidence, also, on structural deformations of the Neogene beds, including large displacements by faulting that can be dated and folding movements that even affect Pleistocene deposits. Therefore, we may examine some of these features.

Three areas contain unusually complete and representative sections of the Neogene System in California. These are (1) the Los Angeles Basin, comprising the very populous area between mountains and the sea where Los Angeles and many suburbs are located; (2) the Ventura Basin, along the coast approximately 65 miles northwest of Los Angeles; and (3) the southern part of the San Joaquin Valley near Bakersfield, about 100 miles northeast of Los Angeles.

Los Angeles Basin. The area of this basin, 50 miles long and about 20 miles wide, is nearly 1,000 square miles (Fig. 18.19). Its Cenozoic deposits have an aggregate maximum thickness of approximately 43,500 feet, of which 37,500 feet is Neogene. These extraordinary amounts do not apply to the rock succession in any one part of the basin but are derived by adding together the thickest known local developments of individual formations. Even so, a huge quantity of predominantly marine deposits of Neogene age is found in this area. Of the total given, Miocene beds account for about 27,000 feet; Pliocene, 9,000 feet; and Pleistocene, 1,500 feet. More

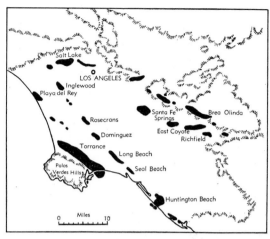

Fig. 18.19 Los Angeles Basin in southern California. The map shows outline of the basin as defined by bordering uplands and the sea. The oil fields (black) all produce from Neogene strata.

Fig. 18.20 Middle Miocene siliceous shale (Monterey) in the Los Angeles Basin. The upper view shows a gentle anticlinal fold in the shale; the lower one is a close-up (with 6-inch scale). The white-weathering bands are composed almost wholly of diatom shells. The deposit is marine. (*M. N. Bramlette, courtesy of U.S. Geol. Survey.*)

than half of the deposits are shales and silt-stones, the remainder being mostly rather coarse sandstone and some conglomerate. An example of the shaly beds is the white-weathering, evenly bedded Monterey Shale, of Miocene age, which is largely composed of the microscopic siliceous shells of diatoms (Fig. 18.20). The deposits are judged to be conformable in central parts of the basin, even though unconformities are common in mar-

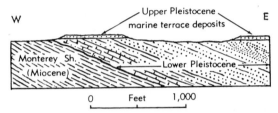

Fig. 18.21   Section showing angular unconformity between late Pleistocene and older Neogene beds. The section is based on outcrops near the southern extremity of the Palos Verdes Hills (Fig. 18.19), in the city of San Pedro. (*Data from A. O. Woodford and others, California Division of Mines.*)

ginal locations; this indicates that edges of the generally subsiding depression in the crust were least regular in sinking, sometimes being subjected to nondeposition, with or without accompanying erosion.

The Neogene and underlying rocks are gently to moderately folded in parallel manner, without noteworthy angular unconformities up to and including early Pleistocene deposits, which indicates that the folding is geologically very young. At least locally, fossiliferous late Pleistocene lying horizontally on a marine terrace (Fig. 18.21) is found to extend across the beveled edges of distinctly folded early Pleistocene and Pliocene beds, and this evidence dates the folding as mid-Pleistocene. Faults occur also in the Los Angeles Basin, some of them being causally related to the distinct alignment of oil fields (such as the row of fields that includes the Inglewood and Huntington Beach fields, Fig. 18.19).

The marine terraces found along the coast near Los Angeles and elsewhere from south-

Fig. 18.22   Pleistocene marine terraces west of the Los Angeles Basin. The sketch shows the seaward side of Palos Verdes Hills, terraces visible in this view being numbered serially in order of their relative age (1–6), with planation at present sea level indicated at the base of the sea cliffs (7). Actually, 13 different terrace levels (counting 6 of the drawing as lowest) are recognized in the Los Angeles area. (*From air photograph by J. S. Shelton and R. C. Frampton, California Division of Mines.*)

ern California to Washington are late Neogene (Pleistocene) features of considerable interest (Fig. 18.22). The evenness of their elevation above present sea level throughout long distances does not fit the suggestion that the terraces represent marine planation associated with crustal upwarping but indicates different levels of the sea itself. The highest of 13 terraces recognized in the Los Angeles area is 1,300 feet above the sea.

The oil fields of the Los Angeles Basin, which are among the chief producers in California, all obtain their oil from Neogene formations. A typical producing area is Signal Hill in the Long Beach field (Fig. 18.23). More than 3,200 million barrels of oil have come from this and other fields in the Los Angeles Basin.

Ventura Basin. The area of the Ventura Basin, including parts in the Santa Barbara Channel submerged by a shallow sea, is considerably larger than the Los Angeles Basin, for it is 120 miles long and an average of 30 miles wide. It contains approximately 50,000 feet of Cenozoic deposits, of which 35,000 feet or more belongs to the Neogene System. In lithologic characters, the section is generally similar to that of the Los Angeles area, containing a predominance of marine deposits. The Ventura Basin is noteworthy on account of the large thickness of Pliocene beds (more than 15,000 feet) and Pleistocene deposits (4,000 to 5,000 feet), both largely marine (Fig. 18.24). They are strongly folded and affected by thrust faults with displacements ranging to more than 15,000 feet; the deformation is dated as mid-Pleistocene.

San Joaquin Valley. This is another region of thick Neogene sedimentation where the Miocene deposits (mostly marine shale) are 12,000 to 13,000 feet thick, the Pliocene (claystones and permeable sandstones, marine in the lower two thirds) 8,000 to 9,000 feet thick, and the Pleistocene (almost entirely nonmarine clays, sands, and conglomerates) 8,000 to 10,000 feet thick. These units are very extensive, continuing with lithologic and thickness changes northward into the Sacramento Valley. In oil fields near Bakersfield, the strata

Fig. 18.23 Signal Hill in the Long Beach oil field, Los Angeles Basin, California. This highly productive field, like others in the basin, obtains oil from Neogene strata. Anticlinal structure of the field that controls oil accumulation is expressed topographically by the shape of the hill. (*Courtesy of Spence Air Photos.*)

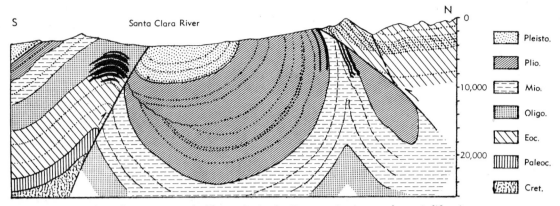

S   Santa Clara River   N

0

10,000

20,000

Pleisto.

Plio.

Mio.

Oligo.

Eoc.

Paleoc.

Cret.

Fig. 18.24 Section of Neogene and older rocks in the Ventura Basin, southern California.
In parts of this area Pliocene and Pleistocene deposits are unusually thick and are steeply
folded. Oil (shown in black) of the South Mountain field (at left) comes from Paleogene rocks.
(*Redrawn from T. L. Bailey, California Division of Mines.*)

**Fig. 18.25 Anticlinal fold in Neogene strata, Kettleman Hills oil field, San Joaquin
Valley, California.** The surface beds in this field, located 75 miles northwest of Bakersfield, are
Pliocene and Pleistocene in age; oil production comes from Miocene rocks. (*Courtesy of R. D.
Reed, The Texas Company.*)

Fig. 18.26 Late Neogene deposits in the Buena Vista oil field, southern San Joaquin Valley, California. This field, located 25 miles southwest of Bakersfield, obtains oil from Miocene beds unconformably overlapped by Pliocene. Exposed strata are Pleistocene and Pliocene. (*Courtesy of Spence Air Photos.*)

are gently to moderately folded (Figs. 18.25, 18.26). Rather pronounced orogeny near the end of Miocene time resulted in tilting the Miocene and older beds basinward as much as 30 degrees; this was followed by erosion that beveled the various formations and then transgression of Pliocene seas. Great oil accumulations are trapped in beds beneath the angular unconformity at the base of the Pliocene. As in other California districts, the most intense mountain-building movements occurred in mid-Pleistocene time; it was then that nearly all the prominent folds and faults of this region were produced.

San Andreas fault. The displacement of crustal blocks in upward, downward, and lateral directions is a very important feature of Neogene history in the California region. It affected the nature and thickness of local sedi-

mentation, and it is prominently expressed in Neogene structures. One of the largest and best-known faults is named San Andreas (Figs. 18.27 to 18.30). It is traced from the vicinity of Point Reyes, north of San Francisco, more than 500 miles southeastward into Mexico, angling slightly away from the coast. Recurrent movements along this fracture in the earth's crust have produced earthquakes, including the disastrous one of 1906 in which San Francisco was largely destroyed. Vertical components have been recognized in the movements, but the displacements have resulted chiefly in relative shifting of the block nearest the coast northward. This is determinable by matching offset features on opposite sides of the fault, and study of such offsets affecting deposits or structures of different geologic age that once were unbroken across

Fig. 18.27 San Andreas fault in the Indio Hills east of Los Angeles. The view looks north-westward along the fault in the central part of the photograph. The crustal block on the left has been displaced in a direction away from the observer, as compared with that on the right. (*Courtesy of Spence Air Photos.*)

the fault trace indicates both (1) great antiquity of the fault and (2) approximate amounts of lateral shifting along the fault since various geologic dates (Figs. 18.29, 18.30). During Neogene time the southern coastal part of California is thus shown to have been thrust northward an aggregate distance of 175 miles or more along the San Andreas fault. This fault is the most outstanding structure of the sort in the world.

Neogene Glacial Deposits

We come now logically to consideration of late Neogene sediments associated with glaciation, so far only mentioned as belonging with other deposits of nonmarine and marine origin that are post-Paleogene in age. These occur in the central and northern parts of North America. They form an integral part of Neogene geologic history but so special that study of them appropriately may be reserved for a separate chapter. Therefore, we turn to other subjects.

Erosion of the Appalachian and Mississippi Valley Regions

It is certain that the eastern and northern interior parts of North America, inside the coastal plain belt, were undergoing erosion throughout Neogene time. Evidence supporting this conclusion includes the fact that (1) no deposits of consequence (alluvium of stream valleys and the like excepted) belonging to this period occur anywhere in the re-

Fig. 18.28 Geologic relief map of Point Reyes area north of San Francisco, California. This quadrangle shows a striking topographic expression of the San Andreas fault, which her runs through Tomales Bay and out to sea. Jurassic rocks occur in areas ruled horizontally (gran ite) and obliquely (highly deformed sedimentary and volcanic rocks of the Franciscan Group); areas of Miocene marine deposits are vertically ruled and of Pliocene beds stippled. (*Relief map courtesy of Aero Service Corporation.*)

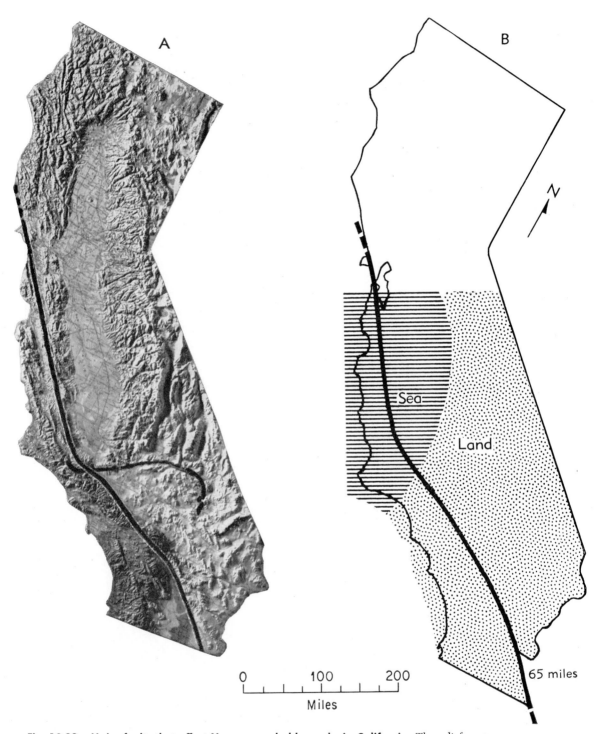

Fig. 18.29 Major faults that affect Neogene and older rocks in California. The relief map (*A*) shows the location of the San Andreas fault subparallel to the coast and an important transverse fault (Garlock). The map at the right (*B*) shows the inferred position of crustal blocks displaced by the San Andreas fault as they were in late Miocene time, based on matching the late Miocene strand lines, which now are found to be offset about 65 miles; the block on the left has been pushed southward accordingly. (*Relief map courtesy of Aero Service Corporation; map B redrawn from M. L. Hill, California Division of Mines.*)

gion mentioned; if such deposits had been formed, they could hardly have been stripped away entirely. (2) Study of the post-Cretaceous coastal plains sediments indicates their derivations from the interior of the continent, in part from areas closely adjacent to the plains and in part from distant sources, just as the present Mississippi River drainage carries sediment from headwaters of the Ohio and Missouri to the Gulf. (3) Effects of geologically recent erosion are found in features of the present land surface in the continent interior.

Peneplanation. The marks of prolonged erosion are most clearly evident in the Appalachian Mountains, where upturned edges of folded rocks are found smoothly beveled. Such even truncation of inclined rocks can be accomplished by wave work along a coast line, but in a broad inland area, such as the Appalachian region, it can mean only thorough peneplanation by the work of streams. The even sky line of Appalachian mountain ridges, as typically shown in eastern Pennsylvania, marks the trace of an erosion surface that is known as the Schooley peneplain. Undoubtedly much erosion occurred during the Mesozoic Era, but several lines of evidence indicate that the Schooley peneplain is not much, if any, older than Neogene.

When this peneplain was formed, the land surface was near base level, a few scores of feet at most above the sea. Except for monadnocks and unreduced uplands, such as the White Mountains area in New England and country of the Great Smokies in western North Carolina, the Appalachians were reduced to a featureless lowland that merged with the coastal plain. Rivers on this lowland crossed hard and soft rocks, uninfluenced by the structure of rocks composing the plain (Fig. 18.31). This was the nature of the land surface throughout much of Cenozoic time. Then, in the latter part of the Neogene Period there was a change. The whole region was moved vertically upward several hundred feet, and parts were upwarped more than 2,000 feet. This caused rejuvenation of the streams and relatively rapid erosion of weak rock belts, but

hard rocks were worn down little. Main streams, like the Susquehanna and Delaware Rivers, were able to maintain their courses across hard rocks, and the places where they cut through the mountain ridges are known as water gaps; lesser streams became adjusted to the outcrop belts of weak strata. Eventually, lowlands were etched out slightly above the new base level, the relatively even surface of these lowlands being cut across the edges of weak formations. This is known as the Harrisburg erosion surface (Fig. 18.31D). A second rejuvenation has caused streams to incise their valleys to depths of several hundred feet below the Harrisburg surface, and accordingly, remnants of the Schooley peneplain are very high above the present valley bottoms. The greatest height of the warped Schooley peneplain above present sea level is about 4,000 feet.

Neogene erosion in the Appalachian Mountains region thus comprises the completion of base leveling recorded by the Schooley peneplain, carving of valleys beneath the level of the Schooley peneplain down to the Harrisburg surface, and probably part of the erosion

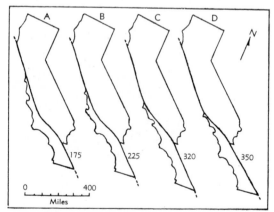

Fig. 18.30   Relative positions of crustal blocks bordering the San Andreas fault at different geologic dates. By matching offset features amounts of displacement along the fault can be determined approximately (A) since early Miocene time, (B) since Eocene time, (C) since Cretaceous time, and (D) since Jurassic time. The figures with each map indicate total miles of displacement. (*Data from M. L. Hill, California Division of Mines.*)

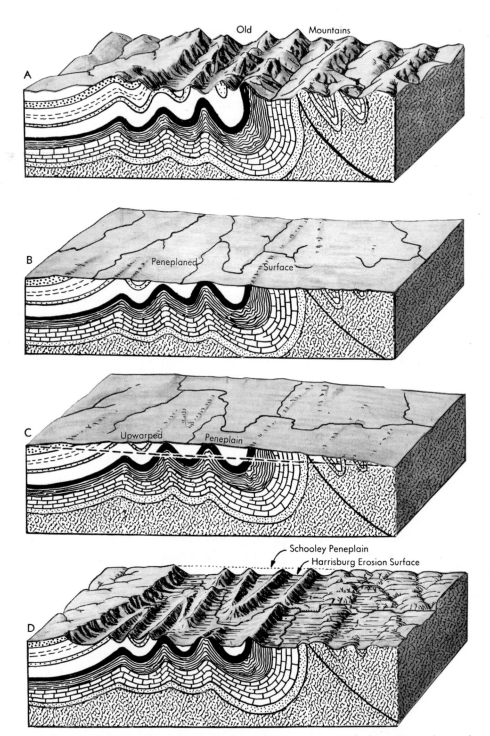

Fig. 18.31 Development of physiographic features in the Appalachian Mountains region.
——*A*. Irregular mountainous topography developed on folded rocks after the Appalachian revolution near the close of Paleozoic time.——*B*. Peneplaned surface produced by very prolonged erosion (Schooley peneplain before uplift).——*C*. Upwarped peneplain, amount of uplift being measured by the dotted line on the near face of the diagram.——*D*. Present state of topographic development in the Appalachian Mountains after successive uplifts; weak strata have been carved into valleys, whereas the summit levels of hard rocks furnish trace of the Schooley peneplain. Note alternative possibilities discussed in the text.

represented by valleys lying below the level of the Harrisburg surface. It is important to observe that, whereas the structure of the Appalachian Mountains was determined by earth movements during parts of the Paleozoic Era, the mountainous relief of this region is due entirely to erosion in late Cenozoic time, after upwarping of the Schooley peneplain.

An alternative explanation of the origin of physiographic features in the Appalachian Mountains just described deserves notice. This was suggested by the late Prof. D. W. Johnson of Columbia University. Pointing out that, in terms of the many million years included in geologic periods, the time from late Paleozoic mountain building in the Appalachian region to beginning of the Cretaceous Period is more than sufficient to allow for complete denudation of the Appalachian chain, he postulated equivalence of the Schooley peneplain to the even erosion surface at the base of Cretaceous deposits in the Atlantic Coastal Plain. This correlation, if correct, would signify a pre-Cretaceous, rather than mid-Cenozoic, age of the Schooley peneplain. Suppose, then, that when the Schooley surface was very low, barely above sea level, nonmarine and marine Cretaceous sediments came to be deposited over much of it, exactly as on the pre-Cretaceous peneplain in the coastal region. Upwarping of the Cretaceous-covered mountain belt in Cenozoic time would provide conditions leading to the removal of Cretaceous beds and establishment of drainage lines superposed on the folded Paleozoic rocks formerly buried by the Cretaceous. Such a historical sequence is very possible. Also, if upwarping and stripping were delayed until Neogene time, objections to the hypothesis advanced by Johnson on the ground of lack of much antiquity in carving present-day Appalachian valleys would lack force. In the light of present knowledge, decision of this problem cannot be made soundly.

The nearly flat-lying rocks of the Mississippi Valley and Great Lakes regions were also subject to erosion in Neogene time. Some upland surfaces in this region may correspond to the Schooley peneplain in the Appalachians, but remnants of peneplaned surfaces are much less easily and definitely recognized in flat-rock country than where beveling of folded rocks is found. Also, the Mississippi Basin seems not to have been much uplifted during recent geologic history.

Erosion in Western North America

Neogene history in western North America is recorded not only by huge quantities of sedimentary and igneous rocks formed but also by erosion on a scale that is difficult to comprehend. Virtually all shaping of the land surface by agents of denudation in this part of the continent is of late Neogene origin, preponderantly belonging to the Pleistocene Epoch. Before information was available for demonstrating the geologic recency of such features as the Grand Canyon in Arizona and lofty mountains in the Alps or other ranges, it was generally thought that erosion responsible for shaping these must have required a very long time, that is, many millions of years. For example, all Cenozoic time and possibly even part of Mesozoic time was called on. This is erroneous. The Neogene Period alone is more than sufficient to account for the erosion accomplished in removing the many ten-thousand cubic miles of rock materials represented by excavation of present-day valleys and other lowering of the land surface.

The vastness and variety of Neogene erosion products in the western part of our continent defy brief description. In mountain areas we find remnants of peneplains and commonly other surfaces bearing topographic evidence of the maturity of erosion; there are also innumerable deep-cut canyons and in many places such features as cirques, U-shaped valleys, and broad pediments. In plateau regions we encounter nearly base-leveled surfaces now occurring at high elevations, little dissected or with mature topography of great relief; on the other hand, we may see marks of only a single cycle of erosion, possibly little advanced, as indicated by vertical-walled chasms. In rolling lowlands and plains country we are likely to overlook the unimposing features produced by degradation, because these are so common and inconspicuous, yet they deserve notice and study. In some deserts we find that winds have

contributed appreciably by abrasion and abla-
tion to shaping the landscape. All these mentioned aspects of erosive work belong to historical geology and to study of the Neogene.
However, since it is impossible to examine
the record comprehensively here, attention is
confined to two selected examples, which are
mountain country in the Rockies just west of
Denver and part of the Colorado River canyons.

Central eastern Colorado Rockies. The
Rocky Mountains came into being as products
of the Laramian revolution, as we have seen
(Chap. 15). Crustal deformation near the
close of Cretaceous time and early in the
Paleogene Period strongly uplifted Precambrian crystalline rocks and their cover of Paleozoic and Mesozoic strata in the Colorado re-

gion, forming mountains or, rather, providing
the necessary conditions for carving out mountains by work of streams. These streams carried their load of rock debris into adjacent
basin areas, chiefly in Colorado, Wyoming,
and Utah, thus building the thick deposits
classed as Paleogene. By the time the basins
became filled, the mountain area that was the
chief source of the sediments was worn very
low, as must be inferred from the very fine-
grained nature of the silts and clays of the
youngest Paleogene (for example, Oligocene
clays of the South Dakota Badlands). In these
ways the stage was set for Neogene conditions
and events in the area of the Colorado
Rockies.

The early and middle Paleogene Rocky
Mountains were gone, and in their place was

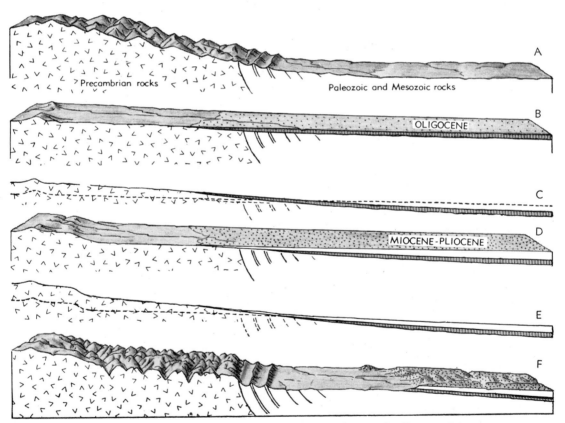

**Fig. 18.32 Diagrams illustrating evolution of the Colorado Rockies and adjacent plains
country.** West-east sections across the mountain border (*A*) in mid-Paleogene time, (*B*) at
end of Paleogene time, (*C*) showing upwarp in the mountain area at beginning of Neogene
time, (*D*) approximately at end of Pliocene time, (*E*) showing upwarp of the mountain area
at beginning of Pleistocene time, and (*F*) at the present time.

Fig. 18.33 Colorado Rockies near Berthoud Pass, west of Denver. This view, looking westward, shows remnants of the Flattop peneplain (*F*) in the distance and rugged terrain, mainly ice-carved, below it. Photographed 3 miles southwest of Berthoud Pass. (*T. S. Lovering, courtesy of U.S. Geol. Survey.*)

a peneplaned broad area cut mainly in Pre-cambrian crystalline rocks, but along their eastern edge beveling upturned Paleozoic and Mesozoic stratified rocks (Fig. 18.32*B*). Remnants of the peneplain are identified in the erosion surface named Flattop, now observed at elevations of 11,000 feet or a little more in high parts of the Front Range, as in Rocky Mountain National Park and elsewhere (Fig. 18.33). Scattered prominences with rounded summits attain heights of 1,000 to 3,000 feet above the Flattop peneplain; these are monad-nocks that persist. Indication that the Flattop surface had been made by the end of Paleogene time is given by its relation to the earliest Miocene deposits locally preserved in the mountain area and by projecting the upper surface of Oligocene deposits on the plains toward the mountains but, even more, by cor-relation of a prominent erosion surface (Rocky Mountains peneplain) at lower level with the top of Miocene-Pliocene deposits east of the Rockies.

Much more striking than the Flattop sur-face is the remarkable accordance of summit levels in large mountain areas of the Front Range (Fig. 18.34). The erosion surface thus marked is known as the Rocky Mountains peneplain. Other erosion surfaces have been distinguished, but this one is the most promi-nent and significant. It is dated as late Plio-cene, since its eastward projection coincides with the surface of Neogene deposits on the plains that include Miocene below and Plio-cene above. In southeastern Wyoming, south-east of Laramie, a connection (known as the "Gangplank") between the peneplain and sedimentary deposits formed by its degrada-tion products is preserved. The Union Pacific Railroad uses this way of ascent for crossing the Rockies, without need to follow mountain canyons or excavate expensive tunnels; the smooth near-level peneplain here is traversed at an elevation of about 8,000 feet. The erosion in early and middle Neogene time leading to the formation of the Rocky Moun-

Fig. 18.34 Rocky Mountains peneplain in the Colorado Front Range. This erosion surface is easily distinguished by the accordance of mountain summits in the nearest areas. *A.* View looking north-northwest from Golden. *B.* View south-southwest toward Pikes Peak from Dawson Butte. *C.* View westward from Garden of the Gods near Colorado Springs. (*T. S. Lovering, courtesy of U.S. Geol. Survey.*)

tains peneplain is very great; it resulted from uplift of the Flattop surface, presumably near the beginning of Neogene time (Fig. 18.32*C*).

Present elevations in the Colorado Rockies and the many deep canyons intersecting the range are the result of Pleistocene uplift and erosion (Fig. 18.32*E, F*). The blanket of Miocene-Pliocene sediments that formerly merged with the smooth surface of the Rocky Mountains peneplain has been stripped away near the mountains, exhuming the edges of upturned Paleozoic and Mesozoic formations, and because most of these are little resistant to erosion, they have been cut to a lower level than Neogene-capped areas farther east.

A resultant of the peneplanations described, accompanied by spread of sedimentary deposits over erosion-beveled older rocks, is the superposition of several rivers in courses that are quite independent of rock structure. For example, the Arkansas River turns from its shallow valley in sedimentary strata of South Park Basin to cut a narrow pathway through resistant Precambrian granite of the Front Range, thus making the 1,400-foot chasm of Royal Gorge. The South Platte River, Laramie River, Green River, and others in the Rocky Mountains area locally flow through similar canyons in hard rocks instead of following easy courses in weak rocks, which they would do if adjusted to rock structure. They are superposed and thus furnish evidence of old erosion surfaces that have been obliterated by Neogene erosion.

Colorado River canyons. Erosion of the canyon and mesa country of western Colorado, Utah, and northern Arizona accomplished during Neogene time is stupendous. Studies in various parts of this region provide knowledge pertinent to understanding important aspects of the erosion, such as placement of main drainageways in courses that ignore rock structures or that locally are well adjusted to them, relation to crustal movements that occurred while denudation was progressing, and existence of clearly distinct stages in downcutting the land surface. A great deal of additional work is needed, however, before an integrated story of Neogene erosion in the Colorado River drainage area can be written, even with qualifications necessary because of obliterated evidence. It is a fact that the very extensiveness of degradation has destroyed traces of conditions or events in erosion history that otherwise would provide records of unmistakable meaning.

We shall confine attention to the Colorado River and notice its canyon-type valley in two places. The first of these is at Dead Horse Point, about 10 miles southwest of Moab, Utah, and 25 miles above the confluence of the Colorado and Green Rivers (Fig. 18.35). Here we may observe smoothly curved meanders like those of the lower Mississippi River, but walled in by cliffs of sandstone (Triassic and Jurassic in this area). Many such intrenched meanders can be seen elsewhere on the Colorado, Green, San Juan, and other rivers of southeastern Utah, as suggested by such names as "Loop," "Bow Knot," "Goosenecks," and the like that are applied to some of the intrenched meanders. These features are inherited from meanders on a vanished flood plain where the river flowed at grade. A mature (possibly late mature) stage had been attained when the flood-plain meanders were formed. Since the present cycle of canyon cutting began, according to evidence judged reliable, stream channels in different places have been lowered 1,200 to more than 2,000 feet. The canyon cutting surely all belongs to Pleistocene time.

Next, we turn to the Grand Canyon. Parts of the course of the Colorado River in the Grand Canyon area seem plainly to be influenced by the structure of the rocks, as in a western section (near Diamond Creek) where the river follows a fault line for many miles, but generally the pathway of the river is not influenced by rock structure. Is the Colorado an antecedent stream, or has its course been determined wholly or largely by superposition? If we take account of geologic observations along tributaries of the Colorado and consider the plateau region in its entirety, little or nothing is found to support the antecedent-stream hypothesis, whereas superposition is probable (Fig. 18.36). Paleogene deposits capping the High Plateaus north of the Grand Canyon rest with angular unconformity on beveled Cretaceous and Jurassic formations; in the Chuska Mountains, east of the Grand Canyon, horizontal Paleogene beds similarly lie on the edges of tilted Cretaceous, Jurassic, and Triassic strata. The Mesozoic and older rocks of the plateau region, after deformation of Laramian date, were peneplaned and then buried by Paleogene deposits, which now are mostly stripped away. The course of the Colorado River in the Grand Canyon area most reasonably is explained as an inheritance from its early Neogene course across Paleogene sediments blanketing the region.

When uplift (probably Miocene) caused active downcutting, relatively rapid erosion of Paleogene and Triassic strata adjacent to the river presumably occurred, accompanied by some removal of exhumed Jurassic and Cretaceous rocks to the north. The Permian is more resistant, but a shallow canyon, seemingly defined by broad benches (named Esplanade) in upper parts of the modern canyon, was eroded before the river became graded and downward cutting became retarded or ceased. The erosion cycle thus indicated, marked by initial stripping of the plateaus and carving of upper Paleozoic rocks along the course of the canyon, fits with evidence from upstream parts of the river and many tributaries pointing to maturely graded conditions in what may be called the pre-canyon cycle (Fig. 18.36, middle section).

Renewal of uplift, doubtless in Pleistocene time (although when is uncertain), introduced the present cycle of canyon cutting. The Colorado River is approximately adjusted to its work of erosion in hard rocks throughout the

Fig. 18.35   Meander bend of the Colorado River above Cataract Canyon in southeastern Utah. The river here has cut downward through flat-lying Jurassic and Triassic strata, preserving its meandering course that was developed on a graded flood plain now uplifted and obliterated. (*Courtesy of D. L. Hopwood, Denver, Colorado.*)

Grand Canyon, but its average gradient of 12 feet per mile, the presence of numerous rapids, and the lack of any flood plain prove that it is still much above grade. A vast amount of rock has been excavated, but the steep walls and many rugged buttes within the canyon indicate how very much more work remains to be done within or beyond Neogene time.

Below the mouth of the Grand Canyon, where the river crosses the great fault (Grand Wash) that bounds the plateau on the west, are gravelly sand deposits (Muddy Creek Formation) built of materials carried by the Colorado. They contain vertebrate remains identified as Pliocene or possibly Miocene.

If Miocene, this means that erosion was proceeding upstream at least as early as in this part of the Neogene Period.

Climate

Evidence from all sides, derived from marine invertebrate assemblages and from occurrence of temperature-controlled plants and animals on land, points to a contrast between prevailing climates of Paleogene and Neogene time. In the Paleogene Period warmth extended even to Arctic latitudes; climates were equable. In Neogene time temperatures declined and moist conditions on land gradually gave way to semiaridity or aridity. These

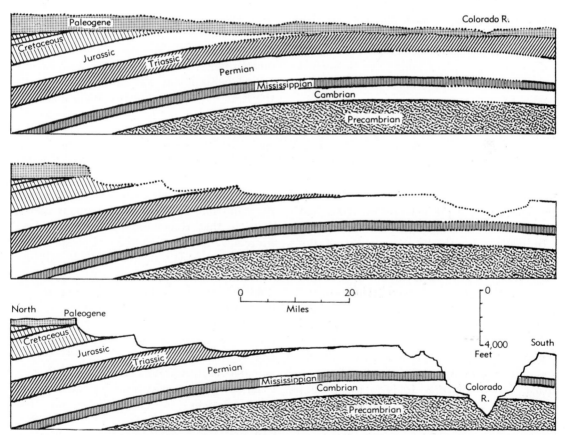

Fig. 18.36 Sections of the Grand Canyon region in Arizona and southern Utah showing inferred stages in development of the canyon. The lowermost section indicates present-day conditions, and the uppermost represents postulated conditions approximately at the beginning of Neogene time (solid lines showing known positions of rock boundaries and dotted lines reconstructed positions). The middle section pictures the canyon region at a stage after early Neogene erosion when a mature erosion surface had been produced (indicated by a variety of evidence), probably near the end of Pliocene time. Strong Pleistocene renewal of uplift has led to carving the present Grand Canyon.

changes are recognized by observing the distribution of marine species sensitive to temperature, for example; thus, warm-water species are found to be restricted to more and more southerly distribution along the North American coasts, while cold-water forms reach more southerly latitudes. On land, similar changes in distribution of plants and animals occur. Increased cooling led without perceptible boundary other than the initiation of glacial conditions into the Pleistocene Epoch.

Mountain Building

Pronounced crustal deformations that resulted in mountain building are a feature of Neogene time. For example, in the Alps Mountains, which had been involved in Laramian and Paleogene movements, the greatest disturbance is identified as Miocene in age, although folding continued in later Neogene time. Great recumbent folds were developed and pushed northward as a series of rock masses termed *nappes;* resultant rock structures are extremely complex. Strong folding, accompanied by thrust faulting, affected the Carpathians, Caucasus, Elburz, and mountains farther east. The Himalayas, which had been folded in early Cenozoic time, were involved also in Neogene deformation, in which southern foothills were pushed upward 6,000 feet or more since middle Pleistocene time.

In western North America, uplift of the Cascade Mountains began in late Miocene or early Pliocene time after outpouring of the enormous flows of basaltic lava that form the Columbia Plateau. Miocene orogenic movements are identified in California also, especially in the San Joaquin Valley. The greatest deformation, however, along the Pacific Border of North America is mid-Pleistocene in age, for at this time folds in the coastal ranges and a majority of the oil-yielding anticlines in southern California fields were formed. This crustal deformation has been called the *Pasadenan orogeny.*

Unlike the deformative movements that produce folds and faults, but important in giving rise to mountains, are the essentially vertical uplifts that rejuvenate belts earlier subjected to mountain-building deformations. An example is the Rocky Mountains, and another the Appalachians. The Rockies, after being pushed upward in Neogene time, have been attacked by erosion so that newly shaped mountains and deep canyons have been carved out. In the Appalachians, weak rocks have been excavated so as to accentuate relief produced by hard rocks.

Economic Resources

Petroleum. Neogene deposits surpass all others as sources of oil and gas. This is true in North America, where in California, for example, approximately 95 per cent of total production comes from Miocene and Pliocene strata, and in the Gulf Coastal region of Louisiana and Texas, in spite of the great yield of Paleogene sands. In foreign oil fields, predominance of Neogene oil production is outstanding, for this includes most of the output of fields in the Middle East, Venezuela, the East Indies, and the rich Baku district of Russia.

Metals. Associated with igneous activity that specially characterizes Neogene history in western North America are many rich deposits of gold, silver, copper, and various other metals, in aggregate value totaling several thousand millions of dollars. Famous mining districts that contribute to this wealth are Morenci, Arizona (copper); Comstock and Tonopah, Nevada (silver); Goldfield, Nevada; and Cripple Creek, Colorado (gold). Placer gold deposits in Cailfornia, of Neogene age, have been rich sources since 1849.

Nonmetallic materials. A large variety of useful nonmetallic substances comes from Neogene sources. Among these are phosphates, valuable as fertilizer; boron (in addition to other uses, now sought as an ingredient in new types of fuels), which comes chiefly from borax deposits in southeastern California lake beds; bromine; calcium chloride; diatomite (also known as diatomaceous earth), used for filters and insulation and chiefly obtained from Miocene deposits in California; perlite and pumice, volcanic materials that are increasingly used for lightweight aggregate in concrete; sodium carbonate and sulfate, used for detergents and cleansers; sulfur, for making acid, compounding rubber, and other uses, obtained in great quantities from the cap rock of some Gulf Coast salt domes; clay deposits of many grades; sand; gravel; stone; and a host of other materials.

More than most geologic systems, Neogene rocks are extremely important containers of ground water, which is used both for domestic and municipal supply in many areas and as an important source of water for irrigation. The economic worth of this water cannot be calculated.

READINGS

DUNBAR, C. O., 1949, *Historical geology*, John Wiley & Sons, Inc., New York (567 pp.), Physical history of the Cenozoic Era, pp. 395–435.
    Good discussion of Neogene history in western regions.
FENNEMAN, N. M., 1931, *Physiography of western United States*, McGraw-Hill Book Company, Inc., New York (534 pp.). [1] The Columbia Plateau, pp. 225–273. [2] Colorado Plateau province, pp. 274–325. [3] Basin and Range province, pp. 326–395. [4] Sierra Cascade province, pp. 396–441. [5] Pacific Border province, pp. 442–510.
    All exceptionally useful descriptions containing discussion of Neogene features; recommended.
FISK, H. N., 1943, *Summary of the geology of the lower alluvial valley of the Mississippi River*, Mississippi River Commission, Vicksburg (49 pp.).
    Important description of late Neogene history of part of Gulf region with many new data.
GILLULY, JAMES, 1949, Distribution of mountain building in geologic time: *Geol. Soc. America Bull.*, vol. 60, pp. 561–590.
    Presidential address referring to dating problems of Neogene and other mountain-making; "must" reading for geology major students.
HILL, M. L., 1954, Tectonics of faulting in southern California, Geology of southern California: *Calif. Div. Mines Bull.* 170, chap. 4, pp. 5–13.
    Describes and interprets San Andreas and other faults.
HOOTS, H. W., BEAR, T. L., and KLEINPELL, W. D., 1954, Geological summary of the San Joaquin Valley, California: *Calif. Div. Mines Bull.* 170, chap. 2, pp. 113–130.
    Good account of Neogene history of an important area.
MOORE, R. C., 1926, Significance of inclosed meanders in the physiographic history of the Colorado Plateau country: *Jour. Geology*, vol. 34, pp. 97–130.
    Explains significance of canyons in study of Neogene erosion cycles.
MURRAY, G. E., 1947, Cenozoic deposits of central Gulf Coastal Plain: *Am. Assoc. Petroleum Geologists Bull.*, vol. 31, pp. 1825–1850.
    Good summary of geologic features of Mississippi Embayment.
PRATT, W. E., 1947, Petroleum on continental shelves: *Am. Assoc. Petroleum Geologists Bull.*, vol. 31, pp. 657–672.
WOODFORD, A. O., SCHOELHAMER, J. E., VEDDER, J. G., and YERKES, R. F., 1954, Geology of the Los Angeles Basin, Geology of southern California: *Calif. Div. Mines Bull.* 170, chap. 2, pp. 65–82.
    Excellent account of a chiefly important Neogene area.

QUESTIONS

1. The lava that invaded the Grand Canyon (Fig. 18.3) at the place known as Toroweap is stated to have dammed the Colorado River to a height of about 300 feet. (a) What sorts of evidence can be suggested as worthy of search if you could study this area in the field, seeking to prove or disprove the former existence of such a dam? (b) Why would a dam formed by invasion of a lava flow, as at this place, constitute a very temporary obstruction as compared with a man-built dam of the same height using crushed lava for concrete aggregate? (c) How can you explain the existence of even-topped lava benches resembling river-terrace remnants distributed 1 or 2 miles apart far down canyon from Toroweap, each bench having the same height (within a few feet) above the river? (d) Indians of the

lower canyon country (Havasupai) hand down a story that the river in the canyon formerly was swallowed whole by the earth. Is this a geologic possibility, and if so, explain?

2. Referring to the map of Neogene formations (Fig. 18.5),

(a) What is the probable explanation of isolated outcrops of Neogene deposits in North and South Carolina? From examination of the map can you determine whether they represent Miocene, Pliocene, or Pleistocene? Could this question be settled in the field and, if so, by what means and with what reliability?

(b) What basis can you suggest for indicating subsea Neogene off the coast of Maine and adjacent to the Maritime Provinces of eastern Canada?

(c) Why is the outline of Neogene deposits in the Great Plains area so very different from that of Neogene formations in southeastern Texas?

3. Comparing Figs. 18.10 and 18.11, can you account for the distribution of Pleistocene terrace deposits near the head of the Mississippi Embayment? Why are such terrace deposits absent along the margin of pre-Paleocene rocks east of the Mississippi River? What reasons can be given for the much greater width of the terrace deposits near the Gulf than inland?

4. What indications are found in the salt dome diagram (Fig. 18.12) that upward movement of the salt plug partly antedates Pliocene time? That some upward thrust is pre-Paleogene?

5. Referring to the geologic relief map of the Mt. Rainier area (Fig. 18.16), what topographic feature or features point to the geologically younger age of rocks forming the mountain as compared with surrounding rocks? What indications of antiquity of the mountain are distinguishable, in spite of its assignment to the Pleistocene Epoch?

6. The marine terraces illustrated in Fig. 18.22 are reported to be due to eustatic movements. What does this mean? What is the significance of the considerably greater width of terrace 6 than that of higher terraces (possibly excepting 1)? Is it possible that the order of the terraces from oldest to youngest is 6, 5, 4, 3, 2, 1? Why? Some other order? How should the terraces differ from actually observed terraces if they originated by crustal upwarping of old coast lines?

7. What features of geologic history are indicated by the southward diminution in thickness of Pliocene deposits plotted in Fig. 18.24? What inferences can be drawn from the diagram as to the age of the folding? Of thrust-faulting?

8. What evidence is observable from study of the geologic relief map of the Point Reyes area (Fig. 18.28) that a prominent fault intersects the quadrangle? To what extent can the age of the displacement along the fault be determined? Does the map furnish indication of predominant lateral movement (shear) along the fault rather than vertical movement mainly? Given knowledge that the San Andreas fault crosses this region, where would you seek to find possible occurrence of Jurassic granite on the northeast side of the fault, matching that on the southwest? If such outcrops could be found, what significance would they have, if any?

9. Can you account for the offset areas of alluvium seen in the photograph (Fig. 18.27) of the San Andreas fault east of Los Angeles?

10. Referring to the relief map of California (Fig. 18.29A), the transverse fault (Garlock) that seems to cross the San Andreas fault without interruption actually is offset by a distance of about 5 miles, the western continuation of the transverse fault being displaced northwestward. What is the significance of this concerning movement along the San Andreas fault and concerning the age of the transverse fault?

11. From study of Figs. 18.32 to 18.34, why should the Flattop peneplain be interpreted as distinctly older than the Rocky Mountains peneplain? What time or times of erosion have contributed to shaping Cretaceous hogbacks along the Rocky Mountains front? What is the evidence?

12. Referring to Fig. 18.36 and accepting the premise that the upper section is approximately correct in representing conditions in the Grand Canyon area near the beginning of Neogene time, is the volume of erosion indicated by the middle section greater or less than that required to produce modern conditions (lower section) by removal of rock indicated as still present in the middle section? What inference can be drawn from your answer to this question? Why does the position of Cretaceous and Jurassic fronts (lower section), as seen today, call for considerably less post-Paleogene stripping of these rocks than is needed to account for position of the Triassic front (Chocolate Cliffs)?

19.

CENOZOIC ERA:

NEOGENE PERIOD (PLEISTOCENE EPOCH)

Glacial cirques near Berthoud Pass in the high Rockies west of Denver.

T. S. Lovering, courtesy of U.S. Geol. Survey.

The outstanding reason for setting apart the division of Cenozoic time designated as the Pleistocene Epoch is climatic change that during the last few hundred thousand years has led to widespread glaciation, especially in the Northern Hemisphere. In contrast to the Paleogene Period, characterized by prevailing warmth even in high latitudes, Neogene history is marked by a progressive trend toward cooler temperatures, accompanied in many places by decreased rainfall. At length, this trend culminated in making snow fields that persisted from one year to the next, gradually increasing in size until glaciers developed in mountain areas and icecaps began to grow in high latitudes. Glaciation

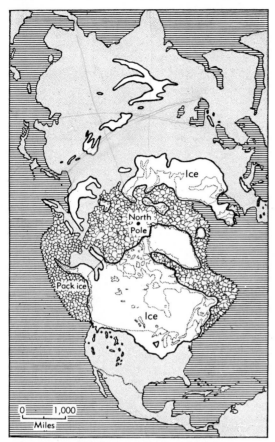

Fig. 19.1   Maximum distribution of Pleistocene ice in North America and Eurasia. In addition to pack ice in the Arctic, Pacific, and Atlantic Oceans, the ice sheets on land and adjacent continental-shelf areas here shown cover more than 7.5 million square miles. Ice in Antarctica, South America, Africa, and Australia occupied at least 5 million square miles.

and plants almost univerally was modified in some degree, if not changed drastically; and innumerable effects of glaciation are to be seen in nearly all territory invaded by the ice. The geologic recency of Pleistocene glaciation greatly facilitates study of it, because the evidence of glacial conditions and events has not yet been appreciably obscured or destroyed. The importance of Pleistocene glaciation justifies the allotment to it of a separate chapter.

It was not at first understood that the widespread glacial materials of northern Europe and North America were deposits made by great continental ice sheets. These deposits were called *drift*, because it was thought that they were carried by icebergs that drifted in waters of Noah's flood. When the boulder-laden bergs chanced to graze bedrock beneath the water, scratches (striae) were made on the bedrock and boulders.

When Agassiz, in 1837, pointed to evidence that glaciers of the Alps had formerly spread far out on the plains at the foot of the mountains and suggested that all northern Europe had been buried by a huge glacier in comparatively recent geologic time, the scientific world was incredulous. The correctness of Agassiz's deductions, however, has been established completely and irrefutably. The deposits of continental glaciers have foremost importance among Pleistocene formations, and as commonly defined, the Pleistocene Epoch is considered to have begun with initiation of the continental glaciation that followed the making of Pliocene deposits.

Pleistocene Deposits in North America

Nature of deposits. Throughout the glaciated portions of North America, deposits formed by ice (till) and by melt water from ice (fluvioglacial deposits) are readily identified as belonging to the Pleistocene Series. They include sediment laid down during the last few hundred years and being formed now by glaciers in some mountain areas and by the icecap that covers most of Greenland, because time classed as Recent is considered now to be a somewhat arbitrarily distinguished sub-

was inaugurated. The ice spread until more than 12 million square miles of the earth's surface was covered and directly or indirectly the entire world was affected by changes originating from this enormous accumulation of ice (Fig. 19.1). For example, sea level everywhere was lowered very appreciably (possibly more than 350 feet) by removal of water to make the continental ice sheets; shore lines were changed in outline, being shifted seaward; downcutting by many streams was vigorously accelerated as a result of lowered sea level; climates on land and temperatures in the sea were altered; distribution of animals division of the Pleistocene rather than ranked (as formerly) as an independent post-Pleisto-cene epoch of the so-called Quaternary Period.

Glacial till resulting from the work of con-tinental ice sheets is widely spread as ground moraine deposits, interspersed with linear belts of terminal and recessional moraines. These are characterized by their heterogeneous mix-ture of rock materials, ranging in size from large boulders to fine rock flour and clay and commonly containing kinds of rock foreign to the bedrock of the till-covered region (Figs. 19.2, 19.3). The foreign materials, from peb-ble-size upward, are termed erratics. Many glacial erratics are as large as a small house and by their lithology can be identified with sources hundreds of miles distant from the place where they were dropped by the ice (Fig. 19.4). One such erratic, a huge granite boulder, was observed by Agassiz and other geologists in the 1830s high on a mountain side of Jurassic rocks above the University of Neuchâtel in northwestern Switzerland; the

boulder is separated from outcrops of similar granite in the Alps by the broad expanse of Lake Neuchâtel and lowland country many miles wide. The Jurassic limestone near the boulder is smoothly rounded and marked by parallel scratches pointing toward the Alps. Agassiz deduced a former great extension of the glacial ice still found in lofty Alpine valleys carved in the granite, concluding that the erratic boulder was transported to its present resting place by this enlarged glacier. Of course, he was quite right. In North America, the sources of many distinctive boulders in Pleistocene drift can be identified more or less precisely, thus furnishing indication of the direction of transport by glacial ice (Fig. 19.5).

Different sorts of till deposits commonly are associated with distinguishing topographic features, especially if the deposits are of late Pleistocene age, so that running water or other geologic agents have had insufficient time to modify the ice-made topography ap-

Fig. 19.2 Exposure of typical glacial till forming part of a moraine that runs the length of Long Island, New York. Deposits formed by melting of glacial ice are a characteristic type of sedimentary record of Pleistocene time in glaciated parts of North America. These regions also contain much stratified drift. (*W. C. Alden, courtesy of U.S. Geol. Survey.*)

preciably. Among such features are gently rolling or nearly flat plains underlain by ground moraine, almost invariably poorly drained and in many places largely covered with shallow lakes (Fig. 19.6); ridgelike hummocky belts marking the location of terminal and recessional moraines that by their looped pattern on a map show their relation to broad lobate divisions of the continental ice sheet (Fig. 19.7); and the elongate, inverted spoon-shaped hills called drumlins, which are aligned with their long axes parallel to the direction of ice movement (Figs. 19.8, 19.9). In areas of mountain glaciation, till deposits may occur in lateral moraines

that form prominent ridges along valley sides, as well as in other moraines.

Fluvioglacial deposits are widespread, some covering or flanking glacial till and some extending far beyond the margins of ice-occupied land. They include kames, eskers, valley trains, and outwash plains, each distinguished by the more or less well-stratified nature of its constituents and topographic expression (Fig. 19.10).

Loess and dune sand are wind-blown sediments generally derived from glacial outwash. The sand deposits are localized, but loess sheets are found distributed over many thousand square miles.

Fig. 19.3 A glacial erratic, 8 inches in longer diameter, scratched and smoothly abraded on one face by ice action. This boulder, from glacial drift in Iowa, shows nearly uniform direction of fine striations, which signifies that it was held rigidly in the ice during abrasion. Naturally, such striae on a boulder are valueless in throwing light on the direction of ice movement in the area where the boulder was deposited. (*W. C. Alden, courtesy of U.S. Geol. Survey.*)

Glacial lake deposits are quantitatively less important than till and fluvioglacial sediment, but if account is taken of temporary water bodies along margins of the continental ice sheets, as well as lakes and ponds left behind after the disappearance of the glaciers, a vast amount of sediment accumulated in standing fresh water during Pleistocene time. The lake deposits are characterized by evenness and generally fineness of the horizontally bedded clay, silt, and fine sand that predominate (Fig. 19.11); locally there are fresh-water limestones and peaty layers of plant remains.

In land areas of the continent that never were covered by Pleistocene glaciers are many nonmarine and some marine sedimentary deposits that belong to post-Pliocene Cenozoic time. They include flood-plain and terrace deposits of streams, clastic and chemical sediments laid down in lakes, dune sands, and various other materials; among marine deposits, some of which are 900 feet above present sea level, are clays, sands, and beach gravels. Nearly all are unconsolidated. Their Pleistocene age is indicated variously —by fossils, stratigraphic or structural relations to older Cenozoic rocks, topographic evidence, and some by C^{14} age determinations.

Precise correlation of the glacial and nonglacial deposits generally is difficult and under varying circumstances may be impossible. On the other hand, many reliable means of establishing correspondence between the diverse kinds of Pleistocene deposits have been and are being developed, so that ultimately we may hope to possess well-integrated understanding of Pleistocene history. An example of how a very trustworthy correlation between some glacial and nonglacial deposits can be obtained is found in Kansas, Nebraska, and Iowa, where a thin bed of volcanic ash has been traced very widely across country and identified in both glacial and nonglacial successions. The ash (named Pearlette) was distributed over the plains country by westerly winds and by its mode of origin can be considered as a deposit having

Fig. 19.4 Erratic boulder of Pleistocene ground moraine near Charles City, Iowa. Two views of a boulder that measures 40 by 50 feet horizontally and 11.5 feet in height above ground. (*W. C. Alden, courtesy of U.S. Geol. Survey.*)

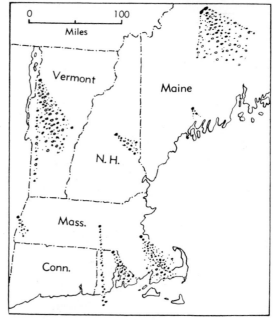

Fig. 19.5 Dispersal of erratics from known sources in New England. Each of the fan-shaped distribution areas of boulders having distinctive lithologic characters is pointed toward the bedrock source. Transportation by the ice was southward to southeastward. (*Data from R. F. Flint.*)

Fig. 19.6 Lake-covered ground-moraine plain in northern Saskatchewan. In this area, east of Frobisher Lake, the continental glacier traversed an evenly peneplaned bedrock surface, which undoubtedly was well drained in spite of its flatness. The irregular ground-moraine deposits have changed the landscape completely. (*Courtesy of Royal Canadian Air Force.*)

geologically precise contemporaneity in all its parts. Its occurrence in glaciated and non-glaciated areas furnishes a valuable tie for correlating the various unlike kinds of deposits that lie next below and above the ash. Such correlations are confirmed by identification almost everywhere of a zone of molluscan fossils beneath the ash and of another zone of partly differing mollusks above the ash.

Divisions. Pleistocene deposits, both glacial and nonglacial, are classifiable with varying reliability and exactness into age-defined parts designated as stages (Fig. 19.12). These are primarily based on the succession of sedimentary units found in the Great Lakes and upper Mississippi Valley regions that were overridden by continental ice sheets. In this territory,

glacial deposits, especially till, are most prominent, but in many places young till is found to overlie old till, commonly with a deeply weathered zone or deposits not formed directly by ice, or with both of these, occurring beneath the younger till. Such evidence of multiple glaciation is described in more detail later. Here, it is sufficient to note that successive stages characterized by dominance of glacial deposits alternate with stages that reflect relatively warm-temperature interglacial conditions. Thus, the Nebraskan Stage is distinguished in the Nebraska-Kansas-Missouri region by the Nebraska Till as its chief component (Fig. 19.13). The next-younger Aftonian Stage contains interglacial deposits in the Great Lakes-Mississippi Valley area (although glacial and fluvioglacial sediment of Aftonian

Fig. 19.7 Glacial moraines and direction of ice movement in parts of Michigan, Indiana, and Ohio. The morainal pattern of late Wisconsinan drift is more clearly defined than that of earlier Pleistocene drift. The moraines mark successive edges of ice tongues called *lobes*. (*After Taylor and Leverett, U.S. Geol. Survey.*)

age theoretically could occur in very high latitudes where "interglacial" glaciers may have persisted, as they do today in Greenland and Antarctica). The Kansan Stage is represented especially by the very widespread Kansas Till (Fig. 19.13), the Yarmouthian Stage by interglacial deposits and soil formation under "normal" nonglacial conditions, and so on.

Geologists are agreed in recognizing the Pleistocene stages just mentioned and likewise those named Illinoisan (pronounced Illinoian,

Fig. 19.8   Drumlin near Newark, New York. The smoothly rounded hill on the skyline is a drumlin, seen from right angle to its longitudinal axis. It is composed of till. (*G. K. Gilbert, courtesy of U.S. Geol. Survey.*)

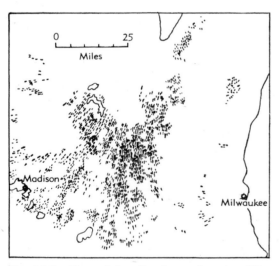

Fig. 19.9   Map of drumlins in southeastern Wisconsin. Radially divergent movement of ice belonging to the Green Bay lobe of a late Pleistocene continental glacier is indicated by the pattern of the drumlins, long axes of which are parallel to the ice flow. Drumlins just west of Milwaukee reflect westward local movement of the Lake Michigan lobe. (*After W. C. Alden, U.S. Geol. Survey.*)

as often spelled) and Sangamonian, but agreement has not been reached on classification of late Pleistocene deposits. For many years, the Iowa Till was considered to represent a glaciation quite independent of that known as Wisconsinan, but recently it has become customary to treat Iowan as a substage of Wisconsinan, because the time of warm climate that followed the recession of the Iowan ice sheet was thought to be distinctly less prolonged than in earlier interglacial ages. In this book the Iowan Stage is separately distinguished, partly because of studies of deposits in the Great Plains area outside the glaciated region but mostly because of evidence of erosion and deposition in the lower Mississippi Valley correlated with glaciation and deglaciation, as explained subsequently.

Distribution of Pleistocene formations. Glacial till deposits formed by the successive Pleistocene ice sheets and expanded mountain glaciers occupy an area of 4.8 million square miles located mostly north of the Missouri and Ohio Rivers. This neglects consideration of bare-rock tracts, which are very common in the Canadian Shield and some other regions, but takes account of unglaciated territory in the northwestern part of the continent (Fig. 19.1) and the so-called driftless area in southwestern Wisconsin and parts of adjacent states that has an extent of approximately 10,000 square miles (Figs. 19.13, 19.14). The southern limit of maximum coverage by glacial ice is traced from Long Island across northern New Jersey and northeastern Pennsylvania into southwestern New York and thence southwestward in an irregular line mostly a little north of the Ohio River to southern Illinois. From the vicinity of St. Louis the boundary runs westward to Kansas City, curves northward across northeastern Kansas and eastern Nebraska, and then lies close to the course of the Missouri River to its headwaters in the Montana Rockies. In the western United States are about 75 areas of noteworthy mountain glaciation, isolated from the continental ice sheets, the largest of these being located in northwestern Wyoming (about 20,-000 square miles) and the Sierra Nevada of eastern California (10,000 square miles) (Fig. 19.15).

Deposits of eolian origin consisting of dune sand (in many places more or less admixed with clay) and silt (loess) form an important part of the Pleistocene Series in North America (Fig. 19.16). They occur in both the glaciated and unglaciated parts of the continent, being most widespread in the Central and Great Plains States. Predominantly, they are late Pleistocene. The loess commonly attains thicknesses of 60 to 125 feet along the bluffs that border the flood plains of the Mississippi and Missouri Rivers, thinning away from the rivers to a featheredge. Plainly, this loess was derived from glacial outwash carried by the rivers. Loess deposits that cover the plains of eastern Colorado, western Kansas, and Nebraska probably were derived largely from silt carried eastward by streams such as the Platte River that rise in the Rocky Mountains, where glacial erosion was very active during Pleistocene time, but some of the silt doubtless was carried southward and westward from Missouri River

outwash. The volume of the loess deposits is surprisingly great, those in Kansas alone being estimated to exceed 50,000 cubic miles. Two relatively large areas of loess are found in the Pacific Northwest, where some 80,000 square miles in Washington, Oregon, and Idaho are blanketed by wind-deposited silt that makes fertile wheat land and by irrigation is suited for raising many other crops.

The Atlantic Coastal Plain, from New Jersey to Florida, is discontinuously veneered by Pleistocene deposits consisting of clay, loam, sand, gravel, and peat or swamp muck. These materials, partly marine and partly nonmarine, conceal older formations in interstream areas, especially where elevation above sea level is less than 250 feet. They lie unconformably on strata ranging in age from Pliocene to Triassic, as well as on Precambrian crystalline rocks. Well-defined terraces, carved and built by the sea at different levels, show that at different times in the Pleistocene Epoch the level of the sea was higher than now. A considerable part of Florida is mantled by marine sand,

Fig. 19.10 Fluvioglacial sand and gravel near Renfrew, Ontario. The stratified, unevenly interbedded sand and gravel were deposited by a stream or streams of glacial melt water. (*Courtesy of Geol. Survey Canada.*)

clay, and highly fossiliferous calcareous beds, similar to deposits that are accumulating offshore at the present time.

The plains region bordering the Gulf of Mexico contains marine sand and clay, as well as fluviatile deposits, of Pleistocene age; these are exposed in a belt 15 to 20 miles wide along the coast from western Florida to southern Mississippi. Flat lowland, 50 to 100 miles wide along the Louisiana and Texas coast, is composed of Pleistocene clay, sand, and calcareous sediment. As shown by well records, the thickness of these deposits locally exceeds 2,000 feet, showing that the coastal region has progressively sunk as sediment was laid down.

Stream deposits are a very important part of Pleistocene formations in the Gulf region, for they comprise not only the great deltas (at least five successively built in different locations) and flood plain of the lower Mississippi but alluvial deposits of many other streams. During Pleistocene time the Mississippi deltaic area was built seaward not less than 125 miles (Fig. 19.17). Northeastward and northwestward from New Orleans are broad flat-surface areas that stand distinctly above the Mississippi River flood plain and delta; they are the southern extremities of terraces built of stream-carried gravel, sand, and clay that were deposited in a pre-Wisconsinan interglacial age when sea level stood higher than now. The

Fig. 19.11 Glacial-lake silt deposits in southwestern Montana. Deposition of the sediment in standing water is indicated by the very even horizontal bedding. These strata were formed in the extensive temporary Pleistocene water body known as Lake Missoula. (*W. C. Alden, courtesy of U.S. Geol. Survey.*)

deposits of the terrace (Prairie Formation) extend far up river and throughout most of this distance are found to be paralleled by three higher terraces, the highest (Williana) about 350 feet above the flood plain (Fig. 19.12). Between the times of fluviatile sedimentation recorded by these terrace deposits were times of accelerated erosion, during which the valley was deepened in bedrock. The intervals when erosion predominated are correlated with glacial invasions farther north, and the times of dominant sedimentation with interglacial ages.

In the great interior plains region south of glaciated country, the chief sedimentary record of the Pleistocene Epoch consists of deposits made by streams and winds. Part of the calcium-carbonate-cemented gravel, sand, and silt that mantle the High Plains east of the Rockies is undoubtedly of Pleistocene age, as indicated by fossils and by tracing some layers into the glaciated territory where their relation to deposits of the glacial succession can be determined. The calcium carbonate is carried by percolating ground water and deposited from it by evaporation, forming caliche. It forms a cap rock, which retards stream erosion and serves to preserve great areas of featureless nearly flat plains, as especially well shown in northwestern Texas and parts of western Kansas.

The succession of fluviatile and wind-laid deposits in unglaciated portions of the plains country now is known to range in age from earliest to latest Pleistocene (Figs. 19.12, 19.18). The various formations, some of which contain numerous fossils, are discontinuously spread over uplands and they form terraces along stream valleys, the highest terraces being the oldest. As in the lower Mississippi Valley, deepening of valleys in the plains region seems to correspond to times of ice-sheet expansion, and aggradation was most pronounced during ice recession and in the early part of interglacial ages. Widely traceable buried soils (paleosols) that furnish record of prolonged weathering of the land surface in warm interglacial parts of Pleistocene time are separately identi-

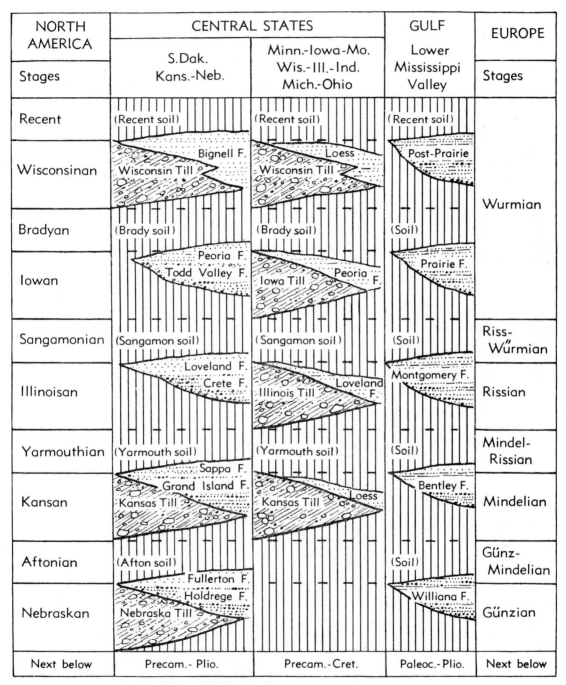

Fig. 19.12 Time-rock divisions of the Pleistocene Series and rock units assigned to them in important successions of North America. The vertical scale does not represent time duration or thickness of deposits but is determined by suitability for plotting the various recognized stratigraphic units, placement of which indicates correlation in age. Vertically ruled areas denote absence of deposits.

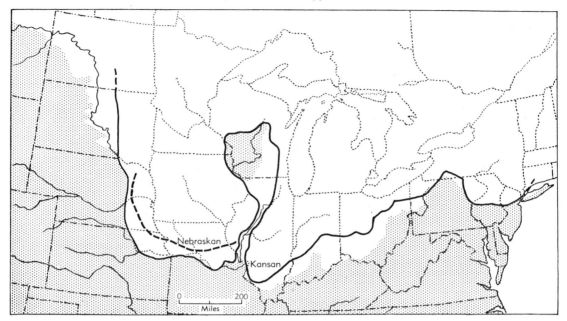

Fig. 19.13 Maximum extent of Nebraskan and Kansan glaciations. Territory not covered by ice during the Pleistocene Epoch is shown by the stippled pattern.

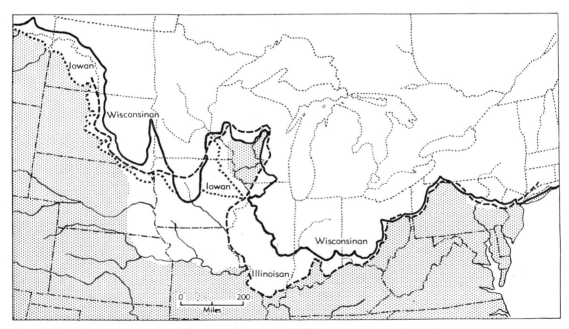

Fig. 19.14 Maximum extent of Illinoisan, Iowan, and Wisconsinan glaciations. Territory not covered by ice during the Pleistocene Epoch is shown by the stippled pattern.

fiable by their relation to the various formations and are helpful in stratigraphic studies
(Figs. 19.12, 19.18).

In the Rocky Mountains region and mountainous areas farther west, Pleistocene deposits
include huge quantities of boulders, gravel,
sand, alluvium, clay, and calcareous material
in valley bottoms, lake beds, talus piles, alluvial fans, landslides, and spring deposits.
Formation of all of these is taking place at the
present time. The deposits of streams and
sheet wash vastly predominate over those of
lakes, wind, and other agents of sedimentation.
The large depressions between the many
mountain ranges of the Great Basin are deeply
filled with water-borne waste, the thickness of
which is measured locally in thousands of feet.
Boulders, cobbles, and finer detritus are carried downward from the mountains by torrents
and deposited in rudely stratified fans sloping

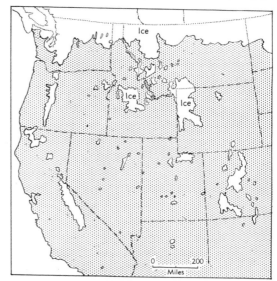

**Fig. 19.15 Maximum extent of Pleistocene glacia-
tion in mountain areas of western United States.**
Territory not covered by ice shown by the stippled
pattern.

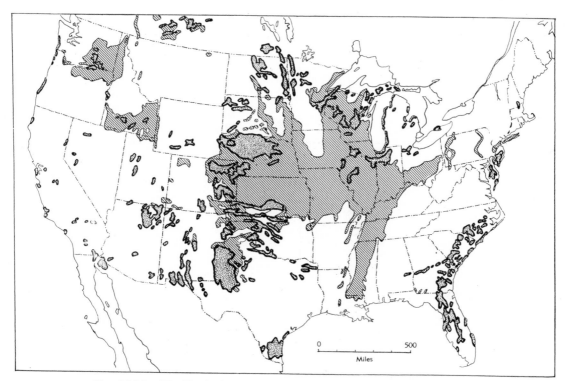

Fig. 19.16 Wind-laid Pleistocene deposits in the United States and southern Canada.
These consist of widespread loess (oblique-ruled), both within glaciated territory and outside
it, and sand deposits (stippled). (*Data from James Thorp, H. T. U. Smith, et al., Pleistocene
eolian deposits of North America, Geological Society of America.*)

toward depressions, which may be occupied temporarily by shallow lakes (playas).

The Pacific Border region contains very thick accumulations of Pleistocene fluviatile gravels, sands, and clays, as well as marine deposits near the coast, which in places are nearly 1,000 feet above present sea level. Diastrophic movements, involving folding and faulting of the rocks, accompanied by earthquakes, have been so numerous in late geologic time that the region is undergoing change from this cause almost continuously. Steeply tilted and faulted Pleistocene beds are found. Some narrow coastal plains are recently elevated portions of the sea floor.

Igneous rocks of Pleistocene age are generally not clearly differentiated from those belonging to the Pliocene, but the western part of North America contains many extensive lava flows and cinder cones that clearly are geologically very young. Some of the lava covers comparatively recent alluvium of stream valleys, and in many places the surface of the flows shows ropy and cindery structure identical with recently congealed lava of the Hawaiian volcanoes. Because there is little or no soil, vegetation has as yet not been able to gain a

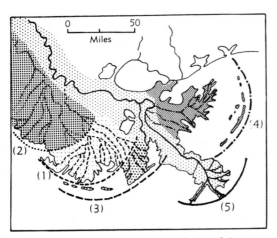

Fig. 19.17 Successively built late Pleistocene deltas of the Mississippi River. The different areas of delta formation are indicated by shading, and their order of development by numbers, the modern "birdfoot" delta (5) being the most recent, mostly formed during the last 500 years. (*Data from H. N. Fisk.*)

foothold upon the lava. Cinder cones appear as though they were formed but yesterday and might at any time resume their growth.

Pleistocene Glaciation

Features of Pleistocene geologic history, except glaciation, have been described in the preceding chapter. Now, the subject of recurrent advance and retreat of great ice sheets, which chiefly distinguish the Pleistocene Epoch, calls for attention, and with this belongs consideration of the causes and effects of glaciation and the nature of evidence concerning duration of the epoch.

Origin and growth of ice sheets. During each glacial age of Pleistocene time, three major ice sheets spread out over North America: (1) the Laurentide ice sheet, much the largest, which occupied the Canadian Shield region and Arctic Archipelago, as well as the central northern part of the United States (*L* and *K* of Fig. 19.19*A*); (2) the Greenland ice sheet, which persists today (shown in black, Fig. 19.19*A*); and the Cordilleran ice sheet (*C* of Fig. 19.19*A*).

In each of these areas, there is little doubt that the initial stage of ice-sheet development consisted of valley glaciers in highlands favorably situated to intercept moisture-laden winds (Fig. 19.20*A*). Such highlands occur in the Cordilleran belt adjacent to the Pacific and throughout Pleistocene time, as today, caused heavy precipitation from winds blowing eastward from the ocean. In the Laurentide ice-sheet area, mountainous highlands exist in Labrador and northern Quebec, near the St. Lawrence River in the vicinity of Montreal, in Newfoundland, and especially in eastern Baffinland, Devon, and Ellesmereland, where extensive glaciers now exist. These parts of northeastern North America are the probable sites of the first accumulation of ice that eventually grew to make the great Laurentide continental glacier (Fig. 19.19*B*). Expansion of valley glaciers may be presumed to have formed piedmont glaciers (Fig. 19.20*B*), and enlargement of these continued on and on until millions of square miles became ice-covered. According to present views, the maxi-

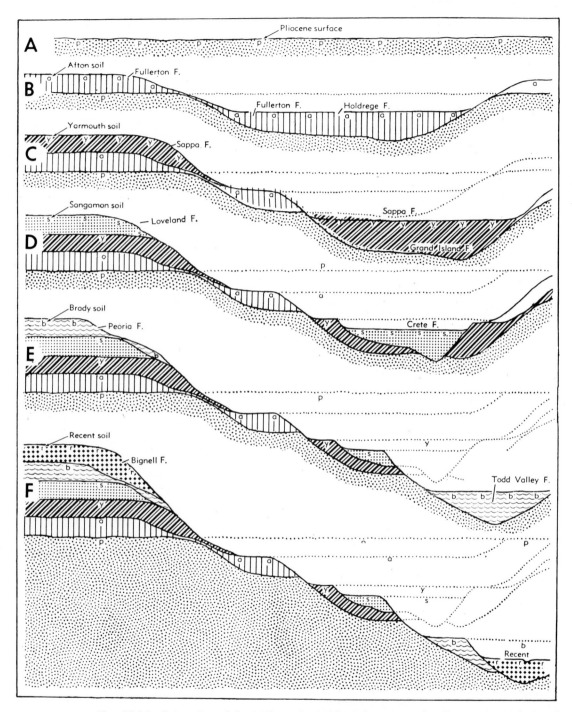

Fig. 19.18 Succession of fluviatile and wind-laid deposits and soil zones in unglaciated plains country. The sections *A–F* diagrammatically represent uplands and valleys in the Nebraska-Kansas region during the Pleistocene Epoch: (*A*) beginning of the epoch; (*B*) just before Kansan time; (*C*) just before Illinoisan time; (*D*) just before Iowan time; (*E*) just before Wisconsinan time; and (*F*) at the present time. (*Data from J. C. Frye, personal communication.*)

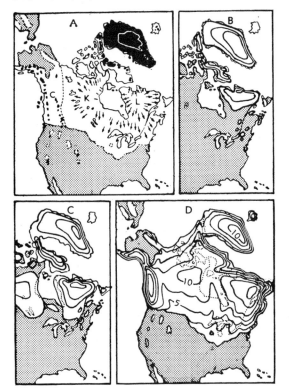

Fig. 19.19 Pleistocene ice sheets of North America.——*A.* Present distribution of glaciers (black; white contour on Greenland icecap indicating elevation of 2,500 feet), stippled areas not glaciated. *C* marks the Cordilleran ice sheet; the area east of the broken line belongs to the Laurentide ice sheet, in which *L* denotes the Labrador center and *K* the Keewatin center, defined by radial disposition of bedrock striae, eskers, and linear features of topography (diagrammatically indicated by arrows).——*B.* Postulated very early stage of ice-sheet growth, showing accumulation of ice in northern Labrador and Baffinland-Ellesmere highlands and in Greenland (contours marking 2,500 and 5,000 feet above sea level).——*C.* Intermediate stage of ice-sheet growth.——*D.* Maximum stage of ice-sheet growth (contours on ice surface with interval of 2,500 feet, figures indicating thousands of feet).

mum accumulation of snow and ice was not necessarily in the areas distinguished as centers of ice dispersal (*L*, *K*, Labrador and Keewatin centers, Fig. 19.19*A*), but because of effects of the ice on air movements and precipitation, it is probable that marginal parts of the ice sheet (particularly in the southeast) were progressively thickened and thus caused to move outward ahead of semistagnant ice in central portions of the glacier (Fig. 19.20*C*). In any case, the directions of ice flow are clearly defined in many places by striations on bedrock, orientation of drumlins and eskers, and trend of end moraines (approximately normal to ice movement).

Multiple glaciation. The upper Mississippi Valley and adjacent Great Lakes region of the United States contain a remarkable record of at least four (probably five) entirely distinct glaciations, of long interglacial ages that separated the successive glaciations, and of so-called postglacial (Recent) history.

Wisconsin, Minnesota, and neighboring country are a land of lakes and irregular hummocky topography, characterized by variously shaped, unevenly disposed hills and poorly drained depressions. Bedrock is mostly concealed by a mantle of glacial till, boulders, gravel, and sand. There are drumlins, kames, eskers, outwash plains, terminal moraines, recessional moraines, and large areas of ground moraine. The insignificant alteration of this glacial topography by stream work or other erosive agencies, since the time of glaciation, and the lack of appreciable weathering in the materials composing the drift attest the comparative recency of glaciation.

It was naturally supposed at first that the glaciation evidenced by these topographic features and by the little-weathered till constituted the entire glacial record of Pleistocene

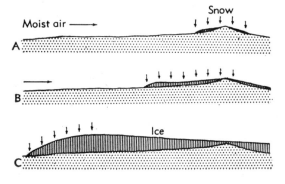

Fig. 19.20 Stages in the development of an ice sheet.——*A.* Valley glacier stage, precipitation largely localized by highland.——*B.* Piedmont glacier stage.——*C.* Ice-sheet stage, precipitation mostly near ice margin, localizing increase in thickness of the glacier. (*Modified from R. F. Flint.*)

time. Increasing cold at the beginning of this epoch led to the formation of an ice sheet that spread widely, and increasing warmth toward the close of the Pleistocene caused melting and disappearance of the ice sheet.

This simple picture does not accord, however, with observations that in Illinois, Iowa, and elsewhere there are widespread deposits of deeply weathered glacial till and, furthermore, that characteristic features of glacial topography are almost lacking in these regions. Seemingly, this much-weathered drift represents glaciation altogether different from, and very much older than, that marked by practically unaltered till and unmodified glacial topography. If this is the case, the older glaciation evidently extended considerably farther south than the later. Most exposures of glacial till in the north show only one drift sheet, the most recent, resting on ice-eroded bedrock. In the south, however, there are many places where one drift sheet overlies another, the contact being marked by change from the much-weathered and decayed upper portion of the older drift to the fresh unweathered drift at the base of the overlying sheet (Figs. 19.21, 19.22). In places, there are beds of peat and old soils, some with remains of land animals and roots of forest trees, above the older drift and buried by the younger. The later ice advance formed a veneer of deposits overlying the older, but in many areas it removed little or none of the underlying material.

Study of the weathering of glacial drift shows that, under the influence of dissolved oxygen and carbon dioxide in water that soaks into the ground, there are progressive chemical changes, which extend downward at unequal rates. Oxidation of iron compounds takes place, making yellowish, brownish, and reddish colors, and more slowly there are solution

Fig. 19.21 Superposed deposits of glacial till and loess near Rhodes, Iowa. Comparatively fresh Wisconsin Till (*A*) rests on wind-laid loess (Peoria Formation, *B*), which in turn lies on weathered Kansas Till (gumbotil, *C*) that is clearly distinguished from subjacent unweathered Kansas Till (*D*). (*W. C. Alden, courtesy of U.S. Geol. Survey.*)

Fig. 19.22 Late Pleistocene deposits at Farmdale, near Peoria, Illinois. The exposure shows Wisconsinan deposits (Tazewell Loess and Till, *A, B*) resting on loess (Peoria Formation, *C*; Farmdale Loess, *D*), which overlies Illinois Till (*E*) with a weathered zone (dark band) at its top. (*Photograph made for this book, courtesy of J. C. Frye, Illinois Geol. Survey.*)

and removal of calcareous material. Still slower than leaching of calcium carbonate is the removal of the soluble parts of silicate minerals. The zones defined by these unequally progressive changes form the so-called soil profile, whose nature and thickness are a measure of the extent (and, other things being equal, the time) to which weathering has proceeded. Under topographic conditions of poor drainage that are common in glaciated areas, the characteristic final alteration product of till is a dark, sticky gumbo-like clay, called *gumbotil*, the dark color of which is due to the reduction of iron by organic compounds derived from overlying vegetation. A gumbotil thus marks very prolonged weathering of a till.

Drift sheets and interglacial materials. The oldest known glacial deposits of the Mississippi Valley region comprise the Nebraska drift sheet, which is seen in Nebraska, Kansas, Missouri, Iowa, and possibly farther east. The deposits left by the Nebraskan glacier consist of boulder clay or till and associated sands and gravels, the thickness in some places being 200 feet or more. The southern limit of the Nebraskan invasion is marked approximately by the lower course of the Missouri River (Fig. 19.13). The ice that occupied the western Mississippi Valley region came from the Keewatin center. The extent of the Nebraskan glaciation in the east and northwest is unknown, because the deposits have been subsequently obliterated or concealed or they are unrecognized. The Nebraska drift, treated as a time-rock unit, comprises the *Nebraskan Stage* (glacial).

When the Nebraskan ice disappeared, the till that it had formed began to be weathered. Most of the topography seems to have been that of a nearly flat, poorly drained ground-moraine plain, upon which chemical weathering was effective and erosion negligible. The weathering continued until an average thickness of more than 8 feet of gumbotil was formed by alteration of the Nebraska Till. Beds of peat, containing tree stumps and branches, and water-laid sediments, containing remains of animals that indicate a cool temperate climate, are associated with the gumbotil. All of these deposits belong to the *Aftonian Stage* (interglacial) (See Fig. 19.12).

A second Pleistocene glaciation is shown by the occurrence of till and fluvioglacial sand and gravel above the Nebraska drift and Afton gumbotil and soil. The younger deposits, called Kansas drift, occupy about the same area as the Nebraska, and their average thickness is about 50 feet. Locally, the Kansas Till is 150 feet thick. An ancient drift in central Ohio, which contains copper derived from the Lake Superior region, is possibly equivalent to the Kansas. The Kansas drift comprises the *Kansan Stage* (glacial).

After melting of the Kansan ice, the poorly drained ground-moraine deposits were subjected to weathering, and an average thickness of 12 feet of gumbotil was formed on the Kansas Till before the next glaciation occurred. Deposits of peat, loess, and gravel were formed at this time. These materials represent the *Yarmouthian Stage* (interglacial).

A third ice sheet, termed Illinoisan, came mainly from the Labrador center and extended over a large part of Illinois, Indiana, and Ohio. A lobe of the glacier extended westward into Iowa, displacing the Mississippi River for a time. The average thickness of the Illinois drift is about 30 feet. Large areas of its surface are nearly flat ground moraine, but in some belts, the topography is distinctly hummocky, denoting terminal and recessional moraines. The Illinois drift makes up the *Illinoisan Stage* (glacial).

During another interglacial age that followed, the Illinois Till was weathered to form 4 to 6 feet of gumbotil in many places. Peat occurs locally. The prolonged weathering that produced the gumbotil was followed by deposition of loess, which consists of wind-blown materials spread widely over the weathered Kansas drift in Iowa, Missouri, Nebraska, and Kansas and over weathered Illinois drift in Illinois and Indiana. Volcanic ash, interbedded with the loess, has been found in western Iowa. Calcareous materials of the loess were leached to a depth of 3 to 5 feet before glacial ice advanced again over parts of the region. These nonglacial deposits are classed as the *Sangamonian Stage* (interglacial).

The next advance of continental ice sheets led to making deposits of till that is found to overlie the Illinois Till or Sangamon soil, in some places occurring also next above Kansas Till or Yarmouth soil. These deposits belong to the *Iowan Stage*. They are named from exposures in eastern Iowa where till deposited by this glaciation comprises the surface materials in several counties. The drift sheet is old enough to have lost traces of morainal topography, and lakes are lacking. The Iowa drift occurs in Iowa, Minnesota, and probably farther west. Although leaching of this drift has reached a depth of about 6 feet, all the time since retreat of the Iowan ice sheet has been insufficient to produce gumbotil. The Iowan glaciation is thus relatively recent. Extensive deposition of loess (Peoria) is the next recorded item of Iowan history. The loess is clearly of wind-blown origin, as indicated by occurrence of the thickest accumulations (nearly 100 feet) along the tops of the bluffs and uplands adjacent to the large river valleys and a progressive thinning away from them. Presumably, it was derived from silt exposed in flats of the valley bottoms that was swirled aloft by air currents and sifted over adjacent land.

Warm climate that succeeded advance of the Iowan ice sheet is recorded by a relatively prolonged time of weathering that produced a soil named Brady. The interglacial stage is called *Bradyan.*

The youngest of the drift sheets is the Wisconsin. Its distinctive youthful features are the almost unmodified glacial topography and slight weathering, which contrast greatly to the characters of the older glacial deposits. Although ice of Wisconsinan time did not reach as far south, in general, as preceding glacial invasions, the area covered by Wisconsin drift is much more extensive than that in which any of the older drifts are now found. The obvious reason for this is that, wherever the Wisconsin deposits occur, they overlie and conceal older drift unless the latter was removed before deposition of the Wisconsin. The margins of the Wisconsinan ice sheets were strongly lobate, as shown by the looped arrangement of the terminal and recessional moraines, and the distribution of the lobes indicates that the ice movement was influenced by major topographic features of the area invaded, being accelerated by broad smooth lowlands and impeded by rough uplands. Thus we find that the hummocky morainal belts of the Wisconsin drift are concentric with the Great Lakes depressions. The Wisconsin glacial deposits comprise the *Wisconsinan Stage* (glacial).

Study of deposits left by the various Wisconsinan ice lobes shows that the history of this glaciation is complex. It is known that the edge of the ice advanced, retreated, advanced again, receded, halted, receded, and so on, with innumerable local variations. In places, after the advance and partial retreat of one lobe, an adjoining lobe overrode deposits previously left by the other. The glacial deposits classed as Wisconsin include three main divisions that represent advances and retreats of a single great ice sheet during this epoch. The successive till deposits are named Tazewell, Cary, and Mankato.

The Tazewell Till forms the surface of a large part of Illinois, Indiana, and southwestern Ohio. It is younger than the Peoria Loess, which it overlies. Not much difference in amount of weathering is shown by early and late parts of the Wisconsin drift, but the topography of Tazewell areas is more modified by erosion and has fewer lakes and swamps than younger divisions of the drift. The Tazewell drift is classed as the *Tazewellian Substage.*

The Cary Till, which is identified in northern and eastern Wisconsin, at the southern tip of Lake Michigan near Chicago, and throughout most of Michigan, Ohio, northern Pennsylvania, and New Jersey, represents the greatest advance of Wisconsinan ice sheets in Ohio and farther east. The Cary drift comprises the *Caryan Substage.*

The youngest part of the Wisconsin glacial deposits, named Mankato Till, is least modified by weathering and erosion. It is mostly poorly drained, and its area contains thousands of lakes, ponds, and swamps. This drift is widely distributed west of the Mississippi Valley in Minnesota, Iowa, and the Dakotas but was restricted in the east to the borders of the Superior, Michigan, Huron, and Ontario lake basins, and the borders of the St. Lawrence Valley. The late Wisconsinan glacial deposits cover a large part of Canada and collectively constitute the *Mankatoan Substage.*

Definition of post-Wisconsinan deposits, classed as the *Recent Stage,* is mostly so lacking in precision that this division of the Pleistocene Series is a unit recognized simply by custom and by reason of convenience. Large glaciers persist today, even though most of the great ice sheets of the last extensive glaciation have disappeared. The return of sea level approximately to its present position after the depression suffered in Wisconsinan time probably is the best marker for the beginning of the so-called Recent Age.

Formation of the Great Lakes. One of the most interesting and important physiographic results of continental glaciation in North America was the formation of the Great Lakes, several large temporary glacial lakes now vanished, and an unnumbered multitude of smaller lakes. All these lakes are due to the formation of depressions made by erosion or deposition of the ice or by the ponding of waters between parts of the glacial ice and the adjacent land.

The recorded history of the Great Lakes

began when the ice lobes retreated north of the St. Lawrence-Mississippi divide, and water from the normal drainage and the melting ice rose until it found the lowest available outlet. The levels of water bodies thus formed were maintained until some other outlet at lower elevation was uncovered. Shore-line features, such as beaches and wave-cut cliffs, and deposits on the lake bottoms furnish evidence of successive steps in evolution of the lakes—features that are defined in proportion to the duration of the lake levels.

In addition to the effect of changing positions of the ice front, a general slow tilting of the land surface influenced the history of the lakes. Under the enormous weight of the continental ice sheet, which was thousands of cubic miles in aggregate volume, the northern part of the continent was depressed, but when this weight was removed by melting of the ice, the land rose in resilient manner. The upward movement was slow. It was least in the southwest and greatest in the northeast, where it amounts to some hundreds of feet. The differential nature of the warping is clearly defined by the gently tilted attitude of the lake beaches, which were horizontal originally. The main steps in the development of the Great Lakes are given in the following summary and annexed maps (Fig. 19.23).

1. Formation of lakes at the tip of the Michigan and Erie ice lobes; outlets by way of Illinois-Des Plaines and Wabash Rivers to the Mississippi (Fig. 19.23A).

2. Retreat of ice, forming larger lakes; abandonment of Wabash River outlet because of the uncovering of a new outlet, which drained waters of the Erie basin northward into a lake formed at the tip of the Saginaw ice lobe, and thence westward across Michigan (Fig. 19.23B).

3. Retreat of the ice margin north of the Straits of Mackinac, uncovering most of the Great Lakes region and (partly because of low level of country in the north and east depressed by weight of the ice sheet) providing northeastward outlets for the lakes that were materially smaller and lower in level than now; the Ontario and St. Lawrence Valley presumably invaded by the sea (Fig. 19.23C).

4. Readvance of the glacier, making a broadly confluent lake in the Erie and southern Huron depressions that drained westward into Lake Chicago and thence to the Mississippi (Fig. 19.23D).

5. Retreat of the ice, forming a lake in the Superior basin and opening outlet for waters of the Huron-Erie basin by way of Mohawk River into the Hudson; outlet of the Lake Michigan basin still southwestward from Chicago (Fig. 19.23E).

6. Further deglaciation, uncovering a channel across Ontario from the Huron basin and producing another very low-water stage (drainage way subsequently uplifted about 600 feet) (Fig. 19.23F).

7. Disappearance of ice sheet in the Great Lakes region, accompanied by differential uplift of the crust that lifted northern areas more rapidly than southern, raising the lake levels; drainage for a time across Ontario and southwestward from Lake Michigan but later the eastward outlet from Lake Huron was cut off (Fig. 19.23G).

8. Additional elevation of country in the north, introducing present conditions.

Retreat of the ice from the Red River basin, northwest of Lake Superior, produced Lake Agassiz, which vastly exceeded in dimensions any of the existing Great Lakes (Fig. 19.24). It is marked by lake deposits and well-formed beaches. The lake drained southeastward by way of valleys now occupied by the Minnesota and Mississippi Rivers. Eventually, when the ice retreated far enough north to permit discharge of waters into Hudson Bay, the lake was drained, except for its present remnants, Lake Winnipeg, Rainy Lake, and other smaller water bodies.

Drainage changes. Pre-Pleistocene drainage ways in parts of North America that later were covered by ice sheets certainly differed more or less radically from the present pattern. This is a reasonable presumption on theoretical grounds, for erosion and deposition by a continental glacier could not fail to carve depressions, modify slopes, fill valleys, and make new divides, and derangement of stream courses resulting from glaciation happened not once but repeatedly. Moreover, the ef-

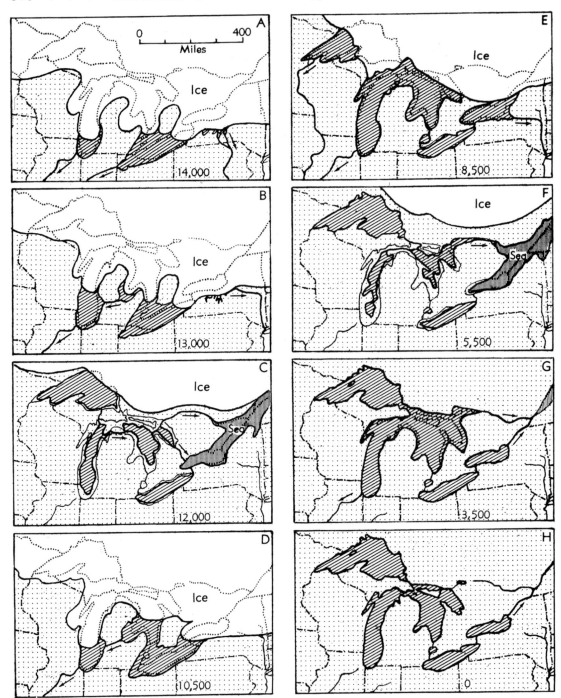

Fig. 19.23 Evolution of the Great Lakes. The figures accompanying each map indicate the approximate number of years before the present time, based on C[14] dates. Arrows mark the direction of flow along outlets from lakes (oblique-ruled).——*A.* Lake Maumee stage.——*B.* Lake Whittlesey stage.——*C.* Bowmanville low-water stage.——*D.* Lake Warren stage.——*E.* Lake Algonquin stage.——*F.* Lake Chippewa stage.——*G.* Nipissing Great Lakes stage.—— *H.* Present stage. (*A–F, modified from R. F. Flint.*)

fects of crustal warping influenced by weight of the ice and elastic rebound when ice disappeared are extremely important. As it happens, there is no need to rely on theory and generalized sorts of deductions, for a wealth of geologic evidence concerning drainage changes in late Pleistocene time at least is available. On the other hand, trustworthy information about stream courses in latest Pliocene, early Pleistocene, and middle Pleistocene times, as far as the glaciated parts of the continent are concerned, is almost entirely lacking.

Valleys filled by glacial deposits have been found in many places by drilling for the purpose of locating and developing supplies of ground water. Sand and gravel in such valleys almost invariably are highly pervious and water-saturated. Some of the buried valleys are found well north of the limits of glaciation, whereas others are marginal, owing their content of deposits mostly to local blocking of drainage by the ice. Examples are a west-flowing major stream (named Teays) traced from southern Ohio across northern Indiana to a large buried channel that led to confluence with the Mississippi in central Illinois (Fig. 19.25) and valleys in northwestern Missouri and northwestern Iowa that trend across modern drainage lines. Pre-Wisconsinan streams in territory now traversed by the Missouri River were almost entirely reorganized as a result of glaciation, those in Montana and North Dakota being diverted from a northward course leading to Hudson Bay so as to become tributary to Gulf of Mexico drainage.

A striking example of stream erosion caused by a glacier-made dam is found in Grand Coulee, east of the Cascade Mountains in Washington. When a lobe of the Cordilleran ice sheet moved southward into and across the west-trending canyon of Columbia River, approximately 1,500 feet deep, a lake was

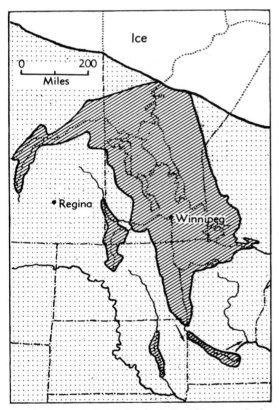

Fig. 19.24 Glacial Lake Agassiz. This water body, much larger than any of the modern Great Lakes, occupied most of southern Manitoba; its outlet was southward by way of the present Minnesota and Mississippi River Valleys. When ice that blocked outlet to the north melted, the ponded water was drained from all of the area except depressions that hold modern Lake Winnipeg and nearby lakes. (*Modified from Taylor and Leverett, U.S. Geol. Survey.*)

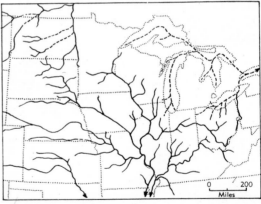

Fig. 19.25 Pre-Wisconsinan stream courses in the North Central States. The most obvious differences between drainage ways here shown and those of the present are absence of the Missouri and Ohio Rivers as trunk streams and the course of the Mississippi River across central Illinois. Whether or not water bodies existed in parts of the Great Lakes depressions is unknown, but drainage of this area probably was toward the northeast into the St. Lawrence River. (*Modified from R. F. Flint.*)

formed, and the level of this lake rose until water spilled over into Grand Coulee. The great discharge that passed along this outlet deepened the coulee and formed conspicuous falls in places where the water tumbled over high basalt cliffs. The detour thus forced upon the Columbia was about 100 miles in length. When the glacier receded, the river was enabled to resume its former course.

Mountain glaciation. During the Pleistocene Epoch, large quantities of snow and ice accumulated in mountain ranges of the western

Fig. 19.26 Mountain glaciation in northern British Columbia. Air photograph of part of Eagle glacier and its snow field in the Coastal Range near the southeastern Alaskan border. This very late Pleistocene (modern) glacier doubtless illustrates accurately local conditions belonging to an incipient stage of making the Cordilleran ice sheet. (*U.S. Air Force, courtesy of Geol. Survey Canada.*)

United States and Canada (Fig. 19.26). Mountain glaciation occurred on a grand scale. At times of maximum growth, the glaciers scoured out and considerably deepened gorges previously cut by the mountain streams. Tongues of ice reached many miles down the valleys and in places spread out as lobes on the adjacent lowlands, building great lateral and terminal moraines. Many topographic features in these mountain areas, where ice is now absent, are due to Pleistocene glaciation (Figs. 19.27, 19.28). The effects of glaciation are recorded as far south as Arizona and southern California.

Early drift lies on remnants of a piedmont terrace bordering the Rocky Mountains in Montana. The elevation of the drift-bearing terrace is as much as 1,000 feet above the present drainage. Much younger glacial deposits are found in the lower parts of the valleys, which, subsequent to the early glaciation, were cut far below the high terrace levels. Three, and possibly four, glaciations are recognized in the mountains of western Wyoming. The oldest deposits lie on remnants of high piedmont terraces, which are separated by valleys that have been carved 1,000 feet in bedrock since the early glaciation. The San Juan Mountains of southwestern Colorado, the Sierra Nevada, and many other mountains show evidence of two or more glaciations.

Glaciation in Europe. During Pleistocene time northern Europe was subjected to recurrent invasion by continental ice sheets in almost exactly the same way and, with reasonable certainty, at the same times as in North America. The area covered by ice during maximum glaciation includes all the Scandinavian countries and Finland, the northern part of the British Isles, most of Denmark, northern Germany and Poland, Latvia, Lithuania, Estonia, and northwestern European Russia (Fig. 19.29). Although large, this territory, approximately 1.5 million square miles in extent, is less than one-third of the glaciated land in North America. In addition to the continental glacier, generally known as the Scandinavian ice sheet, glaciers in the Alps of Switzerland and Austria were expanded greatly, and on a

Fig. 19.27   U-shaped valley of the Merced River in Yosemite National Park. This valley, carved in massive igneous rocks that form the core of the Sierra Nevada, shows typical sculpture produced by mountain glaciation. (*F. E. Matthes, courtesy of U.S. Geol. Survey.*)

smaller scale there was glaciation in the Pyrenees, Carpathians, and Apennines.

In Europe, a classification of glacial and interglacial deposits, accompanied by a reasonably agreed set of names for them, based on the observed succession in areas covered by the Scandinavian ice sheet, does not exist. Instead, the standard for all Europe consists of divisions recognized in the Alps region, even though equivalences between the geographically separated mountain-glacial and continental-ice-sheet successions are by no means firmly determined. This is unfortunate. Deep erosion in the Alps, moreover, has destroyed most of the record of early Pleistocene glaciations, and partly as a consequence of this, correlations within the Alps region itself (particularly as regards the northern and southern flanks of the mountains) lack agreement. The sequence has been worked out mainly from studies of glacial outwash deposits, using topographic expression, soil profiles, relations

to interbedded loess sheets, depth of erosion in bedrock, and similar criteria as evidence for interpreting relative age. On this basis, four glacial stages and three interglacial stages are recognized. In order, from oldest to youngest, the glacial divisions are named Günz, Mindel, Riss, and Würm, and the interglacial units are designated by combining the names of the two glacials that bound them, as Günz-Mindel, Mindel-Riss, and Riss-Würm (Fig. 19.12). Areal distribution of the glacial deposits indicates that the most widespread glaciation was the Mindel, which generally has been correlated with the Kansan glaciation in North America. A complication that bears on intercontinental correlation of the Pleistocene deposits and accuracy of understanding history of the epoch is discovery of pre-Günz drift in the northern Alps, subsequently correlated with cold-climate deposits found on the southern flank of the mountains. These pre-Günz glacial sediments have been termed the *Donau*

Fig. 19.28 Glacial erosion in summit portions of the Uinta Mountains, northeastern Utah. This view, at the head of the west fork of Sheep Creek, excellently shows an old (probably early Pleistocene) erosion surface reduced to remnants by cirque cutting of late Pleistocene (Wisconsinan) date. (*W. H. Bradley, courtesy of U.S. Geol. Survey.*)

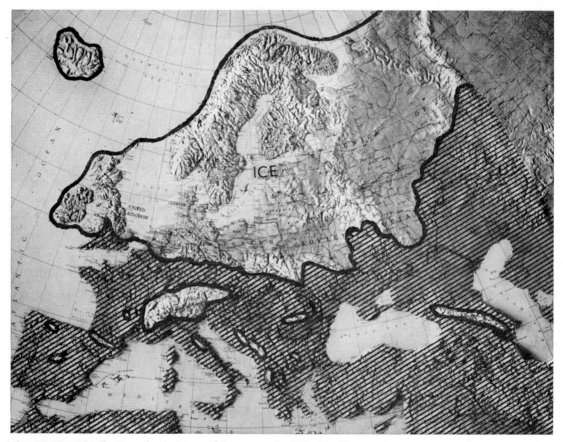

Fig. 19.29 Distribution of maximum Pleistocene glaciation in Europe. Areas not covered by ice sheets and expanded mountain glaciers are indicated by oblique ruling. (*Relief map courtesy of Aero Service Corporation.*)

Stage. Five glacial stages are defined in North America, counting Iowan as separate from Wisconsinan. Is the Donau Stage equivalent to Nebraskan and the Günz to the Kansan, and does the Mindel correspond to Illinoisan rather than Kansan? These questions are not resolved, but one can hardly escape the conclusion that alternating cold and warm climates of Pleistocene time should have affected Europe and North America simultaneously and nearly equally.

A feature of the record of Pleistocene time in Europe that is much more detailed than in North America is evidence of fossil man and of successive human cultures. Unquestionably, there were human beings who lived in Europe before the last ice age (Würmian). The geologic record of man is the subject of Chap. 21, and therefore discussion is omitted here.

Duration of Pleistocene Time

Evidence from weathering of drift sheets. An approximate measure of the duration of Pleistocene time is based on depth of leaching and decomposition of the materials of the drift sheets. For example, if calcareous constituents of the late Wisconsinan (Mankato) drift have been leached to an average depth of 2½ feet in the time since this glaciation, the observed average depth of leaching of the Iowan drift, of 5 to 6 feet, may be interpreted to mean that the time since the Iowan glaciation is slightly more than twice as long as that since the retreat of the late Wisconsinan glacier. Gumbotil, the ultimate product of chemical decay of till in flat, poorly drained areas, is found at the top of the Illinois, Kansas, and Nebraska Tills, but not on the Wisconsin Tills, even where the topographic conditions are favorable. Evidently, gumbotils do not begin to be formed until there has been time for leaching of calcium carbonate to a depth of at least 6 feet. Study of these results of weathering of the drift leads to the following determination of the minimum comparative time values represented by the weathering. If the time since maximum spread of the Mankatoan ice is designated as 1, then post-Iowan time is about 2.2, Sangamonian interglacial time about 4.8,

Yarmouthian interglacial time 12, and Aftonian interglacial time 8. To convert these values to years, we must know as accurately as possible the time value of 1, and to derive a figure for the duration of the Pleistocene Epoch, the time involved in the glaciations must be added to the figures for interglacial and postglacial times.

Evidence from recession of river falls. Attempts have been made to measure the time since the Wisconsinan ice retreated by study of the rate and total amount of the recession of certain river falls that came into existence immediately after the last glaciation. Chief of these are Niagara Falls and St. Anthony Falls, the latter on the Mississippi River at Minneapolis.

The beginning of Niagara Falls can be dated at the time when the Wisconsinan ice retreated north of the escarpment of Niagaran limestone in western New York. Drainage from streams, lakes, and part of the ice front to the west followed the present course of the Niagara River and tumbled over the escarpment near the town of Lewiston. From this point, the falls have subsequently receded about 7 miles to their present position, forming the Niagara Gorge (Fig. 19.30). Dividing the total length of the gorge by the present average annual amount of recession, which is determined at 3.8 feet, the length of time required for the making of the gorge is figured to be about 10,000 years. This method of computation is inaccurate both because the stated figure for average annual recession has been found to be too small and because this recession rate depends on the volume of discharge of the present Niagara River, which drains all the Great Lakes above Ontario. During much of the past when the waters of Lakes Huron, Michigan, and Superior had a different outlet, the flow of Niagara River was correspondingly reduced and the rate of recession of the falls greatly retarded. Estimates of the time required for the recession of Niagara Falls from its original position thus have ranged from 20,000 to as much as 39,000 years. All this has been invalidated by a recent discovery from borings made in connection with construction

Fig. 19.30 Niagara Falls looking toward Goat Island and the Canadian Falls. The recession of this falls, as the capping limestone is undercut and carried away, furnishes a measure of the time since waters from Lake Erie established outlet by way of the Niagara River. This river initially tumbled over the Niagara escarpment at a point coinciding with the lower end of the gorge that now extends several miles below the falls. The geologic relations are illustrated in Figs. 7.12 and 7.13 (page 134), which show the rock succession and regional setting.

of a bridge that a middle section of the gorge is filled by glacial drift and thus must antedate the last glaciation of western New York. Accordingly, no reliable conclusions as to time values can be drawn.

Saint Anthony Falls originated near the present confluence of the Mississippi and Minnesota Rivers, where the waters of the newly formed Mississippi were precipitated into a broad valley, which had served as the outlet for glacial Lake Agassiz in the North Dakota-Manitoba country. The minimum time required for the recession of these falls, which have receded northward a little over 8 miles, is estimated to be 12,000 to 16,000 years. Measured variation in the rate of recession during the period of observation invalidates these estimates also.

Evidence from seasonally banded clay deposits. Another method of time measurement, which is accurate as applied to considerable portions of late Pleistocene time, is the study of the seasonally banded layers (varves) of clay or fine silt deposited in temporary glacial lakes (Fig. 19.31). A varve consists of two layers, a thick one and a thin one. The thicker, slightly coarser, and generally lighter colored layers represent the more rapid deposition in the summer period, when the melting of ice was greatest, whereas the thinner, finer, and darker colored deposits represent the winter season. Count of the pairs of bands in any one deposit gives a measure of the years represented in making the deposit, while careful measurements of the successive bands afford basis for correlation of banded deposits in different lakes and areas. The record may be pieced together to give a fairly continuous time record. Study of these banded clays in New England and eastern Canada indicates that the retreat of the ice in this region required 28,000 to 29,000 years.

Radiocarbon dating. The most reliable means of measuring time intervals in the late part of the Pleistocene Epoch, reaching as far as 35,000 or 40,000 years before present time, is by employment of the C^{14} method. Samples of wood, charcoal, peat, shells of invertebrates, and chemically precipitated carbonates furnish information that can be translated into statements of time elapsed since their origin. In this way, many late Pleistocene deposits have been dated and time before the present when various conditions or events of recent geologic history occurred can be ascertained. In general, radiocarbon dates point to smaller time values for Pleistocene divisions than those arrived at otherwise. With some confidence, we now may say that the Wisconsinan glaciation occurred within the last 30,000 years and the Pleistocene Epoch embraces at least 300,-000 years; the estimate that Pleistocene time amounts to 1 million years may not be too great.

Causes of Glaciation

The problem of finding an explanation for climatic changes that in Pleistocene time led to recurrent spreading out of great ice sheets and subsequent more or less complete melting away of these sheets during warm interglacial ages is a difficult one. In all probability, there was no single cause, but rather a combination of causes. Among items of knowledge that seem pertinent to our inquiry are the following: (1) Climatic change is an inherent feature of the geologic record, conditions that produce glaciation being the expression only of greater than average climatic oscillation, which is not confined to the Pleistocene Epoch; extensive sheets of ice were formed at other times in earth history, as in Pennsylvanian and Permian time and near the beginning of the Cambrian Period. (2) Climatic changes of appreciable magnitude have occurred within the last 100 years during which instrumental measurements of various sorts and direct observations furnish reliable information; in this period temperatures generally have risen, contributing to deglaciation, some elevation of mean sea level, and migration of plants and animals into higher latitudes and altitudes (though some very considerable shifts of range are associated with measured increase of mean temperature amounting to less than 1°F.). (3) Evidence of

several sorts indicates that the extreme range of mean annual air temperature during Pleistocene time was little, if any, more than 15°F., at least in middle latitudes; surface sea water in tropical regions fluctuated only to the extent of 11°F. in mean annual temperature. Neither of these changes is profound. (4) Distribution of existing glaciers and the pattern of present atmospheric circulation are correlated with climatic belts corresponding to those inferred from maximum extents of Pleistocene ice sheets, indicating that the continents and poles have not shifted their relative positions appreciably during this epoch. (5) Obviously, high-latitude highlands in the pathway of moist air coming from oceanic areas are most favorable sites for origin of glaciers.

The chief hypotheses advanced to account for climatic fluctuations of the sort leading to extensive glaciation and deglaciation are based on postulated (1) variation in solar radiation received by the earth; (2) relation of Pleistocene glaciers to late Cenozoic mountains and highlands; (3) variations in con-

Fig. 19.31 Banded clay deposits laid down in a glacial lake. Each pair of light and dark bands in this deposit near Kazabazua, Quebec, comprises sedimentation made during one year. It is thus readily possible to compute the time required to make the entire thickness of the deposits. (*Courtesy of Geol. Survey Canada.*)

stituents of the atmosphere, some of which exert a deciding blanketing effect on transmission of short-wave solar radiation and long-wave terrestrial radiation, thus affecting temperature; (4) displacement of land masses with respect to polar regions; and (5) changes in oceanic currents.

The amount of radiant energy entering the earth's atmosphere from the sun formerly was supposed to be uniform in any specified unit of time and hence was referred to as the solar constant. The possibility of fluctuation in this value was realized, however, in the early 1880s, and subsequent observations, especially since 1920, demonstrate that appreciable variations actually exist, although mostly less than 2 per cent. Times of increased solar radiation, as between 1925 and 1950, coincide with slight warming of the earth's atmosphere. It is possible that the kind of radiation (for example, in the ultraviolet band of the solar spectrum), varying in intensity through a considerable range, may be much more important than the total amount of radiation. Changes of this sort occur in phase with sun-spot activity, which varies cyclically. Although available measurements point to temperature fluctuations not exceeding 2°F. at a given place on the earth's surface since 1750, the Pleistocene record, including evidence from fossil spores of various plants, indicates a range several times greater, up to 15°F. or even more. This larger amplitude possibly is due to (1) greater variation in emission of radiant energy from the sun, (2) longer sustained small fluctuations of temperature, comparable to those actually measured in the last two centuries, or (3) a combination of these. Each of the suggested possibilities is reasonable and furnishes adequate causes of both temperature and atmospheric circulation changes that occurred in the Pleistocene Epoch.

Favorably situated mountains induce large precipitation from moist winds forced to rise in crossing them, and low temperatures at high altitudes make snow and sleet predominant forms of precipitation in mountains and lofty highlands. The result is the appearance of glaciers. When Pleistocene glaciation was thought to represent simply an unusually great expansion of ice in mountain areas and high latitudes, it seemed reasonable to correlate this with uplift of late Cenozoic mountains by crustal deformation, for the appearance of mountains would provide the conditions necessary to make glaciers. Later, when irrefutable evidence of multiple glaciation in Pleistocene time was discovered, the four or five successive great ice expansions, separated by long interglacial warmth, could hardly be attributed to mountain making alone, for this would mean excessive up-and-down movements of the crust. It is still true that existence of mountains is a factor contributing importantly to the origin of glacial ice, but now it is evident that other factors have a controlling influence.

Changes in the atmospheric content of water vapor, carbon dioxide, and ozone may affect climate, decreases in any of these operating to cool the atmosphere and increases to warm it. In similar manner, abundance of solid particles in the air, such as wind-raised dust and explosively ejected volcanic ash that may be carried upward many miles and remain suspended for years, affects atmospheric temperatures, increase of these particles producing lowered temperatures. Qualitatively, variations in atmospheric constituents must be recognized as potential factors influencing climates, but quantitatively and in relation to time, they seem to be quite inadequate to account for Pleistocene glaciations.

Crustal displacements of the earth with respect to its axis have been considered in trying to explain the occurrence of glaciation in various regions during parts of earth history, including Pleistocene time. Evidence bearing on hypotheses of this sort is discordant but mostly is judged wholly insufficient to merit serious consideration, especially as regards the repeated Pleistocene ice advances.

Ocean currents greatly influence climates by transferring heat from low latitudes to high and carrying cold water from polar regions toward the equator. This is demonstrated by surface currents like the warm Gulf Stream and cold Labrador Current; in addition, deep oceanic circulation now brings toward the equator relatively dense cold water that sinks in polar areas. Theoretically, changes in the outline of ocean borders, as by submerging the Panama land barrier between Atlantic and Pacific waters, could modify ocean currents drastically, and under certain conditions deep oceanic circulation could be reversed to cause rise of warm water in high latitudes, but there is no indication that in Pleistocene time the nature and distribution of oceanic currents were changed materially. Lowering of sea level at times of maximum glaciation undoubtedly served to impede water movements between the Arctic and northern Pacific and Atlantic, thus tending to

cool adjacent lands; however, oceanic currents can hardly have been a primary factor affecting glacial and interglacial climates.

In sum, a complex interplay of changing causal factors seems to control the Pleistocene glaciations and deglaciations. Among these factors, variations in solar energy received by the earth probably are most important and the others discussed are secondary in varying degree. It is well to remind ourselves that Pleistocene time continues to run along daily and that within historic time we have the opportunity to observe directly part (however small) of the climatic conditions belonging to the epoch.

READINGS

Antevs, Ernst, 1929, Maps of the Pleistocene glaciations: *Geol. Soc. America Bull.*, vol. 40, pp. 631–720.

Bretz, J. H., 1932, The Grand Coulee: *Am. Geog. Soc. Spec. Publ.* 15 (89 pp.).

Demorest, Max, 1943, Ice sheets: *Geol. Soc. America Bull.*, vol. 54, pp. 363–400.

Durham, J. W., 1950, Cenozoic marine climates of the Pacific coast: *Geol. Soc. America Bull.*, vol. 61, pp. 1243–1264.

Flint, R. F., 1957, *Glacial and Pleistocene geology*, John Wiley & Sons, Inc., New York (553 pp.). [1] Pleistocene facts and basic concepts, pp. 1–10. [2] Crustal warping [in relation to glaciation and deglaciation], pp. 240–257. [3] Fluctuation of sea level [in Pleistocene time], pp. 258–271. [4] Stratigraphy [of Pleistocene deposits], pp. 272–288. [5] Chronology [of Pleistocene Epoch], pp. 289–301. [6] Geography of North America during the latest glaciation, pp. 302–327. [7] [Pleistocene] stratigraphy of central North America, pp. 335–354. [8] Problem of causes [of glaciation], pp. 481–509.

Leighton, M. M., and Willman, H. B., 1950, Loess formations of the Mississippi Valley: *Jour. Geology*, vol. 58, pp. 599–623.

QUESTIONS

1. How is flatness of the face of the cobble illustrated in Fig. 19.3 explained? What is the significance of parallel orientation of a majority of the striae? Why are some striations disposed at an angle to the majority?

2. Referring to Fig. 19.5, how can you account for the fan-shaped areas of distribution of the distinctive groups of erratic boulders shown? Why are some of the fans, like those mapped in Maine and Vermont, so much wider than others, notably that extending from central Massachusetts across western Rhode Island?

3. As indicated in Fig. 19.7, what is the explanation of divergent arrows in areas of the Saginaw and Huron-Erie lobes? Since orientation of indicated ice movements in western Michigan (upper left part of figure) is either west-east or east-west, what reasons can be given from study of the map for concluding that the ice flowed in opposed directions rather than all in the same direction? How can you account for the difference in topographic features of glaciated territory on opposite sides of the line marking the limit of late Wisconsinan drift?

4. How can the sand and gravel deposit shown in Fig. 19.10 be identified as fluvioglacial in origin rather than merely stream-laid? What sorts of evidence can you suggest as suited to indicate most reliably the age of this deposit in the succession of the Pleistocene Series?

5. Why are deposits made by streams and wind (all those indicated in Fig. 19.12 excepting glacial till) placed as belonging to late parts of glacial stages and early parts of

interglacial stages? Why are the Afton, Yarmouth, Sangamon, and Brady soils placed as interglacial? Can you suggest why these soils are not shown graphically as Pleistocene deposits, the names on the chart being enclosed in parentheses? In the column for the lower Mississippi Valley, all the Pleistocene deposits designated, except post-Prairie, are constituents of river terraces found at different elevations above the modern Mississippi River flood plain. What explanation can you give for origin of these terrace deposits and for the hiatuses (indicated by vertical ruling) between them?

6. Referring to Fig. 19.13, can you suggest why Nebraskan drift is indicated only west of the Illinois River? Since everywhere the margin of Kansan drift is shown to be farther south than the limit of the Nebraskan, what sort of evidence is acceptable for showing the outer boundary of Nebraskan drift?

7. In Fig. 19.14, the driftless area located mostly in southwestern Wisconsin is shown to be bounded by drifts of different age; accordingly, how is the absence of an ice cover in this region during any part of Pleistocene time to be explained? What topographic and other evidence is employed for distinguishing the different limits of deposits belonging to the Illinoisan, Iowan, and Wisconsinan Stages? In what ways is unglaciated territory distinguishable from that which was ice-covered during Pleistocene time?

8. What are the factors chiefly governing distribution of glaciers of Pleistocene time in mountain areas, as indicated in Fig. 19.15?

9. Why are Pleistocene wind-laid deposits most extensive and continuous in the Central States, as shown in Fig. 19.16? What is the probable origin of sandy eolian deposits of the Atlantic Coastal Plain area?

10. Referring to Fig. 19.18, why are successively younger Pleistocene terrace deposits found to be distributed from high to low positions along stream valleys whereas in interstream areas younger deposits occur above older? What divisions of Pleistocene time are represented by sedimentation in unglaciated parts of the plains country and what divisions by downcutting of valleys? What is the significance of these relations?

11. What differences are distinguishable between presumed ice accumulations of an early stage of a Pleistocene glaciation (Fig. 19.19B) and present distribution of glaciers (Fig. 19.19A)? Why do some contours on the ice-sheet surface at the stage of maximum glaciation (Fig. 19.19D) terminate at the margin of the ice sheet? Why is maximum surface elevation of the ice sheet inferred to have been located in eastern Quebec (Fig. 19.19D)?

12. During development of a Pleistocene ice sheet, as indicated diagrammatically in Fig. 19.20, why is the area of main ice accumulation shifted toward peripheral parts of the sheet despite existence of highlands that influenced early development of glaciers? If glacier growth was largely effected by marginal accretions (Fig. 19.20C), where was ice movement most active and why?

13. How can the even contact at the base of the Wisconsin Till (B in Fig. 19.22) be explained? What inferences concerning the age of the Farmdale Loess (D in Fig. 19.22) can be drawn from its occurrence and the nature of underlying and overlying deposits?

14. Referring to Fig. 19.23, how is occurrence of the lakes shown in A and location of their outlets explained? How is abandonment of the southwestward outlet of the lake in the Erie basin indicated in B accounted for, inasmuch as southwestward and eastward outlets for ponded waters at the ice-sheet margin persist? In C why are lake levels indicated to be lower than those of the present Great Lakes? What is the explanation of differences between patterns of the Great Lakes and their outlets as indicated in G and H?

15. Referring to Fig. 19.25, what reasons can be given for change of pre-Wisconsinan drainage patterns to those of the present time, especially as regards the origin of the Ohio and Missouri Rivers?

20.

NATURE AND EVOLUTION
OF CENOZOIC LIFE

**Pleistocene flesh-eaters assembled at the Rancho
La Brea tar pools in Los Angeles, California.**

*C. R. Knight, courtesy of Chicago
Natural History Museum*

The record of changing life on land and in the sea during the Cenozoic Era is better known than in the ancient geologic periods, and this life is particularly interesting to us because here we find the immediate ancestors of living animals and plants. The evolution of many groups of organisms can be traced step by step from primitive general-ized forms to specialized modern species. There are also numerous Cenozoic lines that have ended in extinction. Prominence of flowering plants is the main characteristic of Cenozoic time in the plant world.

The outstanding Cenozoic animals are the mammals, which include the highest type of living creatures, and therefore, the era is pre-

Fig. 20.1 Standing trunk of petrified tree in the Yellowstone Park Fossil Forest. Several successive levels of petrified trees in this area furnish record of Cenozoic forests that were killed off by volcanic ash falls. Silica from the volcanic rocks replaced the woody tissue of the plants. (*J. P. Iddings, courtesy of U.S. Geol. Survey.*)

eminently the Age of Mammals. This advance seems especially important to us, because we ourselves are mammals. We find in the Paleogene rocks the beginning of most of our modern domestic and wild animals. The fossil record is nearly all that could be asked for. Fossils are abundant and generally very well preserved. A few groups, such as the horses, are well represented by species which show each stage in evolution, from near the beginning to the present, and which show branching of various offshoots.

PLANTS

All collections of fossil plants from Cenozoic deposits show marked similarities to existing floras. The flowering plants, or angiosperms, which made their appearance late in the Mesozoic Era, had assumed definite leadership. In an astonishingly short time, geologically speaking, this group not only has come to outnumber all others but has spread over practically the entire earth, adapting itself alike to the sweltering heat of the tropics and the bitter cold within 5 to 6 degrees of the Pole, to sea level or hundreds of feet below in some inland basins and to mountain heights of 14,000 feet or more, to regions having an annual rainfall of 500 inches and burning deserts where rain may fall only at intervals of years. Some find a congenial home in marshes, while others have waded boldly into the water and compete with the algae. In size they range from adults less than 0.1 inch long to the redwood big trees of California, which have a diameter up to 30 feet and attain a maximum known height of 340 feet. In length of life, they range from herbs that die in a summer to trees like the baobab that may survive for several thousand years. The variety seems illimitable (Figs. 20.1, 20.2).

Many of the Eocene genera are the same as today, but the species were different from those in the Neogene Epoch. The Miocene and Pliocene deposits contain many plants that apparently have persisted without noticeable change to the present.

The Pleistocene glaciers obliterated the vegetation of the north and forced persisting species southward. At times of greatest advance of the ice, such northern trees as the balsam, fir, and tamarack lived in the central and southern United States, but during interglacial ages these invaders moved back northward.

Interglacial plants in a clay deposit near Toronto, Canada, include remains of the Osage orange, papaw, and others that grow today only in a latitude several hundred miles farther south. The climate around Toronto, therefore, must have been appreciably warmer at that time than now.

Associated with advanced-type plants in the Cenozoic fossil record are very numerous less specialized kinds, among which groups such as calcareous algae, ferns, conifers, cycads, and ginkgos are represented by much earlier antecedents. For example, abundant concentrically laminated rounded masses of calcium carbonate found along margins of lake deposits (Green River) of Eocene age are deposits made by calcareous algae not very different from those known from early Paleozoic and even from Cryptozoic rocks (Fig. 20.3).

PROTISTA

Protozoans

In variety of species and uncountable numbers of individuals, the fossil protozoans of the Cenozoic Era exceed all other parts of the geologic record, not excepting the Cretaceous

chalk (Fig. 20.4). During the Paleogene and Neogene Periods, as now, these tiny shells accumulated on the sea bottom in such myriads that in places they form the major part of deposits hundreds of feet thick. Both sand-shelled and calcareous forms occur abundantly, but the latter are greatly preponderant. Most species are very minute and can be identified only under a microscope. These furnish the chief basis for correlating Cenozoic formations in the oil-field regions of the Pacific Coast and Gulf of Mexico.

In warm waters of subtropic and tropic seas, one group of foraminifers built large shells with complex internal structure, the maximum size being about 2½ inches in diameter. These are chiefly disk-shaped (like *Nummulites*).

INVERTEBRATES

Invertebrate life of the Cenozoic Era is rich and varied. Thousands of fossil species

Fig. 20.2 Fossil leaves from Neogene formations of the western United States. The leaf at left is a maple (*Acer*); those at right are two species of walnut (*Juglans*). Three-fourths natural size.

have been collected and described, and each year brings important additions to knowledge. The outstanding characters of Cenozoic invertebrates as a whole are (1) progressively increased resemblance to the living fauna, (2) dominance of pelecypods and gastropods, and (3) common very perfect preservation of the shells, which may be altered hardly at all. Many localities are famous for the abundance and variety of their fossil shells.

Sponges and Corals

Since the marine Cenozoic deposits that have been studied are almost entirely of shallow-water origin, it is not surprising to find few siliceous sponges, for these live chiefly in deeper water. One of the two orders of calcareous sponges apparently became extinct at the close of the Cretaceous period.

The corals of Cenozoic time are abundant and highly varied. Many new genera and some new families appeared. They belong to the group characterized by sixfold symmetry (Fig. 20.5). Coral reefs are found in the Eocene of Georgia, Florida, Alabama, Mexico, Central America, and the West Indies, and they occur in rocks of this age in parts of the Old World.

Fig. 20.3 Calcareous algae of Eocene age from Wyoming. These fossils occur in marginal parts of the Green River Formation, a lacustrine deposit that contains an enormous volume of oil shale. The photographs were taken in Sweetwater County, Wyoming. (*W. H. Bradley, courtesy of U.S. Geol. Survey.*)

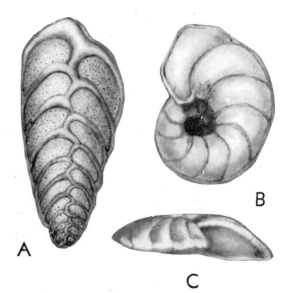

Fig. 20.4 Miocene foraminifers. A biserially chambered shell (*A*), *Bolivina*, and two views of a coiled form (*B, C*), *Cibicides* (approximately ×25).

Miocene, Pliocene, and Pleistocene deposits show that such reefs have become more and more restricted to the tropics.

Echinoderms

Living echinoderms include the echinoids, starfishes, crinoids, brittle stars, and holothurians, of which the first two are much the most important.

Among echinoids, practically all the Mesozoic families are represented in the Paleogene and Neogene today. Both the regularly symmetrical rounded shells with coarse spines and the irregular, flattened, or heart-shaped shells with short spines are common. These echinoderms are essentially at the peak of their career.

Starfishes and brittle stars are well known and varied in modern seas, but their fossil record is not important. A few are found in Cenozoic rocks.

Modern crinoids are a vigorous, cosmopolitan stock confined mainly to deeper oceanic waters. About 650 species of living crinoids are known, 90 per cent of which are free-swimming, stemless forms. Post-Mesozoic fossil crinoids, however, are extremely rare.

Bryozoans and Brachiopods

Bryozoans are exceedingly abundant in many Cenozoic strata of North America and Europe, and the numbers of species is surprisingly large. Nearly 1,000 species have been described from the eastern United States. Some soft marly formations are mainly composed of bryozoan remains which may easily be washed free in any desired quantity for study.

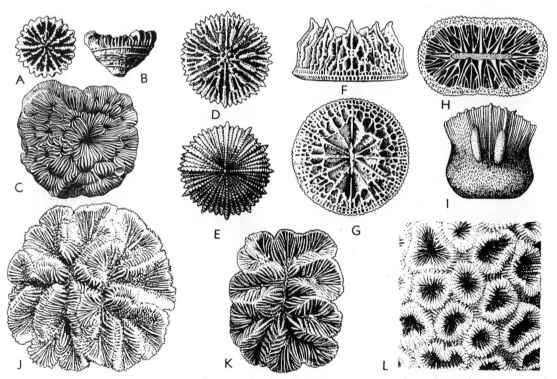

Fig. 20.5 Cenozoic solitary and colonial corals.——*A, B. Trochocyathus,* Paleocene, top and side, ×4.——*C. Cyathoseris,* Oligocene, top, ×0.6.——*D, E. Deltocyathus,* Miocene, top and bottom, ×1.——*F, G. Stephanophyllia,* Miocene, side and top, ×1.——*H, I. Endopachys,* Eocene, top and side, ×2.——*J. Isophyllia,* Pleistocene, top, ×0.5.——*K. Meandrina,* Pleistocene, top, ×0.5.——*L. Favia,* Pleistocene, top, ×1. (*J. W. Wells, Treatise on Invertebrate Paleontology, courtesy of Geological Society of America and University of Kansas Press.*)

Brachiopods are even less important in the marine faunas of Cenozoic time than in the Mesozoic Era. The number of known species is roughly comparable to that of the present day.

Mollusks

Dominant place among Cenozoic invertebrates was held by the mollusks, even though cephalopods were far less important than in Mesozoic time. Species of pelecypods and gastropods are numbered by thousands (Figs. 20.6, 20.7). They show no very radical changes in structure, and peculiarly specialized shells, like some of the Cretaceous pelecypods, are absent. There is a progressive trend toward types of the present day, like the common scallops and oysters or the periwinkles and larger

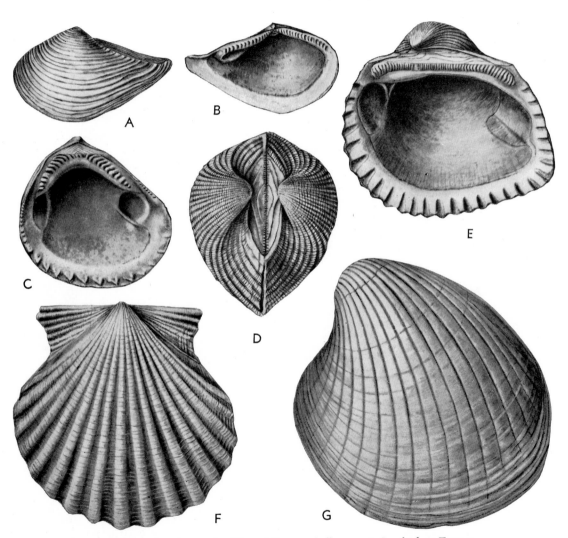

Fig. 20.6 Types of Cenozoic pelecypods. All are Miocene shells, except *G*, which is Eocene. ——*A, B. Leda,* exterior and interior, showing hinge teeth, ×6.——*C. Glycimeris,* interior, showing large rounded muscle scars, hinge teeth, and ligament area beneath the beak, ×1.—— *D, E. Diluvarca,* interior and dorsal view, showing both valves and ligament areas, ×1.5. ——*F. Chlamys,* a scallop, ×2.5.——*G. Venericardia,* characterized by wide flat plications, ×1. (*U.S. Geol. Survey.*)

gastropods that one finds along modern sea-shores. The great majority of Paleogene molluscan genera are still living, but the species are almost entirely extinct. Neogene species, however, are closely related to or identical with living forms. The pelecypods and gastropods have always been a fairly conservative, little-changing stock; their abundance and variety in the Cenozoic, which marks the peak of their development, indicate that they have retained a high degree of racial virility and, though ancient in origin, they are expanding rather than declining in importance. The Neogene gastropods are more highly ornamented on the average than their predecessors.

The great contrast between Mesozoic and Cenozoic marine faunas is seen especially in the cephalopod element. The horde of ammonites that distinguished the older era was completely gone, and only a few nautiloids and two-gilled cephalopods remained. After millions of years in which the cephalopods held a leading place in marine life, they have receded to an inconspicuous part of the background.

Arthropods

The jointed-leg invertebrates, which in number of different kinds far exceeds all other animals combined, are well represented by fossils in Cenozoic formations. Among marine forms are crabs, lobsters, shrimps, and especially a host of varied ostracodes (Fig. 20.8), distinguished by their bivalve shells of microscopic size; many species of ostracodes are very useful for stratigraphic correlations.

Land arthropods are represented especially by insects and spiders, although conditions favorable for their preservation generally are less favorable than for marine invertebrates. Amber (fossilized resin) from Oligocene deposits in the Baltic region of Europe is famous for the large number of remarkably preserved insects and spiders found in it. Some lake deposits of Cenozoic age, such as the Green River (Eocene) and Florissant (Miocene) beds of western United States, contain a variety of fossil insects (Fig. 20.9).

VERTEBRATES

Fishes

The chief characteristic of Cenozoic fishes is the rise of the bony teleosts to a position of dominance in which they outnumber all other kinds more than 20 to 1. They include the salmon, herrings, carps, perches, mackerels, and many other familiar and some extinct groups of marine and fresh-water fishes.

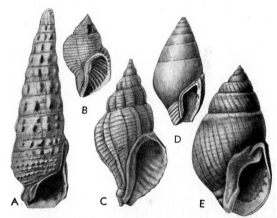

Fig. 20.7 Cenozoic gastropods.—*A. Cerithium,* a very high-spired form, Pliocene, ×1.—*B. Cancellaria,* Miocene, ×1.—*C. Urosalpinx,* Pliocene, ×1.—*D. Columbella,* Pleistocene, ×3.5.—*E. Ilyanassa,* ×1.2. (*Maryland Geol. Survey.*)

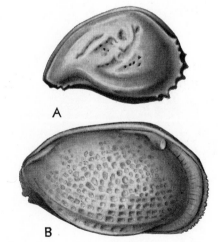

Fig. 20.8 Paleogene ostracodes.—*A. Haplocytheridea,* Eocene, Alabama, ×65.—*B. Brachycythere,* Paleocene, Texas, ×60. (*After C. I. Alexander.*)

Fig. 20.9 Eocene insects. The wings, body (with well-defined abdominal segments), and some of the appendages are preserved in lake sediments (Green River) of northwestern Colorado, ×5. (*W. H. Bradley, courtesy of U.S. Geol. Survey.*)

A famous Eocene fish fauna occurs in the Green River beds in southwestern Wyoming, where large numbers of beautifully preserved complete skeletons have been collected (Fig. 20.10). Among the marine fishes, there were sharks (*Carcharodon*) that had sharp-edged triangular cutting teeth up to 6 inches long (Fig. 20.11). Based on comparison with similarly shaped teeth of living sharks, it is estimated that some of these fossil species attained a length of 80 feet.

Amphibians and Reptiles

Amphibians were relatively no more important in Paleogene and early Neogene time than now. Fossil salamanders, frogs, and toads occur.

Reptiles of post-Cretaceous age are distinguished chiefly by their modern appearance, dinosaurs and other strange reptilian creatures of Mesozoic times having disappeared. Their Cenozoic descendants included especially large numbers of turtles, crocodiles, lizards, and snakes.

Birds

Birds are relatively rare as fossils, but more than 500 genera are known from Cenozoic deposits. These represent most of the modern families, including gulls, ducks, herons, storks, pigeons, grouse, owls, hawks, parrots, and a great many others. Among large, flightless

Fig. 20.10 Skeleton of Eocene fresh-water fish. The fossil, one of the teleosts (*Cockerellites*), is found on a bedding plane of the Green River Formation in Wyoming, ×1. (*Courtesy of American Museum of Natural History.*)

birds are some of very massive build that attained a height of 6 or 7 feet; one of these (*Phororhacos*) had a powerful hooked beak and a skull equal in size to that of a horse (Fig. 20.12).

Mammals

The history of mammals dates back at least to Triassic time. Development was retarded, however, until the sudden acceleration of evolutional change that occurred in the oldest Paleogene. This led in Eocene time to increase in average size, larger mental capacity, and special adaptations for different modes of life. In the Oligocene Epoch, there was further improvement, with appearance of some new lines and extinction of others. Miocene and Pliocene time was marked by culmination of several groups and continued approach toward modern characters. The peak of the career of mammals in variety and average large size was attained in the Miocene.

Adaptation of mammals. The adaptation of mammals to almost all possible modes of life parallels that of the reptiles in Mesozoic time, and except for greater intelligence, the mammals do not seem to have done much better than corresponding reptilian forms. The bat is doubtless a better flying animal than the pterosaur, but the dolphin and whale are hardly more fishlike than the ichthyosaur. Many swift-running mammals of the plains, like the horse and antelope, must excel any of the dinosaurs. The tyrannosaur was a more ponderous and powerful carnivore than any flesh-eating mammal, but the lion or tiger is probably a more efficient and dangerous beast of prey because of a superior brain. The significant point to observe is that different branches of the mammals gradually fitted themselves for all sorts of life, grazing on the plains and able to run swiftly (horse, deer, bison), living in rivers and swamps (hippopotamus, beaver), dwelling in trees (sloth, monkey), digging underground (mole, rodent), feeding on flesh in the forest (tiger) and plain (wolf), swimming in the sea (dolphin, whale, seal), and flying in the air (bat). Man is able by mechanical means to conquer the physical world and to adapt himself to almost any set of conditions.

This adaptation produces gradual changes of form and structure. It is biologically characteristic of the youthful, plastic stage of a group. Early in its career, an animal assemblage seems to possess capacity for change, which, as the unit becomes old and fixed, disappears. The generalized types of organisms retain longest the ability to make adjustments when required, and it is from them that new, fecund stocks take origin—certainly not from any specialized end products. So, in the mammals, we witness the birth, plastic spread in many directions, increasing specialization, and in some branches the extinction, which we have learned from observation of the geologic record of life is a characteristic of the evolution of life.

Fig. 20.11 Tooth of a Miocene shark, *Carcharodon.* The smooth, enamel-covered part of the tooth bears a sharp sawlike cutting edge; the lower bony part was embedded in the jaw, ×0.65. (*Courtesy of American Museum of Natural History.*)

Fossilization of mammals. Remains of mammals are found in stream-laid deposits, lake and swamp beds, wind-blown dust and sand, volcanic ash, asphalt, cave earth, marine sediments (mostly marine mammals), and other materials. The kinds of mammals, numbers, and state of preservation depend largely on the nature of the deposit and its geologic age.

The great majority of Cenozoic mammal fossils occur in sediments of ancient valleys and plains; they indicate burial after drown-

ing or suffocation in streams, quicksands, shallow lakes, swamps, or wind deposits. It is easy to imagine how numbers of animals might be caught and buried, for such capture and burial are not infrequent in modern time. Especially in periods of drought, starved and thirst-crazed animals seek watering places in large numbers and, very much weakened, are unable to escape from clinging mud. Or in exhausted condition, they drink to excess, and, especially if the water is strongly mineralized, this is almost immediately fatal.

In arid regions, animals may suffocate in dust storms or die from thirst, and the skeletons become buried in wind-blown sand.

Fossil mammals are not evenly distributed through the beds but are found to occur in "pockets," with numbers of individuals crowded together. Some layers contain numerous fossils, whereas others are entirely barren.

An interesting occurrence of fossil mammals is the Rancho La Brea asphalt deposits near Los Angeles (Fig. 20.13). The asphalt was formed by oxidation and solidification of petroleum that seeped upward through Pleistocene deposits from oil-bearing strata below. In the change from petroleum to asphalt, very viscous, sticky tar pools were formed on the surface of the ground. These pools entrapped a multitude of Pleistocene mammals and birds, sealing their bones perfectly from decay. Just as in modern time, animals caught in the tar were quickly rendered helpless by the gummy stuff, which bound their feet and eventually engulfed the whole body. The struggles and cries of trapped creatures served to lure carnivorous mammals and birds, which too late discovered themselves in the hopeless predicament of their intended prey. Thus, the skeletons in this deposit include a preponderance of carnivorous mammals and birds, which is unusual, for the carnivores are rarely found in numbers.

Fig. 20.12 Mid-Cenozoic flightless bird of prey, *Phororhacos.* This South American carnivore was as tall as a man and a swift runner; its large skull armed with a powerful curved beak contributed to making it a formidable creature. Its remains are found in Oligocene and Miocene beds. (*Courtesy of J. Augusta and Z. Burian, Praha; published by permission.*)

Archaic Hoofed Mammals

Paleogene formations contain three assemblages of primitive hoofed mammals that include ancestors of the varied host of later hoofed animals (ungulates), as well as unsuccessful offshoots.

Condylarths. One group, designated as *condylarths*, had five digits on each foot, a generalized type of body, and a long heavy tail, resembling in many ways some of the early clawed mammals. The skull was long and low, the brain case small, and the teeth unspecialized and low-crowned. A typical representative of these animals was about the size of a small shepherd dog. The condylarths were most common in Paleocene and early Eocene time.

Amblypods. A second group, known as *amblypods,* was distinguished by stout limbs ending in short blunt feet like those of an elephant, by the archaic nature of their teeth and skull, and by their small brain capacity. The earliest of these animals, of Paleocene age, was about the size of a sheep, but they were distinguished by short legs and broad feet. Evidently, they were slow-footed, as the name amblypod signifies. The Eocene representatives of this group were much larger than their Paleocene predecessors.

Uintatheres. A third group of archaic mammals consists of the *uintatheres* (Fig. 20.14), which range from Paleocene to the close of the Eocene, flourishing especially in late Eocene time. They were grotesque creatures, somewhat resembling a small elephant in appearance and bulk but having no trunk. The top of the long skull carried three pairs of horns, the front pair, above the nose, possibly sheathed with horn, as in the rhinoceros, the middle pair above the eyes and the back pair at the base of the skull being rounded at the ends and probably covered with skin, as in the giraffe. The top of the back part of the skull was peculiarly dish-shaped, leaving little space for the brain, which was indeed small. The males carried long curved tusks projecting downward from the upper jaws.

Odd-toed Hoofed Mammals

One of the chief divisions of hoofed mammals is the so-called odd-toed group (peris-

Fig. 20.13 Restoration of part of Rancho La Brea tar pool in southern California. Skeletons of numerous Pleistocene animals trapped and buried here have been discovered. The view shows a helpless elephant being attacked by a saber-toothed lion, with carrion-eating birds ready to feed on both animals caught in the tar when they have the chance. (*Courtesy of J. Augusta and Z. Burian, Praha; published by permission.*)

sodactyls), in which the central toe is larger than the others because it bears more of the weight. It includes the horse, man's comrade and most valued domestic animal, and mammals such as the rhinoceroses, tapirs, and the very strange extinct animals called *titanotheres* and *chalicotheres.*

Horses. The horse is a highly and efficiently specialized mammal, distinguished chiefly by characters of the limbs and teeth (Figs. 20.15, 20.16). The limbs are wonderfully fitted for running, which is the horse's chief means of self-preservation. The teeth are specially adapted for grazing on the tough grasses of the plains.

Fig. 20.14 Uintatheres and a group of tiny four-toed Eocene horses. The uintatheres are the largest and most specialized of the primitive hoofed mammals. (*C. R. Knight, courtesy of Chicago Natural History Museum.*)

The limbs and feet of the horse differ from those of all other living hoofed mammals in that there is but a single functional toe on each foot. Comparison with other animals shows that the horse walks on the very tip of fingers and toes, the wrist is the "knee," the ankle is the "hock," and the elbow and real knee are close up to the body. Thus, the long slender limb of the horse has been developed essentially by lengthening the lower bones; the upper ones, which remain relatively short, carry the powerful well-bunched muscles that propel the lower limbs by means of thin strong ligaments. Although the lower limb consists of a single digit, the bones are so increased in size that they form an adequate support. The joints are fitted with a tongue-and-groove arrangement, so that only forward and backward motion is possible. Altogether, the limb struc-

ture is so perfectly designed for running swiftly that one may well doubt the possibility of further development along this line in an animal of the size of the horse.

The teeth consist of long-crowned cropping teeth (incisors) in front, very long-crowned grinding teeth (molars and premolars) behind, and in the males, but rarely in females, tusks or canines. The incisors are peculiar in having a deep pit in the cutting face of the tooth, which is due to an infolding of the hard enamel, like the pushed-in end of the finger of a glove. As the teeth are worn down, the size of the pit is reduced; this fact is used in determining a horse's age. The grinding teeth are nearly square in cross section, and the three elements of the tooth structure—enamel, dentine, and cement—are elaborately infolded, so as to give a characteristic pattern of the resistant enamel upon the wearing surface. The teeth have an excessively long crown, so that years of wear are compensated by gradual outward growth of the grinders. In extreme old age, they are worn down near the roots. The premolars of the horse have assumed the characters of the molars. The long grinding teeth are accommodated in the skull by a deep lower jaw and by elongation of the skull, the eye orbit being pushed well back so as to give room for the teeth in the upper jaw.

Horses have attained a size that is exceeded only by a few kinds of land mammals. Some horses reach a shoulder height of 6 feet 4 inches and a weight of 2,400 pounds. The horse is a very intelligent animal. The brain not only is large but is of a relatively high type, well convoluted. Like man and the elephant, the horse has shown the ability to adapt himself to all climatic environments. In the natural wild state, however, horses are restricted to parts of Asia and Africa, all living horses of other continents, including the wild mustangs of western North America, having been introduced by man.

Evolution of horses. The oldest known horses are diminutive creatures, about 1 foot high, skeletons of which occur in Eocene deposits of North America and southern England (Fig. 20.17). These would fail of recognition as primitive horses except for the almost complete series of intergrading fossils in later Cenozoic rocks that definitely connect them with living horses. The small Eocene horses had four complete toes on the forefoot and three, with remnant of a fourth, on the hind foot. The two bones of the forearm and foreleg are separate and normal. The animal was adapted for running but did not walk on the tips of the digits, as later horses. The teeth are very unlike those of the modern horse in that the crown is short and the grinding surface consists of cusps that begin to show the structure of the teeth only when worn well down by use. These teeth were fitted for browsing rather than grazing and suggest that the earliest horses were creatures of the forests and not of the open plains.

Neogene beds contain larger and less primitive fossil horses. Climatic changes in Oligocene and Miocene time, with decrease of forests and increase of meadow and plains country, were probably responsible for the chief modifications seen in the several types of fossil horses from deposits belonging to these epochs. There was a distinct but gradual increase in size, the toes on each foot were reduced to three, and the teeth, especially in some, became more like those of the modern horse.

Pliocene horses carried these modifications further, and we find here the first one-toed horse, in which the remnants of side toes are represented merely by bony splints below the wrist and ankle (Fig. 20.18). Some Pliocene horses, however, still retained complete side toes.

Pleistocene deposits of North and South America contain abundant remains of horses which are essentially modern, but for unex-

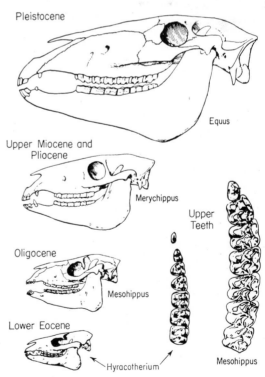

Pleistocene

Equus

Upper Miocene and Pliocene

Merychippus

Upper Teeth

Oligocene

Mesohippus

Lower Eocene

Hyracotherium

Mesohippus

Fig. 20.15 Skulls and teeth of Cenozoic fossil horses, showing evolution in shape and size. (*After Scott.*)

plained reasons, horses became extinct in the Western Hemisphere before the beginning of the Recent geologic epoch. If Old World species, which are probably migrants or descendants of migrants from North America, had not survived, we should know the horse only as we do the amblypod, from fossil bones.

The evolution of the horse, more completely shown by discovered fossils than probably any other mammal group, reveals clearly (1) lengthening of the limbs, (2) change of foot posture from digits with much of the length to only the tip in contact with the ground, (3) reduction in the number of digits on each foot to one, (4) reduction of smaller bones (ulna and fibula) of the limbs, (5) modification and complication of the teeth from a type adapted for browsing to one adapted for grazing, (6) elongation of the skull and neck, and (7) marked increase in size.

Rhinoceroses. The fossil record of rhinoceroses is second only to that of the horses in abundance and completeness. Modern repre-

sentatives of this family are restricted to Africa, India, Java, and Sumatra, and therefore they seem quite foreign to the North American continent. Yet rhinoceroses were very much at home here during most of Cenozoic time, and it is indeed possible that they originated in the western United States. They migrated to all parts of the world except South America and Australia.

The modern rhinoceroses are large beasts, 4 to 6½ feet high at the shoulders, with long body, short elephant-like legs, and a long head that bears one horn on the nose or one on the nose and another on the forehead. These horns are unlike those of other horned mammals, such as deer or cattle, in that they consist of solid horny substance without a bone core. The horns are not preserved as fossils, but their place of attachment is shown by roughened thickenings of the skull. Living rhinoceroses have three toes on each foot, the central one the largest; this is true of many fossil forms also, but the more primitive had four

Fore limbs   Hind limbs

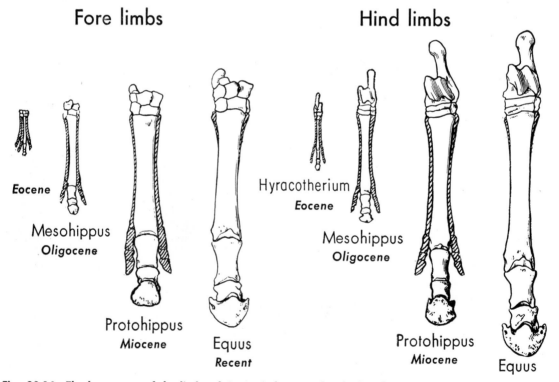

Fig. 20.16   The lower part of the limbs of Cenozoic horses. The chief evolutionary change is progressive enlargement of the central digit and gradual disappearance of the side toes. (*Modified from Scott.*)

toes on the front feet. The initial five-toed ancestor is unknown.

Middle Eocene beds contain several species of primitive rhinoceroses about the size of a sheep. From this stock, characterized by the unspecialized nature of the skeleton, came at least four divergent lines of descent: (1) relatively light-bodied, hornless animals with slender limbs adapted for running (hyracodonts); (2) large-bodied, short, and heavy-legged aquatic animals (amynodonts); (3) gigantic long-necked, long-headed hornless forms (baluchitheres); and (4) the true rhinoceroses, which are generally horned.

The Oligocene, Miocene, and lower Pliocene beds of western America contain abundant remains of rhinoceroses, some deposits forming veritable bone beds. One type (*Teleoceras*), which lived in large numbers along streams and marshy areas in western Nebraska and Kansas in late Miocene and early Pliocene time, had a long, large barrel-like body and absurdly short legs.

Although not known in North America, we may notice the baluchitheres (named from Baluchistan, central Asia, where they were discovered). These are the largest known land mammals, attaining a height of more than 16 feet at the shoulders and a total length of about 25 feet (Fig. 20.19). The head, armed with two powerful tusks, was about 4½ feet long, and the neck was also unusually extended. The legs were elongated, making the whole appearance somewhat giraffe-like, but much heavier. This branch of the rhinoceros group doubtless fed on the foliage of trees. It lived in the late Oligocene or early Miocene.

In Pleistocene time, the woolly rhinoceros roamed the European and Siberian country close to the border of the ice sheet, and its remains, like those of mammoths, have been found with soft parts preserved intact in frozen ground (Fig. 20.20). Modern descendants have withdrawn from cold-climate environments and today are found only in subtropical parts of Africa.

Titanotheres. A very strange branch of the odd-toed hoofed mammals that inhabited the western United States in Paleogene time comprises the titanotheres (name signifying gigantic beasts). The group is most abundantly represented by fossils from North America but is now known also from Asia and Europe. The earliest known titanothere was a trifle smaller than a sheep, the skull long and narrow, bearing tusks but no horns. The fore limbs had four toes, and the hind limbs three. Later titanotheres increased in size, reaching elephantine proportions. The limbs were stout and pillar-like, and as in the elephant, the short feet were supported by thick pads. The most striking modifications are seen in the skull, which developed bony knobs and eventually great bony paired horns over the nose. The skull became long, very broad, and strengthened to withstand the impact when the horns were put to use. Despite the large bulk of the later titanotheres, the brain was very small, not larger than a man's fist, indicating a low order of intelligence.

Fig. 20.17 Model of *Hyracotherium* of the Eocene Epoch. This diminutive forerunner of modern horses, little more than 12 inches in height, is horselike in appearance in spite of extra toes. The name *Eohippus* ("dawn horse") is a synonym of *Hyracotherium*, accepted because of its earlier publication. (*Courtesy of Chicago Natural History Museum.*)

Fig. 20.18   Pliocene horses and elephants of western North America. Both horses and elephants became extinct on this continent in Pleistocene time. (*C. R. Knight, courtesy of American Museum of Natural History.*)

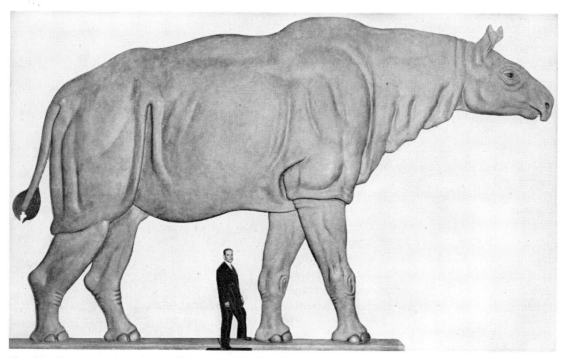

Fig. 20.19   Restoration of *Baluchitherium*. This hornless rhinoceros, which roamed central Asia in mid-Cenozoic time, stood more than 16 feet high at the shoulders. (*Courtesy of American Museum of Natural History.*)

Chalicotheres. The strangest perissodactyls are animals called *chalicotheres,* from North America, Asia, Africa, and Europe, which are found in middle Eocene to Pleistocene beds (Fig. 20.21). The skull and remainder of the skeleton, except limbs and feet, are not greatly unlike those of a horse, although there are many differences. The feet are armed with great claws, and when the first specimens were discovered, in disconnected form, they were referred to an order entirely different from that in which the skull had been placed. Complete skeletons now known show that the horselike body and clawed feet actually belong together. That this grotesque animal fed on plants is plainly shown by the teeth. The claws probably served in grubbing roots and tubers. Some of the chalicotheres considerably exceed a good-sized horse in height and bulk.

Even-toed Hoofed Mammals

The great group of even-toed hoofed mammals (artiodactyls) is distinguished by characters of the limbs and teeth, which separate them readily from the odd-toed mammals and yet serve clearly to show relationship among such apparently unlike animals as the pig, camel, deer, giraffe, and hippopotamus. The axis of the foot lies between the third and fourth digits, which are equal in size and symmetrical. The number of toes is four or two, although in some primitive forms a vestige of the fifth toe remains. A peculiar and very characteristic structure of the ankle bones is found in all. There are two types of chewing teeth, the more primitive having conelike cusps and the more specialized showing crescent-shaped grinding ridges of enamel. Even-toed hoofed

Fig. 20.20 Woolly rhinoceroses of the Ice Age (Pleistocene) in northern Eurasia. These animals (*Coelodonta*), companions of the mammoth, attained a length of 12 feet and height of 6 feet, with the front horn in old males as long as 3.5 feet. They were contemporaries of prehistoric man, who hunted and ate them and made beautifully executed drawings of them on cave walls. (*Courtesy of J. Augusta and Z. Burian, Praha; published by permission.*)

Fig. 20.21 Part of western Nebraska in Miocene time. The wild hogs (entelodonts) shown in foreground were about 6 feet high at the shoulders; at right is a chalicothere. (*C. R. Knight, courtesy of Chicago Natural History Museum.*)

animals are very abundant as fossils, the remains of different kinds being found in each of the Cenozoic Epochs from Eocene to Pleistocene.

Oreodonts. The most common kind of mammals in some of the Oligocene deposits of the western United States are extinct creatures having the size of a small sheep and combining certain characters of pig, deer, and camel. They are called *oreodonts*. These animals are restricted to North America and are known from late Eocene to early Pliocene times. During part of their career, they must have roamed the plains and river valleys in enormous numbers. Skeletons are frequently found in little-disturbed condition. An interesting specimen, mounted by students at the South Dakota School of Mines, shows the well-formed skeleton of an unborn young oreodont within the body of the mother.

Giant pigs and peccaries. The swine may claim rank as one of the "first families" of the Cenozoic. They trace their ancestry to Eocene time and were represented in North America as late as the Pleistocene (including Recent) by large, highly developed peccaries. The strangest, or at least the most uncouth, are so-called giant pigs (entelodonts) that lived in the Oligocene and early Miocene Epochs (Fig. 20.21). These attained a height of 6 feet at the shoulders and were exceeded in bulk among members of the swine family only by the hippopotamus. The skull of the giant pig was very elongate, and it bore peculiar bony excrescences below the eyes and on the underside of the jaw. There were stout but not long tusks. The brain was almost reptile-like in its diminutive size; the animal must have been profoundly stupid.

Camels. The desert regions of central Asia and northern Africa are the home of one living genus of camels, and the cold parts of South America of the other (llama). The ancestral dwelling place of this family, however, was North America. They developed gradually along various lines, increasing greatly in size and in specialization of teeth and limbs. In the Neogene Period, they migrated to the Old World and into South America, while after mid-Pleistocene time, they became extinct in the continent of their birth. The earliest known camels, from Upper Eocene beds, were smaller than a tiny lamb. The forefoot had four toes, but the hind foot was already so modified that there were only two functional toes, although vestiges of two others are present. The development of the camels shows many interesting parallels with that of the horses, but the irreducible number of toes on each foot is two, instead of one. Some of the mid-Cenozoic American camels were slender, graceful creatures resembling antelopes (Fig. 20.22), and one kind is distinguished by its extremely elongated neck and long legs, an adaptation like that of the giraffe for browsing on leaves of trees.

Deer and cattle. Interesting representatives of the deer family are found as fossils in the American Cenozoic as far back as the Oligocene. Some were hornless, others had short pronglike horns, and still others had antlers with branches. One very peculiar group, which is really distinct from the true deer, had a pair of prominent bony plates above the eyes and another pair on the nose. The moose and caribou are immigrants from the Old World that are first known on this continent in Pleistocene time.

The cattle family is represented in America by the bison, musk ox, and wild sheep. Domestic cattle and sheep are derived from Asiatic species and have been introduced in the Western Hemisphere by man. The bison, which roamed the plains in such enormous herds before the advance of civilization destroyed them, were present in the Pleistocene Epoch but are not known earlier. One kind of fossil bison was distinctly larger than the Recent species and was characterized by a huge hump; another had a horn spread of more than 6 feet. There is proof that man was contemporaneous with some of these extinct species of bison.

Elephants

Elephants rank with the horse in point of interest and instructiveness of the fossil record. The lineage of this largest living land mammal may be traced far back in Cenozoic time, and the gradual acquirement of proboscidian peculiarities may be observed step by step. Like the horse and man, the elephant is one of the few kinds of mammals that became adapted to almost all sorts of environments and spread

Fig. 20.22   A herd of Miocene camels. Skeletal remains show that these llama-like camels roamed North American western plains in large numbers. (*E. M. Fulda, courtesy of American Museum of Natural History.*)

over practically the whole world. Teeth and bones of elephants are found in stream and other deposits of Pleistocene age in almost every part of the United States, testifying to the abundance and wide distribution of these animals in North America until comparatively recent time.

The chief distinguishing characters of the elephants are in the head, which is unusually massive and abnormally shortened and bears the long powerful trunk (Fig. 20.23). The shape of the skull, the enormously thick but light cranial bones, and the short neck are all modifications that aid in carrying the weight of the head. The trunk is a very muscular development of the upper lip and nose, the nostrils running the entire length to the tip. Elephants are not the only animals with an elon-

Fig. 20.23 Largest of the American fossil elephants, of Pleistocene age. This animal (*Archidiskodon*) is known as the "imperial elephant." (*Courtesy of American Museum of Natural History.*)

Fig. 20.24 Grinding surface of an elephant tooth from Pleistocene deposits in Kansas. This tooth, very similar to the molars of living elephants, shows the projecting transverse ridges of hard enamel that adapt the tooth for grinding. (*Courtesy of University of Kansas Natural History Museum.*)

gated proboscis or trunk, but no others have this organ so highly developed. Since elongation of the snout is always correlated with a recession of the nasal bones and with a thickening of adjacent bones for muscular attachment, it is possible to determine, from study of a fossil skull, whether an animal had a trunk and approximately how large it was.

The teeth of the elephant are distinctive. The tusks are remarkably enlarged long incisors, which in the African elephant may exceed 10 feet in length and 2 feet in circumference at the base and weigh 230 pounds or more apiece. Some of the fossil elephants had tusks 13 feet or exceptionally even 16 feet in length. The grinding teeth are very large, and there is normally only one tooth on each side of the upper and lower jaws (Fig. 20.24). However, as a tooth is worn down to the roots, it is gradually displaced by a new one that pushes in from behind. Thus the grinding teeth grow in successively, the last, or backmost, molars appearing at about age forty-five and serving for the rest of the animal's life. The character of these teeth differs notably in different species, that of the modern Indian elephant having numerous parallel grinding ridges, that of the African elephant having a simpler pattern, and those of several extinct forms showing a series of large conelike cusps.

Evolution of the elephants. The earliest definitely distinguishable representatives (*Moeritherium, Palaeomastodon*) of the elephant family occurs in upper Eocene and lower Oligocene deposits of northern Africa and southern Asia. These animals had about the size and build of a small baby elephant, but the trunk was undoubtedly very short, the head and neck relatively more elongate, and all the grinding teeth were present at the same time. There were short downward-curving tusks in the upper jaw and very short tusks also in the long lower jaw.

In Miocene time, different kinds of elephants are known to have spread to Europe and North America. One type (*Deinotherium*), which occurs in Europe and Asia, had no tusks on the upper jaw, but on the lower there were large tusks curving downward and backward (Fig. 20.25). Other kinds from eastern Asia and North America had four large straight tusks, two on the upper jaw and two on the lower. They continued into the Pliocene Epoch, a specimen of this age from Nebraska having a lower jaw and flat shovel-like tusks at least 6 feet long (Fig. 20.26).

The most abundant and best-known fossil elephants in North America are those of the great Ice Age. One type, called the American mastodon, is distinguished partly by the large-cusped grinding teeth, which differ markedly from those of the true elephants. The mastodon had about the height of the modern Indian elephant but was much stockier. It was apparently a forest-dwelling animal. Its remains have been found chiefly in drainage excavations in boggy lands of the Northern States, one specimen found in New York having a quantity of long shaggy dark brown hair with the bones. True elephants are represented in North America: by the imperial elephant, which had remarkably long curving tusks and attained a height of 13 feet (Fig. 20.23); the columbian elephant, which was somewhat smaller than the imperial; and the hairy or woolly mammoth (Fig. 20.27). This last was circumpolar in range, being known in Europe and northern Asia as well as on this continent. It had a thick coat of coarse long black hair with a dense brown wool covering beneath. Specimens of this animal have been discovered frozen in the Siberian tundras.

The main evolutionary changes in the development of the elephants are increase in size; modification in shape and structure of bones of the skull; loss of incisors and canines, except two incisors of each jaw (or of one jaw) that are modified as tusks; increase in size and complexity of the grinding teeth; their reduction in number; development of the peculiar method of tooth succession; and the growth of the trunk.

Carnivores

The carnivorous mammals, including chiefly the cat and dog families, are distinguished by clawed feet and by teeth adapted for grasping and cutting flesh, the long sharp canines and shearlike molars. In the Paleogene time, there were primitive flesh-eaters (creodonts), which in some respects resembled the early hoofed mammals but in others show ancestral relationship to the later carnivores.

The best-known Cenozoic cats are the saber-tooths, characterized by unusual enlargement of the canines of the upper jaw. These animals were evidently ferocious beasts of prey that ranged over the whole Northern Hemisphere, and in Neogene time extended to South America. The culmination of this race is found in a Pleistocene cat (*Smilodon*) of the western United States and South America, which had great curved scimitar-like upper canines 8 inches or even more in length. We find it hard to understand how these great tusks, blocking entrance to the mouth, could have been used effectively unless the creature could open its mouth much more widely than any living cat. There were only one or two large cutting teeth at the back of each jaw. The form and structure of the skeleton indicate an unusually powerful animal.

Fossil dogs are well known from late Cenozoic deposits, but the doglike animals of earlier time are increasingly generalized. Dogs are a central line of carnivore evolution among the mammals, several lines of which became extinct during the Cenozoic.

In addition to the mammalian flesh-eaters adapted for life on land are flipper-limbed (pinniped) aquatic carnivores such as the seals, sea lions, and walruses. These do not appear in the fossil record until Miocene time, and it is not now possible to identify their Paleogene ancestors that lived on land. We simply know that adaptation toward beautifully streamlined body shape and powerful swimming appendages began in pre-Neogene time.

Cetaceans

Whales and porpoises are mammals collectively termed cetaceans. Their remarkably perfect adaptation for life in the sea has led to an appearance that is entirely fishlike and certainly very unlike the form of ancestors provided with legs for running or walking on

Fig. 20.25 *Deinotherium*, **representative of a specialized elephant family.** These animals, known from Miocene and Pliocene deposits of Europe, are characterized chiefly by downward curving tusks in the lower jaw. (*Courtesy of J. Augusta and Z. Burian, Praha; published by permission.*)

land. The body is smoothly streamlined, the tail is modified into a powerful propeller, and the limbs are transformed into steering and balancing paddles. These adaptations closely parallel those of the ichthyosaurs among Mesozoic reptiles and thus furnish exceptionally good illustrations of convergent evolution.

The oldest known whales are Middle Eocene forms that already indicate the trend toward large size characteristic of these animals; some of the Eocene fossils denote a length of 60 feet and show that the fore limbs were modified into paddles, the hind limbs being suppressed. During late Eocene and Oligocene time, modern types of whales appeared, most of which possess teeth. The largest living whales, which reach lengths of 100 feet and weights of 150 tons, lack teeth, being provided with a straining structure of so-called whalebone for capture of planktonic organisms used as food. These, like the small toothed whales classed as porpoises and dolphins, are found as fossils in Miocene deposits and occur rather commonly in later Neogene marine strata.

Insectivores, Rodents, and Other Groups

Under this heading we may notice briefly several mammal groups such as the insectivores (moles, shrews, hedgehogs, and others), bats, edentates (sloths, anteaters, armadillos, glyptodonts), rodents (squirrels, rats, mice, porcupines), and rabbits. These are extremely varied and collectively are important in the Cenozoic record of mammal differentiation. Early representatives of some groups occur in Paleogene deposits, but the fossil record is chiefly Neogene. Primitive insectivores are found in Cretaceous formations.

The largest mammals among the groups just mentioned are extinct relatives of the armadillos, named *glyptodonts*, and ground sloths. Both are well known as fossils in North America and South America, especially in

Fig. 20.26   A shovel-toothed elephant (*Platybelodon*) from Neogene deposits of Mongolia and the western United States. In Miocene and Pliocene time, this specialized branch of the elephant stock was distributed from the Dakotas to Texas. Probably their spadelike teeth and lower jaw were used for grubbing succulent roots in swampy ground. (*Courtesy of American Museum of Natural History.*)

Fig. 20.27 The mammoth (*Elephas primigenius*), best-known and most characteristic animal of the Ice Age. This elephant, about 12 feet in average height, was characterized by its relatively large head and unusually long, curved tusks. Its body was covered by long, dense hair. Specimens with the soft parts preserved have been found in frozen ground of Siberia, and abundant remains occur in North America. (*Courtesy of J. Augusta and Z. Burian, Praha; published by permission.*)

Pleistocene deposits. The glyptodonts were distinguished by a heavily armored body, the largest attaining a length of about 9 feet. The ground sloths were equipped with powerful claws. Some exceeded an elephant in size, with length up to 20 feet (Fig. 20.28). In Patagonia and southwestern United States, remains of ground sloths with parts of the hide and dried tendons attached to bones have been found in caves, and there is evidence that some of these animals were killed by man.

Primates

The group of mammals that includes man is the primates. As a whole, these are generalized, rather than highly specialized, nail- or claw-bearing mammals (unguiculates) that are rather closely related to the insectivores, from which, with little doubt, they descended.

The assemblages classed as primates are varied in form and size, ranging from the diminutive Oriental tree shrew (*Tupaia*) through the lemurs and large-eyed tarsiers to the monkeys, anthropoid apes, and man. Ancestral primates, like a majority of their living descendants, were arboreal mammals characterized by alertness and possession of binocular vision but generally having a poor sense of smell. The digits are developed for grasping, and joints of the limbs allow much rotation of the bones. Another peculiarity is rather slow postnatal development that necessitates an extended period of parental care for the young. Both anatomical inheritances and mode of life have contributed to gradual evolution of the enlarged brain capacity and superior intelligence that above all else distinguish the primates, providing them with means for sur-

Fig. 20.28 Pleistocene ground sloths, *Megatherium*. These are edentates characterized by unusually massive bodies and length up to 20 feet. They occur in both North and South America, the latest being contemporaries of early man. The name *Megatherium* means huge beast. (*Courtesy of J. Augusta and Z. Burian, Praha; published by permission.*)

vival. On the basis of fact, and not egotism, man may classify himself as a culminating product of mammalian development that began with the appearance of primitive Paleocene primates derived from insectivore ancestors. In any case, the geological record of man is a sufficiently important subject to warrant consideration of it in a separate chapter.

READINGS

COLBERT, E. H., 1955, *Evolution of the vertebrates,* John Wiley & Sons, Inc., New York (479 pp., 122 figs.). [1] Introduction to the placentals [mammals], pp. 249–257. [2] Carnivores [mammals], pp. 310–327. [3] Ancient hoofed mammals, pp. 328–336. [4] Perissodactyls [mammals], pp. 350–371. [5]Artiodactyls [mammals], pp. 372–399. [6] Elephants and their kin, pp. 400–416. [7] The Age of Mammals, pp. 417–431.
Authoritative, well-written, not too technical account of the nature and evolution of various mammal groups.
ROMER, A. S., 1945, *Vertebrate paleontology,* University of Chicago Press, Chicago (687 pp., 377 figs.), Cenozoic vertebrates, pp. 546–572.
A good summary of the nature of Cenozoic mammal-bearing deposits and successive faunas of each epoch.

QUESTIONS

1. How is the observation that distribution of most species of land plants today reflects temperature and moisture conditions of their environment applicable to interpretation of earlier Cenozoic land floras? What inference can be drawn as to Paleocene climate in Montana from the discovery of numerous large fossil palm leaves in deposits of that age (Fort Union)

in various parts of the state? On what premise does such inference depend? How can you explain the occurrence of local assemblages of plant fossils, all identified as Pliocene and all collected in approximately the same latitude, in California and Nevada, (a) some consisting exclusively of moderately warm-climate, moisture-loving plants, (b) some containing a mixture of temperate and cool-climate plants, (c) some composed solely of hardy cold-climate evergreens, and (d) some dominated by warm- and dry-climate (xerophytic) plants?

2. Can you suggest reasons that may satisfactorily explain each of the following observations relating to Cenozoic Foraminifera? (a) Various species of pelagic foraminifers are more widely useful and trustworthy indicators of age equivalence than bottom-dwelling (benthonic) forms. (b) Relatively large foraminifers with various sorts of complex internal structures (such as *Nummulites* and allied forms) are valuable guide fossils for defining zones and correlating strata, whereas diminutive shells of simple structure commonly lack such value. (c) Marine strata of the Gulf Coastal Plain and California, for example, generally can be correlated accurately by study of their contained foraminiferal shells, but in Cenozoic deposits of the Western Interior, including such evenly stratified formations as the Green River (Eocene), such fossils have no value.

3. What distinctions are observed between Cenozoic corals and those of Paleozoic age? Why are Paleogene and Neogene coral reefs lacking in high-latitude belts?

4. What group or groups of mollusks are found as fossils in Cenozoic deposits (a) of marine origin only, (b) of both marine and fresh-water origin, (c) of marine, fresh-water, and eolian origin? How do Cenozoic cephalopods as a group differ from their predecessors of Mesozoic age?

5. Although many hundred species of Cenozoic fishes, amphibians, reptiles, and birds are known, why are none of these groups used to any extent for identification of Cenozoic formations?

6. Why are the skeletons of exceptionally numerous vertebrate animals (chiefly mammals, some birds) localized in the Rancho La Brea area of Los Angeles, California? Why are the skeletons mostly complete and almost perfectly preserved? Why is the proportion of carnivorous animals in the fossils collected much greater than normal for southern California today?

7. What parts of the skeleton chiefly are influenced in evolution of horses during Cenozoic time? Can you suggest reasons for differential modification of the skeletal parts thus mainly affected? How does anatomy of the perissodactyl group differ most radically from that of the artiodactyl group?

8. Why is *Baluchitherium,* which lacks a horn or horns on the skull, classed as a member of the rhinoceros group? How is the presence or absence of horns in extinct rhinoceroses ascertained (horns themselves not being preserved)? What basis exists for concluding that the woolly rhinoceros of Pleistocene age was warmly covered by a heavy coat of hairy fur?

9. What are the characters that distinguish fossil camels from antelopes or deer, since humps on the back are not present in all camels and are not preservable in fossils anyway? What evidence can be cited to prove that camels of Pleistocene and pre-Pleistocene age are by no means adapted exclusively to desert and semidesert environments?

10. What are the chief attributes of the elephant group (proboscideans) among mammals? What are the specializations of skull and teeth observed in *Elephas? Platybelodon? Deinotherium?* What noteworthy peculiarity characterizes the development of the grinding teeth (molars) among elephants? How are features of the skull correlated with degree of development of the trunk among elephants? How is modern distribution of elephants as compared with that in Pliocene and early to mid-Pleistocene time, when these mammals were common in North America, to be explained? What is the nature of the distinctions between present-day Asian and African elephants, and how can you account for them?

11. Why are seals thought to be more closely related to wolves than to dolphins? In what ways has the adaptation of seals, sea lions, and walruses to marine life differed from that observed in whales?

12. What explanation can be suggested for attainment of by far the greatest size of any mammal that is seen in the blue whale?

21.

GEOLOGIC RECORD OF MAN

Neanderthal cave man.   *F. L. Jaques, courtesy of American Museum of Natural History*

The bare-skinned, warm-blooded animal called man, which has been the dominant creature of the earth during at least the last several thousand years, differs from all other living things in his ability to reason and to devise and make tools for use in accomplishing all sorts of purposes. Many past and present inhabitants of the earth have achieved high specialization of structure that adapt them to different modes of life, but no other has learned to make and use implements or has achieved the mental and spiritual consciousness leading to ethical, aesthetic, and religious concepts such as those belonging to man. Accordingly, we say that man stands apart from the lower animals.

553

Fig. 21.1 Gorilla, largest of the living manlike apes. Although the gorilla corresponds closely to man in many features of structure and embryological development, his hands and feet are considerably modified from human form. (*Courtesy of Peabody Museum, Yale University.*)

Because man seems to belong in a sphere of his own, it is appropriate to inquire if his origin is different from that of the rest of the organic world. Is he a wholly distinct type of being that suddenly appeared in a fully developed state very recently—say, about 4000 B.C.—by special creation? Or opposed to this, do we find evidence that antiquity of man on the earth is measured in many ten-thousand or even several hundred-thousand years? Do we observe that early human types are less sharply differentiated from lower animals than men composing the modern Caucasian, Mongolian, and Negro races are distinguished from one another?

Study of man's origin, his expanding distribution over the earth, and his physical and cultural development prior to earliest written history belongs in the field of geology, though the later parts of the prehistoric human record are commonly embraced in archaeology.

Evidence of Man's Origin

Several independent lines of evidence throw light on the question of how man originated. All testimony points toward his derivation by processes of evolution such as have produced the many other kinds of animals inhabiting the earth. It indicates, furthermore, that he developed during Late Neogene geologic history from the branch of mammals that includes the lemurs, apes, and monkeys. This branch comprises animals that collectively are known as the *primates* (Latin *primus*, first), a name given by Linné to signify their development to first rank in the animal kingdom. The chief lines of evidence relating to man's origin are found in studies of comparative anatomy, embryology, vestigial organs, blood tests, and paleontology.

Structural relationships. Man's body very plainly is patterned on the mammalian plan. Part for part, his skeleton, musculature, nervous system, and internal organs correspond to those of other mammals, identity of features being especially close between man and other primates. Most closely similar to man in physical structure are the gorilla and chimpanzee, and not much less like man are the orangutan and gibbon (Figs. 21.1–21.3). At least one-fourth of man's structural peculiarities also characterize the gorilla or chimpanzee or both but are not found in other animals. A few features are common to man and the orangutan or gibbon, but not to others. An example of these peculiarities is one of the wristbones (centrale) that is lacking in adult man, gorilla, and chimpanzee but is present in all three before birth and is found

generally in all other adult primates. Another example are the air chambers that branch off the nasal cavity, which are identical in number and arrangement in man, gorilla, and chimpanzee but different in other primates. Such facts have rational meaning if these animals are related in evolutionary development. They are surely not duplication of characters produced by pure chance.

The developing human embryo undergoes a series of peculiar changes in the mother's womb, and it is a significant fact that in only

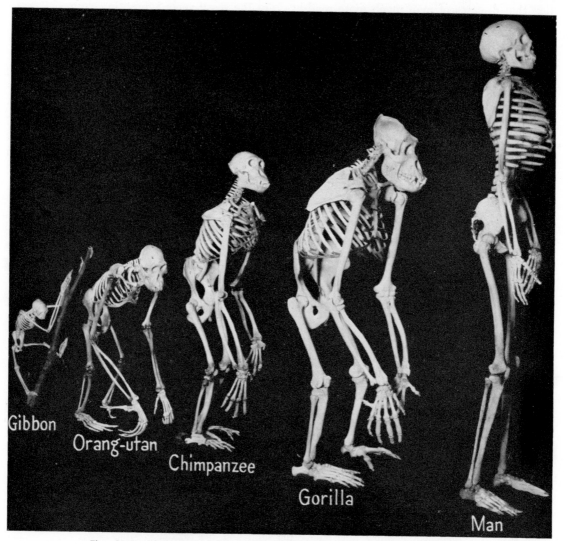

Fig. 21.2 Skeletons of man and of the four primates that most closely resemble him.
(*Courtesy of Peabody Museum, Yale University.*)

four other living mammals—gorilla, chimpanzee, orangutan, and gibbon—are identical changes found to occur. One of these similar features of development is the appearance of an external jointed tail that is seen in the fifth week of development but shrivels and disappears by the eighth week.

Sensitive tests based on biochemical properties of blood have been found to be a reliable measure of biologic relationship. This sort of study proves that man is close kin to the manlike apes and more distantly related to other primates. Confirming such evidence is observation that diseases of man much more readily affect the gorilla and chimpanzee, for example, than any of the monkeys, and when some of these are successfully inoculated, they are likely to have the disease in mildest form.

Fossil remains. Whereas structural relationships just considered provide strong inferential basis of man's antiquity and common ancestry with the higher apes, the discovery of fossilized human remains, buried in association with extinct Pleistocene animals of vari-

ous sorts, furnishes indisputable proof that races of men existed on the earth during the Ice Age. Almost certain, but not established beyond doubt, is the appearance of the earliest creatures classifiable as human during the Pliocene Epoch. No skeletal remains of Pliocene man have been found, but stone implements (*eoliths*), classifiable as marking the beginning of human culture, are found buried in Pliocene deposits. Thus, fossil remains give convincing confirmation of conclusions concerning man's origin based on other lines of study. We shall now review main features in the fossil record, omitting notice of man's distant Paleogene ancestors (Fig. 21.4).

Ape Men of Eastern Asia

Relatively numerous kinds of human fossils, representing primitive types of men that possess many apelike characters, have been reported from eastern Asia. These fossils have been obtained from the island of Java in the East Indies and from China. They occur in river-terrace and cave deposits containing

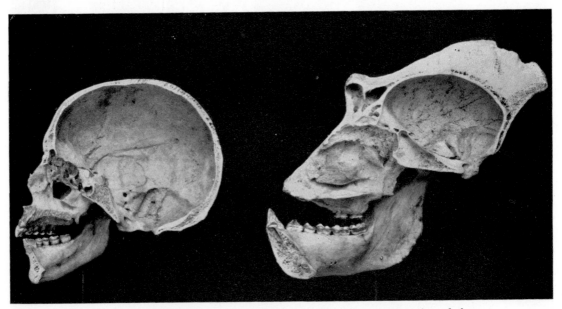

Fig. 21.3 Skulls of man and gorilla cut longitudinally to show comparative size of the brain case. The prominent eyebrow ridge above the orbit and the sagittal crest on the top of the skull of the gorilla are features which, with the low facial angle and absence of chin, distinguish the apes from men. (*Courtesy of Peabody Museum, Yale University.*)

Fig. 21.4 An early member of the order of primates. This animal (*Notharctus*), which is represented by nearly complete skeletal remains in Eocene deposits of North America, is a primitive lemur that may be a very distant ancestor of man. (*F. L. Jaques, courtesy of American Museum of Natural History.*)

undisturbed remains of extinct mammals, which are interpreted to denote mid-Pleistocene age.

Ape man of Java. The first discovery of very ancient primitive man in Asia was in 1892 when excavation in ash beds on the banks of the Solo River in eastern Java yielded human teeth and bones associated with remains of various extinct animals, then thought to represent latest Pliocene or earliest Pleistocene time. The fossils are now considered to belong to the middle part of the Pleistocene Epoch and are estimated to be approximately 400,000 to 500,000 years old. The first found evidence of human existence in such remote past time consisted of three teeth, the top part of a skull, and an upper leg bone (femur). The skullcap is apelike in having very prominent bony ridges over the eye orbits, but it differs greatly from that of any ape in lacking a median crest and in having a very much larger brain cavity. The size of the brain of this early Java man was approximately two-thirds that of a modern adult European and roughly twice as large as that of the biggest

ape brain, which is found in a full-grown gorilla. A cast of the interior of the Java ape man's skullcap shows the position and shape of brain convolutions, and this definitely confirms classification of the owner of the skull as a primitive human being who probably possessed at least the rudiments of speech. The structure of the leg bone shows that it belonged to an erect-walking primate. Inasmuch as the skull and leg bone were found some 20 feet apart, although in the same deposit, it is by no means certain that they belong to the same individual. They are confidently judged, however, to represent a race of erect-walking primitive men and accordingly have been named *Pithecanthropus erectus* (erect ape man) (Fig. 21.5).

Excavation of the Solo River deposits, especially in the years from 1936 to 1939, has yielded important additional remains of *Pithecanthropus*. These include three more skullcaps, upper and lower jaws, four leg bones, and the skull of a child. They agree in character with the original find and furnish information, previously wanting, concerning the face (Fig. 21.6A). Despite lack of most of the skeleton, the essential nature of the Java ape man is fairly well known.

China ape man. In 1927 or shortly before, paleontological collecting from limestone caves some 40 miles southwest of Peking, China, resulted in finding three teeth that belonged to either a primitive man or a large manlike ape. In 1929, a well-preserved skullcap, almost identical in size and shape with that of the Java ape man, was discovered. The human affinities of these fossils could no longer remain doubtful, and the name *Sinanthropus pekingensis* (China man of Peking) was applied. Subsequent excavations of the cave deposits have yielded a full series of skeletal remains belonging to about three dozen young and adult individuals of both sexes. Although no complete skull has been found, comparison of different specimens now provides full knowledge of the skull, including the lower jaw (Fig. 21.6B). It is judged that the Peking man belongs to the same race as

Fig. 21.5   Restoration of the Java ape man (Pithecanthropus). (*J. H. McGregor, courtesy of American Museum of Natural History.*)

the Java ape man and therefore may be called *Pithecanthropus* instead of *Sinanthropus*.

Stone implements and remains of hearths prove that the Peking ape man was a user of tools and knew how to make fire. The fact that every brain case has been broken open from below indicates that the brains were sought for food, and we must judge that the *Pithecanthropus* individuals of China were cannibals. This is confirmed by the condition of the limb bones, all of which have been split so as to get at the marrow.

Associated extinct fossils near Peking indicate that the Chinese ape men belong to mid-Pleistocene time like those of eastern Java.

Giant primates. In recent years, fragmentary jaws and teeth of gigantic ape men or manlike apes (*Meganthropus, Gigantopithecus*) have been found in Java and southern China. These indicate creatures considerably larger than the biggest full-sized gorilla. They are not well enough known to permit more than a guess as to whether they are in the direct line of human ancestry or an offshoot branch of primates.

Near-human Remains from Africa

Cave deposits in the Transvaal and Rhodesia, South Africa, have yielded varyingly complete skulls and other bones that prove the existence of primitive near-human beings. As judged by fossil animals found with them, they belong to middle or late Pleistocene time. These primate fossils (*Australopithecus*) are more like apes than men, even though the brain capacity is slightly larger than that of a gorilla and dentition closely follows the human pattern. One almost perfect skull from Rhodesia combines several very primitive characters with others that are specialized. There are very heavy brow ridges, and the face rather suggests that of an ape, but the brain case has only slightly smaller capacity than that of an adult modern European. The Rhodesian man ape is not very unlike early human cave dwellers of western Europe who lived during late Pleistocene time.

Prehistoric Men in Europe

River terraces and cave deposits in various parts of western Europe have yielded fairly numerous cultural remains of prehistoric man. These show definitely progressive advancement of his skill in making weapons and many sorts of implements. Except skeletons of late Pleistocene age, fossil human bones are uncommon.

Heidelberg man. Perhaps the oldest human bone yet discovered anywhere in the world is a man's jaw found in a deposit of river sand

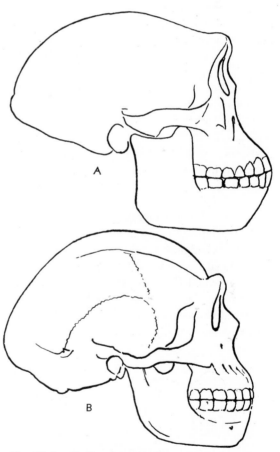

Fig. 21.6 Skulls of Java and China ape men.— *A.* Java ape man (*Pithecanthropus erectus*), partly restored, showing low skull cap, very prominent eyebrow ridges, oblique facial angle, and rounded chin. —*B.* China ape man (*Sinanthropus pekingensis*), with larger brain case, less oblique facial angle, and less rounded chin than in the Java ape man.

about 80 feet below the surface near the German town of Heidelberg (Fig. 21.7). Associated bones of elephants, rhinoceroses, lions, and other mammals indicate the age of the deposit as early Pleistocene. The jaw is very large and heavily built. It lacks a chin prominence, but the teeth and other structural features have definite human characters. Nothing is known of the cultural stage of Heidelberg human beings, because no man-made implements have been found in the river deposit associated with the bone.

Supposed "dawn man" from England. Until recently, one of the almost universally accepted records of very early man in Europe comprised an incomplete human skull and apelike lower jaw reported to have been found together in early Pleistocene deposits of southeastern England known as the Piltdown gravels. These remains were named *Eoanthropus,* signifying dawn man. From the outset some specialists were skeptical that the skull and jaw could belong to the same creature, and now, by application of various ingenious tests that include measurements of the fluorine content of the bones, the microchemical nature of discolored surficial parts of the bones, and others, proof beyond doubt has been obtained that the skull and jaw actually differ widely in age and almost surely were "planted" in the deposits where they were "discovered." Thus, so-called *Eoanthropus* must be rejected, being recognized as a scientific fraud cleverly perpetrated for unknown reasons by a presumedly trustworthy archaeologist who now is dead.

Neanderthal man. A race of prehistoric men that during the last interglacial age of Pleistocene time and the early part of the final (Würmian) glaciation lived throughout Europe, western Asia, and the north coast of Africa is Neanderthal man (Fig. 21.8). This name is derived from the locality in western Germany where the first recognized specimen was found in a cave deposit in 1856. Many complete skeletons now are known, and the bones are associated in many places with an abundance of stone implements that show a high degree of skill in manufacture. The Neanderthalers were primarily cave dwellers and hunters (Fig. 21.9) The average height of adult men was not over 5½ feet, and of women about 5 feet. The brain capacity was as large as that of the highest type of living races, but the shape of the skull, especially the receding forehead and heavy eyebrow ridges, is quite unlike the rounded contours of the modern European head. The jaw was chinless, and there are many other structural differences between the Neanderthal race and modern man.

Modern man. In late Pleistocene time, during the retreating phase of the last ice sheets, a new race of men, decidedly unlike the Neanderthalers who suddenly disappeared, took possession of Europe. The newcomers, sometimes known as Cro-Magnon man, from a locality in France where many skeletal remains have been found, are entirely indistinguishable structurally from well-built modern men. Their bones are especially abundant in cave deposits of central France, and

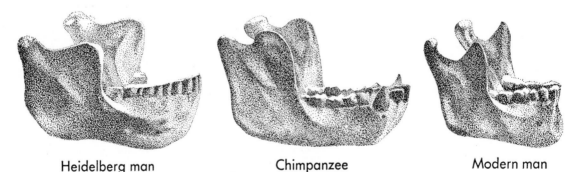

Heidelberg man   Chimpanzee   Modern man

Fig. 21.7 The jaw of Heidelberg man compared to that of an ape and modern man. (*Courtesy of K. F. Mather, "Sons of the Earth," W. W. Norton & Company, Inc.*)

altogether about 100 nearly complete skeletons are known. Many of the males exceed 6 feet in height. The skulls have a high forehead and well-rounded contours, and the lower jaws bear a well-developed chin. These prehistoric "modern" men were skilled workers in flint and bone, and they have left records of artistic talent in paintings and sculpture found in many caves (Figs. 21.10, 21.11).

Early Man in the Americas

Extensive and varied remains of prehistoric human cultures have been found in both North and South America, but there is no proof that the oldest of these belongs as far back as 25,000 B.C. Man's antiquity in the Western Hemisphere does not seem to approach that of the early and middle Pleistocene remains found in various parts of the Old World. Moreover, information concerning man in the Americas is derived mostly from his works rather than from skeletal remains. It is true that human bones have been found associated with fossil skeletal parts of extinct mammals, such as camels, elephants, and ground sloths, but either it is not established that the human remains are as old as the associated mammals (occurrence together being due to secondary deposition) or there is no reason to suppose that the extinct mammals themselves are very ancient.

Folsom remains. The oldest American flint implements are those of so-called Folsom man, named from a locality in New Mexico where specimens of this sort of prehistoric human handicraft were first discovered. Most common are spearheads, which are readily differentiated from flints shaped by the later American Indians, all of which lack the sort of groove that is cut on each side of the Folsom points (Fig. 21.12). Some of the latter implements have been found embedded in matrix between bones of extinct species of bison, and one in northeastern Colorado was found beneath the pelvis of a fossil mammoth. These finds prove the contemporaneity of Folsom man and the now extinct Pleistocene animals hunted by him. On the basis of carbon-14 age determinations that now are available, the

Fig. 21.8   Restoration of Neanderthal man. (*J. H. McGregor, courtesy of American Museum of Natural History.*)

Folsom culture can be dated as ranging from 8,000 to 10,000 years before the present.

Although the very distinctive, skillfully made Folsom points are widely distributed, as indicated by finds now recorded in every state of the United States, in southern Canada, and in northern Mexico, no human remains have been identified in association with them. Consequently, we can only guess about the physical appearance of the Folsom men themselves. Surely they were quite as advanced human beings as contemporaneous Cro-Magnon man in Europe, whom they excelled in shaping flint weapons. Undoubtedly, also, they were descendants of Mongoloid immigrants from eastern Asia who crossed into North America by way of Alaska and thus may be presumed to have possessed attributes of this Oriental race.

Minnesota man. In 1931, near Pelican Rapids, northwestern Minnesota, a complete

Fig. 21.9 Neanderthal men in eastern Europe. This restoration shows a family group taking notice of a pair of woolly rhinoceroses in the background; the youngster at the right holds the skull of a Pleistocene cave bear. (*Courtesy of J. Augusta and Z. Burian, Praha; published by permission.*)

human skeleton, claimed to be the oldest yet discovered in North America, was found in undisturbed glacial-lake banded clay deposits approximately 10 feet below the surface. The find was made in the course of excavation for a state highway, examination of the site and removal of the bones being competently undertaken by scientists from the University of Minnesota. The specimen, designated as Minnesota man, actually is the skeleton of a girl approximately fifteen years old who is thought to have encountered some sort of accident that led to her being drowned and subsequently buried in lake-bottom sediment. The published estimate of 20,000 years for the age of the skeleton probably is considerably too great, and instead, the Minnesota maiden may not be older than Folsom man. At any rate, detailed anatomical studies lead to the conclusion that she belonged to a physically well-advanced tribe resembling modern Eskimos more closely than present Asian Mongoloids.

Patagonian early man. Seemingly, the oldest authentic human remains yet found in the New World are several human skeletons found in two caves in Patagonia, South America. These bones were found near the bottom of undisturbed earth and ashes that largely fill the caves, and associated with them were bones of an extinct sloth and American wild horse. Excavation showed four distinct layers of successive human cultures in deposits that had accumulated above the skeletons. The skulls are of Mongoloid type, not very unlike those of some American Indians. They are by no means primitive in structural characters.

Migrations from eastern Asia. Comparatively modern, though prehistoric, are remarkable stone structures and carvings that are records of early Inca, Maya, and other cultures of South and Central America, but in places there are relics of a very different pre-Inca people. These may represent some of the earliest invaders of America who, in all probability, migrated from eastern Asia by way of the

Bering Strait, which now narrowly divides Alaska from the eastern tip of Siberia.

During late Pleistocene time, it is very probable that man need not have traveled by water in order to reach Alaska, and it is not necessary to postulate existence of an ice bridge in order to permit passage of land animals from one continent to the other. Water removed from ocean areas to make the enormous volume of glacial ice formed in Pleistocene time is computed to have lowered the mean sea level by an amount greater than 300 feet. Submarine surveys in the Bering region show that, if the present sea level dropped only a little more than 100 feet, a dry roadway could be built so as to join North America with Asia. Not only is this northwestern route a most plausible pathway for migration, but no other reasonably possible alternative route is offered. The Asiatic origin of the Indian inhabitants of both North and South America is shown by their physical character, for extremely close resemblance between Indian and Mongolian types persists to the present day. We conclude that the earliest human inhabitants of the Americas were all immigrants who traveled eastward from Asia and that Indian tribes of North and South America are descendants of Asiatic immigrants. The first arrivals probably came in the late part of Pleistocene time, perhaps 25,000 years ago, and in course of time spread throughout vast areas of game-filled wilderness and plains country in the Americas. Eventually they peopled both continents and built civilizations that were old when Columbus crossed the Atlantic.

Successive human cultures. Based on stratigraphic evidence such as superposed layers of cave deposits containing man-made weapons, tools, and articles of other kinds, the nature of many successive human cultures has been defined, beginning with that of the most primitive, very early Old Stone Age and extending toward the present. Types are named from localities in Europe. Thus, the Old Stone Age (Paleolithic) includes classic divisions designated (from oldest to youngest) Chellean, Acheulean, Mousterian (Fig. 21.10),

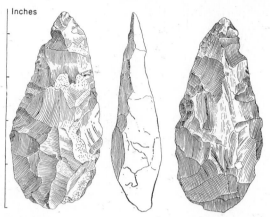

Fig. 21.10 Edge and side views of an early Stone Age flint used for striking blows or for cutting and scraping. (*Courtesy of K. F. Mather, "Sons of the Earth," W. W. Norton & Company, Inc.*)

Fig. 21.11 Carving on a cave wall at Les Combarelles, in central France. (*After l'Abbé H. Breuil.*)

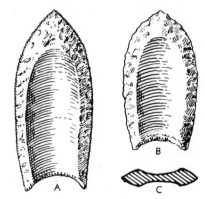

Fig. 21.12 Folsom points. This type of flint weapon is characterized by broad, evenly concave excavations on the opposite faces.——A. An elongate point.——B, C. A shorter point and cross section.

Fig. 21.13 Cliff dwellings in Mesa Verde National Park. (*Courtesy of D. L. Hopwood, Denver, Colorado.*)

Aurignacian, Solutrean, and Magdalenian. Then comes the New Stone Age (Neolithic), which began in Europe approximately 15,000 years ago. When man learned how to use metals, about 5,000 years ago, the Bronze Age was initiated, followed later by the Iron Age, and in modern time by the Steel Age. Most recently and as yet barely started, the Atomic Age has been added to the list. All these mark forward steps in man's expanding knowledge and skills, introduced at accelerated pace.

In North America, human cultures of the last 10,000 years vary a good deal according to localities, but in general, a post-Folsom Archaic stage of development is recognized, dated by C¹⁴ age measurements as ranging to within approximately 2,500 years of the present. One of the places where exceptionally

well-documented evidence of Archaic man's flint, bone, and stone implements occurs is the so-called Modoc Rock Shelter in western Illinois, along bluffs of the Mississippi River south of St. Louis. Here, implements of many sorts were found in successive layers of silt and clay distributed from 5 to 28 feet below the surface in an area where projecting rocks provided a sheltering overhang. The flints are less skillfully shaped than those of Folsom man. The Modoc men and their contemporaries were hunters who had not learned to obtain the fruits of agriculture.

More recent cultures in the plains country of the continental interior include those of the burial-mound builders (about 1,200 to 2,500 years before the present) and temple-mound builders (400 to 1,200 years before the present), both of whom were farming people. They made pottery and learned the use of bows and arrows. Overlapping the mound builders in time were tribes that constructed stone houses in rock shelters and on mesa tops in the Southwestern States; these are the cliff dwellers and pueblo Indians, who developed the art of irrigation (Fig. 21.13). In coastal areas, many semipermanent communities became established, persisting to the time of invasion by white men. The people of these settlements depended largely on marine invertebrates and fishes for food, as attested by large middens (mounds of waste) composed predominantly of shells. Mixed with kitchen refuse are bits of pottery, land-animal bones, ashes, and earth.

At many places in the western United States, carvings and inscriptions on rock surfaces have been found (Fig. 21.14). These were made by men who antedate the Indians encountered by the early Spanish and other Europeans. The Indian descendants of the various peoples who built mounds and pueblos, who farmed and hunted, and who learned how to make many kinds of tools and weapons lacked horses when white men discovered them, for horses had become extinct in North America before the Wisconsinan glaciation of Pleistocene time culminated. All the Indian ponies and herds of wild mustangs belonging to the times of the early wagon trains and stagecoaches came from horses brought to North America by white men. The geologic record of man includes various accessory items such as this, affecting distribution of other animals, and more important, it includes innumerable works that have reshaped physical features of the earth's surface. Man is justified in claiming preeminence among all forms of life known on the globe.

Fig. 21.14 Inscriptions on sandstone of the Colorado River canyon, about 85 miles below the mouth of Green River, Utah. These carvings, well preserved in the dry air of the Southwest, are not demonstrably of great antiquity, but they were made by men unknown to modern Indians.

READINGS

CAMP, C. L., 1952, *Earth song*, University of California Press, Berkeley, Calif. (127 pp.), Rise of man, pp. 73–85.
Good brief account of Folsom man and later prehistoric peoples of Southwest and Pacific Border.
DUNBAR, C. O., 1949, *Historical geology*, John Wiley & Sons, Inc., New York (567 pp., 350 figs.), The coming of man, pp. 497–518.
Well-written, very short summary.
HILL, W. C. O., 1954, *Man's ancestry*, William Heinemann, Ltd., London (194 pp., 100 figs.). [1] The rise of the anthropoids, pp. 84–103. [2] The emergence of man, pp. 104–115. [3] Fossil men, pp. 116–148. [4] From Palaeolithic to present, pp. 149–160.
Specially readable, authoritative descriptions and discussion.
MACCURDY, G. G., 1932, *The coming of man*, University Society, New York (157 pp.).
Good general survey of prehistoric man.
SELLARDS, E. H., 1947, Early man in America: *Geol. Soc. America Bull.*, vol. 58, pp. 955–978.
Summarizes records of fossil men in North America.
WORMINGTON, H. M., 1949, *Ancient man in North America:* Colo. Museum Nat. History, Popular ser., no. 4, ed. 2 (198 pp.).

QUESTIONS

1. Why are primates such as the monkeys and especially the manlike apes (including the chimpanzee, orangutan, and gorilla) considered to be "cousins" of man rather than possible ancestors?

2. Can you specify at least four very obvious anatomical characters that distinguish the skull of a gorilla from that of man?

3. What reasons are adduced for concluding that the Java ape man and China ape man are properly classifiable as human whereas manlike fossils from South Africa are considered to be man-apes and thus not regarded as human beings?

4. Why is Neanderthal man (*Homo neanderthalensis*) considered to be a species distinct from Cro-Magnon and modern men (*Homo sapiens*)?

5. What features distinguish early Paleolithic from late Paleolithic cultures and both of these from Neolithic cultures?

6. On what grounds are prehistoric men of North America interpreted to be immigrants from eastern Asia? How, presumably, were they able to reach this continent?

Appendix A

CHARACTERS OF ORGANISMS REPRESENTED AMONG FOSSILS

Model of the pelagic foraminifer, Globigerina.   *Courtesy of American Museum of Natural History*

Classification of Organisms

Prior to the time of Linné, whose epoch-making work *Systema Naturae* appeared in the year 1735, the comparatively few animals and plants described were designated either by some simple common name or by a long and cumbersome descriptive title. Linné in-

troduced the binomial nomenclature which now has universal scientific use.

The group (genus) to which an animal or plant belongs is designated by the first name, generally derived from the Greek, and the individual kind (species) by the second name, generally derived from the Latin. For example, *Felis domesticus*, the common cat;

Felis leo, the lion; *Felis concolor,* the puma; and a number of others are all species of the genus of cats. Obviously they are all closely related to one another. *Smilodon* and *Hoplophoneus* are extinct genera of cats characterized by unusually elongated saber-like canine teeth and distinguished in other respects from modern *Felis,* but we group together all the cats in the family Felidae.

Thus, in ascending scale of comprehensiveness, there are species, genus, family, order, class, phylum, and kingdom. In addition to these categories, recognized as standard, various intermediate ones (designated by such terms as tribe, cohort, section, subfamily, superfamily, and the like) are needed to express significant groupings, especially among animals, but agreement is general that the fundamental unit of major rank within a kingdom is *phylum.* Hence, in outlines of classification that follow, the names of phyla are distinguished by printing in boldface type. Because of differences in knowledge or in judgment as to relationships and points of distinction among the innumerable kinds of organisms, there is by no means complete accord on the subject of biologic classification.

The organic world traditionally has been divided into two kingdoms that on the whole have obviously contrasted characters; these are the plants (Plantae) and the animals (Animalia). Actually, a large number of organisms of unicellular construction are strictly neither plants nor animals but plant-animals, for in varying degree they possess attributes of both plants and animals. This was recognized approximately a century ago (1860) by Haeckel's proposal to segregate the one-celled plant-animals in a separate kingdom called Protista, and such classification seems logical both intrinsically and because it avoids conflict between botanists and zoologists who claim the in-between organisms as belonging in their domain. Unquestionably, protistans were the first forms of life on earth, and from them the plant and animal kingdoms have been derived.

PROTISTANS

The kingdom of Protista includes the relatively simplest of all organisms, having basically unicellular structure, with varying developed characters of both plants and animals. Several groups are represented importantly by fossils, whereas others have little importance or are unknown as fossils. A tabular outline of classification showing main divisions of the protistans is followed by brief descriptions of some groups having geologic interest. The names of phyla are printed in boldface type. The range of Protista is *Algonkian-Neogene (Recent).*

Main Divisions of Protistans

Monera. Cells lacking a definite nucleus. *Algonkian-Neogene (Recent).*
 Schizophyta. Bacteria. *Algonk.-Neog.(Rec.)*
 Myxophyta. Blue-green algae. *Algonk.-Neog.(Rec.)*
Protoctista. Cells provided with a distinct nucleus. *Algonk.-Neog. (Rec.)*
 Chlorophyta. Grass-green algae. *Algonk.-Neog. (Rec.)*
 Chrysophyta. Diatoms, silicoflagellates, coccoliths. *?Cam.-?Trias., Jur.-Neog.(Rec.)*
 Pyrrhophyta. Dinoflagellates, etc. *?Penn., Jur.-Neog.(Rec.)*
 Rhodophyta. Red algae. *Ord.-Neog.(Rec.)*
 Phaeophyta. Brown algae. *?Sil.-?Jur., Cret.-Neog. (Rec.)*
 Myxomycetes. Slime molds, yeasts. *Neog.(Rec.)*
 Eumycophyta. Fungi, mushrooms, common molds. *Algonk.-Neog.(Rec.)*
 Protozoa. Characteristically mobile, animal-like. *?Algonk., Cam.-Neog.(Rec.)*
  Foraminifera, *Cam.-Neog.(Rec.);* Radiolaria, *?Algonk., Cam.-Neog.(Rec.);* Tintinnina, *Jur.-Neog.(Rec.)*

Bacteria (Schizophyta). Bacteria are the simplest and smallest directly visible forms of life, some measuring less than 0.0002 millimeter in diameter or length. They thrive in all environments and enormously outnumber all other organisms put together. Possibly viruses, invisible at electron-microscope magnifications of $\times 100,000$, belong to this group, or perhaps they should be grouped separately as a form of life lower than bacteria in organization.

Bacteria exhibit three main shapes: the rod-like bacillus type (Fig. A.1*A, B*), spherical coccus type (Fig. A.1*C*), and spirally twisted spirillum type (Fig. A.1*D*). Many of these are provided with thin, whiplike appendages (flagella) that produce locomotion of the organism by lashing movements. Reproduction is dominantly by subdivision (fission) of the body, which suggests the name Schizophyta (*schizo-*, splitting; *phyta*, plants). Bacteria are known as fossils even in Precambrian rocks, but not commonly, for these lowly protistans lack hard parts.

Blue-green algae (Myxophyta). Modern blue-green algae are filamentous growths of very simple cells joined together and adapted for life in aquatic environments. Some are effective as agents of deposition of calcium carbonate secreted outside the cells or between them in a manner not suited to show distinctive structural features. Many fossils characterized by obscure to well-defined laminated concentric structure are considered to be deposits formed by these protistans, mostly marine (Figs. A.2, 4.39, 4.40*B*). They include the numerous fossils called *stromatolites* (*stromato-*, layered; *lite*, rock), which are common in some Cryptozoic and many Phanerozoic formations. The blue-green algae thus are important as rock builders, and some that exhibit distinctive growth are guide fossils.

Grass-green algae (Chlorophyta). In this group belongs a host of marine and some fresh-water algae that are distinguished by the grass-green color of their pigment. They consist of cells grouped together in bundles that give to calcium carbonate secreted around them a characteristic pattern of small tubes. A considerable number of these are common as fossils. One type distinguished by relatively complex reproductive structures is the so-called stonewort (*Chara*) assemblage, in which the calcareous spheroidal spore capsules are prominently marked by spiral grooves and ridges (Fig. A.3); such capsules are common in various fresh-water deposits from Devonian to Neogene (Recent) in age.

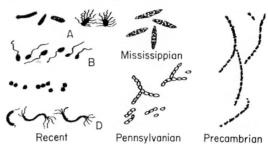

Fig. A.1 Bacteria. Flagellate and nonflagellate types are shown, some of the latter grouped in chainlike series, ×250. Illustrated Recent forms include (*A*) *Bacillus*, (*B*) *Pseudomonas*, (*C*) *Pneumococcus*, and (*D*) *Spirillum*.

Fig. A.2 Stromatolites. Weathered surface of Lower Ordovician rocks near Saratoga Springs, New York, showing concentrically laminated growths of the type called *cryptozoön*. (*Courtesy of D. W. Fisher.*)

Fig. A.3 Fossil charophytes.—*A, B. Trochiliscus,* Lower Mississippian, side and top, ×15.—*C. Sicidium,* Lower Mississippian, ×15.—*D. Atopochara,* Cretaceous, ×15. (*After R. E. Peck.*)

Diatoms, silicoflagellates, coccoliths (Chrysophyta). These are protistans that grow separately, not joined together in colonial growths, all being very minute in size. They include a multitude of genera that secrete hard parts and thus are capable of fossilization. Diatoms and silicoflagellates possess a siliceous skeleton (Fig. A.4), whereas the hard parts of coccoliths are calcareous. The latter are extremely small discoid and variously shaped bodies that under high magnification reveal delicate surface markings. These and the diatoms are most important as rock builders.

Dinoflagellates (Pyrrhophyta). The dinoflagellates are abundant solitary protistans with a complex organic shell covering that may be mineralized by silica or calcium carbonate. The skeleton is characterized by an equatorial band that girdles the cell. Dinoflagellates are abundant in modern oceans, and many occur as fossils, having considerable value for correlation (Fig. A.5). The best preserved specimens, some with fine hairy projections, are found in chert. There are other kinds of pyrrhophytes, but only the dinoflagellates are concerned in the fossil record.

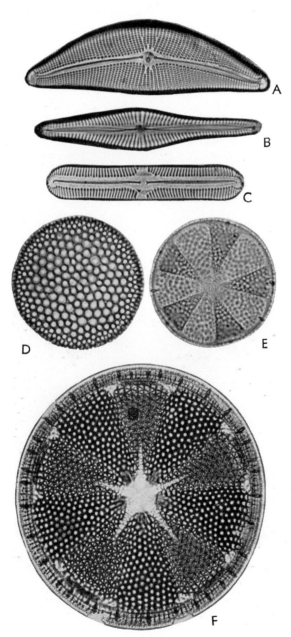

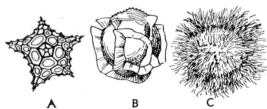

Fig. A.5 Dinoflagellates. The fossil representatives of this protistan group illustrated include (A) *Actiniscus,* Neog. (Mio.); (B) *Ceratocorys,* Cret.; (C) *Cometodinium,* Cret., a hystrichosphere type; all enlarged. (*After G. Deflandre.*)

Fig. A.4 Fossil fresh-water and marine diatoms. —*A–C.* Pleistocene fresh-water forms; *A, Cymbella,* Utah, ×535; *B, Gomphonema,* Wyoming, ×1,000; *C, Pinnularia,* Oregon, ×725.—*D, E.* Pleistocene marine forms from North Atlantic cores; *D, Coscinodiscus,* ×930; *E, Actinoptychus,* ×1,000.—*F.* Miocene marine form; *Actinoptychus,* Maryland, ×300. (*Courtesy of K. E. Lohman, U.S. Geol. Survey.*)

Red algae (Rhodophyta). The red algae characteristically grow as colonial structures that in living forms are distinguished by their red pigment. Some of them secrete calcium carbonate and are preserved as fossils, identified by rows of closely packed cells with polygonal cross sections (Fig. A.6).

Brown algae (Phaeophyta). This group is mostly not well adapted for fossilization, but in some strata calcareous strands of parallel threads that match features belonging to modern brown algae have been identified among fossils.

Fungi (Eumycophyta). The fungi are a very large group characterized in part by the lack of green coloring matter (chlorophyll). Although they are unicellular organisms, individuals are joined together in the form of branching filaments. They do not possess ability to synthesize carbohydrates and thus are dependent on other organisms for nourishment. Reproduction is by means of spores. The cells build tubes (hyphae) of character-istic pattern, and the spores are concentrated in spherical enlargements (sporangia) of these tubes. Fungi are known as fossils ranging from late Cryptozoic to the present, but they are not common.

Foraminifera (Protozoa). The shell-bearing protistans known as Foraminifera are the most important group of protozoans represented by fossils. The shell of nearly all foraminifers is composed of calcium carbonate, but a few secrete silica, and some have a covering that consists of foreign particles such as sand grains, sponge spicules, mica flakes, and the like, cemented by calcium carbonate, iron oxide, or a complex organic compound known as chitin. The name of the group is derived from the presence of minute openings (foramina) in the test, through which threadlike projections of the body protoplasm extend (Appendix A, frontispiece illustration). The simplest types of foraminiferal shells consist of a single globular or cylindrical chamber with a rounded aperture (Fig. A.7A). In

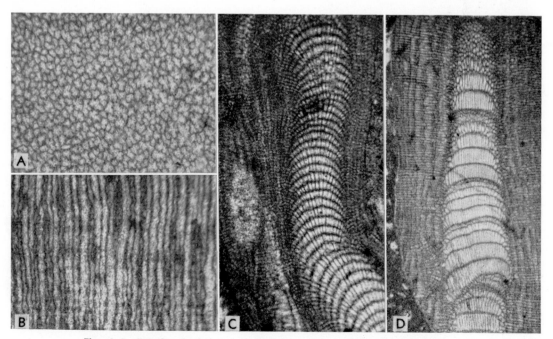

Fig. A.6 Fossil red algae.—*A, B. Solenopora,* U. Ord., Kentucky, transv. and long. secs., ×50.—*C. Lithophyllum,* Neog.(Mio.), Saipan, a so-called coralline alga, long. sec., ×100. —*D. Amphiroa,* Neog.(Pleist.), Saipan, another coralline alga, long. sec., ×75. (*Courtesy of J. H. Johnson.*)

more advanced types, an initial chamber (proloculus) is surrounded spirally by a long undivided tube or by numerous chambers arranged spirally, in a single straight or curved series, or in two or more rows with chambers arranged in alternate positions (Fig. A.7). Some fossil foraminifers have an extremely complex internal structure that may be revealed by breaking away the outer shell or by cutting sections through the shell (Fig. A.8). Reproduction in the Foraminifera is both asexual (by fission of an adult individual) and sexual, the latter calling for union of minute cells (gametes) produced by different individuals. A shell formed by asexual reproduction is distinguished by the large size of its initial chamber, and that formed by conjugation of gametes is distinguished by the relatively small size of the initial chamber. The first type, with large proloculus, is called megalospheric, and the second type is known as microspheric.

Radiolaria (Protozoa). Hard parts secreted by the protozoans termed Radiolaria are mainly internal rather than outside the proto-plasm of the protistan. The skeleton consists of one or more concentric capsules of delicately lacy silica (or of strontium sulfate in some) coupled with radially directed bars or spines (Fig. A.9). Variation in form is extremely great, and the number of individuals, chiefly living in the sea, is enormous. Fossil radiolarians are widely distributed in geologic time, being found in rocks of all ages from late Cryptozoic to Recent.

Tintinnina (Protozoa). A group of protozoans quite unlike either of those just described consists of the tintinnines. These have a conical to trumpet-shaped chitinous covering of the soft parts that, although not rigid, is capable of fossilization (Fig. A.10). The remains, generally flattened, are found in late Mesozoic and Cenozoic deposits.

PLANTS

The plant kingdom, defined to exclude the algae and other organisms classed as basically one-celled, consists of immobile multicellular growths mostly characterized by structure

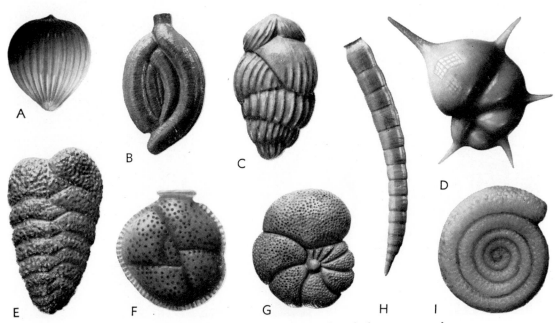

Fig. A.7 Models of foraminiferal shells. In addition to the relatively large aperture borne by the last-formed chamber, numerous small openings (foramina) through the shell wall are visible in some specimens (especially *F* and *G*). Particles of sand are incorporated in the shells of some foraminifers (*E, I*). (*Courtesy of Chicago Natural History Museum.*)

(termed vascular) adapted for passage of fluids and able to secrete chlorophyll. The plants are adapted to all sorts of environments and range in size from individuals approximately 1 millimeter in maximum dimensions to giant trees 100 meters in height and trunk diameter of 12 meters or more. Their known distribution in the fossil record extends from Silurian to the Neogene (Pleistocene) and many thousand species are living at the present time. Only a few groups are entirely ex-

tinct. An outline of classification showing main divisions of plants follows (names of phyla in boldface type and extinct groups marked by an asterisk).

Main Divisions of Plants

Bryophyta. Mosses, liverworts. *Miss.-Neog.(Rec.)*
Tracheophyta. Vascular plants, with specialized conducting cells (xylem, phloem) and mostly having multicellular sex structures (archegonia). *Sil.-Neog.(Rec.)*
 Psilopsida. Primitive, mostly leafless plants. *Sil.-Neog.(Rec.)*
  Psilophytales*. *Sil.-Dev.*
  Psilotales. *Neog.(Rec.)*
 Lycopsida. Club mosses and allies. *Sil.-Neog.(Rec.)*
  Lepidodendrales*. Giant club mosses. *Sil.-Perm.*
  Lycopodiales, Selaginellales, Isoetales. Modern club mosses and allies; about 950 species. *Neog.(Rec.)*
 Sphenopsida. Horsetail rushes and allies. *Dev.-Neog.(Rec.)*
  Sphenophyllales*. Wedge-shaped leaves. *Miss.-Perm.*

Fig. A.8 Large fusulinid foraminifer. Section through middle of the shell of *Polydiexodina*, M. Perm., western Texas, cut parallel to long axis. The initial chamber (proloculus) and complex structure surrounding it are readily seen. (*Courtesy of Moore, Lalicker, and Fischer, Invertebrate Fossils, McGraw-Hill Book Company, Inc., New York.*)

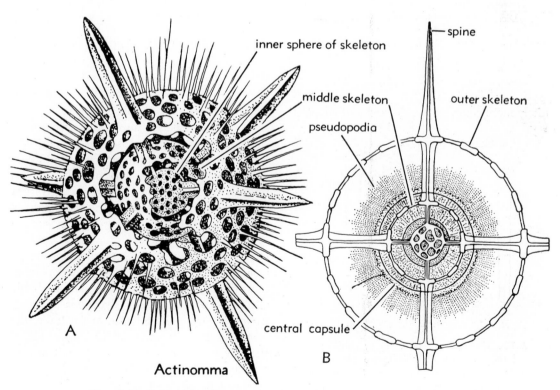

Fig. A.9 Concentric siliceous shells of radiolarian.—*A.* Outer and intermediate shells partly broken away to reveal interior.—*B.* Cross section showing relation of skeleton to soft parts. (*After Bütschli.*)

Calamitales°. Noded ribbed stems. *Dev.-Trias.*
Equisetales. Modern horsetail rushes. *Neog.* (*Rec.*)
Pteropsida. Ferns and seed plants. *Dev.-Neog.* (*Rec.*)
Filicineae. Ferns. *Dev.-Neog.*(*Rec.*)
Filicales. Typical ferns. Approximately 9,000 species. *Dev.-Neog.*(*Rec.*)
Ophioglossales, Marattiales. Modified ferns. 300 species. *Neog.*(*Rec.*)
Gymnospermae. Naked-seed plants. *?Dev., Miss.-Neog.*(*Rec.*)
Pteridospermales°. Seed ferns. *?Dev., Miss.-Jur.*
Bennettitales°. Cycadeoids (cycad-like plants). *Trias.-Cret.*
Cycadales. Cycads. *?Trias., Neog.*(*Rec.*)
Cordaitales°. Early conifers with straplike leaves. *Miss.-Perm., ?Trias.*
Ginkgoales. Maidenhair trees. *?Dev., Penn.-Neog.*(*Rec.*)
Coniferales. Conifers. *?Dev., Penn.-Neog.* (*Rec.*)
Gnetales. Minor group intermediate between gymnosperms and angiosperms. *Neog.* (*Rec.*)
Angiospermae. Flowering plants with inclosed seeds. *Jur.-Neog.*(*Rec.*)
Dicotyledonales. Most trees and woody shrubs. *Jur.-Neog.*(*Rec.*)
Monocotyledonales. Grasses, herbs, some trees. *Cret.-Neog.*(*Rec.*)

Mosses, liverworts (Bryophyta). The bryophytes are like algae in some respects but definitely more complexly organized and adapted for life in moist environments on land. Both the mosses (Musci) and liverworts (Hepaticae) are very diminutive plants that lack specialized cell structures found in higher groups. Reproduction is by means of spores. Definitely identified fossil liverworts are known from rocks of Mississippian age in England.

Psilopsida. The psilopsid plants are primitive tracheophytes having stems but no true roots (growing from runners) and mostly lacking leaves; if leaves occur, they are very small and simple. Spore cases (sporangia) are borne at the tips of shoots or branches (Fig. A.11). Cross sections of the stems show an outer layer several cells thick and an inner grouping of vascular cells. The aerial part of the plant, which was naked, spiny, or covered by diminutive scalelike leaves, rose from a creeping underground structure (rhizome). The psilopsids were evidently semiaquatic or moisture-loving plants adapted for a swampy environment, as indicated by the known Silurian and Devonian fossils (Figs. 8.24C, 12.1). Two living genera are distant relatives of the Paleozoic forms.

Lycopsida. The group of plants known as club mosses, including the giant types of Paleozoic age sometimes designated as scale trees, are characterized by their unjointed stem or trunk and simple structure of their single-veined scaly, needle-like, or strap-shaped leaves, which mostly are small. The leaves are distributed in spiral or longitudinal rows along the trunk and branches or arranged irregularly but never in whorls. The spore cases (sporangia) are placed singly in axils (angle between stem and upper surface of leaf) of fertile leaves (sporophylls), which commonly are grouped in terminal conelike assemblages (strobiles). In the modern club moss (*Lycopodium*, Fig. A.12A) and probably also the oldest known lycopods (*Baragwanathia*) from the Silurian of Australia, the spore cases are located on the upper side of the leaves where they join the stem. The very regular pattern of diamond-shaped leaf scars, arranged in intersecting rows oblique to the

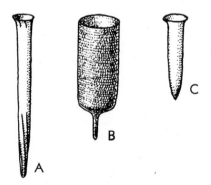

Fig. A.10 Tintinnines. The vase- or goblet-shaped form of the chitinous body inclosure (lorica) preserved as a fossil is illustrated: A, C, Cretaceous, ×175; B, Jurassic, ×100.

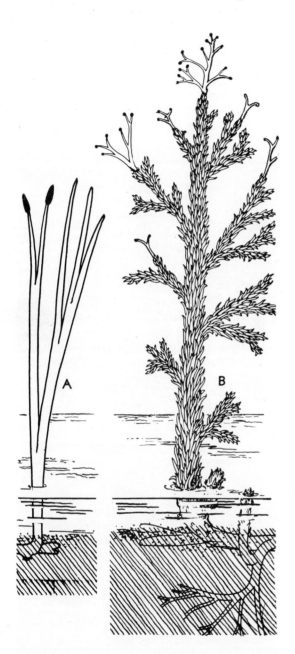

Fig. A.11 Psilopsid plants from a silicified Devonian peat bog (Rhynie Chert) in Scotland.——*A. Rhynia,* a leafless plant, showing spore cases (sporangia) on fertile shoots at left.——*B. Asteroxylon,* covered with short scaly leaves except at tips of some branches that bear sporangia. (*A* and *B,* approx. ×0.5, are represented as growing in a shallow pool with runners in earth.) (*Modified from Kidston and Lang.*)

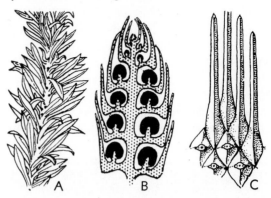

Fig. A.12 Lycopod leaves and spore-bearing structures.——*A.* Modern club moss (*Lycopodium*) showing sporangia (black bodies) along branch at base of sharp-pointed leaves. (*H. N. Andrews, Jr., courtesy of Comstock Publishing Associates, Inc.*)——*B.* Median section through cone of a club moss with sporangia (black) near base of spore-carrying leaves (sporophylls).——*C.* Spinelike leaves of a Pennsylvanian lycopod tree (*Lepidodendron*) and scars left behind when leaves drop off.

axis of the trunk or branch, characterizes the abundant late Paleozoic trees called *Protolepidodendron* (Fig. 8.24*B*) and *Lepidodendron* (Figs. A.13, 2.10*A*, 12.3, 12.5). The leaves taper gradually from the base to a sharp-pointed tip (Fig. A.12*C*).

Sphenopsida. The group of plants called sphenopsids contains approximately 400 species, mostly Paleozoic, that now are extinct and 25 living species of horsetail rushes. They are characterized by jointed stems or trunks bearing longitudinal ribs (Figs. 2.10*B*, 8.24*A*, 12.1, 12.4) and whorls of pointed or wedge-shaped leaves (Figs. A.14, A.15). Spore cases are grouped along the conelike terminal parts (sporangiophores) of fertile stalks.

Ferns (Pteropsida, Filicineae). The ferns are plants that reproduce by means of spores that mostly are borne on the underside of fertile leaves termed sporophylls. The fronds of ferns consist typically of rows of leaflets arranged along main stems or branches diverging from them in feather-like manner (Figs.

A.16, 1.14, 2.10*C*, 12.2, 12.5). So-called tree ferns, both ancient and modern, have a woody trunk, some attaining a height of 80 feet. Ferns mostly are classified on the basis of shape and arrangement of the leaflets and features of the spore cases (sporangia) in covered or uncovered clusters. The number of spores produced by a single plant is prodi-

gious, in some species amounting to 1,000 million in a year. The spores are dispersed widely by winds and water currents, many of them becoming buried in sediment and preserved as fossils.

Seed ferns (Pteropsida, Gymnospermae, Pteridospermales). Plants that resemble tree ferns in mode of growth but distinguished by

Fig. A.13 Leaf scars of Pennsylvanian lycopod. The arrangement of the diamond-shaped scars in regular obliquely intersecting rows is characteristic of *Lepidodendron*, ×1. (*Courtesy of Chicago Natural History Museum.*)

Fig. A.14 Restoration of Pennsylvanian sphenopsid. The wedge-shaped leaves of this shrublike plant (*Sphenophyllum*) are arranged in whorls; a conelike spore-bearing structure (sporangiophore) is shown on one branch, ×0.5. (*Courtesy of Chicago Natural History Museum.*)

the presence of seeds borne on the leaves are known as seed ferns. Seeds differ from spores in their relatively large size and (more importantly) in being classifiable as fertilized eggs. Each pteridosperm seed, uninclosed in a protective sheath, occurs at the tip of a slightly modified leaf stem. The seed ferns are known only as fossils and undoubtedly are the most primitive known type of seed-bearing plants (Fig. 8.24*D*).

Cycadeoids (Pteropsida, Gymnospermae, Bennettitales). The cycadeoids are cycad-like plants generally having thick unbranched stems and a crown of palmlike leaves. They are known only as fossils in Mesozoic rocks and are abundant enough to warrant recognition of them as dominant plants of the era. Some attained large size (Fig. 13.17). As a group they are distinguished by their large pinnate leaves and structural features of their flower-like organs associated with naked seeds (Figs. 16.7 to 16.9).

Cycads (Pteropsida, Gymnospermae, Cycadales). The cycads closely resemble palms in appearance but differ from them in lacking true flowers (Fig. 16.6). Their male and female reproductive structures commonly occur in cones. Although the extinct cycadeoids are important in the fossil record, cycads are not, for only a few specimens from Paleogene and Neogene strata are known. Approximately 90 species are living.

Early conifers (Pteropsida, Gymnospermae, Cordaitales). Late Paleozoic deposits contain abundant remains of tall, slender trees that bore simple, very elongate leaves. These are a group of primitive conifers readily distinguished by their straplike leaves and concentration of their naked seeds in catkin-like cones (Fig. A.17). Some had a trunk diameter of 5 feet with cells of woody tissue exceptionally well preserved.

Ginkgos (Pteropsida, Gymnospermae, Ginkgoales). The modern maidenhair tree (*Ginkgo*) is the sole surviving representative of a gymnosperm group that was widely common in Mesozoic time and now recognized as having been introduced by known late Pale-

Fig. A.15 Leaves of Pennsylvanian horsetail rush (*Annularia*). This fossil comes from Mazon Creek, Illinois; ×1. (*Courtesy of Chicago Natural History Museum.*)

ozoic plants (*Baiera, Dichophyllum*). The ginkgos have dichotomously veined fan-shaped leaves of unique type, and the seeds are borne in persimmon-like fruits (Fig. A.18).

Conifers (Pteropsida, Gymnospermae, Coniferales). The most important single group of naked-seed plants are the conifers, comprising the evergreens, or softwoods, which are represented by about 550 living species. They are characterized by their scalelike or needle-like leaves and grouping of the seeds in cones. Many are trees that grow to large size, such as the giant redwoods (*Sequoia*) that may attain a height of 300 feet and a trunk diameter of 40 feet. The conifers are common as fossils from late Paleozoic time onward (Figs. 10.23, 16.10).

Angiosperms (Pteropsida, Angiospermae). The flowering plants, called angiosperms, greatly predominate over all others in the plant kingdom, for they include at least 250,000 known living species as well as numerous fossil forms distributed through Cretaceous and younger rocks. Actually, this group existed in Jurassic time, as proved by the identification of undoubted angiosperm pollen grains in a Jurassic coal of Scotland and a few leaf impressions from England and eastern Greenland, but distinctive leaves are common as fossils only in Cretaceous, Paleogene, and Neogene deposits. The leaves are typically broad (Fig. 20.2), and the flowers complexly organized, seeds being produced in an inclosure of carpels, which are one of the four structures (petals, sepals, stamens, carpels) of a complete flower. The angiosperms include the grasses and grains, all common vegetables and garden flowers, a multitude of

Fig. A.16 Pennsylvanian ferns from Illinois. These fossils show typical features of leaflets and fronds: (*A, B*) *Neuropteris,* different species, with bases of leaflets rounded and free; (*C*) *Alethopteris,* with entire bases of leaflets attached to stem; all ×1. (*Courtesy of Chicago Natural History Museum.*)

shrubs and trees with deciduous leaves, and many kinds of palms. Familiar seeds of angiosperms are acorns, walnuts, cocoanuts, peas, beans, grains of wheat, corn, and the like.

The angiosperms are divided into two major assemblages (Dicotyledonales, Monocotyledonales) on the basis of the nature of first-formed leaves (cotyledons) derived from the seed and by characteristics of leaf venation.

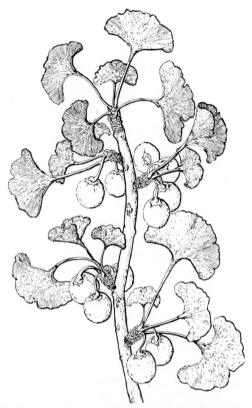

Fig. A.18 Twig of living Ginkgo. The fan-shaped leaves with bifurcating fine veins and seeds in persimmon-like fruits are distinguishing characters of this plant (*Ginkgo biloba*), ×1. (*Courtesy of H. N. Andrews, Jr., and Comstock Publishing Associates, Inc.*)

Fig. A.17 Reconstruction of Pennsylvanian primitive conifer. This tree (*Cordaites*) is mainly distinguished by the straplike nature of its parallel-veined leaves. (*Courtesy of Chicago Natural History Museum.*)

ANIMALS

The animal kingdom comprises 1 million or more known kinds of living and extinct multi-celled organisms that generally are characterized by constancy of body form, complexity of internal structure, inability to sustain themselves by use of inorganic substances alone as food, and more or less pronounced irritability providing quick response to stimuli. Some animals resemble plants in growing in fixed locations, but a greatly preponderant majority are mobile. The cells of animals are inclosed by delicate membranes, and tissues are kept moist by water containing dissolved common salt (NaCl). Metabolism is based on complex organic materials derived from plants or other animals as food and on oxygen obtained from water or air for respiration. Growth commonly is differential, affecting various parts unequally during development from infant to adult life stages and thus producing changes in body proportions.

Although some protistans are closely similar to animals, these one-celled organisms here are classed in the separate kingdom of Protista. Members of the kingdom Animalia are composed of many cells, yet some of them are small enough to be visible only with a microscope; maximum size is represented by the modern blue whale, which may reach a length of 100 feet and weight of 150 tons. Utmost variety is found in their modes of life and adaptation to different environments. The known distribution of animals in geologic time ranges from late Cryptozoic (Algonkian) to the present, although nearly all fossil remains are confined to Phanerozoic (Cambrian-Neogene) rocks. Only a few major groups (phyla) are entirely extinct.

For the purpose of showing relationships among the numerous larger natural assemblages of animals, a tabular outline of classification is given, with names of phyla printed in boldface type and extinct groups marked by an asterisk (*). The table is simplified by omission of various animal groups that are absent or unimportant in the paleontological record.

Main Divisions of Animals

Parazoa. Animals possessing an outer cell layer (ectoderm) but no inner one (endoderm), and lacking mouth, nervous tissue, and internal organs. *Algonk.-Neog.(Rec.)*

Archaeocyatha*. Skeleton typically conical in form, calcareous, double-walled, porous. *Cam.*

Porifera. S p o n g e s . *Algonk.-Neog.(Rec.)*

Eumetazoa. Animals with cells organized in tissue and organs. *Algonk.-Neog.(Rec.)*

Radiata. Characterized by primary radial symmetry, with two tissue layers inclosing digestive cavity but lacking additional open body spaces (coeloms). *Algonk.-Neog.(Rec.)*

Coelenterata. Body interior serving to carry on all vital functions, without differentiated alimentary tract. *Algonk.-Neog.(Rec.)*

Cnidaria. Mainly distinguished by presence of stinging capsules; includes nearly all coelenterates. *Algonk.-Neog.(Rec.)*

Protomedusae*. Primitive free-swimming cnidarians with prominent radial pouches. *Algonk.-Ord., ?Penn.*

Dipleurozoa*. Umbrella-shaped (medusoid) forms with bilateral symmetry. *Cam.*

Scyphozoa. Free-swimming or attached marine cnidarians with prominent 4-fold symmetry. *Cam.-Neog. (Rec.)*

Conulata*. Mostly steep-sided pyramidal forms with quadrangular cross section and extremely thin skeletal covering of calcium phosphate, attached or free. *Cam.-Trias.*

Scyphomedusae. Jellyfishes, typically bowl- or umbrella-shaped, free-swimming. *Jur.-Neog.(Rec.)*

Hydrozoa. Mostly small, body interior without radial partitions; includes attached polyps and free-swimming medusae. *Cam.-Neog.(Rec.)*

Trachylinida. Medusoids distinguished by arrangement of tentacles and body lobes. *?Cam., Jur.-Neog. (Rec.)*

Milleporida, Stylasterida. Colonial hydrozoans with diminutive dimorphic (two forms) types of polyps that secrete calcareous skeleton. *Cret.-Neog.(Rec.)*

Stromatoporoidea*. Colonial hydrozoans that secrete massive calcareous skeletons with lamina-and-pillar structure. *Cam.-Cret.*

Spongiomorphida*. Generally like stromatoporoids. *Trias.-Jur.*

Hydroida. Branching colonies of minute polyps, some with horny hard parts. *Cam.-Neog.(Rec.)*

Anthozoa. Corals; body interior divided by radial partitions. *Ord.-Neog.(Rec.)*

Ceriantipatharia. Black corals and some without hard parts. *Neog.(Mio.-Rec.)*

Octocorallia. Colonial corals with 8-fold symmetry, mostly with discrete calcareous hard parts. *?Sil., Perm.-Neog.(Rec.)*

Zoantharia. Most corals. *Ord.-Neog.(Rec.)*

Rugosa*. Colonial and solitary corals with dominant 4-fold symmetry, t e t r a c o r a l s . *Ord.-Perm.*

Heterocorallia*. Colonial, with distinctive septal pattern. *Miss.*

Scleractinia. Colonial and solitary corals with dominant 6-fold symmetry; h e x a c o r a l s . *Trias.-Neog.(Rec.)*

■ Tabulata*. Minute colonial polyps that mostly build massive growths. *Ord.-Perm., ?Trias.-?Eoc.*

Ctenophora. Comb-jellies. *?Cam., Neog.(Rec.)*

Bilateria. Characterized by primary bilateral symmetry and generally having three tissue layers (ecto-, meso-, endoderm). *?Algonk., Cam.-Neog.(Rec.)*

Eucoelomata. With open body cavity (coelom) between digestive tract and body wall; includes all higher in-
■ vertebrates and vertebrates. *?Algonk., Cam.-Neog.(Rec.)*

Schizocoela. Coelom originating as space in mesoderm. *?Algonk., Cam.-Neog.(Rec.)*

Bryozoa. Minute colonial forms that secrete varied types of delicate skeletons, mostly calcareous; b r y o -
z o a n s . *?Cam., Ord.-Neog.(Rec.)*

Brachiopoda. Bivalves with one shell larger than the other, each typically showing bilateral symmetry;
b r a c h i o p o d s . *?Algonk., Cam.-Neog.(Rec.)*

Mollusca. Unsegmented body with well-developed digestive and nervous systems, with distinctive larval
stage (trochophore). *Cam.-Neog.(Rec.)*

Monoplacophora. Chiton-like forms with single dorsal shell. *Cam.-Neog.(Rec.)*

Amphineura. Elongate body bearing skeleton of 8 articulating plates; c h i t o n s . *Ord.-Neog.(Rec.)*

Scaphopoda. Slender tubular skeleton open at both ends; tooth shells. *Dev.-Neog.(Rec.)*

Gastropoda. Snails; body generally asymmetrical, with single cap-shaped or spirally coiled shell not
■ divided into chambers, mostly marine but common in fresh waters and on land; g a s t r o p o d s .
Cam.-Neog.(Rec.)

Pelecypoda. Bivalves, generally with valves equal in size and symmetrical to each other, mainly marine
■ but also common in fresh waters; p e l e c y p o d s , clams, oysters, mussels. *Cam.-Neog.(Rec.)*

Cephalopoda. External shell straight, curved, or spirally coiled, divided into chambers, or with solid in-
■ ternal shell, some naked; exclusively marine; c e p h a l o p o d s . *?Cam., Ord.-Neog.(Rec.)*

Nautiloidea. Cross walls (septa) between chambers of simple type, without fluted margins; n a u t i -
■ l o i d s . *?Cam., Ord.-Neog.(Rec.)*

Ammonoidea*. Septa with fluted margins, marked in fossils by complex sutures; a m m o n o i d s .
■ *Dev.-Cret.*

Decapoda. Characterized by 10 tentacles, fossil forms (Belemnoidea, Sepioidea) with well-developed
■ internal shell; b e l e m n o i d s , squids, cuttlefishes. *?Miss., Perm.-Neog.(Rec.)*

Octopoda. Characterized by 8 tentacles, without shell; octopuses. *Cret.-Neog.(Rec.)*

Annelida. Segmented worms, some with hard jaw parts (scolecodonts) preserved as fossils. *?Algonk., Cam.-
Neog.(Rec.)*

Arthropoda. Segmented invertebrates with chitinous body covering (exoskeleton) and pairs of jointed
appendages attached to many or few segments; crustaceans, arachnids, insects, and others, together
outnumbering all other kinds of animals. *?Algonk., Cam.-Neog.(Rec.)*

Trilobitomorpha*. Arthropods resembling and including t r i l o b i t e s . *?Algonk., Cam.-Perm.*

Trilobitoidea*. *Cam.*

Trilobita*. Characterized by longitudinal and transverse division of dorsal exoskeleton into three
■ parts or lobes, especially common in some early Paleozoic beds. *Cam.-Perm.*

Chelicerata. Head and front part of body fused to form cephalothorax, two front limbs armed with
■ pincer-like claws (chelae), antennae lacking. *Cam.-Neog.(Rec.)*

Merostomata. Cephalothorax broadly joined to abdomen, with compound eyes and bearing six pairs
■ of legs; king crabs, e u r y p t e r i d s . *Cam.-Neog.(Rec.)*

Arachnida. Abdomen without limbs, eyes simple, mostly terrestrial; s p i d e r s , s c o r p i o n s ,
■ ticks, mites. *Sil.-Neog.(Rec.)*

Pyconogonida. Abdomen rudimentary, legs long and slender, marine; sea spiders (rare as fossils). *Dev.-
■ Neog.(Rec.)*

Crustacea. Head with two pairs of antennae, mostly aquatic. *Cam.-Neog.(Rec.)*

Branchiopoda. With leaflike thoracic appendages bearing gills. *Cam.-Neog.(Rec.)*

Ostracoda. With minute bivalved carapace; abundant as fossils; o s t r a c o d e s . *Ord.-Neog.(Rec.)*

Malacostraca. Head fused with front thoracic segments, typically with 19 body segments;
■ l o b s t e r s , c r a b s , crayfishes. *Penn.-Neog.(Rec.)*

Cirripedia. Adults sessile, carapace modified into plates surrounding body; b a r n a c l e s . *Ord.-
■ Neog.(Rec.)*

Myriapoda. Body elongate, wormlike, with many segments, terrestrial; includes centipedes (Chilopoda)
■ and millipedes (Diplopoda). *Penn.-Neog.(Rec.)*

Hexapoda. Head distinct, bearing single pair of antennae, thorax with three pairs of jointed legs; includes
■ i n s e c t s (Insecta) and other groups. *Dev.-Neog.(Rec.)*

Enterocoela. Coelom originating from digestive tract. *Cam.-Neog.(Rec.)*

Echinodermata. Spiny-skinned animals, with skeletal parts of crystalline calcite, typically with 5-fold radial symmetry, exclusively marine. *Cam.-Neog.(Rec.)*

Haplozoa*. Primitive 5-plated unattached forms that may be ancestral to other exhinoderms. *Cam.*

Homalozoa*. Anomalous dorsoventrally compressed forms with irregular plates and taillike "stem," possibly related to primitive chordates. *Cam.-Dev.*

Pelmatozoa. Sessile, generally attached by stalk composed of slightly movable superposed disks. *Cam.-Neog.(Rec.)*

Cystoidea*. Body inclosed by irregularly arranged polygonal plates of highly variable number, some or nearly all perforated by respiratory pores or slits; c y s t o i d s . *Cam.-Dev.*

Blastoidea*. Bud-shaped calyx composed of regularly arranged plates, with numerous threadlike armlets (brachioles) along food-groove areas (ambulacra); b l a s t o i d s . *Ord.-Perm.*

Eocrinoidea*. With irregular imperforate plates. *Cam.-Ord.*

Paracrinoidea*. With combined cystoid and crinoid characters. *Ord.*

Edrioasteroidea*. Body generally discoid, stemless, with curved food grooves on upper surface; e d r i o a s t e r o i d s . *Ord.-Penn.*

Crinoidea. With regularly arranged imperforate plates on dorsal side and distinct tegmen that may bear perforate plates on ventral side, arms free and strongly developed; c r i n o i d s . *Ord.-Neog. (Rec.)*

Eleutherozoa. Free-moving echinoderms with numerous skeletal elements. *Cam.-Neog.(Rec.)*

Asterozoa. Star-shaped. *Cam.-Neog.(Rec.)*

Asteroidea. Body not sharply set off from radiating arms, which are commonly five; s t a r f i s h e s . *Cam.-Neog.(Rec.)*

Ophiuroidea. Discoid body sharply distinct from five long, slender arms; brittle stars, serpent stars. *Miss.-Neog.(Rec.)*

Echinozoa. Body without laterally directed armlike extensions. *Cam.-Neog.(Rec.)*

Echinoidea. Body globular to discoid or egg-shaped, exterior bearing many large or small movable spines; s e a u r c h i n s , sand dollars. *Ord.-Neog.(Rec.)*

Holothuroidea. Body elongate, subcylindrical, with leathery skin containing minute disconnected plates or spicules; sea cucumbers. *Cam.-Neog.(Rec.)*

Chordata. Body supported by cartilaginous or bony column. *Ord.-Neog.(Rec.)*

Hemichordata. With axial structure and other characters lacking in higher chordates. *Ord.-Neog.(Rec.)*

Pterobranchia. *Ord.-Neog.(Rec.)*. Enteropneusta. *Neog.(Rec.)*

Graptolithina*. Colonial marine animals of minute size, free-floating or attached to organisms such as sea weeds, body inclosed by chitinous cover; important early Paleozoic fossils; g r a p t o l i t e s . *Cam.-Miss.*

Vertebrata. Chordates possessing a skull; vertebrates. *Ord.-Neog.(Rec.)*

Pisces. Aquatic, mostly with median and paired lateral fins; f i s h e s . *Ord.-Neog.(Rec.)*

Agnatha. Primitive jawless fishes, mostly with prominent bony covering of head region; o s t r a c o - d e r m s , cyclostomes. *Ord.-Neog.(Rec.)*

Placodermi*. Primitive jaw-bearing fishes, mostly with heavy armor; jointed-neck arthrodires, spiny sharks (a c a n t h o d i a n s) . *Ord.-Perm.*

Chondrichthyes. Cartilaginous fishes; s h a r k s , rays, skates. *Dev.-Neog.(Rec.)*

Osteichthyes. Bony fishes, body generally covered by scales. *Dev.-Neog.(Rec.)*

Choanichthyes. Lobe-finned fishes: c r o s s o p t e r y g i a n s (ancestral to amphibians), lung-fishes. *Dev.-Neog.(Rec.)*

Actinopterygii. Ray-finned fishes; most modern b o n y f i s h e s . *Dev.-Neog.(Rec.)*

Tetrapoda. Four-legged vertebrates, chiefly terrestrial, typically with two pairs of limbs, each bearing 5 digits. *Dev.-Neog.(Rec.)*

Amphibia. Earliest tetrapods adapted for life partly on land, but development of eggs and young dependent on aquatic environment; a m p h i b i a n s , salamanders, frogs, toads, l a b y - r i n t h o d o n t s . *Dev.-Neog.(Rec.)*

Reptilia. Cold-blooded air-breathing tetrapods, eggs and young not dependent on aquatic environment, body covered by scales or armor; r e p t i l e s . *Penn.-Neog.(Rec.)*

Anapsida. Skull completely roofed over, as in amphibians. *Perm.-Neog.(Rec.)*

Cotylosauria*. Primitive land reptiles, probably including ancestors of all higher reptiles, birds, and mammals; c o t y l o s a u r s *. *Perm.-Trias.*

Chelonia. Body more or less completely inclosed by united bony plates; t u r t l e s . *Trias.-Neog.(Rec.)*

Synapsida*. Mammal-like reptiles, with single lateral opening on each side of skull behind eye; fin-backed reptiles (p e l y c o s a u r s) , varied other types (t h e r a p s i d s) . *Penn.-Jur.*

Parapsida*. Like synapsids but with opening behind eye differently placed with reference to skull
 | bones; short-necked fishlike reptiles, i c h t h y o s a u r s. *Trias.-Cret.*

Euryapsida*. Skull differing slightly from that of parapsids, includes long-necked aquatic rep-
 | tiles with chunky bodies and long paddle-like limbs; nothosaurs, p l e s i o s a u r s. *Perm.-*
 | *Cret.*

Diapsida. Skull with two lateral openings on each side behind eye; dominant reptile group that
 | includes all lizards, snakes, crocodiles, dinosaurs, pterosaurs, and others. *Perm.-Neog.(Rec.)*

Lepidosauria. Primitive diapsids; l i z a r d s, s n a k e s, m o s a s a u r s, and others. *Perm.-*
 | *Neog.(Rec.)*

Archosauria. Advanced diapsids. *Trias.-Neog.(Rec.)*

   Thecodontia*. Ancestral archosaurs; includes crocodile-like p h y t o s a u r s*. *Trias.*

   Crocodilia. Advanced aquatic archosaurs; c r o c o d i l e s, a l l i g a t o r s. *Trias.-Neog.*
      (Rec.)

   Pterosauria*. F l y i n g r e p t i l e s. *Jur.-Cret.*

   Saurischia*. Major group of d i n o s a u r s distinguished by lizard-like pelvic structure.
      Trias.-Cret.

      Theropoda*. Small to gigantic carnivorous dinosaurs, bipedal; includes t y r a n n o -
       | s a u r s. *Trias.-Cret.*

      Sauropoda*. Giant semiaquatic herbivorous diosnaurs, quadrupedal; includes b r o n -
       | t o s a u r s. *Jur.-Cret.*

   Ornithischia*. Major group of d i n o s a u r s distinguished by birdlike pelvic structure.
      Trias.-Cret.

      Ornithopoda*. Primitive (c a m p t o s a u r s) to highly specialized (duck-billed t r a -
       | c h o d o n t s), semiaquatic, dominantly bipedal. *Trias.-Cret.*

      Stegosauria*. Heavy quadrupedal dinosaurs with body protected by projecting large
       | plates and spines; s t e g o s a u r s. *Jur.-Cret.*

      Ankylosauria*. Sides and back armored by thick bony plates not projecting outward;
       | a n k y l o s a u r s. *Cret.*

   Ceratopsia*. Quadrupedal, h o r n e d d i n o s a u r s. *Cret.*

Aves. Generally warm-blooded tetrapods with one pair of limbs adapted for flying, feathered;
   b i r d s. *Jur.-Neog.(Rec.)*

Mammalia. Almost exclusively viviparous warm-blooded tetrapods that suckle the young, body
   usually hair-covered; m a m m a l s. *Jur.-Neog.(Rec.)*

Prototheria. Primitive egg-laying mammals. *Neog.(Pleist.)*

Allotheria*. Primitive early mammals with several sharp conical projections on teeth; m u l t i -
 | t u b e r c u l a t e s. *Jur.-Paleog.(Paleoc.)*

Theria. Placental mammals, young born alive. *Jur.-Neog.(Rec.)*

Pantotheria*. Primitive forms, mostly trituberculates, ancestors of higher mammals. *Jur.*

Metatheria. Young born very immature and carried in pouch; m a r s u p i a l s such as opos-
 | sums, kangaroos. *Cret.-Neog.(Rec.)*

Eutheria. Young well developed at birth, not carried in pouch. *Cret.-Neog.(Rec.)*

   Unguiculata. Digits with more or less clawlike nails. *Cret.-Neog.(Rec.)*

      Insectivora. Insect-eaters. *Cret.-Neog.(Rec.)*

      Chiroptera. Bats. *Paleog.(Eoc.)-Neog.(Rec.)*

      Edentata. Sloths, anteaters, armadillos. *Paleog.(Paleoc.)-Neog.(Rec.)*

      Primates. Lemurs, monkeys, a p e s, m e n. *Paleog.(Paleoc.)-Neog.(Rec.)*

   Glires. Gnawers; rodents, rabbits. *Paleog.(Paleoc.)-Neog.(Rec.)*

   Carnivora. Flesh-eaters; c a t s, d o g s, bears, hyenas, raccoons, weasels, seals, sea lions,
      walruses. *Paleog.(Paleoc.)-Neog.(Rec.)*

   Cetacea. W h a l e s, dolphins, porpoises. *Paleog.(Eoc.)-Neog.(Rec.)*

   Ungulata. Hoofed mammals. *Paleog.(Paleoc.)-Neog.(Rec.)*

   Condylarthra*. Ancestral hoofed mammals. *Paleog.(Paleoc.-Oligo.)*

   Amblypoda*. *Paleog.(Paleoc.-Oligo.)*

   Dinocerata*. Uintatheres. *Paleog.(Paleoc.-Eoc.)*

   Sirenia. Sea cows. *Paleog.(Paleoc.)-Neog.(Rec.)*

   Proboscidea. E l e p h a n t s. *Paleog.(Eoc.)-Neog.(Rec.)*

   Perissodactyla. Odd-toed hoofed mammals; h o r s e s, r h i n o c e r o s e s, tapirs, titano-
      thers, chalicotheres. *Paleog.(Eoc.)-Neog.(Rec.)*

   Artiodactyla. Even-toed hoofed mammals; sheep, goats, cattle, deer, swine, camels, ore-
      odonts, hippopotamuses, *Paleog.(Eoc.)-Neog.(Rec.)*

Archaeocyathans

A group of extinct invertebrates, known as fossils only from Lower and Middle Cambrian rocks, now is classified as belonging to an independent phylum named Archaeocyatha. Formerly, the double-walled porous calcareous skeletons of these animals were interpreted as representing a strange sort of sponge or bottom-dwelling marine organism possibly related to the corals, but for several reasons such suggestions must be rejected.

The archaeocyathans developed as solitary individuals or grew together in colonies, their remains being so abundant in some formations that they build reeflike masses many feet thick and traceable scores of miles. Specimens are conical to cylindrical in form, with diameter ranging from 1.5 to 60 millimeters (2.4 inches) and maximum height of 100 millimeters (4 inches). An open central cavity is surrounded by two porous walls that are joined together by numerous radially disposed walls (Fig. A.19). The group is world-wide.

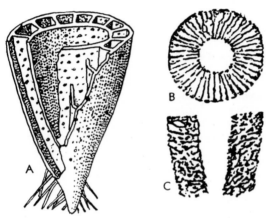

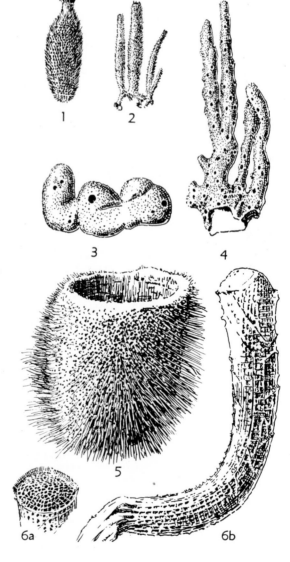

Fig. A.19 Archaeocyathans.——*A*. Diagrammatic sketch of fossil with part cut away to show porous double cones joined by radial walls.——*B*, *C*. Transverse and longitudinal sections of *Archaeocyathus*, from Lower Cambrian rocks of Labrador, ×2.5.

Fig. A.20 Modern sponges of types represented by fossils.——*1*, *2*. Calcareous sponges (*Sycon, Leucosolenia*) with one- to four-rayed spicules.——*3*, *4*. Siliceous sponges (*Chondrilla, Haliclona*) with one- to four-rayed spicules.——*5*, *6*. Siliceous sponges (*Staurocalyptus, Euplectella*) with six-rayed spicules. None to scale. (*After Hyman and Dendy, courtesy of Moore, Lalicker, and Fischer, Invertebrate Fossils, McGraw-Hill Book Company, Inc., New York, 1952.*)

Sponges

In simplest form, the sponges (Porifera) are characterized by a hollow globular or cylindrical structure with a relatively large opening at the top. As a whole, they exhibit extremely diverse form, growing in attached position as single individuals or joined in colonies (Fig. A.20). Most sponges are marine, but a few kinds live in fresh-water bodies. They range in size from that of a pinhead to a height or width of more than 1 meter.

Sponges lack internal organs of any kind, possess no nervous tissue, and are devoid of circulatory or digestive systems. In these respects their organization differs markedly from that found in more advanced types of invertebrates. The body walls are pierced by numerous small openings of canals that lead directly or circuitously by way of small chambers to a central cavity (Fig. A.21). So-called collar cells in the walls of the chambers or central cavity are provided with mobile hair-like appendages (flagella), which by rhythmic motion produce gentle water currents toward the sponge interior. The water carries microscopic food particles used by the animal and ultimately escapes by a vent (osculum) generally located on the upper surface of the sponge. Some sponges have no hard parts and therefore are not capable of fossilization, but a majority possess either siliceous or calcareous

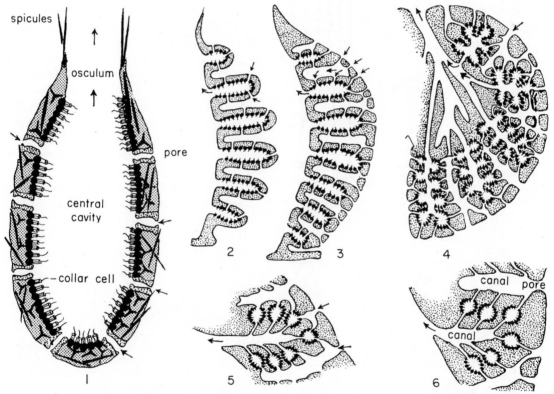

Fig. A.21 Types of sponge structure. Diagrammatic sections showing digestive collar cells (black), which control water movements by means of whiplike flagella, direction of water currents indicated by arrows.——*1.* Ascon type, simplest known form, with single vaselike body.——*2, 3.* Sycon type, with folded walls forming separate chambers lined by collar cells. ——*4–6.* Leucon type, characterized by subdivision of collar-cell chambers. (*Modified from Hyman, courtesy of Moore, Lalicker, and Fischer,* Invertebrate Fossils, *McGraw-Hill Book Company, Inc., New York, 1952.*)

skeletal elements (spicules) that are loosely embedded among soft cells of the body or knit together so as to form a strong framework (Fig. A.22). Disconnected spicules become scattered when the sponge dies and its soft parts decay, thus leaving no trace of the form of the whole animal though the spicules themselves are preserved. Sponges having a skeleton of spicules welded together are abundantly found as fossils, and these are the most interesting and useful in paleontological studies. Distribution of known sponges ranges from the Precambrian (Algonkian) to the present (Figs. 5.26, 8.22, 11.19, 12.6 to 12.10, 16.12).

Coelenterates

The coelenterates are the most simply organized animals having well-developed body tissues. They are aquatic invertebrates of highly varied form that very predominantly live in the sea. A majority grow together as colonies, but solitary individuals are rather common also. Many are attached throughout postlarval life, whereas others, including both individuals and colonies, float or swim about freely. The name of the phylum (*coel*, hollow; *enteron*, gut) refers to the manner in which the body interior functions as a digestive cavity (Fig. A.23). An almost universally distinguishing character is the occurrence of stinging capsules (nematocysts) useful for defense and numbing prey. The size of most individual coelenterates is small, that of attached forms (polyps) ranging from a diameter of less than 1 millimeter to as much as 1 meter but mostly not exceeding a few millimeters. Unattached forms (jellyfishes) of umbrella-like form, known as medusae, commonly have a diameter of 10 to 50 millimeters (2 in.), but a few attain the extraordinary diameter of 2 meters (6.3 feet). Many kinds of coelenterates lack hard parts; among forms provided with a skeleton, the preponderant majority secrete calcium carbonate and only a few have a chitinous covering.

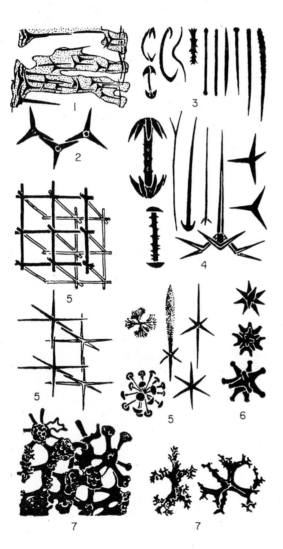

Fig. A.22   Types of sponge spicules.——*1.* Wall of calcareous sponge (*Grantia*) showing arrangement of discrete spicules, exterior at right.——*2.* Triradiate spicules of calcareous sponge in adjoined positions making part of firm skeleton.——*3.* One-rayed spicules (monaxons) of types common in both calcareous and siliceous sponges.——*4.* Four-rayed spicules (tetraxons) found in calcareous and siliceous sponges.—— *5.* Three-rayed spicules (triaxons) common in some siliceous sponges.——*6.* Many-rayed spicules (polyaxons) found in some siliceous sponges.——*7.* Irregular spicules (desmas) of type common to so-called lithistid siliceous sponges. None to scale. (*Courtesy of Moore, Lalicker, and Fischer, Invertebrate Fossils, McGraw-Hill Book Company, Inc., New York, 1952.*)

The phylum of coelenterates is abundantly represented in the fossil record, oldest known forms appearing in Precambrian (Algonkian) rocks (Fig. 4.40D). Owing to the diversity of groups, classification is relatively much ramified and attention here is confined to assemblages having paleontological importance, especially various kinds of corals.

Protomedusae. Primitive coelenterates of free-swimming type characterized by expansion of the body into large and small radial pouches are classed as Protomedusae (Figs. A.24, 4.40D). Known fossils belonging to this group range from late Precambrian to Ordovician and are recorded doubtfully in Pennsylvanian rocks. Probably the coelenterates originated as medusoid forms that generally resembled these.

Dipleurozoans. Rare as fossils but important in the study of organic evolution are the Lower Cambrian fossils from Australia known as dipleurozoans. They are medusoid coelenterates having well-defined bilateral symmetry, thus showing a character that distinguishes the vast majority of more highly organized animals (Fig. A.25).

Conulates (Scyphozoa). The Conulata (composed of the order named Conulariida) are extinct invertebrates represented by rather numerous and widely distributed fossils ranging from Cambrian to Triassic in age. They differ from known kinds of coelenterates generally in having an external covering of calcium phosphate admixed with chitin, and partly for this reason their classification long has been uncertain. Now, with little doubt these fossils are grouped with the scyphozoan jellyfishes, which are chiefly characterized by their prominent fourfold symmetry. Most conulates are steeply pyramidal in form, with quadrangular cross section, some showing inwardly projecting bifurcated septa suggestive of soft-tissue septa found in modern scyphozoans (Fig. A.26A, B). The chitinophosphatic hard parts of conulates are extremely thin, and despite the common occurrence of strengthening transverse ridges on the sides, there is good evidence that the covering was

Fig. A.23 Model of sea anemone. This animal, shown in extended position for feeding, is a typical coelenterate, characterized by a cylindrical body with mouth at the summit surrounded by numerous elongate tentacles armed with abundant stinging capsules (nematocysts). (*Courtesy of American Museum of Natural History.*)

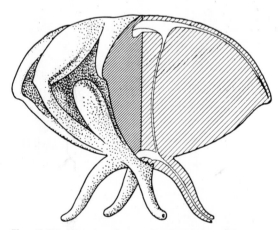

Fig. A.24 Protomedusae. Reconstruction of *Brooksella* (Cam.) partly cut away to show internal structures. (*H. J. Harrington and R. C. Moore, Treatise on Invertebrate Paleontology, courtesy of Geological Society of America and University of Kansas Press.*)

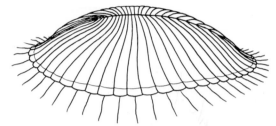

Fig. A.25 Dipleurozoa. Reconstruction of *Dickinsonia* (Cam.), oblique view, showing bilateral symmetry. Each lobe of the body bears a slender tentacle. (*H. J. Harrington and R. C. Moore, Treatise on Invertebrate Paleontology, courtesy of Geological Society of America and University of Kansas Press.*)

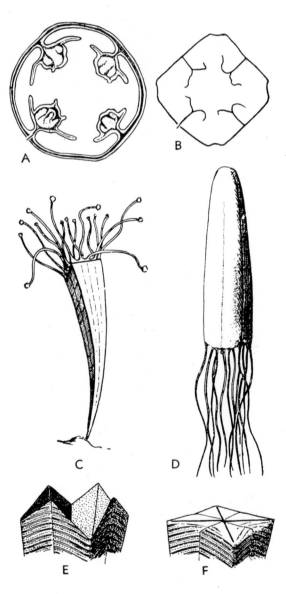

flexible in a manner to allow inbending of the apertural edges (Fig. A.26E, F). In early life stages conulates grew in attached position but later were able to break away and become free-swimming like jellyfishes, the pointed extremity being sealed over in a rounded manner (Fig. A.26C, D).

Scyphomedusae (Scyphozoa). Modern scyphozoans and several fossil forms ranging to as old as Jurassic are designated as Scyphomedusae. Commonly they are 45 centimeters (18 inches) or smaller in diameter, but some species attain dimensions of 2 meters (6.3 feet), being the largest known coelenterates. The umbrella-shaped body bears pendent tentacles around the rim, and angles of the four-cornered mouth are drawn outward in the form of more or less prominent lobes (Fig. A.27). The Scyphomedusae lack hard parts, yet in spite of this, some remarkably preserved impressions occur as fossils (Fig. 16.14).

Hydrozoans. The coelenterates classed as hydrozoans are mostly marine animals of small size that grow in colonies, but some live in fresh waters, and there are solitary polyps, as well as free-swimming individuals of medusoid form. Some build a considerable skeletal deposit of calcium carbonate. Each individual polyp consists of a cylindrical tube composed of two cell layers. It is attached at its base and bears at the free end a ring of tentacles surrounding the so-called mouth, which serves also as vent for the discharge of waste from the primitive digestive cavity (Figs. A.28, A.29). This cavity comprises the entire space

Fig. A.26 Conulata.——*A, B.* Transverse sections of modern scyphomedusan (*Craterolophus*) and Silurian conulate (*Eoconularia*) showing similarity in development of bifurcate septa (*after Kiderlen*).——*C, D.* Reconstruction of an attached conulate (*Archaeoconularia*) and free-swimming form (*Exoconularia*) (*after Kiderlen*).——*E, F.* Diagram showing apertural region of a conulate in open and closed condition. (*R. C. Moore and H. J. Harrington, Treatise on Invertebrate Paleontology, courtesy of Geological Society of America and University of Kansas Press.*)

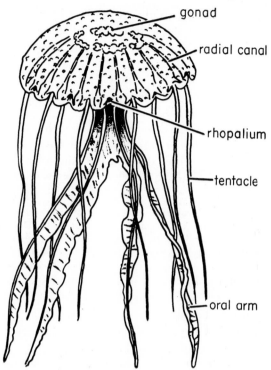

gonad

radial canal

rhopalium

tentacle

oral arm

Fig. A.27 Modern scyphozoan belonging to the Scyphomedusae. This form (*Pelagia*), which inhabits open oceans, is characterized by long oral lobes. (*Courtesy of L. H. Hyman, The Invertebrates: Protozoa through Ctenophora, McGraw-Hill Book Company, Inc., New York, 1940.*)

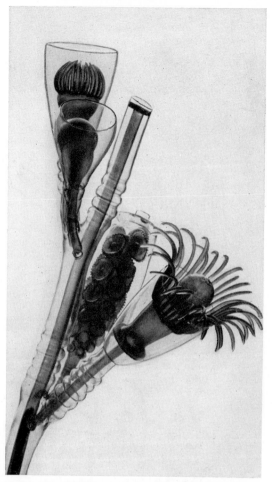

Fig. A.28 Model of modern colonial hydrozoan (Obelia). The polyps branch from a common stalk, that at right, with tentacles around the mouth, being a vegetative individual and that next to it a bud containing young medusae; much enlarged. (*Courtesy of American Museum of Natural History.*)

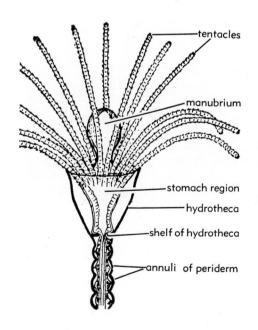

tentacles

manubrium

stomach region

hydrotheca

shelf of hydrotheca

annuli of periderm

Fig. A.29 Structural features of a hydrozoan polyp (Obelia). The corresponding individual in part of the colony illustrated in Fig. A.28 is readily identifiable. (*Courtesy of L. H. Hyman, The Invertebrates: Protozoa through Ctenophora, McGraw-Hill Book Company, Inc., New York, 1940.*)

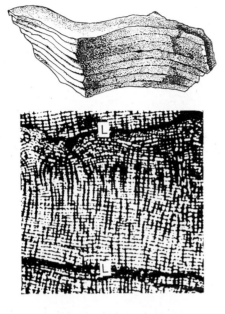

enclosed by the body walls. The hydrozoan colony grows by a sexual budding of new polyps, forming a delicate branching frond or, where the buds arise from a basal expansion, a mosslike felt. Many (hydrocorallines, stromatoporoids) secrete a dense calcareous deposit at the base.

Some of the hydrozoan buds in each colony are very different from those that have been described, for they develop into umbrella-like jellyfishes, or medusae, which break away and

Fig. A.30 Structural characters of stromatoporoids. Fragment of colony (*Stromatopora*, Dev.) showing layered structure (latilaminae), ×1, upper figure; detail, longitudinal section (*Actinostroma*, Dev.), ×3, lower figure. (*M. Lecompte, Treatise on Invertebrate Paleontology, courtesy of Geological Society of America and University of Kansas Press.*)

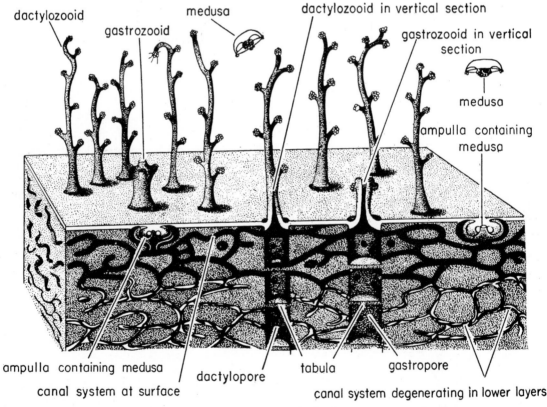

Fig. A.31 Part of milleporid colony. The several individuals show two types of polyps, which are connected to one another by a thin film of living tissue that covers the calcareous colonial skeleton traversed by irregular canals. (*H. Boschma, Treatise on Invertebrate Paleontology, courtesy of Geological Society of America and University of Kansas Press.*)

are free-swimming. The medusae reproduce sexually, forming the vegetative attached polyps or other medusae. There is thus an alternation of generation. Medusae are not adapted for fossilization, since they have no hard parts, but under exceptional conditions, they have been preserved.

Stromatoporoids deposit large masses of calcium carbonate in successive thin layers separated by low rods or pillars (Fig. A.30). Distinctive surface features, such as hummocky elevations with a large central pore and radiating grooves, may be present. Important rock builders in Cretaceous and younger divisions of geologic time are the milleporids and stylasterids, colonies of which are characterized by the dimorphic nature of associated polyps (Fig. A.31). Other groups of hydrozoans (trachylinids, spongiomorphids, hydroids) also appear in the fossil record.

Corals (Anthozoa). The corals are bottom-dwelling marine coelenterates. They are varied in color and, with outspread tentacles, are distinctly flower-like in appearance (*an-thos*, flower; *zoa*, animals). Some are solitary individuals, but a majority grow in colonies, many of which are several feet across. Relatively few of these creatures entirely lack hard parts; most secrete a calcareous skeleton of solid construction or at least produce spicules of calcium carbonate that are disconnectedly embedded in soft tissues of the body (as especially in the group classed as octocorals). Corals chiefly inhabit the very shallow and warmer parts of the sea, where colonies of varied sorts commonly build reefs.

Structurally, the body of the coral polyp differs from that of the hydrozoan in the presence of numerous radial walls of membrane (*mesenteries*), some of which project inward only a short distance from the circumference of the body, others reaching and joining a slitlike gullet that extends part way downward from the mouth (Fig. A.32). The calcium carbonate skeleton is normally secreted by the outer portion of the body wall, which thus encases the lower part of the coral in a cylindrical or conical tube or forms a flattish

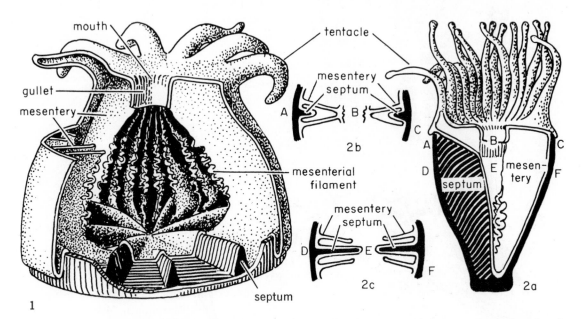

Fig. A.32 Coral polyps showing relation of soft parts to skeleton.——*1*. Coral with soft parts closely similar to those of a sea anemone.——*2*. Simple scleractinian coral; *2a*, longitudinal section cut through a septum at left and between septa at right (septum composed of inclined rows of calcite fibers); *2b*, transverse section through A, B, C of *2a*; *2c*, transverse section through D, E, F of *2a*. (*Courtesy of Moore, Lalicker, and Fischer, Invertebrate Fossils, McGraw-Hill Book Company, Inc., New York, 1952.*)

basal expansion (Fig. A.33). Radial calcareous walls (*septa*) are built by infolded parts of the body covering. The upper edges of these walls generally slope inward from the outer calcareous wall (*theca*) so as to form a central depression (*calyx*). In Mesozoic and younger corals (Scleractinia), there are typically six dominant radiating walls; in most Paleozoic forms (Rugosa), there are only four such primary walls. Among the latter, one or more of these four may be repressed so as to form a furrow (*fossula*) or furrows in the calyx (Fig. A.33). At successive stages in the life of the coral polyp, it may draw upward slightly and deposit a new basal platform (*tabula*) across the tube, and vacated spaces between the radial walls may be partitioned off by small oblique plates (*dissepiments*). Some corals secrete a central rodlike axis

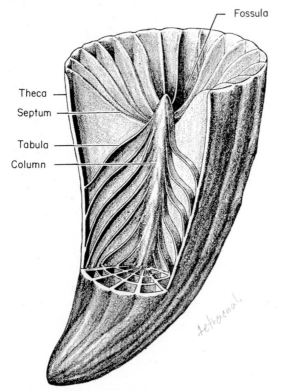

Fossula

Theca

Septum

Tabula

Column

Fig. A.33 Diagram showing structure of a simple horn coral (Lophophyllidium). About one-third of the upper part of the corallite is cut away so as to show the internal structure.

(*column*), which may project into the calyx. These and other structures give complexity and wide variation to the hard parts of different species of corals, which make them the more useful as markers of strata that contain them.

The abundance and variety of fossil corals contribute to their importance as stratigraphic guides in correlation, and in most divisions of the geologic column from the Ordovician onward this group is noteworthy as rock builders. Many kinds are illustrated in foregoing chapters of this book (Figs. 7.21*B*; 7.22*A, B, J*; 8.19*D*; 8.21*B*; 10.22*A*; 11.19*D, E*; 12.11*A* to *C*; 12.12*A* to *L*; 12.30*G*; 16.13; 20.5).

Bryozoans

With exception of a single genus, bryozoans are exclusively colonial animals that secrete a calcareous, horny, or membraneous covering that in different species exhibits a multitudinous variety of form and structure. Of course, only the calcareous forms are adapted for preservation as fossils. The simplest bryozoans build a simple, chainlike series of tubes, one budding from another (Fig. A.34). By branching and lateral confluence of tubes, the more complex types of colonial structures are produced. Some grow in slender tufts; some spread over shells or other foreign objects in a delicate network of interwoven threads; or they form thin, leaflike expansions, rounded branches, lacy fronds, or massive subglobular bodies (Fig. A.35). There are several thousand described fossil species ranging in age from Ordovician to Recent, and during parts of geologic time the bryozoans were important rock builders.

Superficially, the bryozoans resemble certain hydrozoans, but they differ from them radically in the possession of a distinct body cavity, an alimentary canal, a highly developed nervous system, and delicate respiratory tentacles surrounding the mouth (Fig. A.36). The colonial skeleton (*zoarium*) has various structural peculiarities which, with the almost microscopic size of the individual habitations (*zooecia*), make it easy to distinguish the bryozoans from other organisms. Many bryozoans were widely distributed geographically but short-ranging vertically; they are therefore good guide fossils of the formations in which they occur.

Features that are most important in the evolution and classification of the bryozoans are (1) characters of the zooecial apertures, (2) internal structures, and (3) the mode of colonial growth, which determines the form of the zoarium (Figs. 6.23, 9.18, 9.19, 11.19, 12.13, 12.14, 16.17).

Brachiopods

Brachiopods are marine shelled animals that are related to the bryozoans. Their external form, average size, and complete absence of colonial development, however, do not remotely suggest the bryozoans.

Brachiopods have two unequal shells, or valves, each of which is bilaterally symmetrical (Fig. A.37). They consist of calcium carbonate in the great majority of species, but some have chitinous shells, impregnated with

Fig. A.34   Model of a colony of modern bryozoans (*Bugula*). Each small tube of the branching colony houses an individual animal (much enlarged). (*Courtesy of American Museum of Natural History.*)

Fig. A.35   Parts of two Paleogene bryozoan colonies. These fossils belong to the group known as cheilostomes, restricted to post-Paleozoic rocks (much enlarged). (*After F. Canu and R. S. Bassler.*)

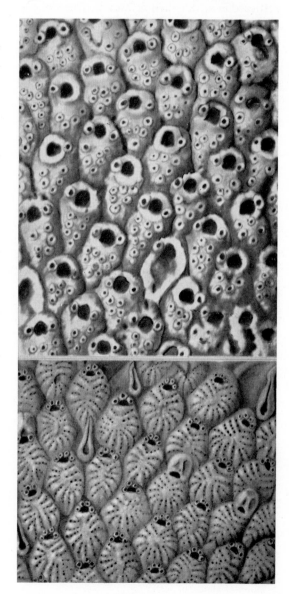

calcium phosphate and carbonate. The form of the shell is variable. Generally both valves are convex, but they may be nearly flat, one or other of the valves may be convex while the opposite is concave, or one valve may be cone-shaped, the other fitting like a lid upon it. The posterior portion of the shell, where the valves are hinged or held closely together, is pointed in a beak. One of the valves is designated as pedicle, and the other as brachial. During all or part of the existence of the brachiopod after the free-swimming larva settles down, the shell is attached to the sea bottom by a fleshy stalk (*pedicle*) that projects posteriorly between the valves or through an opening in the pedicle valve. With increasing age, the pedicle opening may become closed and the pedicle itself atrophied. Some brachiopods are anchored by projecting spines or are cemented to foreign objects by the whole or part of the surface of the pedicle valve.

Many brachiopods are smooth, except for concentric markings that indicate interrupted growth. The greater number, however, develop radiating striae, ribs, or plications that

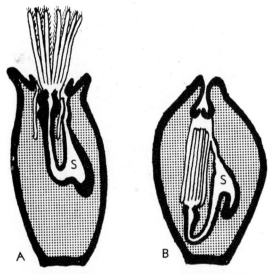

Fig. A.36　Anatomy of a living bryozoan (Alcyonidium). The body wall of this form is membranous and flexible, hard parts being absent. The drawings show longitudinal sections of the animal in extended position (*A*) and retracted (*B*); body cavity shaded, S indicates stomach.

ornament and strengthen the shell materially. The median portion and front margin of one valve are commonly depressed (*sinus*), while the corresponding part of the opposite valve is elevated (*fold*). Spines may be developed in various parts or over the entire surface. Between the beak and the hinge line in many species, a flattened or curved triangular space (*interarea*) is observed. It is more highly developed in the pedicle valve and may be bisected by a small triangular opening (*delthyrium*) for the pedicle. The opening may be partly closed by a plate (*deltidium*) secreted by the pedicle or by a pair of plates (*deltidial plates*) secreted by an extension of the mantle that builds the pedicle valve. The shells of most living species are light-colored and unornamented, but some bear vivid color markings. It is interesting to find at least some fossil brachiopods in which traces of color patterns are preserved. The large, externally sculptured brachiopods of Paleozoic time must have been objects of much beauty.

The more primitive brachiopods (inarticulates) have no definite hinge structure, the valves being held together merely by muscles. More advanced shells (articulates) have hinge teeth on the pedicle valve that fit into sockets on the brachial valve, and the hinge line may be considerably extended laterally. The valves are pulled together by muscles attached to the interior and are opened by other muscles extending from the floor of the pedicle valve to the end of a lever-like projection (*cardinal process*), near the beak of the brachial valve, which passes between and beyond the hinge teeth. These structures may be supplemented and supported by plates of various shape and position inside the shell. Finally, in all advanced types of brachiopods, the delicate fleshy arms (*brachia*) that serve to propel food particles toward the mouth are supported by calcified projections attached near the beak of the brachial valve. These may consist of moderately short, curved processes, of a loop, or of two thin, spirally coiled ribbons (Fig. A.37, *1*).

Numerous representative kinds of brachiopods are illustrated in chapters of this book

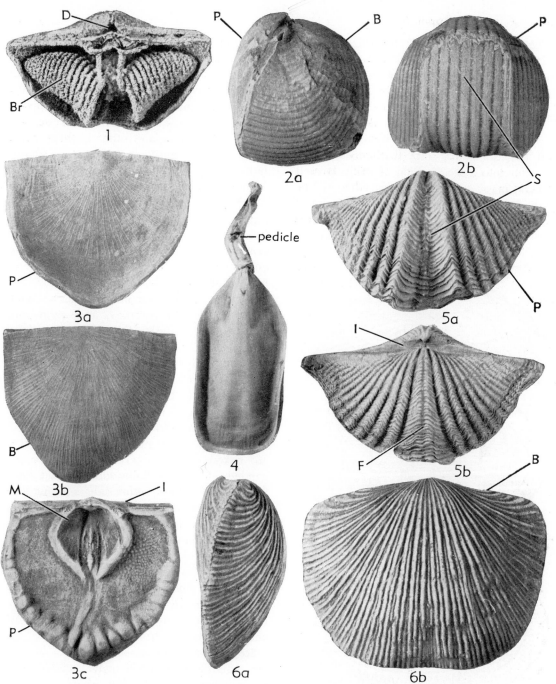

Fig. A.37 Morphological features of typical brachiopods.——*1. Mucrospirifer*, Dev., with most of brachial valve removed to show spiral internal supports of brachia, ×2.——*2. Hypothyridina venustula*, M. Dev., side and front views showing strongly convex brachial valve and prominent interlocking of fold and sinus along front edge of shell, ×1.5.——*3. Strophomena nutans*, U. Ord., a concavo-convex shell, with interior of pedicle valve, ×2.——*4. Lingula*, a modern inarticulate brachiopod, with fleshy pedicle protruding from beak, ×1.5.——*5. Mucrospirifer consobrinus*, M. Dev., ×2.——*6. Plaesiomys subquadrata*, U. Ord., side and brachial views, ×2. (Explanation: *B*, brachial valve; *Br*, brachial support; *D*, delthyrium; *F*, fold; *I*, interarea; *M*, muscle scar; *P*, pedicle valve.) (*Courtesy of G. A. Cooper, U.S. National Museum.*)

(Figs. 1.13*A* to *M*, 5.21*E*, 6.19, 6.20, 7.19*C*, 7.22*I*, 8.19*A* to *C*, 8.21*J*, 10.22*B* to *G*, 11.19*F* to *L*, 11.20, 12.9*C*, *D*, 12.11*I*, 12.12*U* to *W*, 12.15*A* to *H*, 12.16*A* to *E*).

Mollusks

Mollusks are characterized by unsegmented soft bodies (*mollis,* soft) that generally are divisible into a head region, dorsally located visceral mass, and ventrally placed foot. The body is mostly inclosed by a thin skinlike mantle that commonly secretes a protective shell composed of calcium carbonate (arago-

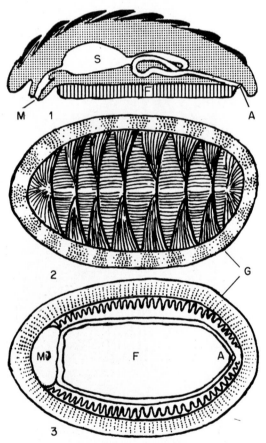

Fig. A.38 Morphological features of chitons.—— *1.* Longitudinal section showing eight dorsally placed plates (black), digestive tract, and foot.——*2.* Dorsal view showing plates and surrounding girdle.——*3.* Ventral view showing rows of gills in mantle cavity between girdle and foot. (Explanation: *A,* anus; *F,* foot; *G,* girdle; *M,* mouth; *S,* stomach.)

nite or calcite or both). The phylum contains six classes, all of which are more or less well represented in the fossil record; they are named Monoplacophora (simple chiton-like forms), Amphineura (chitons), Scaphopoda (secreting tooth shells), Gastropoda (snails), Pelecypoda (clams and other bivalves), and Cephalopoda (nautiloids, ammonoids, squids, and others). These groups are highly diverse in appearance and mode of life. Some (pelecypods) are adapted to both marine and fresh waters, others (gastropods) to these environments and to breathing air so as to travel about on land, and still others (remaining groups) only to life in the seas. A majority of the aquatic mollusks are bottom dwellers (benthonic), but very many kinds are able to swim freely (nektonic), and a few are floaters (planktonic). Mollusks range in size from barely 1 millimeter in greatest dimension to giant squids reported to attain a length of 15 meters (50 feet).

Chitons (Amphineura). The chitons are relatively simple mollusks with an elongate body commonly protected on the dorsal side by eight articulated plates (Fig. A.38); a few are naked. Margins of the mantle are expanded into a thick fleshy girdle, along inner borders of which on either side is a long row of gills extending from the vicinity of the mouth to the anus. The head region is reduced, bearing neither tentacles nor eyes. The foot is a broad, flattened fleshy mass that occupies most of the ventral surface. Chitons are common along the borders of modern seas, and the distinctive plates of their skeleton are found as fossils in various strata, the oldest yet known being Ordovician.

Scaphopods (Scaphopoda). The scaphopods are mollusks with an elongate slender body surrounded by a mantle that secretes a slightly curved and tapered shell open at both ends. This form is the basis for the common name of tooth (or tusk) shells (Fig. A.39). The scaphopods live partly buried obliquely in sand or mud of the sea bottom, ranging to maximum depths of approximately 4,500 meters (15,000 feet). Fossil remains are common in geologically young deposits, and they are known from Devonian onward to the present.

Gastropods (Gastropoda). The gastropods (*gaster*, belly; *podos*, foot), or snails, have a distinct head, which carries the mouth, tentacles, and eyes. They are distinguished by having a broad foot, on which they may crawl slowly, and by the possession of a single spirally coiled or cap-shaped, unchambered shell, on account of which they are frequently termed *univalves* (Figs. A.40, A.41). Some gastropods, however, have no shell at all. The mouth is armed with horny plates and a rasp-like process (*radula*). The esophagus leads into a long coiled intestine, surrounded by a large liver, kidneys, and various glands. A heart and many-branching blood vessels make up the circulatory system, and two cerebral and numerous other paired ganglia, with their connections, compose the nervous system. Most gastropods have tufted or leaflike gills, originally paired but generally becoming single by the atrophy of one. Reproductive organs are specialized. Gastropods are most abundant in the shallow seas, but they live also in fresh waters, and many are air breathers. They feed mostly on plants, but some, including the drills, which can bore a neat round hole through other shells, are carnivorous. A few are scavengers.

The shell of the gastropods, secreted by the mantle on the dorsal side of the body, consists essentially of calcium carbonate in the form of aragonite and hence, like the

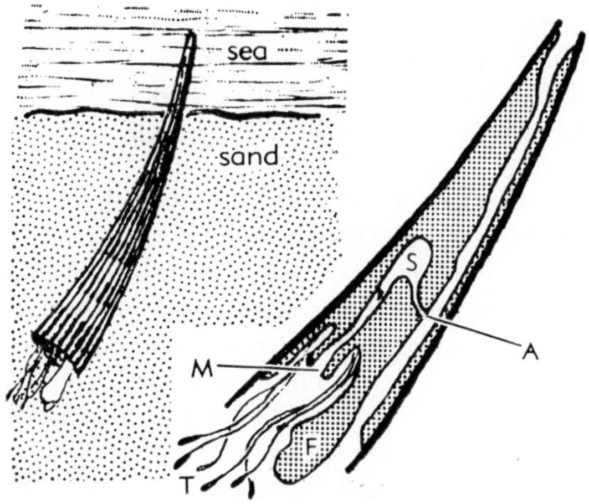

Fig. A.40   Large marine gastropod (*Triton tritonis*). This vividly colored shell is moderately high-spired, ×0.3. (Explanation: *A*, aperture; *B*, body whorl; *I*, inner lip; *O*, outer lip; *S*, spire; *SN*, siphonal notch; *V*, varix, comprising outer lip of aperture at a pause in growth; *W*, whorl.) (*Photograph courtesy of American Museum of Natural History.*)

Fig. A.39   Scaphopods. Diagram at left shows *Dentalium* in living position, mostly buried in sand; longitudinal section at right diagrammatically shows morphological features. (Explanation: *A*, anus; *F*, foot; *M*, mouth; *S*, stomach; *T*, tentacles.)

pearly shell substance in pelecypods, is subject to solution or alteration rather readily in fossilization. Generally, the spire is strongly elevated and screwlike, being carried on the back of the animal with the apex pointed upward and backward and the aperture downward and forward. Most shells are right-handed; that is, the aperture when held downward and facing the observer is on the right side (Fig. A.41, 4). A few are left-handed (Fig. A.41, 5). Some shells are coiled in a plane. Each complete coil is termed a *whorl*. The whorls may wind around a solid axis (*columella*) or leave an open space (*umbili-*

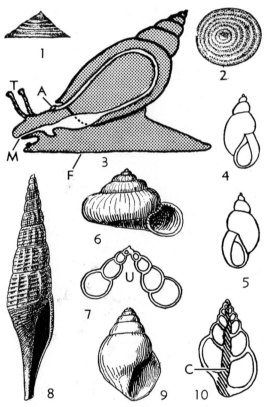

Fig. A.41 Morphological features of gastropods.
——*1, 2.* Simple cap-shaped shell (limpet).——*3.* Diagrammatic section of gastropod carrying its spiral shell, showing (*A*) anal vent, (*F*) foot, (*M*) mouth, and (*T*) tentacles.——*4, 5.* Right- and left-handed spiral shells.——*6, 7.* Exterior and section of spiral shell with umbilicus (*U*).——*8.* High-spired shell with elongate aperture.——*9, 10.* Exterior and section of spiral shell with columella (*C*). (*In part from Winifred Goldring, New York State Museum.*)

cus) (Fig. A.41, *6, 7, 9, 10*). The aperture is generally rounded but may be notched by canals carrying the siphon, which conducts water to the gills, and the anal tube. The position and character of these notches are indicated on the earlier-formed whorls by the configuration of the shell and by deflection of the growth lines. External ornamentation is highly varied; it consists of revolving and transverse lines, grooves, ribs, frills, and spines. In addition, many gastropod shells are beautifully decorated with a diversity of brilliant or delicate hues and patterns.

The body of the gastropod is united to the shell by muscular attachment, and generally the animal may draw itself entirely inside for protection. In many species an accessory plate (*operculum*) secreted by the foot then closes the aperture. This plate is commonly composed of horny material and is not fossilized, but rarely it is calcareous and may be preserved.

A subordinate division among the gastropods, which, however, was very important in parts of Paleozoic time, is that of the *pteropods*. These are rather small, free-swimming forms in which the foot is modified into two winglike fins. The shell is generally a narrow and straight pointed tube, which is circular or triangular in cross section.

Representative fossil gastropods are illustrated in various chapters of this book (Figs. 6.19*E;* 7.22*G, H;* 9.18*B;* 10.22*I* to *K;* 11.19*A;* 12.18*A* to *D;* 15.18*E;* 15.20*E;* 16.18*G;* 20.7*A* to *E*).

Pelecypods (Pelecypoda). The pelecypods are bivalved aquatic mollusks with a bilaterally symmetrical body; fairly well-developed digestive, circulatory, and nervous systems; and a muscular foot that may be used in locomotion. They have no head, and in this respect they are more primitive than the gastropods and cephalopods. In most pelecypods the membranous mantle that encloses the body and secretes the shell is extended backward out of the shell and forms two tubes (*siphons*) (Fig. A.42). These carry currents of water, of which the inflowing one carries oxygen for respiration and microscopic organic matter for food and the outflowing one serves to remove waste products. The tubes can be drawn inside the shell, except where they are unusually elongated. Most clams live on the bottom of the shallow parts of the sea, but some, like the mussels, have become adapted to fresh waters. They may crawl about slowly or burrow into mud, sand, or even wood and stone. The scallop (*Pecten*) can swim a little by clapping its valves together and by forcing water alternately from one side and the other.

The two valves of the pelecypod are typically equal in size and symmetrical one with the other (Fig. A.43); they are carried on the right and left sides of the animal, the line of hingement being dorsal. This is very different from the two valves of the brachiopod, which are dorsal and ventral, one larger than the other and each valve divisible into equal symmetrical halves. The foot of the pelecypod projects forward on the ventral side between the valves, and the siphons backward. The beak of each valve generally, but not invariably, points forward and is located in front of the mid-length of the shell. By this and other means the fossil shell may be oriented readily. The valves are held together in most pelecypods by two large muscles (Fig. A.42), but in some, like the oyster, there is only one such muscle. The valves are fastened together at the hinge by an elastic ligament which, if external, is placed under tension and, if internal, under compression when the muscles close the shell. When the muscles relax, the shell springs open automatically. Articulation of the two valves is aided in very many species by different types of teeth and sockets along the hinge line; the interlocking of these serves to hinder slipping or twisting of one valve on the other. The external ornamentation comprises concentric growth lines, projecting lamellae, ridges, ribs, folds, nodes, and spines. Certain fossil species have a subtriangular space (*cardinal area*) set off by a slight groove between the beak and the hinge line; in others and in many living forms there is a heart-shaped area (*lunule*) bounded by a ridge or groove in front of the beaks and a more elongated one

(*escutcheon*) extending backward from the beaks.

On the inside of the shell are attachment scars of the muscles. A slight furrow (*pallial line*), which marks the place of attachment of the mantle, parallels the ventral border of many pelecypods, and a strong deflection of this furrow (*pallial sinus*) in some shows

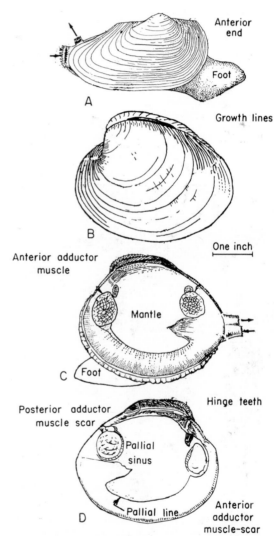

Fig. A.42 Morphological features of pelecypods. ——*A. Anodonta*, a common fresh-water mussel (arrows showing direction of water movement in siphons).——*B–D. Venus*, a shallow-water marine clam; *B*, exterior, viewed obliquely from above so as to show both valves; *C*, soft parts revealed by removal of left valve; *D*, interior of left valve. (*Modified from Winifred Goldring, New York State Museum.*)

where the siphons are drawn into the shell. These internal features are clearly defined on some fossil molds. The fact that the inner pearly layer of pelecypod shells consists of aragonite explains the frequent removal of the shell substance by solution, for aragonite, though identical with calcite in composition, is more soluble. In collecting fossils, one often finds that brachiopods and other shells made

Fig. A.43 Typical modern marine clam shell (*Arca grandis*). The strongly arched valves have regularly spaced ribs diverging radially from the beaks. This species lives along the Atlantic Coast from Cape Cod to the West Indies. (*Courtesy of American Museum of Natural History.*)

Fig. A.44 Types of modern cephalopods. The large central figure shows a swimming nautilus and near it are several squids. At lower left is an octopus. (*Courtesy of Moore, Lalicker, and Fischer, Invertebrate Fossils, McGraw-Hill Book Company, Inc., New York, 1952.*)

up of calcite are well preserved whereas pelecypods and gastropods, whose original shell was largely composed of aragonite, are represented only by molds.

The structures of the hinge region, musculature, and general form of the shell are the chief features used in classifying the pelecypods. In spite of a wide variety of forms, the group has been rather conservative throughout its long period of existence.

Examples of the highly varied genera of pelecypods found as fossils are illustrated in foregoing chapters (Figs. 11.19G, H; 12.17A to F; 15.19A to E; 16.18A to D; 16.19; 20.6A to G).

Cephalopods (Cephalopoda). The cephalopods are the most highly organized class of mollusks. They include the largest and most powerful of all invertebrate animals, and they are one of the most important groups of fossils. The best-known living cephalopods are the pearly nautilus, which has a coiled, many-chambered shell, the octopuses, and the cuttle-fishes, some of which have internal shelly structures (Fig. A.44). The head is well defined in most types and is provided with large eyes. The mouth contains jaws armed with a powerful horny beak and is surrounded by fleshy tentacles, which are used in grasping objects. Among cuttlefishes, the tentacles bear strong sucker disks and hooks. The foot is transformed into a muscular funnel-shaped swimming organ through which water may be ejected so as to propel the cephalopod rapidly backward or sideward. Cephalopods breathe by gills and are exclusively marine. The nervous, circulatory, digestive, and reproductive systems and the sense organs are all specialized and well developed.

Two main classes of cephalopods are distinguished: (1) the *tetrabranchiates*, which have four gills and a chambered external shell, and (2) the *dibranchiates*, which have two gills and an internal shell or none at all. The first group is represented by thousands of fossil species, but only one, the nautilus (Fig. A.45), is still living; the second had a great development in Mesozoic time and includes a variety of living species.

The shell of the nautilus is coiled in a plane and is bilaterally symmetrical. In life the aperture is directed forward, the shell twisting spirally backward and upward above the animal. Accordingly, the outer, convex part of the coiled tube is ventral, and the inner, concave part, is dorsal. In side view, only the last-formed coil (*whorl*) of the shell may be seen, for in the nautilus each coil extends laterally so as to envelop and conceal the inner ones. The cross section of each embracing whorl is therefore strongly crescentic. This type of shell is said to be deeply *involute*, and it is evidently an advanced or specialized form of coiling. Among fossil nautiloids there are many examples in which the outer whorl only partly embraces the inner and many in which the coils are barely in contact at their outer and inner margins. Then there are coiled shells in which the whorls do not touch. There are also curved but uncoiled shells, and finally the most primitive type of all, which is straight.

The body of the nautilus occupies only the end portion of the outer whorl, this part of the shell being known as the body chamber (Fig. A.45). At the inner end of the body chamber is a cross plate (*septum*), which is concave toward the aperture, and at regular short spaces throughout the unoccupied parts of the shell are similar partitions, which were formed at successive stages in the growth of the animal (Fig. A.45). These septa and the chambers into which they divide the nautilus shell are characteristic features which serve to distinguish it very readily from that of planospirally coiled gastropods. Observation shows that each septum is pierced by a round opening, which provides passage for a tube (*siphon*) that extends back to the embryonic chamber in the center of the shell. In many of the ancient nautiloids the siphon was encased in a calcareous tube (*siphuncle*), which, of course, may be preserved in the fossils. The junctions of the septa with the outer wall of the shell are termed *sutures*; they cannot be seen from the exterior unless the outer shell is broken or worn away. The sutures of early Paleozoic cephalopods are straight or gently curved, but those of later time became angulated and extremely complex in pattern. External ornamentation consists merely of color bands and faint curving growth lines in the modern nautilus. The majority of fossil nautiloids have smooth shells, but some had strong ribs or spines, and a few preserve indications of a color pattern.

Ammonoids are distinguished from nautiloids mainly by more or less complex fluting of peripheral parts of the septa that divide the shell into chambers, and this is expressed clearly by the suture pattern (Fig. A.46). Most Paleozoic ammonoids exhibit comparatively simple curved and angulated sutures; collectively they are classed as *goniatites*. Shells characterized by toothlike small indentations on parts of the sutures are *ceratites;* these first appear in Mississippian rocks, are most abundant in the Triassic, and occur among Cretaceous ammonoids. The most complex sutures, some with extremely intricate patterns, typify the *ammonites*, distributed from Pennsylvanian to uppermost Cretaceous, and these are the dominant cephalopods of Mesozoic time.

Squidlike cephalopods possessing a readily fossilizable internal shell are the *belemnoids* and related dibranchiate forms (Fig. A.47). In most of these a small chambered shell (*phragmocone*) is surrounded by a solid structure (*rostrum*) of concentrically laminated, radially fibrous calcite that is posteriorly elongated into a cigar-shaped form; these rostra are most commonly found as fossils.

Illustrated in various chapters of this book are numerous kinds of nautiloids (Figs.

Fig. A.45 Exterior and interior of chambered nautilus (Nautilus pompilius). The exterior view shows growth lines and color markings of the shell but reveals no sutures, because these mark junctions of the chamber divisions (septa) with the outer shell. (Explanation: *A*, aperture; *B*, body chamber; *C*, camera or chamber; *P*, protoconch, initially formed shell; *S*, septum; *Si*, siphuncle.) (*Photographs courtesy of American Museum of Natural History.*)

6.19F, G; 7.19A; 7.22E, F; 7.23C; 8.21G, H; 11.21E; 12.11E, F; 12.19 B, E, G), ammonoids (Figs. 9.18F; 10.22L; 11.1; 12.19A, C, F, H; 13.15A to C; 14.11A to F; 14.12; 15.18A to D; 15.20A, C, D; 16.18H, I; 16.21A to E), and belemnoids (15.20B, 16.18E, 16.20, 16.22).

Annelids

The phylum Annelida comprises a host of segmented worms, which are distinguished by soft bodies composed of many essentially identical segments (somites). They are ill adapted for fossilization, but some possess hard, toothlike mouth parts collectively designated as *scolecodonts* that are found preserved in sedimentary deposits. Exceptionally, as in the Middle Cambrian Burgess Shale of western Canada, the form of whole annelids and hairlike projections from the body are observable (Figs. 5.26E to G, 12.10H). Many

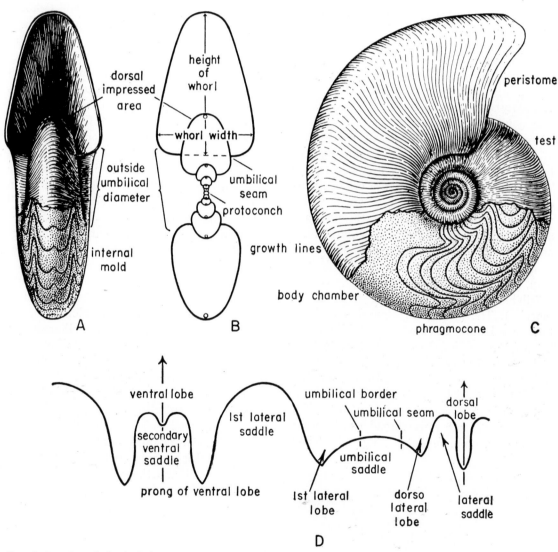

Fig. A.46 Morphological features of ammonoids.——*A–C.* Apertural, section, and side views of a goniatite, shell partly removed to reveal sutures.——*D.* Diagram of suture showing nomenclature of parts; arrows point in direction of shell aperture. (*A. K. Miller and W. M. Furnish, Treatise on Invertebrate Paleontology, courtesy of Geological Society of America and University of Kansas Press.*)

trails and burrows probably made by worms are indirect evidence of annelids or possibly of some representatives of the several phyla of nonsegmented worms (Fig. 4.40A).

Arthropods

A considerable majority (approximately 800,000 species) of all known kinds of animals belongs to the phylum Arthropoda (*arthros,* joint; *podos,* foot), for grouped together in this assemblage are the hosts of insects, spiders, scorpions, centipedes, millipedes, crustaceans, trilobites, and other jointed-leg invertebrates. Virtually all these animals are characterized by a distinctly segmented body that is covered externally by a hard organic skeleton containing chitin, and varied sorts of paired appendages having movable joints are attached to body segments. They are bilaterally symmetrical and during at least part of their life are highly mobile, being able to crawl, swim, or fly about freely. Their nervous system and sense organs, generally including prominent eyes, are well developed. Taken as a whole, the arthropods are adapted to every conceivable environment and are entitled to recognition as the chief competitors of vertebrate animals, including man, for survival.

Trilobitoids (Trilobitoidea, Trilobitomorpha). The arthropods classed as trilobitoids are known chiefly from Middle Cambrian (Burgess Shale) rocks, but they include at least one Lower Devonian form. They are rather heterogeneous in appearance, some being distinguished by prominent hornlike projections of the carapace, others by shrimplike form, and still others by broad exoskeletons somewhat resembling that of king crabs. They

Fig. A.47 Restoration of belemnoid showing internal skeleton. Soft parts of the body are represented as transparent in order to show the shape and position of hard parts, drawn in longitudinal section. (*Modified from Winifred Goldring, New York State Museum.*)

correspond to the trilobites in some respects (hence their name) but are sufficiently distinct from them and other main arthropod groups to be classified separately. Examples are illustrated in chapters on the Cambrian and Paleozoic life (Figs. 5.26A to *D,* 12.10*D* to *F*).

Trilobites (Trilobita, Trilobitomorpha). The most interesting of all invertebrate fossils to the average person are trilobites. This is due partly to the easily recognized character of the head, eyes, segmented body, and tail, and partly to the obvious biologic advancement and approach to such familiar creatures as lobsters, crabs, and insects. Indeed, trilobites are probably the direct or indirect ancestors of all other joint-legged invertebrates. For this reason, and because the trilobites are very numerous and valuable guide fossils in many Paleozoic formations, they occupy a position of importance.

Trilobites were protected on the dorsal side by a hard shelly carapace consisting of chitin impregnated by calcium carbonate. The shell is longitudinally three-lobed, with an axial and two side (*pleural*) regions that are commonly well defined on head (*cephalon*), thorax, and tail (*pygidium*) (Fig. A.48). Since the trilobite skeleton is rather easily separated into segments, one finds these fragments much more frequently than a complete test. As shown by a few remarkably well-preserved fossils, these animals had delicate antennae, numerous legs that were used for crawling or swimming, and breathing organs.

The central lobe of the head (*glabella* and posterior segment defined as *occipital lobe*) is generally well defined (Fig. A.48). Typically, this axial region shows traces of at least five original segments that consolidated to form the head, and these correspond to pairs of appendages on the ventral side of the head. Lateral portions of the trilobite cephalon are each divided by a line of parting (*facial suture*) into an inner part (*fixed cheek,* or *fixigena*) continuous with the glabella and an outer part (*free cheek,* or *librigena*) that carries the eyes. In early types of trilobites, the fixigenae make up nearly the whole of the lateral lobes of the head shield, the facial sutures being marginal. In more advanced orders, the librigenae show clearly on the dorsal side, the sutures intersecting the posterior or lateral margins of the head shield. Most trilobites had a pair of raised, outward-facing compound eyes provided with numerous facets, and in some there was a simple eye located centrally on the occipital lobe. As many as 15,000 facets may occur on one of the compound eyes. Some trilobites were blind. The segments of the thorax were jointed and permitted slight movement, but flexibility sufficient to bring the tail under the head and thus protect the vulnerable ventral parts was not developed in the earliest, most primitive genera. The pygidium, like the head shield, was formed by fusion of several segments, for its superficial markings and the paired appendages beneath it indicate ancestral separated segments.

Stages in the development of the trilobite individual are determinable by means of the successively castoff, or molted, shells. During the larval stage, when only head and tail shields were present, there were commonly several molts; during the adolescent stage, there were molts at the time of adding each thoracic segment; during adult life, there were further molts, which permitted increase in size but did not increase the number of segments. The characters exhibited during these changes are significant in establishing the direction of evolutionary modification in the different groups of trilobites, for the life history of the individual recapitulates more or less completely the history of the race.

Numerous representative trilobites are illustrated in chapters describing the Paleozoic part of geologic time (Figs. 5.16A, B; 5.21A to D; 5.22; 5.23; 6.21; 7.19B; 7.21A; 7.22C, D; 7.23B, D; 8.21I; 10.22H; 12.10C; 12.11G, H; 12.12R; 12.20A to F; 12.21; 12.22; 12.23).

Chelicerates (Chelicerata). The chelicerates are a varied assemblage of arthropods that includes spiders, scorpions, king crabs, eurypterids, and other forms characterized by lack of antennae and mandibles. Typically, the head and thorax are united as a cephalothorax

that is clearly distinct from the abdomen. The cephalothorax bears six pairs of jointed appendages, of which the front pair (*chelicerae*) terminate in claws and the others have varied form in different groups. The chelicerates are divided into two main assemblages (Merostomata, Arachnida), both represented by numerous fossils.

The merostomes comprise the king crabs (Xiphosura) and eurypterids (Eurypterida), among which the cephalothorax (also called *prosoma*) is very broadly joined to the abdomen. At the rear of the abdomen, which may be divided into anterior (*preabdomen*) and posterior (*postabdomen*) parts, is a spikelike tail (*telson*) (Fig. A.49). All merostomes are aquatic animals with paired appendages behind the chelicerae modified for walking or swimming. Both compound eyes, with many lenses, and simple eyes (*ocelli*) are present.

Among arachnids, the second pair of ap-

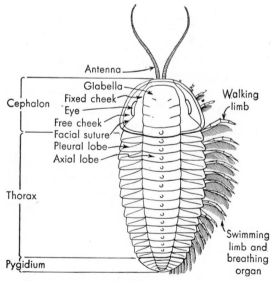

Fig. A.48 Morphological features of a trilobite. The illustrated form is *Triarthrus*, from Ordovician rocks, with limbs on the left side omitted. As now customarily defined, the glabella does not include the posterior axial segment of the cephalon, which is designated as occipital ring; pleural and axial lobes refer to divisions of the carapace extending throughout its length, as well as to parts of individual segments. Approximately ×1.5.

pendages (*pedipalpi*) is modified for capturing and masticating food, and the four pairs behind these are walking legs (Fig. A.50). The clawlike chelicerae are fangs provided with a duct that connects with a poison gland. The pedipalpi of scorpions are much larger than the chelicerae, which they resemble in bearing pincer-like claws, although the pedipalpal claws do not carry poison. Among spiders and ticks, only the chelicerae terminate in pincers. Arachnids lack compound eyes but possess as many as eight simple eyes; some are eyeless.

Fossil chelicerates illustrated in this book include eurypterids (Figs. 7.19, 12.25, 12.26) and spiders (Figs. 12.27F, A.51).

Crustaceans (Crustacea). Arthropods classed as crustaceans (*crusta,* hard shell) are distinguished by the presence of two pairs of antennae at the front of the head, which is formed by the fusion of five anterior segments (*somites*). They include crabs, lobsters, cray-

fishes, shrimps (Malacostraca); forms such as the ostracodes (Ostracoda) and most branchiopods (Branchiopoda) characterized by a bivalved carapace; barnacles (Cirripedia); and other groups not represented by known fossils. Nearly all are aquatic, breathing by means of gills, and a large majority are marine.

The branchiopods are chiefly distinguished by the leaflike gills that border four or more pairs of thoracic appendages. A few of this group lack a carapace, but most have a compressed body inclosed by a bivalved carapace that differs from the skeleton of ostracodes in not being hinged along the dorsal margin (Fig. A.52, 2); some have a low oval covering over the back.

Ostracodes are minute, commonly microscopic, bivalve crustaceans, which (excepting two families) are restricted to the sea. They occur in vast numbers, and a study of the microscopic fossils that may be washed out of

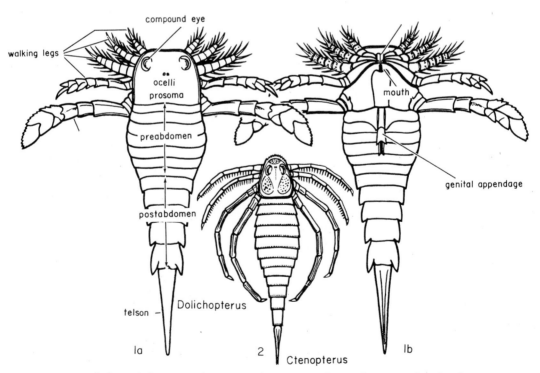

Fig. A.49 Morphological features of eurypterids.—*1.* A Silurian form; *1a,* dorsal side; *1b,* ventral side.—*2.* A Devonian form, dorsal side. (*Leif Stormer, Treatise on Invertebrate Paleontology, courtesy of Geological Society of America and University of Kansas Press.*)

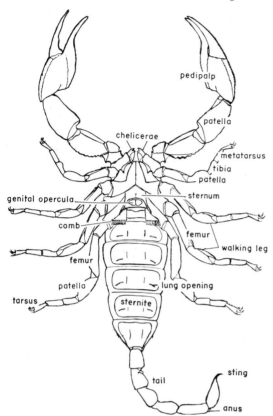

Fig. A.50 Morphology of arachnids. Dorsal side of a scorpion showing small chelicerae and large pincer-bearing pedipalpi, ×1.3. (*A. Petrunkevitch, Treatise on Invertebrate Paleontology, courtesy of Geological Society of America and University of Kansas Press.*)

Fig. A.51 Fossil spider from Pennsylvanian rocks. Dorsal side of *Eophrynus* from England, ×2.5. (*A. Petrunkevitch, Treatise on Invertebrate Paleontology, courtesy of Geological Society of America and University of Kansas Press.*)

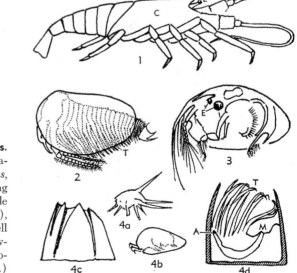

Fig. A.52 Morphological features of crustaceans. —*1.* A marine decapod (*Panulirus*, modern malacostracan).—*2.* Fresh-water conchostracan (*Cyzicus*, modern).—*3.* An ostracode (*Cypridina*) showing animal in shell, left valve removed.—*4.* A barnacle (*Balanus*) showing early nauplius larval stage (*4a*), ostracode-like free-swimming larval stage (*4b*), shell exterior of adult (*4c*), and section of adult. Drawings not to scale. (Explanation: *A*, anus; *C*, cephalothorax; *E*, eye; *M*, mouth; *T*, thoracic appendages.)

most marine shale or shaly limestone deposits shows that ostracodes are common and highly varied in rocks of all ages back to the Early Ordovician. The majority of genera and species are not long-ranging vertically, which fact, together with wide geographic distribution and large numbers, makes them valuable index fossils. In recent years they have served especially in helping to identify and correlate the rocks penetrated in oil wells, for, in spite of the action of drilling tools, many perfect specimens can often be found in the well cuttings. The valves of the ostracode shell are generally somewhat elliptical in outline; commonly they have a straight hinge line and exhibit a diversity of surface markings, which consist chiefly of raised lobes and depressed grooves or pits (Fig. A.51). Some have a beautiful network surface ornamentation, broad flangelike frills, or projecting spines (Fig. A.53).

The malacostracans are a highly diverse group that includes the largest crustaceans, some 2 feet or more in length. The group (Decapoda) that includes the lobsters, crabs, and shrimps is characterized by a large carapace that is fused to the thorax and covers all this region as well as the head (Figs. A.52, *1*, 12.27A, *D, H, I*, 16.23). The appendages are modified in various ways in different assemblages; in some all thoracic appendages are two-branched (biramous), whereas in others they are mostly uniramous.

The cirripeds, or barnacles, are hermaphroditic crustaceans that have become highly modified as a consequence of their attached existence except in larval life stages. After hatching from an egg, the young individual swims, feeds, and molts in normal crustacean manner (so-called nauplius stage) with increase of size and slight changes in shape; then it spends a few days or several weeks as a bivalved ostracode-like form that is able to move about freely; ultimately it finds a place where the front antennae become cemented to the foreign surface as an anchor, and profound change in shape marks the beginning of adult life and development of a multivalved shell in fixed position (Fig. A.52, *4*). In feeding, long thoracic appendages fan outward and by quick curving movements carry food particles to the mouth. Fossil barnacles as old as Ordovician are known.

Myriapods (Myriapoda). Wormlike arthropods characterized by numerous segments that bear similar pairs of walking legs are millipedes and centipedes, which are classed as myriapods. They are not very common as fossils, although well-preserved specimens occur in Pennsylvanian and some younger rocks (Fig. 12.27B, *E*).

Insects (Insecta, Hexapoda). As previously noted, the numerically most important group of arthropods (and of animals as a whole) comprises the insects. Thousands of fossil insects are known, distributed from Devonian to Pleistocene, and yet they do not contribute so importantly as might be expected to the paleontological record. Many of the remains are fragmentary, for example consisting of isolated wings, and generally each described species is represented by a very small number of specimens, perhaps only a single one. Even so, they call for attention.

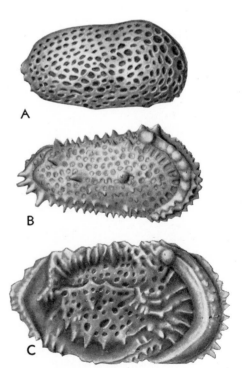

Fig. A.53 Fossil ostracodes. Side views of Paleogene species.——A. *Cythereis russelli*, Eocene, ×65.—— B. *Cythereis spiniferrima*, Paleocene, ×60.——C. *Cythereis hilgardi*, Eocene, ×80.

Insects have a distinct head that bears a single pair of antennae, and their thorax carries three pairs of jointed limbs. Very generally they possess one or two pairs of wings, which are double-layered outgrowths of the insect body wall (Figs. A.54; 2.10; 12.5; 12.27C, G; 20.9). The insects are exclusively air breathers in adult life, but many aquatic larvae obtain oxygen by means of tracheal gills.

Echinoderms

The echinoderms (spiny skin) comprise a host of exclusively marine animals that are highly varied in appearance and size, but nearly all are characterized by combined bilateral and radial symmetry, and all are distinguished by the presence of a skeleton consisting of crystalline calcareous plates embedded in the skin. Most familiar are the starfishes and sea urchins, which crawl about on the shallow sea bottom. Less generally known, but important geologically, is a group of

sedentary echinoderms, the crinoids, which are represented by living species, and the cystoids and blastoids, both of which are confined to rocks of Paleozoic age. The mouth is located on the ventral side. In free-moving echinoderms, the ventral side is normally downward, but in attached forms it is upward, and the animal is fastened by a stalk growing from the dorsal side. The echinoderms are much more highly organized than the coelenterates, for they have a true digestive canal, a distinct body cavity, a vascular and water circulatory system, a more highly developed nervous system, complex skeletal and structural elements, and an exclusively sexual mode of reproduction.

Cystoids (Cystoidea, Pelmatozoa). One of the oldest and most primitive groups of echinoderms consists of the cystoids, which have a skeleton of irregularly arranged plates joined rigidly together to form a saclike calyx, 1 or 2 inches in average diameter (Figs. A.55, 12.30A). The calyx was attached to the sea bottom or some foreign object by a short stem. Like other sedentary echinoderms, the cystoids fed on microscopic organic matter in the sea water, which was carried to the mouth along canals (*ambulacral grooves*) on the upper surface of the calyx or on the arms. Some species had two or more rather simple arms; a majority show peculiar perforations of the plates.

Blastoids (Blastoidea, Pelmatozoa). A second group of stemmed echinoderms is known

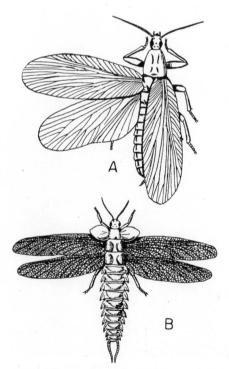

Fig. A.54 Restorations of primitive winged insects.——A. *Eucaenus,* a Pennsylvanian cockroach from Illinois, ×0.45.——B. *Stenodictya,* a Pennsylvanian orthopteran from France, ×0.65.

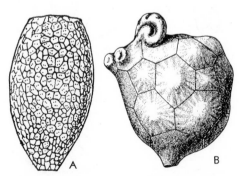

Fig. A.55 An Ordovician cystoid (A, *Eumorphocystis*) and paracrinoid (B, *Canadocystis*). Both side views, ×1. The cystoid has very numerous unevenly arranged plates that are perforated by paired pores.

as the blastoids. These have a symmetrical, budlike calyx, about ½ inch in average diameter, composed of 13 plates (Fig. A.56). Five food-groove ambulacral areas extend downward from the summit along the sides. Exceptionally well-preserved specimens show a multitude of threadlike armlets attached to the borders of the food grooves. Bundles of flattened tubes (*hydrospires*), which probably functioned as respiratory organs, occur inside the calyx. In preceding pages fossil blastoids and restorations of blastoids are illustrated (Figs. 9.18C, 9.20C, 12.30B, 12.31G).

Crinoids (Crinoidea, Pelmatozoa). The most important group of attached echinoderms is that of the crinoids, which embrace rather numerous kinds that are anchored only during larval life, becoming free of attachment as adults. Most crinoids are long-stemmed, with a discoid or rootlike holdfast at the lower extremity and a calyx composed of regularly arranged plates at the top of the stem. The calyx, which contains most of the soft parts of the animal, is provided almost invariably with well-developed movable arms that function in gathering food particles.

The stem consists of numerous superimposed button-like disks, each with a rounded or five-angled opening through the center.

Lateral appendages (*cirri*) may occur at intervals, and near the base they may be modified into rootlike branches that serve for attachment (Fig. A.57). The length of the stem is ordinarily not greater than 2 feet, but some Mesozoic crinoids have stems 50 feet long.

Fig. A.57 Modern crinoid (*Metacrinus*). The branching arms of this form from the southwestern Pacific bear regularly spaced branchlets (pinnules) and the stem also carries whorls of appendages (cirri), ×1.

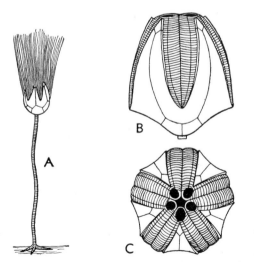

Fig. A.56 A typical blastoid (*Pentremites*), from Mississippian rocks.——*A.* Whole animal, showing stem and calyx with many threadlike armlets (reduced).——*B, C.* Side and top views of calyx, ×1.

The calyx is cup-shaped or globular and encloses the more important organs of the animal (Fig. A.58). The lower (dorsal) portion, below the arms, is characterized by regularly disposed plates, the shape and arrangement of which are constant in each species. The primary symmetry is always fivefold (pentameral), but in very many crinoids the introduction of an additional plate or series of plates (*anals*) on one side of the calyx causes a bilateral symmetry. The crinoids are classified mainly on the basis of the plate arrangements of the calyx. If the plates become separated after death of the animal, or if stem or arm pieces only are found, it is not possible ordinarily to identify the species to which these parts belonged. The upper (ventral) part of the calyx is generally formed of numerous irregularly arranged plates. The mouth is centrally located and externally visible in some forms but concealed beneath the ventral covering in others. The anal vent is also located on the upper surface of the calyx, in some at the end of an elevated tube.

The arms of the crinoid are movable columns of small channeled plates arranged in single or double alternating series. The furrow along the arms, covered by small plates, carries water, with its contained microscopic food matter, to the mouth. Among all the more highly organized crinoids, each plate segment of the arms carries a small branchlet (*pinnule*), similar to the arm in structure and function. Various numbers of arms and types of branching are observed, but the arrangement of arms in all species shows a basic fivefold symmetry.

Living crinoids are highly gregarious and inhabit mainly the shallow, clear, moderately warm portions of the sea.

Numerous illustrations of fossil crinoids ranging in age from Ordovician to Cretaceous are given in chapters of this book (Figs. 6.19*B*; 7.22*K*; 7.23*A*; 9.18*E*; 9.20*A, B, D, E, F*; 12.11*D*; 12.29; 12.30*C* to *F*; 12.31*A, B, D, E, F*; 16.15).

Asterozoans (Asterozoa, Eleutherozoa). The starfishes (Asteroidea) and brittle stars (Ophiuroidea) are bottom-dwelling echinoderms characterized by prominent radial ex-

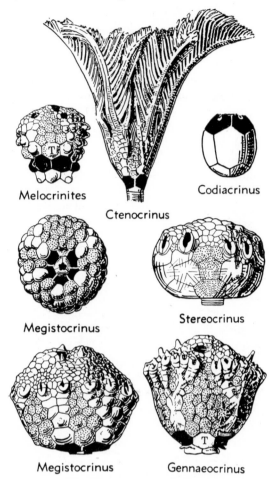

Melocrinites

Ctenocrinus

Codiacrinus

Megistocrinus

Stereocrinus

Megistocrinus

Gennaeocrinus

Fig. A.58 Devonian crinoids. Radial plates are indicated by solid black and interray plates by stippled pattern (*T*, anal plate designated tergal), all ×1. (*Courtesy of Moore, Lalicker, and Fischer, Invertebrate Fossils, McGraw-Hill Book Company, Inc., New York, 1952.*)

tensions from the central body (Fig. A.59). The mouth is located on the underside. Movement of the starfishes is accomplished by means of slender tubular structures (tube feet) that terminate in sucker-like disks capable of clinging to foreign objects; rows of these tube feet occur along the underside of the rays. Ophiuroids crawl around by muscular movement of their snakelike arms that in wriggling manner push and pull the animal along. The skeletal parts of some asterozoans are not joined firmly together, consisting of separate ossicles embedded in the somewhat leathery skin, but in others the calcareous plates and spines are joined together, and such forms are best adapted for preservation as fossils that show the shape of the animal. Some starfishes as old as Cambrian are known; the earliest discovered ophiuroids occur in Mississippian rocks (Fig. 12.31*H*). Cretaceous starfishes are illustrated in Chap. 16 (Fig. 16.16).

Echinozoans (Echinozoa, Eleutherozoa). Unattached echinoderms that lack armlike radial extensions of the body are termed *echinozoans*. They include a host of sea urchins of semiglobular, heart-shaped (Fig. 16.18*F*),

or discoid form (Echinoidea) and elongate, subcylindrical forms with a leathery skin, known generally as sea cucumbers (Holothuroidea). The echinoids are provided with a relatively firm skeleton and thus are well suited for fossilization, whereas the holothuroids possess only discrete hard parts that become scattered on death of the animal.

Echinoids are distinguished from other echinoderms by their general form and shell structure but especially by the presence of innumerable movable spines on the shell exterior. In one large group, the shell is a slightly flattened globe with a moderately

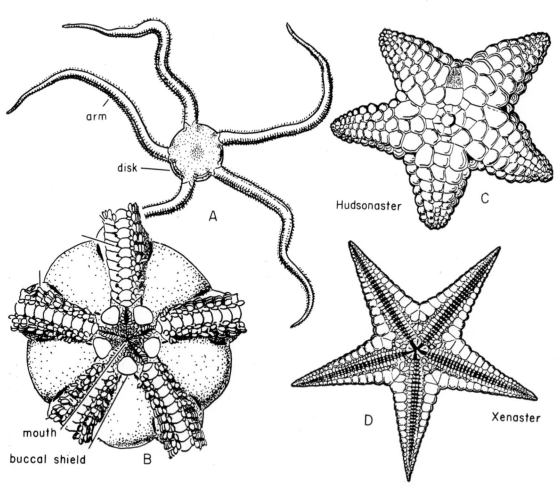

Fig. A.59 Recent and fossil asterozoans.—*A, B.* Dorsal side of modern ophiuroid (*Ophioderma*, ×0.65) and ventral side of disk (×3).—*C.* Simple type of asteroid from Ordovician rocks, dorsal side (×2.7).—*D.* Devonian asteroid, ventral side (×0.9). (*Courtesy of Moore, Lalicker, and Fischer, Invertebrate Fossils, McGraw-Hill Book Company, Inc., New York, 1952.*)

large opening for the mouth, centrally located on the underside, and a small anal aperture near the center of the dorsal side (Fig. A.60*A, D*). The shell is composed of 20 columns of plates arranged in double rows, five of the pairs of rows containing specialized perforated plates (*ambulacra*) through which the delicate tube feet, or tentacles, that are used in locomotion or for respiration are protruded. The spines vary greatly in size, and there may be two or three orders of sizes on the same shell. They have a socket-like hollow at the base, which articulates with a rounded tubercle on the plates of the shell and is movable by muscle fibers that are attached slightly above the base (Fig. A.60*E*). The function of the spines is to support the test, to aid in locomotion, and to serve as a means of defense. Within the mouth of most echinoids is a complicated jaw or masticatory apparatus, known as Aristotle's lantern (Fig. A.60*B*).

A second group of echinoids is distinguished by the more or less irregular outline of the shell which in a large number of species is heart-shaped, by the excentric position of the mouth and anus, and in part by modification of the ambulacral areas into petal-shaped spaces on the dorsal side of the shell (Fig. A.60*C*).

The skeletal parts of holothuroids consist of microscopic calcareous bodies having various shapes, some resembling small wheels and others being hook- or anchor-like. Rarely, soft parts have been preserved as fossils (Figs. 5.26*H*, 12.10*G*).

Graptolites (Graptolithina). Graptolites are an important group of extinct colonial animals in which the rows of tiny cups (*hydrothecae*) that house individuals were composed of resistant but flexible chitin. They have been interpreted as a peculiar type of coelenterates, but presently available evidence indicates close affinity with pterobranchs, which are an assemblage of hemichordates, included in the phylum Chordata along with all vertebrate animals.

Fossil graptolites appear almost exclusively as flattened carbonaceous films on the bedding planes of black shales. In recent years,

however, numerous undistorted specimens have been discovered in limestone, and when these are freed from the inclosing rock by dissolving the limestone in acid, the anatomy of the graptolites can be studied in minute detail.

Most graptolite colonies are straight, simple, or branching stems with hydrothecae on one or both sides, more or less overlapping and resembling the teeth of a saw (Fig. A.61). Some colonies have a leaflike shape (Fig. 6.22*B*), and a few are spirally coiled. The individuals grew by successive budding from a parent housed in the first-formed cup (*sicula*) of the colony. Among highly developed graptolites, the rows of hydrothecae were supported by a slender solid axis.

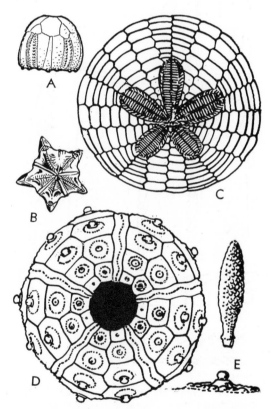

Fig. A.60 Fossil echinoids.——*A. Triadocidaris,* Triassic, side view, ×1.——*B.* Aristotle's lantern of *Encope,* Pliocene, ×2.——*C. Dendraster,* Pleistocene, dorsal side, ×1.——*D. Dorocidaris,* Lower Cretaceous, ventral side, ×1.——*E.* Large spine of *Cidaris,* Jurassic, and side view of interambulacral plate of *Dorocidaris,* showing boss for spine attachment.

Fishes

Fishes (Pisces) have the form and general structure that are best adapted to a mobile life in water. The body is typically compressed, spindle-shaped, and streamlined to offer minimum resistance to motion. The head, which is fastened to the body without a neck, bears the eyes, mouth, and gills. The sharks and lampreys have a series of separate openings for the gills, which are exposed on each side; in other fishes, these are all concealed by an operculum. The body is generally protected by a shingle-like covering of scales, but it may be armored by bony plates, by a flexible mail of quadrangular enamel-like plates, or by small toothlike structures embedded in the skin, or it may have only a leathery skin.

Fins, which enable the fishes to swim easily, belong in two groups: (1) the unpaired fins, which are median projections from the back (dorsal fin), tail (caudal fin), and venter (anal fin), and (2) the paired fins, which consist of pectoral fins, located one on each side near the head, and the pelvic fins, located typically farther back but in front of the anal fin. Three types of tail fins are observed: (1) *diphycercal*, which extends symmetrically and evenly around the end of the vertebral column; (2) *heterocercal*, in which the end of the vertebral column is bent upward (or rarely downward) and the arrangement of the fin is unsymmetrical; and (3) *homocercal*, a more or less fan-shaped symmetrical tail fin that is developed at the abrupt termination of the vertebral column. The fins are supported near the base by cartilaginous or bony structures and farther out by horny rays or, in the paired fins of certain species, by a skeletal structure that suggests the limb bones of higher vertebrates.

The lungfishes possess an internal organ of respiration, which is absent in most other fishes. The higher types (bony fishes) have instead an *air bladder*, which functions as a hydrostatic organ.

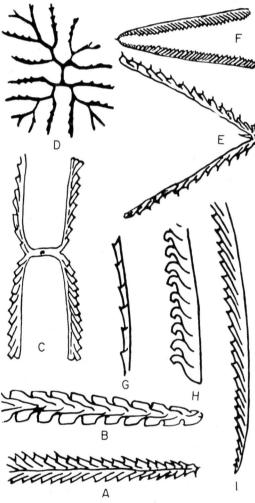

Fig. A.61 Types of graptolite colonies.—*A, B.* Biserial forms, *Diplograptus* ($\times$4), *Climacograptus* ($\times$7), Ord.—*C.* Four-branched form, *Tetragraptus* ($\times$3), Ord.—*D.* Multiple-branched form, *Goniograptus* ($\times$2), Ord.—*E.* Reflexed V-shaped colony, *Dicellograptus* ($\times$3), Ord.—*F.* Two-branched "tuning-fork" type, *Didymograptus* ($\times$1.5), Ord.—*G.* Uniserial type, *Cyrtograptus* ($\times$6), Sil.—*H, I.* Uniserial types, *Monograptus* ($\times$3), Sil.

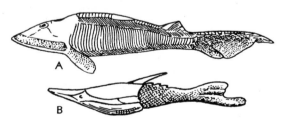

Fig. A.62 Lower Devonian ostracoderms. These jawless fishes are characterized by bony structure of the head region.—*A. Hemicyclaspis,* $\times$0.5.—*B. Pteraspis,* $\times$0.8.

Several different classifications of the fishes have been proposed, the difference in grouping being due to uncertainty as to the significance and relationships of various structures. Present knowledge favors recognition of four main · classes: (1) primitive jawless fishes (Agnatha), which include the ostracoderms (Fig. A.62); (2) plate-armored fishes (Placodermi), having primitive jaws and a bony skeleton (Figs. 8.23, 12.33); (3) sharks and related fishes (Chondrichthyes), having an advanced type of jaw structure but no bony skeleton (Figs. 2.9, 8.22, 12.34, 20.11); and (4) other fishes (Osteichthyes), which have advanced jaw structure and retain a bony skeleton (Figs. 1.17, 2.4, 2.5, 12.32, 12.33, 16.24).

Amphibians

Amphibians resemble the fishes in living for a part or all of their lives in water and breathing by means of gills, in being cold-blooded, in the possession by some forms of a diphycercal tail fin, in the presence of a body covering of scales in many of the fossil species, and in the nature of their eggs and the way these are laid in water without further attention from the parents. They differ from fishes in having legs (Tetrapoda) with fingers and toes (although in some amphibians one or both pairs of limbs have been lost); in the possession by the majority of species of functional lungs, which make them independent of water as a surrounding medium in adult life; and in the structure of the heart, the mobile muscular tongue, and other features. The amphibians were derived from crossopterygian fishes (Fig. A.63, *1, 2*). The skulls of Paleozoic and Triassic amphibians, including especially the heavy-boned stegocephalians, were characterized by their considerable width and relative flatness, the eyes being directed upward as well as outward (Figs. A.63, 2.6, 12.35, 13.18).

Reptiles

The reptiles are tetrapod vertebrates having a well-ossified skeleton and a body covering of bony plates or dry horny scales. They are solely air breathers that show important evolutionary modification from their amphibian ancestors in being freed of dependence on an aquatic environment for birth and initial growth. The ability of reptiles to begin life on land is consequent on development of means for protecting the embryo from desiccation during early life by inclosing it in a liquid-filled sac (*amnion*) associated with a receptacle (*allantois*) for deposit of waste products and a supply of food substance (*yolk*) sufficient to care for growth until the young animal can fend for itself (Fig. A.64). These combined features distinguish the so-called amniote egg, which bears a porous leathery or calcified shell that allows oxygen to pass into the egg and carbon dioxide to escape. Fertilization of the egg occurs within the body of the mother, and among some reptiles embryonic development takes place there also, the young being born alive. Otherwise, the eggs are laid on land and eventually are broken open from within when the time for hatching comes. The almost incredible evolutionary advancement represented by the appearance of the amniote egg is comparable to the "invention" of a lower jaw by altering the nature and function of a forward gill arch of the fishes, which marks the great forward step that produced the placoderms and other jaw-bearing fishes from jawless ancestors.

The two pairs of limbs found in all but specialized reptiles, such as snakes, typically possess five digits on each, and commonly these end in horny claws suited for crawling, running, or climbing. The heart is imperfectly four-chambered, with two auricles and a partly divided ventricle. Body temperature is variable, depending mainly on environment. The reptiles are distinguished from amphibians by the absence of a moist, glandular skin and by their mode of reproduction; they differ from birds and mammals primarily by their lack of feathers or hair as a body covering. First-rank divisions of the reptiles are defined by structural features of the skull (Fig. A.63).

Earliest known reptiles are represented by Lower Pennsylvanian fossils. This group of animals attained maximum variety and great-

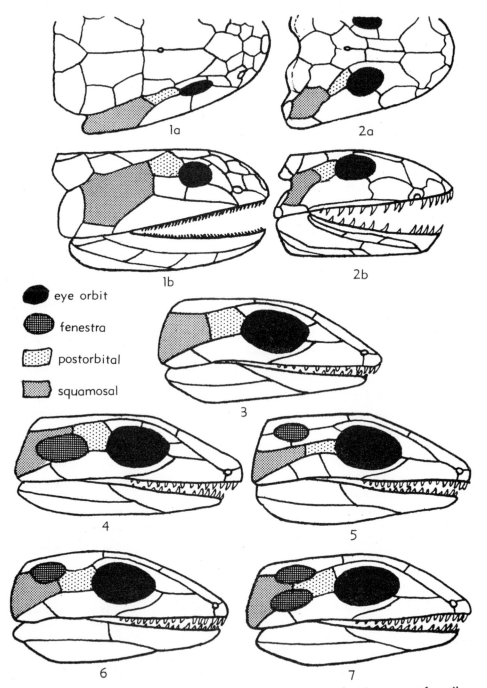

Fig. A.63 Skull structure of crossopterygian fish, amphibian, and main groups of reptiles.
Homologies and differences of skull bones are indicated; openings (fenestrae) appear behind
the eye orbit in four types of reptiles.——1. Crossopterygian fish; *1a, b,* top and side views.——
2. Amphibian; *2a, b,* top and side views.——3. Anapsid reptile (cotylosaurs, turtles).——4.
Synapsid reptile (pelycosaurs, therapsids).——5. Parapsid reptile (ichthyosaurs).——6. Euryapsid reptile (plesiosaurs).——7. Diapsid reptile (lizards, dinosaurs, pterosaurs, crocodiles).
(*1, 2, modified from A. S. Romer; 3–7, modified from E. H. Colbert.*)

est size during the Mesozoic Era, when dinosaurs were rulers of the lands, ichthyosaurs and other marine reptiles dominated the seas, and pterosaurs were almost alone in the skies.

Cotylosaurs (Cotylosauria, Anapsida). The cotylosaurs are primitive Permian-to-Triassic reptiles that resemble amphibians in the absence of any openings on sides of the skull behind the eye orbits (Fig. A.63, 3).

Turtles (Chelonia, Anapsida). Inclosure of the body by a boxlike structure of united bony plates characterizes the turtles, which appear first in the fossil record in Triassic deposits. They became adapted to life in fresh waters and the sea, as well as on land; some marine forms, such as the Cretaceous turtle *Archelon,* attained a length of more than 12 feet.

Pelycosaurs and mammal-like reptiles (Pelycosauria, Therapsida, Synapsida). The pelycosaurs are Late Pennsylvanian and Permian synapsid reptiles generally distinguished by a prominent finlike structure along the back (Figs. A.63, 4, 2.0, 11.18, 12.36, 12.37); they include both herbivorous and carnivorous reptiles, judging by characters of the teeth. Mammal-like reptiles (therapsids) that probably include ancestors of the mammals are a varied Permian and Triassic assemblage known chiefly from South Africa; some of these have prominent canines and cusped cheek teeth (molars) somewhat resembling those of a dog.

Ichthyosaurs (Ichthyosauria, Parapsida). In many ways the most highly specialized marine reptiles are the decidedly fishlike ichthyosaurs (Figs. A.63, 5, 2.9, 16.4, 16.40, 16.41). The earliest known members of this group, from Triassic rocks, differ from typical Jurassic and Cretaceous ichthyosaurs only in having a slightly less elongated skull and paddles that are narrower and shorter.

Plesiosaurs (Plesiosauria, Euryapsida). Relatively long-necked marine reptiles with large paddle-like limbs for swimming are the plesiosaurs (Figs. 16.4, 16.42) and their somewhat less specialized antecedents, the Triassic nothosaurs. Their skull structure (euryapsid) especially distinguishes them from the

ichthyosaurs and other reptiles with a single temporal opening behind the orbit (Fig. A.63, 6). The plesiosaurs are typically Jurassic and Cretaceous reptiles.

Lizards, mosasaurs, snakes (Lepidosauria, Diapsida). Reptiles classed together as lepidosaurs include the lizards, snakes, and extinct marine "sea serpents" known as mosasaurs (Fig. 15.17). They are all characterized by a diapsid-type skull, which has two large openings behind the eye orbit on each side (Fig. A.63, 7). The mosasaurs had an elongate pointed head, paddle-like limbs, and long laterally compressed tail. They had worldwide distribution in Cretaceous time, some attaining a length of 50 feet.

Crocodiles, phytosaurs (Crocodilia, Thecodontia, Archosauria, Diapsida). Aquatic reptiles collectively designated as archosaurs include crocodiles, alligators, and various extinct forms, such as the slender-snouted, gavial-like phytosaurs, which characterize some continental Triassic formations (Fig. 13.19). Most of this group are inhabitants of fresh waters, but a few became adapted to life in the sea. Some attain a length of 20 feet.

Flying reptiles (Pterosauria, Archosauria, Diapsida). Adaptation of tetrapod vertebrates for flying is not known to have occurred until Jurassic time, when a group of reptiles

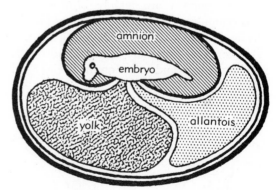

Fig. A.64 Section of reptilian egg. The shell (heavy outer line) incloses a liquid-filled sac (amnion) containing the embryo, to which are joined a food supply (yolk) sufficient for growth within the egg and a receptacle (allantois) for storage of waste products. This type of amniote egg enables reptiles to reproduce on dry land.

(pterosaurs) and feather-clad derivatives of reptiles (birds) appeared in the fossil record. The flying reptiles were numerous and varied during middle and late Mesozoic epochs but did not survive, like the birds, into Cenozoic time. The pterosaurs had a membranous or leathery sort of wing that stretched from the body to the forearm and much-elongated fifth digit (little finger) on each side (Figs. 15.17, 16.5, 16.43, 16.44), thus differing from the wings of a bat, which are partly supported by three fingers of the fore limbs.

Saurischian dinosaurs (Saurischia, Archosauria, Diapsida). The numerous, mostly large to gigantic reptiles known as dinosaurs are divided into two major groups on the basis of their pelvic structure, forms with a lizard-like arrangement of the pelvic bones (Fig. A.65A) being classed as Saurischia and those with a birdlike pelvis (Fig. A.65B) being grouped as Ornithischia. As described in the chapter on Mesozoic life, the bipedal carnivorous saurischians (tyrannosaurs and their allies) comprise one distinct assemblage (Theropoda) (Figs. 13.17, 16.25 to 16.28, 16.45) and the quadrupedal herbivorous saurischians (brontosaurs) are another (Sauropoda) (Figs. 16.2, 16.29 to 16.31).

Ornithischian dinosaurs (Ornithischia, Archosauria, Synapsida). Four main groups of ornithischian dinosaurs are recognized. (1) The Ornithopoda are mainly bipedal land forms (camptosaurs) and aquatic types (duckbills and allies) (Figs. 1.12, 16.25, 16.32). (2) The Stegosauria are heavy quadrupeds with large plates and spines on the back (Figs.

16.34, 16.35). (3) The Ankylosauria are quadrupedal armored dinosaurs characterized by a body covering of thick bony plates (Figs. 16.26, 16.33). (4) The Ceratopsia are the horned dinosaurs, which also are quadrupedal (Figs. 15.16, 16.36 to 16.39).

Birds

The birds (Aves) are prevailingly warm-blooded, feather-covered derivatives of the reptiles that are adapted specially for flying, although some kinds such as ostriches and penguins have lost the power of flight. The front part of the skull is produced as a hard, variously shaped beak that is toothless, except in the Jurassic and Cretaceous birds (Fig. A.66). The skeleton exhibits many modifications that are mostly connected with fitness for flight; for example, parts of the skull, neck vertebrae, and limb bones may be hollow, air-filled means of reducing specific gravity. The flightless birds are characterized by reduction or even the absence of wings and by a broadly flattened breastbone (*sternum*), whereas the flying birds have more or less extended wings and a prominently projecting breastbone that serves for attachment of muscles used in flying. Birds may possess long tail feathers, but the skeletal structure behind the pelvis is much shortened and tends to become fused. Some types of fossil birds are illustrated in preceding chapters (Figs. 2.9, 16.45, 16.46, 20.12, 20.13).

Mammals

The mammals are mostly very active, warm-blooded tetrapods characterized by a body covering of hair or fur. Their name (*mammae*, breasts) refers to the ventrally located glands of females that supply milk for suckling the young. Except for two primitive forms found in Australia (platypus, echidna), which lay eggs, mammals are born alive. The skeleton shows several distinguishing characters as compared with the hard parts of reptiles, the most important being (1) the presence of two articular surfaces (*condyles*) at the base of the skull instead of one; (2) a single external nasal opening in front of the skull; (3) modification of articulating elements between skull

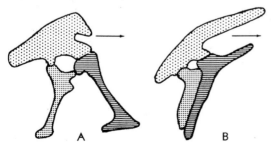

Fig. A.65 Types of pelvic structures in dinosaurs.
——A. Lizard type, characteristic of the Saurischia.——
B. Bird type, characteristic of the Ornithischia. Arrows point toward front of animal.

and jaw of reptiles to make inner ear bones of mammals; (4) a notably enlarged brain case in all but very primitive mammals; (5) differentiated dentition (commonly incisors, canines, premolars, molars), although closely similar differentiation appears in mammal-like reptiles; and (6) fusion of pelvic bones. There are other more or less diagnostic features, but those mentioned are quite sufficient to set the mammals apart from all other vertebrate animals. In the course of their history mammals have become adapted to almost every sort of environment on the surface of the land, burrowing underground, living in fresh waters and the seas, and flying in the air. They exhibit utmost diversity in form and range in size from creatures such as some shrews and small mice, less than 50 millimeters (2 inches) in length, to the largest known animals, which are the blue whales that attain a length of 32 meters (105 feet) and weight of nearly 150 tons.

Multituberculates (Allotheria). One of the earliest known mammal groups, which appeared in Jurassic time and persisted into the Paleocene Epoch, consists of the multituberculates. They were herbivores having a pair of large incisors in their upper and lower jaws separated by a considerable gap from grinding teeth provided with longitudinally arranged rows of cusps and in some a shearing-type, vertically ribbed premolar (Fig. A.67, *1a, b*).

Marsupials (Metatheria, Theria). Mammals characterized by the birth of the young in very immature condition with early postnatal growth in a pouch on the ventral side of the mother are classed as marsupials. The opossums, kangaroos, koalas, wallabies, and other mammals of Australia are examples. Most members of this group are identifiable readily on the basis of skeletal characters, and thus extinct types, including some as old as Cretaceous, can be distinguished. The teeth indicate that some were carnivorous whereas others were herbivorous or omnivorous. Divergent evolution along several lines is observed, one form being a jaguar-sized marsupial that strikingly resembles the saber-toothed cats (Fig. A.67, *2*).

Insectivores (Insectivora, Unguiculata, Eutheria, Theria). One of the most generalized—that is, least specialized—groups of placental mammals (those with young moderately well developed at birth) consists of the insectivores, known from the Cretaceous onward to the present. All are small, and all have a diminutive, primitively developed brain, as illustrated by modern moles and shrews. The teeth are well differentiated, molars being varied in form and commonly marked by minute cusps on the upper surface (Fig. A.67, *3a, b*). The insectivores are interpreted to be the ancestral stock from which other unguiculates and possibly all kinds of placental mammals were derived.

Bats (Chiroptera, Unguiculata, Eutheria, Theria). The bats are the only mammals that have mastered true flight, using a membranous wing supported by the fore limb. Unlike

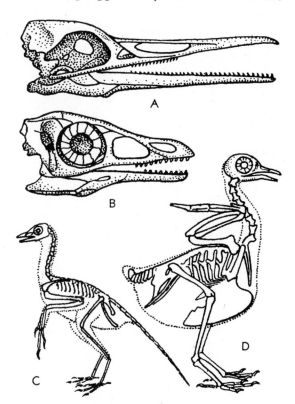

Fig. A.66 Skeletal features of birds.——*A*. Skull of the Cretaceous diving bird, *Hesperornis*, showing teeth in jaws, ×0.3.——*B*. Skull of *Archaeornis*, Jurassic, a close relative of *Archaeopteryx*, ×1.——*C*. Restoration of skeleton of *Archaeornis*, ×0.2.——*D*. Modern pigeon, ×0.5.

the pterosaurs, which used a single elongated digit (fourth) to carry the outer part of the wing, the bats employ all but the first finger to provide umbrella-like ribs for the wing (Fig. A.67, 4). The hind limbs are so weak that bats are rather helpless on the ground, but they have clawed digits used for hanging the body upside down when at rest. Oldest known fossil bats occur in Eocene deposits.

Edentates (Edentata, Unguiculata, Eutheria, Theria). Armadillos, sloths, anteaters, and a few related mammals characterized by reduced or suppressed dentition are grouped in the Edentata. They have various shapes and living habits. A few, such as the heavily armored glyptodonts (Fig. A.67, 5a, b) and

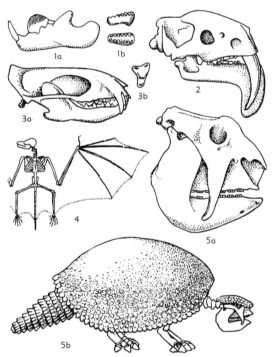

Fig. A.67 Morphological features of unguiculates. ——*1a, b.* Lower jaw and grinding tooth (side and top views) of *Ptilodus*, a Paleocene insectivore, ×0.5, ×2. ——*2.* Skull of *Thylacosmilus*, a saber-toothed marsupial from Pliocene rocks of South America, ×0.1.—— *3a, b.* Skull and grinding surface of molar of *Deltatheridium*, a Cretaceous insectivore, ×1, ×8.——*4.* *Palaeochiropteryx*, an Eocene bat.——*5a, b.* Skull and skeleton of *Glyptodon*, armored edentate from Pleistocene beds of South America, lengths 11 inches, 11 feet.

ground sloths (Fig. 20.31), which attained lengths of 9 and 20 feet, respectively, were very ponderous animals.

Primates (Primates, Unguiculata, Eutheria, Theria). The assemblage of mammals that includes man, together with the apes, monkeys, lemurs, and tarsiers, is distinguished by little skeletal specialization, but the brain case is generally large, and the eyes are capable of binocular vision. This group is described and illustrated in Chaps. 20 and 21.

Rodents, rabbits (Glires, Eutheria, Theria). Relatively small mammals characterized by chisel-like gnawing teeth (incisors) at the front of the jaws comprise the rodents and rabbits. The rodents, which include squirrels, beavers, rats, mice, porcupines, and numerous others, have a single incisor on either side of each jaw, whereas rabbits and hares possess a pair of incisors in these positions. Highly varied representatives of this group are distributed from the Paleocene to the present. Because they are extremely numerous, widely distributed, and adapted to many sorts of environments, they may be rated as a very successful branch of the mammals. Species of rodents outnumber all other species of mammals combined.

Carnivores (Carnivora, Eutheria, Theria). A large group of flesh-eating mammals that includes the cats, dogs, bears, raccoons, weasels, seals, sea lions, and walruses and allied forms are classed as Carnivora. In general, they are characterized by development of the canine teeth as more or less prominent tusks and modification of the cheek teeth (premolars, molars) for shearing or crushing (Figs. A.68, 1, 2, 2.8, 20.13). The oldest known carnivores are Paleocene forms.

Cetaceans (Cetacea, Eutheria, Theria). Whales of several sorts and their close relatives, the porpoises and dolphins, comprise the Cetacea, which are characterized by very perfect adaptation for living in the sea. They all possess a streamlined fishlike form and powerful tail fin that is used in swimming; some have a dorsal fin also. The front limbs are modified into flippers. Hind limbs are lacking. The oldest and most primitive whales, represented by Eocene fossils, were elongate, relatively slender animals with a pointed skull and jaws armed with large sharp teeth. Some of these types (zeuglodonts) attained a length of 70 feet. The largest whales (mysticetes) are toothless, the roof of the mouth being equipped with fine ridges of hardened skin (so-called whalebone) that hang downward as a strainer for catching small invertebrate prey on which these whales depend solely for food (Fig. A.68, 5).

Archaic ungulates (Ungulata, Eutheria, Theria). The ungulates include all types of hoofed mammals, and since these are exclusively herbivorous in habit, their molar teeth are modified for grinding the leaves, grass, or grain on which they feed. The archaic ungulates, all of which are extinct forms found in Paleogene deposits, include the condylarths (Condylarthra), amblypods (Amblypoda), and uintatheres (Dinocerata) (Figs. A.69, 17.14, 17.15). These are characterized by lack of very marked adaptation of the molars for grinding and unspecialized foot structure; also, the proportionally small size of the brain case indicates low intelligence.

Elephants (Proboscidea, Ungulata, Eutheria, Theria). Modern elephants are familiar types of very large land mammals distinguished mainly by their long, highly mobile trunk, great tusks, and pillar-like limbs. They all belong to one or other of two species that are assigned to different genera, respectively found in Asia and Africa. The occurrence of numerous kinds of elephants in strata ranging in age from late Eocene to late Pleistocene indicates that the living representatives of this group are merely remnants of a stock having a long record of evolutionary differentiation. In some, a pair of incisors of the upper jaw are enormously enlarged to form nearly straight or strongly curved tusks, the lower jaw being short and tuskless (Figs. A70, 2, 20.13, 20.18, 20.30); in others, the lower jaw carries straight, shovel-like tusks or pointed, down-curved tusks (Figs. A.70, 1, 20.28). The grinding teeth (premolars, molars) exhibit more or less prominent cone- or ridgelike elevations. Long-jawed elephants have several

grinding teeth in each jaw, but in short-jawed forms there is room for only one or two of these teeth at a time in each jaw, and therefore they are introduced in succession, a new tooth crowding forward to replace a worn-down tooth.

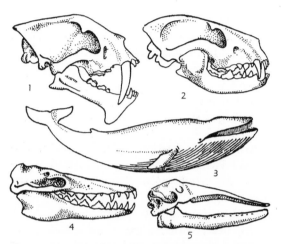

Fig. A.68 Morphological features of carnivores and cetaceans.—*1.* Skull of *Hoplophoneus,* an Oligocene saber-toothed cat, ×0.25.—*2.* Skull of *Cynodesmus,* a Miocene dog, ×0.3.—*3.* Whalebone whale, 100 feet long, modern.—*4.* Skull of *Prozeuglodon,* an archaic toothed whale, Eocene, ×0.05.—*5.* Skull of *Cetotherium,* a Miocene whalebone whale, showing absence of teeth, ×0.05.

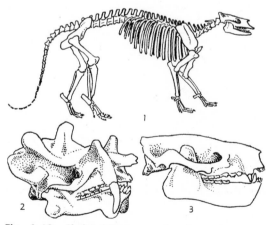

Fig. A.69 Skeletal features of archaic ungulates. —*1. Phenacodus,* a lower Eocene condylarth, length 5.5 feet.—*2.* Skull of *Uintatherium,* Eocene, representing the Dincerata, length 30 inches.—*3.* Skull of *Pantolambda,* a Paleocene amblypod, ×0.25.

Perissodactyls (Perissodactyla, Ungulata, Eutheria, Theria). The so-called odd-toed hoofed mammals, characterized by limbs with an odd number of digits or having one of the middle digits enlarged for support of an extra share of the animal's weight, are classed as perissodactyls (Figs. A.71, *1* to *6*, 20.16). The group includes the horses, rhinoceroses, tapirs, and the extinct forms known as titanotheres and chalicotheres (Figs. 17.16, 17.17, 20.14 to 20.18, 20.22). Archaic perissodactyls commonly have grinding teeth with cusps, whereas advanced types, modern horses and rhinoceroses, have premolars and molars with ridged summits truncated by wear (Fig. 20.15).

Artiodactyls (Artiodactyla, Ungulata, Eutheria, Theria). Most modern hoofed mammals are artiodactyls, characterized by the even number of toes (two or four) on each foot (Fig. A.72, *4* to *6*). They include sheep, goats, deer, cattle, pigs, camels, hippopotamuses, and various extinct assemblages. Their grinding teeth commonly bear crescent-shaped ridges or cusps that tend to be arranged in a crescentic pattern (Fig. A.72, *1* to *3*). Many artiodactyls bear horns. They are common Cenozoic fossils, ranging from Eocene to Pleistocene.

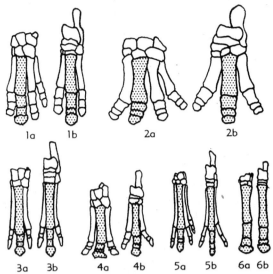

Fig. A.71 Extremities of limbs of perissodactyls. In each pair of figures, the hand is shown at left and the foot at right, axial digits shaded.——*1a, b.* Pleistocene tapir (*Tapirus*).——*2a, b.* Oligocene titanothere (*Brontotherium*).——*3a, b.* Oligocene running rhinoceros (*Hyracodon*).——*4a, b.* Miocene rhinoceros (*Diceratherium*).——*5a, b.* Eocene horse (*Hyracotherium,* more commonly but incorrectly named *Eohippus*).——*6a, b.* Pleistocene horse (*Equus*).

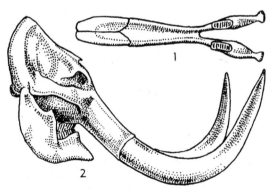

Fig. A.70 Skull and jaw of proboscideans.——*1.* Lower jaw of a Pliocene shovel-tusk elephant, *Amebelodon,* length 7 feet.——*2.* Skull of woolly mammoth, *Mammuthus primigenius,* Pleistocene, length 6.5 feet. (*After A. S. Romer.*)

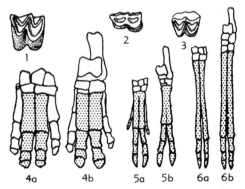

Fig. A.72 Grinding teeth and extremities of limbs of artiodactyls.——*1–3.* Molars of Miocene oreodont, Pleistocene camel, and Pliocene antelope, showing grinding surface.——*4–6.* Hands (left) and feet (right) of Pleistocene hippopotamus, Pleistocene peccary, and Oligocene camel, axial digits shaded.

Appendix B

LITHOLOGIC SYMBOLS
FOR GEOLOGIC SECTIONS

Symbols of unknown meaning carved by prehistoric Indians in basalt along Columbia River.

Graphic Representation of Rock Types

Geologists have abundant need for recording their observations concerning rocks in ways other than by written descriptions. Maps of several sorts serve best for organizing information that relates importantly to distribution of specified rocks or mineral deposits in space, and in various ways such maps may indicate occurrence vertically as well as in horizontal directions. Commonly, patterns or colors or combined patterns and colors are chosen somewhat arbitrarily to represent the selected geologic units, and in order that the map be intelligible, explanation must be furnished as to what each pattern or color signifies. Con-

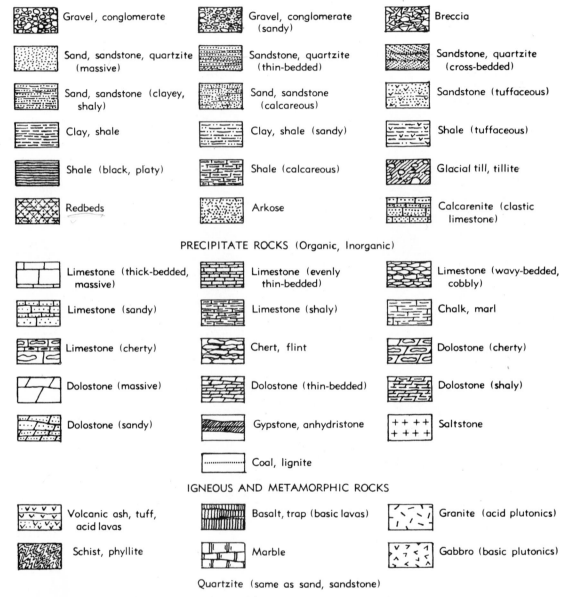

CLASTIC ROCKS

(Formed of more or less sorted mineral and rock fragments derived from pre-existing sources)

Gravel, conglomerate

Gravel, conglomerate (sandy)

Breccia

Sand, sandstone, quartzite (massive)

Sandstone, quartzite (thin-bedded)

Sandstone, quartzite (cross-bedded)

Sand, sandstone (clayey, shaly)

Sand, sandstone (calcareous)

Sandstone (tuffaceous)

Clay, shale

Clay, shale (sandy)

Shale (tuffaceous)

Shale (black, platy)

Shale (calcareous)

Glacial till, tillite

Redbeds

Arkose

Calcarenite (clastic limestone)

PRECIPITATE ROCKS (Organic, Inorganic)

Limestone (thick-bedded, massive)

Limestone (evenly thin-bedded)

Limestone (wavy-bedded, cobbly)

Limestone (sandy)

Limestone (shaly)

Chalk, marl

Limestone (cherty)

Chert, flint

Dolostone (cherty)

Dolostone (massive)

Dolostone (thin-bedded)

Dolostone (shaly)

Dolostone (sandy)

Gypstone, anhydristone

Saltstone

Coal, lignite

IGNEOUS AND METAMORPHIC ROCKS

Volcanic ash, tuff, acid lavas

Basalt, trap (basic lavas)

Granite (acid plutonics)

Schist, phyllite

Marble

Gabbro (basic plutonics)

Quartzite (same as sand, sandstone)

HIATUS IN ROCK SECTIONS OF STRATIGRAPHIC CHARTS

Unconformity (nonconformity, angular unconformity, paraconformity, disconformity) (rocks missing)

Fig. B.1 **Explanation of lithologic symbols used in time-stratigraphic charts.**

ventional symbols for strike and dip or structure contours may be employed to show structure. Graphic geologic sections are really special kinds of geologic maps drawn in a vertical plane, so-called structure sections extending across country along a selected line and columnar sections showing the succession of rocks at a given place. For such sections, especially those depicting rock successions, conventional symbols commonly are used to represent different kinds of rock, and the thickness of each type can be indicated graphically according to some adopted scale.

The purpose of this appendix is to provide explanation of the symbols used in the several charts showing representative rock successions included in each of the geologic systems. This is given in Fig. B.1. Inspection of the symbols will lead to the observation that only a few basically different patterns appear, each of which refers to a "pure" rock type in more or less pictorial manner (as gravel, sand, clay, limestone, dolostone, and chert). Intergrading kinds of rock can be represented by combining the basic patterns (as sandy shale, calcareous shale, shaly limestone, and others). Also, some features of stratification can be suggested graphically. In constructing a columnar section, if the symbols for different rocks are accompanied by a diagrammatic profile that represents hard strata as projecting outward well beyond the surface of soft layers, simulating appearance of the strata in a weathered vertical cliff, additional geologic information of value is portrayed. This device is used in the stratigraphic charts but not in the accompanying explanatory figure (Fig. B.1).

Appendix C
GLOSSARY

absolute age. Time before present stated in years; referring to geologic events, generally based on measurement of radioactive decay rates and products of minerals or rock substances (as uranium-lead method, carbon-14 method, etc.).

abyssal. (1) Deep within the earth, generally signifying depth of some miles (= plutonic). (2) Deep in oceans or lakes, well beyond depth of light penetration, commonly referring to depths of 1,000 feet or more in lakes and 6,000 feet or more in oceans.

acidic. Describing igneous rocks having silica (SiO_2) content greater than two-thirds of total constituents (as rhyolite, granite, etc.) (see basic).

adaptation. Adjustment of structures or modes of living (including methods of reproduction) that better fit an organism to its environment, thereby favoring successful competition with other organisms and survival.

adaptive convergence. Approach by unrelated organisms to similarity of structures or modes of living (as flying reptiles, birds, and bats, which are mammals).

adaptive divergence. Differentiation of related organisms by adaptation to dissimilar environments or modes of living (as horses, wolves, seals, and whales, all mammals).

adaptive radiation. Same as adaptive divergence.

adjusted. Term applied to coast line, drainage pattern, or individual stream with placement controlled by rock hardness or structure or both (as so-called subsequent streams of Appalachian Mountains flowing in weak rocks parallel to strike).

aerial. Pertaining to air or atmosphere (subaerial conditions or processes on land, because directly under the atmosphere).

agate. Banded or cloudy quartz with waxy appearance.

agatized. Applied to silicified fossil (wood, invertebrate shell, vertebrate bone) with the appearance of agate.

age. Any time span in earth history (as absolute age of rock or mineral, relative age of one rock unit compared with another, "age of reptiles," referring to the time when reptiles were dominant animals on the earth).

Age. Time represented by the time-stratigraphic unit called Stage (initial capital letter used in formal nomenclature).

agglomerate. Accumulation of coarse, angular or sub-angular pyroclastics (mostly $>$ 1 inch diameter).

aggradation. Upward building of a surface by deposition of sediment.

alga (pl. **algae**). Aquatic protistan organisms that include many lime-secreting kinds.

algal. Pertaining to algae (as algal limestones and reefs, largely formed by algae; algal structure, generally laminated crusts, oöids and pisoids, some of which may be inorganic, however).

Algoman. Precambrian granite of Canadian Shield region, post-Timiskamingian in age, classified as Archean.

Algonkian. Main division of late Precambrian time and rocks (equivalent to Proterozoic).

allocthon. Large displaced body of rocks (as rock mass moved considerable distance by thrust faulting); opposite is autocthon.

allocthonous. Not formed *in situ*.

alluvial. Pertaining to alluvium (as alluvial cones, fans, plains, etc.).

alluvium. Unconsolidated detrital deposits ranging from clay to gravel sizes, generally poorly sorted, typically fluviatile in origin.

alternation of generations. Succession of sexually and asexually formed groups of offspring belonging to a given species of organisms (as microspheric and megalospheric foraminifers, polyps and medusa stages of some coelenterates, etc.).

amblypod. Moderately large early Paleogene hoofed mammal with blunt, elephant-like feet, small brain case, and unspecialized teeth.

ammonite. Extinct late Paleozoic or Mesozoic cephalopod distinguished mainly by the complexity of the suture pattern of the shell (as *Caloceras*, Fig. 14.11E).

ammonoid. Externally shell-covered cephalopod characterized by strongly curved, angulated, or complex suture patterns and generally by the position of the siphuncle inside the shell differing from that of nautiloids; includes ammonites, ceratites, and goniatites.

amorphous. Without form, referring to rock or other substance lacking observable texture.

amphibian. Four-legged vertebrate (tetrapod) that reproduces only in an aquatic or very moist environment, breathes by means of gills during at least early life, and develops lungs for air breathing; known from Devonian to Recent.

amphibole. Ferromagnesian silicate mineral, common constituent of igneous and metamorphic rocks.

Amphineura. Class of marine mollusks, generally called chitons, characterized by a large flat foot used in crawling and a dorsal side protected by jointed transverse plates.

amygdaloid. Extrusive igneous rock containing many gas-formed vesicles more or less filled by secondary minerals such as quartz, calcite, zeolites, etc.

amygdule. Individual mineral-bearing vesicle of an amygdaloid.

anaerobic. Pertaining to organisms, such as many

bacteria, able to live in an environment that lacks free oxygen.

anastomosing. Branching repeatedly with reunion of the branches to form a netlike pattern.

andesite. Extrusive igneous rock distinguished by content of silica lower than in rhyolites and especially by the nature of its plagioclase feldspar (commonly andesine).

angular unconformity. Structural discordance of stratified rocks produced by erosion of the older beds and deposition of younger beds on the edges of the eroded rocks; angular unconformities signify deformation of the older strata prior to deposition of the younger ones. They may be simulated by cross-bedding and by faulting, distinction of which from angular unconformities generally is recognized easily by various criteria.

anhydristone. Rock composed mainly of anhydrite (also called anhydrock, a much less suitable name, because "stone" rather than "rock" is used by custom in nomenclature of many lithified sedimentary deposits, as sandstone, limestone, etc.).

anhydrite. Mineral consisting of anhydrous calcium sulfate, commonly formed as massive or laminated evaporites; may be altered by hydration to gypsum, as in weathering.

Animikean. Sequence of late Precambrian (Algonkian) rocks recognized in the southern part of the Canadian Shield.

annelid. Type of worm characterized by numerous appendage- or leg-bearing body segments.

anorogenic. Not characterized by or associated with mountain building.

anthozoan. Coelenterate characterized by a radial partition of the body cavity, which is correlated with but not the same as radial septa of skeletal parts; includes nearly all forms called corals.

anthracite. Hard, lustrous coal containing a high percentage of fixed carbon and low percentage of volatile matter, generally formed by dynamic metamorphism but may be produced by contact metamorphism induced by igneous intrusion.

anticlinal. Referring to strata so bent that one portion (limb) slopes upward toward another oppositely inclined.

anticline. Upfold of strata resembling an arch or peaked roof.

anticlinorium. Broad arch of strata folded in anticlines and synclines (= geanticline).

aphanite. Dense homogeneous rock with constituents indeterminable by unaided eyes.

aphanitic. Pertaining to the texture of aphanites; includes microcrystalline, cryptocrystalline, and amorphous.

aplite. Fine-grained, light-colored, granitic dike rock.

aqueous. Pertaining to water or sediment deposited in water.

aquifer. Water-bearing rock, generally stratiform.

arachnid. Jointed-leg invertebrate (arthropod) char-

acterized by a pair of pincer-like appendages (chelicerae) in the head region and mostly four pairs of legs; includes scorpions, spiders, ticks, and several other assemblages but not merostomes or pycnogonids, which are separate groups.

aragonite. Orthorhombic mineral composed of calcium carbonate ($CaCO_3$) dimorphous with calcite.

archaeocyathan. Reef-building calcareous invertebrate with porous double-walled skeleton of cylindrical or conical form, known only from Lower and Middle Cambrian rocks, world-wide in distribution; formerly classified with sponges or corals but now considered to represent an independent extinct phylum.

Archean. Main older division of Precambrian or Cryptozoic rocks and time.

areal. Pertaining to area, as areal geology; not to be confused with aerial.

arenaceous. Sandy (term derived from Latin, *arena,* sand).

argillaceous. Clayey (term derived from Latin, *argillus,* clay).

argillite. Hard clay rock, intermediate in induration between shale and slate.

arkose. Medium- to coarse-grained sedimentary rock largely composed of quartz and feldspar, formed of mechanically weathered minerals of crystalline igneous rock of granitic type.

arkosic. Having more or less well-developed characters of arkose.

artesian. Pertaining to subsurface water under pressure sufficient to make it rise above level of the aquifer (as artesian basin, spring, well, etc.).

arthrodire. Extinct (Devonian) actinopterygian fish characterized by heavy bone armor of the head and front part of body, movably jointed in the neck region; attained the length of 30 feet.

arthropod. Invertebrate with jointed legs; includes trilobites, chelicerates, crustaceans, insects, and others, outnumbering all other animals combined.

articulate. Type of (1) crinoid or (2) brachiopod characterized by muscular hingement of parts of skeleton.

artifact. Prehistoric-made implement or weapon.

asbestos. Fibrous mineral (amphibole) resistant to heat and chemical attack.

asexual. Pertaining to reproduction not involving union of male and female cells (gametes); sometimes called vegetative.

ashstone. Indurated volcanic ash.

ash, volcanic. Fine, unconsolidated pyroclastic material, commonly a product of the explosive eruption of viscous (acidic) lavas.

asphalt. Comparatively nonvolatile bitumen of variable hardness related in origin to petroleum.

asteroid. (1) Echinoderm with radial extensions (arms) not sharply separated from a centrally located body; starfish. (2) Relatively small body revolving in elliptical orbit around sun (= planetoid).

asterozoan. Asteroid (starfish) or ophiuroid (brittle star).

atmosphere. Gaseous envelope surrounding a star or planet, especially the earth.

atoll. Ringlike island or group of islands formed mainly by corals and calcareous algae, surrounding a central lagoon.

atoll reef. Like atoll but may be more or less entirely submerged.

atomic number. Number of protons (or positive charges) in atomic nucleus.

atomic weight. Relative weight of an atom of an element stated in terms of an arbitrary standard of 16 for an oxygen atom.

autocthon. Large body of rocks *in situ*, not displaced; opposite is allocthon.

autocthonous. Formed in place, not foreign.

back reef. Shallow-sea or lagoon shelf area behind a reef, between it and land, commonly characterized by nonfossiliferous deposits of limestones, dolostones, and evaporites, as in the western Texas area of Permian reefs.

baculite. Straight-shelled Cretaceous ammonite.

barite. Mineral consisting of barium sulfate ($BaSO_4$).

basal conglomerate. Generally coarse, more or less well-sorted deposit next above an unconformity, commonly formed by a transgressing shallow sea.

basalt. Dark-colored extrusive igneous rock; many flows marked by columnar jointing.

base level. Lower limit of subaerial erosion by running water, controlled by the level of the water body at stream mouths, may be local and temporary (as where lakes determine the extent of downcutting or in interior basins) or general and semipermanent (as where controlled by mean sea level).

basement complex. Rocks generally with complex structure and distribution of individual rock types (commonly composed largely of crystalline igneous or metamorphic rocks or both) that underlie a sedimentary sequence.

basic. Pertaining to igneous rocks having a silica (SiO_2) content less than two-thirds (generally less than one-half) of total constituents (as basalt, peridotite) (see acidic).

basin. Topographically or both topographically and structurally low area that generally is the site of thicker deposition of sediment than is found elsewhere; basin areas tend progessively to become accentuated by sinking more than the territory outside the basin; in conjunction with shelf, basin refers to adjacent relatively deep water areas.

batholith. Common but etymologically unsuitable equivalent of bathylith.

bathylith. Large mass of deep-seated (therefore, prevailingly coarse-grained) igneous rocks formed by *in situ* fusion of preexisting rocks or by intrusion of magma into preexisting rocks; like stock but much larger.

bauxite. Mineral consisting of hydrated alumina ($Al_2O_3 \cdot 2H_2O$), principal ore of aluminum.

bed. Rock between two next-adjacent bedding planes; commonly the smallest distinguished unit in a stratigraphic succession; stratum.

bedding plane. Parting between two contiguous layers or strata.

beekite. Concretionary calcite ($CaCO_3$) or chalcedony (SiO_2) occurring commonly as small rings, seen on the surface of some weathered fossils.

benthonic. Pertaining to life on sea bottom.

benthos. Collective term for marine bottom-dwelling organisms.

bentonite. Clay formed by decomposition of volcanic ash, generally has the property of absorbing water and swelling accordingly.

biofacies. Spatially distinguished part of sedimentary deposit characterized by its contained organisms.

biogenic. Pertaining to rock or unconsolidated sedimentary deposit formed largely by the agency of organisms.

bioherm. Organically formed reef.

biostratigraphic. Distinguishable by means of contained organisms, commonly referring to classification of parts of sedimentary deposits.

biostrome. Rock layer composed largely of organic remains.

biozone. Rocks distinguished by the presence of a specified kind of organism (species or genus), from lowest to highest and including laterally farthest.

bituminous coal. Coal with moderately high fixed carbon, although less than anthracite, and moderately high volatile matter.

bivalve. Shell consisting of two subequal parts held together by a hinge along one of the margins or by muscles; commonly refers to pelecypods but is applicable to crustaceans (such as ostracodes), brachiopods, etc.

blastoid. Stalked echinoderm with a budlike calyx that bears many delicate armlets (brachioles) but no true arms like those of crinoids.

block faulting. Breaking of large rock masses into blocks bounded by generally normal faults, with or without appreciable tilting of the blocks.

bone bed. Stratum largely composed of fossil bones, teeth, and scales of vertebrates.

borderland. Land mass or island chain bordering a geosyncline, on the side away from the continental interior (as the hypothetical land called Appalachia on the eastern side of the Appalachian geosyncline).

bottom-set beds. Deposits on sea or lake bottom adjacent to the front and sides of a delta.

boulder. Large (>256 millimeter diameter) rounded block of rock, generally transported from a more or less distant source.

brachiopod. Marine invertebrate characterized by a bilaterally symmetrical shell composed of two unequal valves, mostly calcareous and hinged (articulate type) but including phosphatic or chitinophosphatic unhinged valves held together by muscles (inarticulate type).

brackish. Describing water perceptibly salty but less saline than sea water.

breccia. Clastic rock composed of coarse, angular rock fragments.

bryozoan. Colonial invertebrate, almost exclusively marine, with minute individuals, typically secreting a calcareous skeleton of diverse form.

B.t.u. British thermal unit, heat required at sea level to raise the temperature of 1 pound of water 1 degree (between 32° and 212°F.).

calcarenite. Limestone composed of sand-sized grains consisting of more or less worn shell fragments or pieces of an older limestone; a clastic limestone.

calcareous. Containing calcium carbonate ($CaCO_3$).

calcification. Replacement of the original hard parts of an organism by calcium carbonate ($CaCO_3$).

calcilutite. Limestone composed of silt- or clay-sized calcareous particles; a limemud rock of aphanitic texture.

calcisponge. Sponge having calcareous spicules loosely embedded in soft tissue or knit together so as to make a firm skeleton.

calcite. Mineral composed of calcium carbonate ($CaCO_3$).

calcitic dolostone. Carbonate rock composed mainly (51 to 90 per cent) of dolomite but containing 10 to 40 per cent of calcite.

caliche. Deposit of calcium carbonate ($CaCO_3$) found commonly at or near the surface in arid regions; commonly cements noncalcareous gravel-, sand-, silt-, and clay-size particles together to form a porous or compact mass.

Cambrian. Lowest main division of Paleozoic rocks, named from Wales (Cambria); correspondingly, oldest period of Paleozoic Era.

cannel coal. Massive type of easily ignited coal consisting mainly of plant spores and pollen grains deposited in water.

cap rock. Disklike rock mass covering part or all of the top of a salt dome; composed generally of anhydrite, gypsum, limestone, and (in some) sulfur.

carapace. Hard protective covering (exoskeleton) of various invertebrates, especially arthropods; composed of chitin or salts of calcium and phosphorus or both.

carbon-14 (C^{14}). Radioactive isotope of carbon with atomic weight 14; because of relatively rapid decay rate, it is adapted for age measurements of less than 40,000 years.

carbonaceous. Containing appreciable carbon.

carbonate. Compound containing CO_3.

carbonation. Chemical alteration that produces carbonates, as commonly by action of carbonic acid (H_2CO_3) on basic oxides in weathering.

carbonization. Concentration of carbon during fossilization or in coal making.

carbon ratio. Proportion of fixed carbon to total carbon (fixed and volatile) in a coal, expressed in percentage.

cast. Natural or artificial replica of an object, such as a fossil shell, made by filling a mold (impression) of the object; casts of hollow objects may show the shape of both external and internal surfaces. Casts can reproduce none of the microstructure of the original objects but only the shape.

catastrophism. Hypothesis accounting for differences in organic remains found in successive rock layers by assuming destruction of old organisms by a catastrophe and creation of new ones later to replace them.

Cenozoic. Highest major segment of the geologic column and corresponding time, known as Cenozoic Era, which extends from the close of the Mesozoic to the present.

cephalopod. Marine mollusk with tentacles around the mouth and generally (nautiloids, ammonoids) with an external calcareous shell divided into chambers by cross partitions (septa) that produce a distinctive pattern of junctions (sutures) with the covering shell; some forms (belemnoids) with internal shells and others (octopods, sepioids) with none.

ceratite. Ammonoid cephalopod characterized by a distinctive suture pattern of smoothly rounded saddles (curved toward the shell aperture) and jaggedly crenulate lobes (pointed away from the aperture); typical of Triassic deposits but not confined to them.

chain coral. Tabulate coral distinguished by the chainlike appearance of corallites in transverse sections of the colony (*Catenularia*, Ordovician; *Halysites*, Silurian).

chalcedony. Cryptocrystalline quartz, common in siliceous fossils and the substance of agate.

chalk. Soft, white or light-colored variety of limestone, with or without abundant foraminiferal shells.

chat. Finely broken chert that constitutes waste rock (gangue) in mining some ore deposits, as lead and zinc in the Tri-State district of Missouri, Kansas, and Oklahoma.

chemical limestone. Inorganically precipitated nonclastic limestone.

chert. Variously colored cryptocrystalline silica (SiO_2) occurring as nodules or beds in limestone or dolostone; a variety is flint.

chitin. Complex organic compound similar to horn or fingernails secreted as the covering of soft parts by various invertebrates.

chiton. Marine mollusks with a dorsal covering of

eight articulated movable plates extending transversely across a low body (Amphineura).

chordate. Animals with a backbone or notochord, as hemichordates, fishes, tetrapods.

cinder cone. Conical hill of clinker-like volcanic extrusives around a vent.

cirque. Bowl-shaped valley in high mountains carved by glacial ice.

class. Category in zoological or botanical classification intermediate in rank between order and phylum.

clastic. Fragmental, composed of detritus, including broken organic hard parts as well as rock substances of any sort.

clay. Extremely fine unconsolidated sediment (grains mostly <0.005 millimeter) that generally exhibits some degree of plasticity and consists predominantly of hydrous aluminum silicates.

claystone. Indurated clay lacking shaly structure.

coal. Black, compact rock formed by accumulation and alteration of plant remains.

cobble. Rounded rock fragment intermediate in size (64 to 256 millimeters diameter) between pebble and boulder.

coelenterate. Invertebrate characterized by radial symmetry and the possession of stinging capsules, a body cavity without a separate digestive tract; mostly marine; jellyfishes, corals, hydroids.

colonial organisms. Group of individuals belonging to the same species living in close association with independence of separate members partly or wholly lost.

columnar jointing. Cleavage of rock in a manner that produces vertical columns, generally hexagonal in section, as in many basaltic flows.

columnar section. Graphic representation of rock succession in a vertical column with lithology shown by more or less standard symbols and thickness plotted to scale.

conch. Shell of a gastropod (especially a large one) or cephalopod (exclusive of embryonic shell, called protoconch).

conchiolin. Complex organic substance forming the outer thin layer of molluscan shells.

concretion. Generally spheroidal to irregular nodular localized accumulation of mineral matter.

conformable. Superposed strata deposited without interruption in accumulation of sediment, beds parallel.

conformity. State of deposits laid down without interruption.

conglomerate. Lithified gravel; rounded pebbles cemented together.

conifer. Cone-bearing gymnospermous plant, as pine.

conodont. Minute toothlike phosphatic bodies of platy or spiny form belonging to unknown organisms found in many Ordovician to Triassic strata and valuable for correlation.

contact metamorphism. Alteration of rock produced by nearness to igneous intrusions or extrusions.

continental deposits. Sedimentary accumulations formed on continents rather than in seas, that is, made by winds, streams, or in lakes; subaerial.

continental glacier. Ice sheet covering a considerable part of a continent, not confined to valleys.

continental nucleus. Large, relatively rigid part of the earth's crust, consisting of ancient crystalline rocks that form the nearly immobile core of a continent, against and over which younger rocks are deposited so as to enlarge the mass of the continent.

continental shelf. Outer part of a continent submerged by a shallow sea, bounded on the oceanward side by a 100-fathom (600-foot) depth contour.

continental slope. Outer sloping border of a continental mass, extending from a 100-fathom contour downward to oceanic depths.

conulariid. Extinct marine invertebrate characterized by the pyramidal form of its thin chitinophosphatic covering, now classed with scyphozoan coelenterates.

convergent evolution. See adaptive convergence.

coprolite. Fossilized excrement.

coquina. Porous limestone composed of shells and shell fragments cemented together.

coquinoid. Like coquina but solid rock with little porosity.

coral. Bottom-dwelling marine coelenterate that secretes calcareous hard parts; may be solitary or colonial.

coralline. Pertaining to corals or lime-secreting red algae.

corallite. Skeleton of individual coral, solitary or a member of a colony.

coral reef. Topographically upward-projecting mass of limestone formed largely of coral skeletons, at the time of formation reaching close to sea level.

cordillera. Group of mountain ranges. In North America, Cordillera refers to mountainous country between the Central Plains region and the Pacific Ocean.

correlation. Determination of equivalence or correspondence, generally of (1) more or less widely separated outcrops of rock units or (2) different rock units equivalent in age.

country rock. Rocks invaded by igneous intrusions or veins and surrounding them.

craton. Relatively immobile large segment of the earth's crust; continental nuclei are cratons.

Cretaceous. Uppermost Mesozoic system and the last period of the Mesozoic Era; named derived from Latin *creta*, chalk.

crinoid. Generally stalked echinoderm with a calyx composed of regularly arranged plates and provided with arms that radiate from the calyx and function for gathering food.

cross-bedding. Lamination of the stratum oblique to bedding planes.

cryptocrystalline. Very fine crystalline texture with grains not visible to unaided eyes.

cryptogam. Plant that reproduces by spores, as ferns.

Cryptozoic. Oldest major division of earth history, classed as an eon; Precambrian.

cryptozoon. Calcareous algal deposits of hemispheroidal form with concentric laminae.

cup coral. Solitary coral, generally with a cup-shaped depression (calyx) at the summit.

current ripple. Type of ripple mark produced by currents, characterized by an asymmetrical profile and irregular arrangement.

cyclic sedimentation. Deposition of different types of sediment in repeated regular sequences.

cyclothem. Deposits comprising a single sedimentary cycle.

cystoid. Echinoderm with plates of the calyx generally irregular in arrangement and number, perforated by pores or slits, attached by a stalk.

decay constant. Rate of spontaneous disintegration of a radioactive element, unaffected by heat or pressure.

deep. Troughlike depression in the ocean floor, mostly reaching more than 3,000 fathoms (18,000 feet) below sea level.

density current. Highly turbid, relatively dense flow of sediment in water or air, by settling of sediment forming layers that grade upward from coarse to fine (see graded bedding).

detrital. Clastic, consisting of rock or mineral fragments.

detritus. Material produced by mechanical disintegration.

Devonian. Fourth system and period of Paleozoic, named from Devonshire.

diabase. Intrusive igneous rock of basaltic composition but coarser textured than basalt.

diagenesis. Physical and chemical change of sediment leading to lithification.

diastem. Minor interruption in sedimentation, with or without accompanying erosion; if associated with changes in an organism, these are judged to lack significant difference in age.

diastrophism. Deformation of the earth's crust or the process producing such deformation.

diatom. Microscopic protistan with a delicate siliceous shell of generally discoidal form.

diatomaceous earth. Deposit consisting mainly of diatoms.

dike. Intrusive igneous-rock body of tabular form that cuts across the structure of stratified, metamorphosed, or igneous rocks.

dimorphic. Occurring in two forms, as differently shaped shells of males and females or minerals identical in composition but having different crystal forms (calcite, aragonite).

dimorphism. Property of being dimorphic.

dimorphous. Dimorphic.

diorite. Dark-colored plutonic igneous rock, therefore coarse-grained, basic in composition.

dip slope. Inclined land surface parallel to the dip of underlying stratified rocks.

disconformity. Unconformity marked by distinct erosion-produced irregularity of contact between parallel strata below and above the break; commonly greater in time value than diastem (see paraconformity).

discordant. Describing igneous-rock contact that cuts across bedding or foliation of adjacent rocks.

distal. Direction away from a specified or understood reference point (see proximal).

dolomite. Mineral consisting of calcium magnesium carbonate, $CaMg(CO_3)_2$.

dolomitization. Alteration of limestone to dolostone by change of calcite to dolomite.

dolostone. Rock consisting mostly of dolomite.

dome. Upfold shaped like an inverted saucer.

dorsal. Referring to the back or in the position of the back (see ventral).

downwarp. Segment of the earth's crust broadly bent downward.

drift. Rock material transported by glaciers.

drowned valley. Valley partly submerged by the sea or a lake.

drumlin. Elongate elliptical hill of glacial drift (till) with its long axis parallel to the direction of ice movement.

dwarf fauna. Assemblage of fossils subnormal in size, generally inferred to denote adverse environment.

dynamic metamorphism. Pronounced alteration of rocks induced by pressure and accompanying heat.

echinoderm. Exclusively marine invertebrate with a skeleton of crystalline calcite, generally distinguished by prominent pentamerous symmetry; cystoids, blastoids, crinoids, echinoids, asterozoans, and others.

echinoid. Free-moving bottom-dwelling echinoderm with a skeleton of many plates and movable spines; sea urchins.

edrioasteroid. Extinct Paleozoic echinoderm attached to the sea bottom or a shell by the underside of its skeleton.

Eocambrian. Name applied to prevailingly unfossiliferous sedimentary deposits of uncertain classification that occur next below Cambrian rocks in various places; may belong to Paleozoic or to Precambrian.

Eocene. Next to lowest series and next to oldest epoch of Paleogene.

eon. Longest division of geologic time recognized in geochronology.

epeirogenic. Referring to relatively gentle deformation of segments of the earth's crust involving upwarp or downwarp or both (as by tilting) (see orogenic).

epicontinental. Located on a continent, as epicontinental sea.

epoch. First-order division of a geologic period; time corresponding to making rocks of a series.

era. Very long segment of geologic time but smaller than eon, as Paleozoic Era; post-Cryptozoic eras are divided into periods.

erratic. Describing a cobble or boulder displaced from its source by glacial transportation.

esker. Narrow ridge of gravelly or sandy sediment formed by deposition beneath a continental glacier.

euryhaline. Able to tolerate a wide range of salinity, as some invertebrates and fishes.

eurypterid. Extinct type of chelicerate arthropod belonging to the group called merostomes.

eustatic. Referring to simultaneous world-wide changes of sea level.

evaporite. Chemically precipitated sediment formed by evaporation of water containing dissolved mineral matter, as salt, anhydrite, etc.

exoskeleton. Hard protective covering of soft parts, commonly referring to mineralized integument of arthropods.

extrusive rocks. Igneous rocks formed from lava poured out on the earth's surface.

facies. Significantly varying part of a sedimentary rock unit, generally characterized by both lithologic and biologic distinguishing features and segregated areally from other parts of the unit.

family. Assemblage of closely related genera of animals or plants.

fanglomerate. Consolidated gravel and associated sediment deposited as an alluvial fan.

fault. Displacement of rocks along a fracture; the fracture surface or zone along which displacement has occurred.

fauna. Assemblage of animals associated in a particular area or belonging to a particular rock or time-rock unit.

feldspar. Light-colored aluminum silicate mineral, important as the primary constituent of many igneous and some metamorphic rocks but found also in some sedimentary rocks as deposit derived from igneous or metamorphic rocks or originating in the sediment (authigenic).

flint. Dense variety of chert that breaks with conchoidal fracture.

flora. Assemblage of plants associated in a particular area or belonging to a particular rock or time-rock unit.

fluviatile. Belonging to a river or stream.

fluvioglacial. Pertaining to streams of glacial melt water or deposits made by them.

fold. Bend in strata; rounded elevation extending from the beak of a brachiopod along the mid-line of the brachial valve.

foliation. Laminated structure in metamorphosed rocks produced by segregation of different minerals into layers parallel to schistosity.

foraminifer. Protozoan commonly bearing a calcareous shell of varied form with one or more chambers, but the shell may be siliceous or composed of cemented foreign particles.

formation. Rock unit distinguished primarily on lithologic characters and defined as a unit for geologic mapping.

fossil. Remains or traces of organism preserved in rocks (arbitrarily excluding Recent remains or traces).

fucoid. Ridgelike marking on bedding plane of uncertain origin but inferred to represent seaweed (*Fucus*) impression.

fusulinid. Spindle-shaped to globose foraminifer with a calcareous spirally coiled shell divided into numerous chambers, abundant in many Pennsylvanian and Permian strata.

gabbro. Dark-colored, plutonic igneous rock.

gastrolith. Well-rounded, polished pebble found with some fossil reptile skeletons, considered to be stomach stone.

gastropod. Molluscan invertebrate generally with a spirally coiled calcareous shell; snail.

geanticline. Broad, linear, crustal upwarp paralleling a geosyncline and presumed to be the chief source of sediment deposited in the geosyncline.

genus. Group of closely related species of animals or plants.

geochronology. Time as applied to earth history; including classification of geologic time in eons, eras, periods, epochs, and ages.

geosyncline. Large troughlike depression generally scores of miles wide and many hundreds of miles long that receives thick sedimentary deposits and progressively subsides during accumulation of the deposits.

glacial lake. Lake formed by erosional or depositional work of glacial ice or by both; also water ponded against glacial ice.

glacial lobe. Tonguelike extension of a glacial ice sheet.

glacial striae. Scratches made by the work of glaciers on bedrock or rock fragments (pebble to boulder size) transported by glacial ice.

glacier. Slow-moving mass of ice on land.

glauconite. Greenish mineral consisting of hydrous potassium iron silicate, commonly formed in marine environment.

globigerina ooze. Deep-sea sediment composed largely of shells of the planktonic foraminifer *Globigerina*.

gneiss. Coarse-grained, banded metamorphic rock.

Gondwanaland. Hypothetical continent of the Southern Hemisphere extending from Australia to India, Africa, and South America.

goniatite. Ammonoid cephalopod characterized by a relatively simple suture pattern of angulated lobes and rounded saddles.

graben. Downthrown block of the earth's crust bounded by faults (see horst).

graded bedding. Sorting of clastic sediment in a manner that produces progressive decrease in coarseness of grains from the base to the top of a stratum; characteristic of density-current deposits.

granite. Coarse-grained, light-colored igneous rock consisting of alkalic feldspar, quartz, and accessory minerals.

granite gneiss. Banded rock of granitic texture and composition.

granodiorite. Plutonic igneous rock somewhat more basic than granite and less basic than diorite.

graphite. Black to steel-gray carbon (C) mineral.

graptolite. Extinct marine colonial invertebrate with chitinous hard parts, now classed as hemichordate; especially common in many Ordovician and Silurian dark-colored shales.

gravel. Unconsolidated rounded pebbles, cobbles, or boulders.

graywacke. Fine-grained clastic rock composed of varied sorts of rock fragments and mineral grains.

greensand. Sandy sediment consisting largely of glauconite.

ground moraine. Deposits formed below the body of a glacier, generally distinguished by low topographic relief.

ground water. Subsurface water occurring in rocks or unconsolidated sedimentary deposits within the zone of saturation.

guide fossil. Any remains of an organism useful for correlating strata and for age determination (see index fossil).

gypstone. Rock composed chiefly of gypsum.

gypsum. Light-colored mineral consisting of hydrous calcium sulfate ($CaSO_4 \cdot 2H_2O$).

half life. Time in which one-half of the initial number of atoms of a radioactive element decays.

halite. Mineral consisting of sodium chloride, common salt.

hematite. Reddish brown mineral composed of iron oxide (Fe_2O_3), the principal ore of iron.

hemichordate. Animal intermediate between invertebrates and chordates.

hexacoral. Coral distinguished by hexameral symmetry; scleractinian.

hiatus. Gap in the sedimentary record indicating nondeposition, with or without accompanying removal of sediment by erosion (signifies unconformity).

hinge line. Line marking the position of articulation between two shells of bivalve invertebrates, generally dorsal (pelecypods, ostracodes, etc.) but may be posterior (brachiopods).

hogback. Ridge formed by tilted strata or a dike.

holothuroid. Soft-bodied, generally elongate echinoderm; sea cucumber.

homeomorph. Unrelated species that closely resemble one another in form.

honeycomb coral. Tabulate coral with small polygonal corallites, *Favosites.*

horizon. Surface of contact between two rock layers, lacking thickness; as commonly used refers to a stratigraphic level such as marked by the occurrence of a designated fossil.

hornblende. Ferromagnesian silicate mineral, common constituent of igneous and metamorphic rocks.

horn coral. Conical solitary coral, straight or curved, shaped like a horn.

horst. Upraised block of the earth's crust bounded by faults (see graben).

Huronian. Sequence of Algonkian rocks (Precambrian).

hydrozoan. Simple type of coelenterate, some of which secrete calcareous hard parts, prevailingly marine.

hypersaline. Abnormally high in salinity.

index fossil. Fossil with a narrow stratigraphic range and wide geographic distribution chosen as namegiver to a zone, otherwise the same as guide fossil.

inlier. Area of rock outcrop surrounded by outcrops of younger rocks.

interfingered, interfingering. Describing laterally contiguous rock units with extensions of each projecting into the other so as to make a zigzag boundary between them.

intertongued, intertonguing. Same as interfingered, interfingering.

intraformational conglomerate. Consolidated pebble bed within a formation produced by breaking up of a lithified or semilithified stratum of the formation and therefore not involving appreciable transportation of the generally flat, little-rounded pebbles.

intrusive rocks. Igneous rocks formed by cooling of magma forced into or displacing other rocks, as dikes, sills, bathyliths, etc.

isoclinal. Dipping equally in same direction, as limbs of isoclinal fold.

isomorphous. Applied to minerals with different ions that may replace one another without altering the crystal form.

isopach. Line on a map drawn through points of equal thickness of a designated rock unit or assemblage of beds.

isostasy. Balance of segments of the earth's crust causing blocks of average low specific gravity to stand topographically higher than those with high specific gravity; thus continental masses, being relatively light, project well above oceanic crustal segments, which are much heavier.

isostatic adjustment. Compensation of mass deficiencies in blocks of the earth's crust by elevation of the surface that brings them into balance with neighboring heavy blocks with lower surface, or conversely, by depression of heavy blocks that brings them into balance with elevated light blocks.

isotope. Variety of an element having a standard number of protons in the nucleus of each atom but a number of neutrons differing from those of other isotopes; hence isotopes have identical atomic number but differing atomic weights and slightly dissimilar chemical properties.

jasper. Slightly translucent cryptocrystalline quartz of red, brown, or green color.

jet. Dense black lignite that takes a good polish, used in jewelry.

Jurassic. Middle system and period of Mesozoic, named from the Jura Mountains.

kame. Hill composed of fluvioglacial sand or gravel.

kaolin. Rock composed of clay minerals of the kaolinite group, which are hydrous aluminum silicates, used in making porcelain and chinaware.

karst. Limestone area having many sinks separated by abrupt ridges or irregular hills; generally honeycombed below the surface by tunnels and caves resulting from solution by ground water.

Keewatin. Oldest recognized division of Archean (Precambrian) rocks in the Canadian Shield region.

Keweenawan. Uppermost and youngest division of Algonkian (Precambrian) rocks in the Canadian Shield region.

laccolith. Lenticular, intrusive igneous rock body with its convex upper surface concordant with overlying domed strata and its flat or downwardly convex lower surface parallel to subjacent strata.

lacustrine. Produced by or belonging to lakes.

lag concentrate. Coarse sediment accumulated residually by removal of formerly associated fine materials, as in forming some bone beds and pebbles of so-called desert pavement.

lagoon. Salt-water lake near the sea or a shallow sea nearly enclosed by land.

lamellibranch. Pelecypod; name referring to leaflike gills.

lamp shell. Brachiopod, especially terebratuloid shells that resemble a Roman lamp.

Laurentian. Precambrian granite of the Canadian Shield region, classed as Archean.

law of superposition. Principle that underlying strata must be older than overlying beds where the rock succession is not disturbed by overturning or overthrusting.

lead-uranium ratio. Proportion of lead and uranium in rock or mineral or amounts of isotopes of these elements, used in radioactive age measurements.

lentil. Lenticular subdivision of a formation.

lignite. Brownish black coal with high content of volatile carbon, composed of plant remains more altered than in peat but less than in bituminous coal.

limestone. Sedimentary deposit consisting mainly of calcium carbonate ($CaCO_3$), generally bedded.

lineation. Parallel orientation of structural features of rocks expressed by lines rather than planes, as long dimensions of minerals or pebbles, striae on slickensides, intersection of bedding with cleavage, etc.

lithification. Consolidation of loose sediment into coherent rock.

lithofacies. Rock record of any sedimentary environment, including both physical and organic aspects.

lithology. Description of rocks, generally megascopic.

littoral zone. Shore areas between low and high tide.

loess. Homogeneous nonstratified silt deposit, mostly, if not exclusively, eolian in origin.

lutite. Rock formed from mud, hence composed of silt or clay or both.

magma. Hot fluid rock matter within the earth's crust, capable of intrusion or extrusion, producing igneous rocks by cooling.

mammal. Warm-blooded, more or less densely hair-covered vertebrate that (except two egg-laying forms) brings forth its young alive and suckles them.

marble. Metamorphosed limestone or dolostone with more or less coarse-grained crystalline structure; some nonmetamorphosed carbonate rocks containing abundant crystalline calcite (as echinoderm fragments and intergrain precipitates from ground water) and dolomite are incorrectly called marble.

marine-cut plain. Nearly flat surface carved by sea waves or current scour.

marker bed. Distinctive stratum that is more or less easily identifiable and widely traceable, useful in correlations; also, stratum chosen as a reference for structure mapping.

marl. Unconsolidated or only semiconsolidated calcareous clay, silt, or sand containing glauconite.

marlstone. Indurated calcareous clay, normally with 25 to 75 per cent clay.

massive. Nonstratified or very thick-bedded.

matrix. Rock substance in which coarse crystals, fossils, pebbles, etc., may be embedded, normally finer grained than the constituents embedded.

mega-. Combining term meaning large.

megalospheric. Foraminiferal shell with a relatively large initial chamber (proloculus), formed by asexual reproduction.

megascopic. Observable with unaided eyes.

merostome. Type of chelicerate arthropod; includes king crab (*Limulus*), eurypterids.

Mesozoic. Major time division classed as era, succeeding Paleozoic and preceding Cenozoic, name meaning medieval life; also rocks formed during this era.

metamorphic rock. Product of large changes in temperature, pressure, and chemical environment affecting already formed rock, as schist, phyllite, gneiss; may be classed as meta-igneous (derived from igneous rocks) or metasedimentary (derived from sedimentary rocks).

metamorphism. Change in texture, with or without change in composition, of rock produced by heat, pressure, and possibly altered chemical environment resulting from deformation or igneous activity.

metasomatism. Replacement of one mineral by another resulting from simultaneously effected solution and deposition; term commonly applied to altered mineral aggregates but equally applicable to fossils formed by petrifaction involving change in mineral composition.

metastable. Stable only under undisturbed conditions, changing to more stable condition when disturbed, as in the common alteration of aragonite (metastable $CaCO_3$) to calcite (stable $CaCO_3$), which importantly affects the preservation of many fossils.

metazoan. Multicelled animal having tissue formed of cell layers.

meteorite. Metallic or stony body fallen to the earth from outer space.

micaceous. Containing more or less abundant mica, especially muscovite.

microcrystalline. Describing rock composed of minute crystals visible only with a microscope.

microfossil. Remains of a microscopic organism, including commonly colonies of megascopic size (as bryozoans) that require microscopic study for identification.

micropaleontology. Study of microfossils, including identification, classification, nomenclature, description, and observation of occurrence.

Miocene. Series and epoch of mid-Cenozoic age, next younger than Oligocene and older than Pliocene.

Mississippian. System and period of Paleozoic age, next younger than Devonian and older than Pennsylvanian.

mold. Impression of the exterior (external mold) or interior (internal mold) of a shell or other organism; may be natural or artificial.

mollusk. Invertebrate, generally shell-bearing, of univalve (cephalopod, gastropod, scaphopod), bivalve (pelecypod), or multivalve (chiton) type, but some naked.

monocline. Strata inclined in a single direction, especially a steplike fold produced by local downbending of nearly horizontal strata or locally steepened dip of gently inclined beds.

moraine. Glacial drift with constructional topography.

mudstone. Nonfissile rock composed of clay- to silt-size clastic grains.

myriapod. Arthropod characterized by very numerous leg-bearing segments (centipedes, millipedes).

nappe. Large body of rocks moved laterally a considerable distance (generally one or more miles) by overfolding or thrust-faulting.

natural cement. Product made by burning limestone that contains a specified clay content, the rock having a composition corresponding approximately to the mixture of limestone and shale used in making portland cement.

natural selection. Survival of organic types by reason of greater fitness than competitors.

nautiloid. Externally shelled cephalopod characterized by simple sutures (not distinctly angulated), with straight, curved, or coiled shells.

negative segment. Part of the earth's crust that tends progressively to sink during geologic time.

nektonic. Pertaining to marine swimming animals.

Neogene. System and period of late Cenozoic age, comprising Miocene, Pliocene, and Pleistocene Series and Epochs.

neritic. Marine environment extending from low tide to the outer edge of the continental shelf where the depth is approximately 100 fathoms (600 feet).

nonconformity. Unconformity formed by deposition of rock strata on massive crystalline rock.

normal fault. Fault with hanging wall depressed relative to foot wall.

nummulite. Relatively large, multichambered, discoid foraminifer.

obsidian. Volcanic glass, generally black and typically with well-marked conchoidal fracture.

offlap. Progressively more restricted sedimentary units in upward succession resulting from diminution in the area of sedimentation, as in marine regression.

oil shale. Shale that yields appreciable quantities of oil on slow distillation.

Oligocene. Series and epoch of Cenozoic age, next older than Miocene and younger than Eocene.

onlap. Progressively more extensive sedimentary units in upward succession resulting from expansion in the area of sedimentation, as during transgression of a shallow sea (= overlap).

ontogeny. Life history or development of an individual organism (see phylogeny).

oölite. Limestone composed of minute spheroidal concretionary grains resembling fish eggs.

order. Category of zoological or botanical classification intermediate in rank between family and class.

Ordovician. System and period of early Paleozoic age, next younger than Cambrian and older than Silurian, named from Ordovices, an ancient Celtic tribe that lived in western England and Wales.

orogenic. Pertaining to mountain-building crustal deformation (orogeny).

ostracode. Minute bean-shaped, bivalve crustacean, common as fossils.

outlier. Detached portion of a sedimentary unit separated from the main body by erosion.

outwash. Stratified glacial drift deposited by melt water beyond the margin of a glacier.

overlap. Lateral extension of a rock unit beyond the limits of the next underlying units (see onlap).

overthrust. Generally low-angle fault with hanging wall pushed over foot wall.

paleobotany. Study of fossil plant remains.

Paleocene. Series and epoch of early Cenozoic age, next younger than Cretaceous, older than Eocene.

paleoecology. Study of the relationship of pre-Recent organisms to environment.

Paleogene. System and period of early Cenozoic age, next younger than Cretaceous and older than Neogene; includes Paleocene, Eocene, and Oligocene Series and Epochs.

paleogeography. Study of geographic features belonging to any division of past geologic time.

paleogeology. Study of geologic features (such as distribution of outcrops of various rock divisions) belonging to any part of past geologic time.

paleontology. Study of fossil organisms, including protistans, plants, and animals.

Paleozoic. Major division (era) of geologic time characterized by relative abundance of ancient organic remains, which sharply distinguishes it from older (Precambrian) eras that lack evidence of living things, except locally and rarely; also rocks belonging to the era.

paleozoology. Study of fossil animal remains, commonly divided into studies of invertebrates and vertebrates.

paraconformity. Unconformity distinguished by even contact of parallel beds, may be continuous laterally with disconformity, angular unconformity, or nonconformity.

parazoan. Multicelled animal lacking cells organized as tissue.

peat. Dark brown or black residue produced by partial decomposition of accumulated plant remains, high in volatile carbon, burns with smoky flame.

pebble. Rounded rock fragment 2 to 64 mm. diam.

pediment. Sloping plain carved in bedrock, thinly and discontinuously veneered with sediment, bordering mountains in semiarid and arid regions.

pelagic. Free-swimming (nektonic) or floating (planktonic) organisms of the sea, not living on the bottom (benthonic).

peneplain. Broad, nearly flat plain produced by very prolonged degradation of land that lowers it essentially to base level.

Pennsylvanian. System and period of late Paleozoic age, younger than Mississippian, older than Permian.

period. Large division of geologic time corresponding to rocks classed as a geologic system, next lower in rank than era and divisible into epochs.

Permian. System and period of late Paleozoic age, younger than Pennsylvanian, older than Triassic.

phylogeny. Line of descent of organisms.

phylum. Main division of organisms, next lower in rank than kingdom; divided into classes, orders, families, etc. (as Mollusca, Chordata).

planetesimal. Referring to a small body revolving about the sun in manner of planets but mostly with strongly elliptical orbits.

planktonic. Applied to floating organisms of the sea.

Pleistocene. Series and epoch of latest Cenozoic age, next younger than Pliocene, includes Recent; especially characterized by extensive glaciation.

Pliocene. Series and epoch of late Cenozoic age, next younger than Miocene and older than Pleistocene; subdivision of Neogene System and Period.

plutonic. Deep-seated igneous rocks, generally coarsely equigranular in texture.

portland cement. Hydraulic cement made by semifusing a chemically controlled mixture of limestone and shale and fine grinding the resultant clinker.

positive segment. Part of the earth's crust that tends progressively to rise during geologic time.

Precambrian. Geologic time before the Cambrian Period and all rocks formed in this part of earth history (= Cryptozoic, pre-Paleozoic).

profile of equilibrium. Marine wave-cut platform merging with an offshore-built platform sloping gently seaward at an angle that yields a balance between erosion and deposition; may be expressed in rock succession by conformity, disconformity, paraconformity, angular unconformity, or nonconformity, depending on local conditions.

Proterozoic. Era of late Cryptozoic age and rocks formed during this part of Precambrian time (= Algonkian).

protistan. One-celled organism lacking characters of multicelled plants and animals.

protozoan. Type of protistan that includes foraminifers and radiolarians, important as fossils and in many places as rock builders.

proximal. Pertaining to direction toward a specified or understood reference point (see distal).

pseudomorph. Natural cast of mineral crystal or fossil composed of a substance differing from the original composition of the replaced object.

pteropod. Nektonic gastropod with a foot modified into winglike form for swimming, commonly with a thin, narrowly conical shell.

pumice. Very finely cellular volcanic glass.

pyrite. Brassy yellow mineral composed of iron sulfide.

pyroclastic. Fragmented rock of igneous origin (ash, tuff, agglomerate, etc.).

pyroxene. Ferromagnesian silicate mineral, common constituent of igneous rocks.

quartz. Mineral composed of silica (SiO_2), hard, very common constituent of igneous, sedimentary, and metamorphic rocks.

quartzite. Rock composed of quartz grains cemented by silica, commonly in crystallographic continuity with the grains.

quartzose. Largely composed of quartz.

Quaternary. Designation of youngest major division of geologic column and geologic time in commonly used but outmoded classification, next younger than Tertiary.

radioactive age determination. Computation of the time elapsed since the formation of a radioactive mineral or rock based on constant decay rates of the parent substance and measurement of its quantity in relation to decay products.

radiocarbon age determination. Age measurement based on carbon-14.

radiolarian. Minute protistan with a delicate, generally complex siliceous or strontium sulfate shell, important as fossils.

Recent. Vaguely and variably defined latest part of Pleistocene Epoch and rocks or deposits belonging to this part of geologic time.

recessional moraine. Marginal glacial deposits marking a halt of the ice front during its retreat.

redbeds. Prevailingly red-colored sedimentary deposits, mostly sandstone and shale or clay.

reef. Rounded or ridgelike elevation of the sea bottom reaching close to sea level; also the rock mass composing a reef.

reef-core rock. Massive central part of a reef, without bedding, in organically built reefs with organisms (as corals, stromatoporoids, algae) commonly in position of growth.

reef-flank rock. Generally rather strongly inclined bedded rock along the edges of reef-core rock; may be formed largely of reef detritus built outward as submarine talus.

rhyolite. Fine-grained, light-colored extrusive igneous rock with a composition corresponding to that of granite.

rill mark. Groove in beach sand or mud produced by the current of an outgoing tide in the lee of a small obstruction such as a shell or pebble.

ripple mark. Undulatory surface of sand or silt produced by currents of air or water or by agitation of water due to waves.

roche moutonée. Glacially smoothed bare-rock hillock.

salt dome. Pluglike mass of salt pushed upward through relatively incompetent sedimentary strata upturning the edges of penetrated rock layers next to the salt and doming strata above the salt.

saltstone. Rock layer or mass composed of common salt (halite, NaCl).

sand. Detrital material composed of grains $\frac{1}{16}$ to 2 millimeters in diameter.

sandstone. Consolidated sand, generally used only for rock composed of quartz sand grains predominantly.

schist. Metamorphic rock characterized by foliated structure, splitting into thin irregular platy fragments.

schistosity. Foliated structure of the sort seen in schist.

scoria. Dark-colored, vesicular, extrusive igneous rock with slaglike or cindery appearance.

seamount. Submarine mountain, mostly rising more than 3,000 feet above ocean floor.

section. In geology, exposure of a succession of rocks or graphic representation of such a succession.

sediment. Material deposited by settling from a fluid transporting medium such as water or air.

sedimentary. Descriptive term for unconsolidated or consolidated deposits composed mostly of sediment.

sedimentary cycle. Succession of different kinds of sedimentary deposits repeated in constant order.

sedimentation. Process of deriving, transporting, and depositing sedimentary particles, including broken (clastic), inorganic, and organic materials and more or less unbroken organic remains.

sequence. Major division of rocks formed during many million years of Precambrian time (without criteria for precise definition of magnitude but corresponding roughly to systemic divisions of Paleozoic, Mesozoic, and Cenozoic rocks); may be divided into parts called sub-sequences that correspond approximately to series in post-Cryptozoic rocks.

series. Time-stratigraphic term applied to the main division of a system; commonly only two or three such parts of any one system are recognized; time corresponding to series is designated as epoch.

shale. Laminated, fine-grained, clastic sedimentary rock.

shallow sea. Marginal or inland extension of the ocean having depths prevailingly less than 600 feet.

shelf. Relatively broad area of the shallow-sea bottom adjacent to a deeper water basin, as in western Texas during Permian time.

shield. Relatively large continental segment of the earth's crust that has been little raised, lowered, or affected by folding during a long part of geologic time, as Canadian Shield.

sial. Major subdivision of the earth's crust occurring mainly beneath continents, characterized by relatively low specific gravity (approximately 2.7), composed mainly of siliceous (Si) and aluminous (Al) rock materials.

silica. Silicon dioxide (SiO_2).

silicate. Chemically formed substance essentially characterized by content of SiO_4 (orthosilicate) or SiO_3 (metasilicate).

siliceous. Containing silica (SiO_2).

silicification. Replacement of mineral or rock substance by silica (SiO_2) or significant change of composition due to introduction of silica.

sill. Relatively thin tabular body of intrusive igneous rock parallel to bedding or schistosity of enclosing rocks.

silt. Unconsolidated clastic particles ranging in diameter from $\frac{1}{256}$ to $\frac{1}{16}$ millimeter, finer than sand and coarser than clay.

siltstone. Nonlaminated rock composed of silt.

Silurian. System and period of Paleozoic age, next younger than Ordovician and older than Devonian; named from the ancient Celtic tribe of Silures that lived in western England and Wales.

sima. Major subdivision of the earth's crust occurring mainly beneath ocean areas, characterized by relative high specific gravity (approximately 3.3), composed mainly of siliceous (Si), magnesian (Mg), and aluminous (Al) materials.

sub-sequence. Main division of rocks designated as a sequence; applied to Precambrian rocks in manner corresponding to series of Phanerozoic rocks.

synclinal. Referring to strata so bent that one portion (limb) slopes downward toward another oppositely inclined.

syncline. Downfold of strata resembling a trough.

synclinorium. Broad syncline with superimposed minor folds.

system. Major division of the geologic column applicable generally throughout the world, comprising rocks formed during a geologic period, which is the first-rank division of a geologic era.

talus. Accumulation of loose rock fragments at the foot of a cliff or slope.

tectonic. Referring to rock structures formed by movements of the earth's crust.

tepee butte. Conical hill resembling an Indian wigwam.

terrace. Relatively flat land surface bounded by an escarpment on one side and a rise to higher terrain on the other.

Tertiary. Widely used designation of Cenozoic rocks classed as a system and of time classed as a period in outmoded classification; next younger than Cretaceous and older than Quaternary.

thrust fault. Generally low-angle displacement of rocks along a fracture with the hanging wall pushed over the foot wall.

till. Unconsolidated, nonsorted, nonstratified glacial deposit.

tillite. Consolidated till.

time. Duration; whole or part of geologic chronology; instant defined in relation to preceding and succeeding points or parts of geologic time.

time-rock. Same as time-stratigraphic.

time-stratigraphic. Referring to rock units bounded by time-defined initial and terminal limits that at least in theory are respectively synchronous.

tongue. As applied to rocks, division of a formation that extends laterally into another formation or between other formations.

trap rock. Dark-colored igneous rock composing sill, dike, or extrusive sheet that typically crops out with steplike topographic expression (derived from Teutonic word for stair).

travertine. Compact, usually concretionary calcium carbonate ($CaCO_3$) deposited by surface and ground waters.

Triassic. System and period of early Mesozoic age, next younger than Permian and older than Jurassic.

trilobite. Paleozoic arthropod characterized by longitudinal and transverse division of carapace into three parts or lobes, most abundant in Cambrian and Ordovician rocks.

tufa. Sedimentary rock composed of calcium carbonate ($CaCO_3$) or silica (SiO_2) precipitated from spring, lake, or ground water.

tuff. Igneous rock consisting of compacted volcanic fragments.

type locality. Place from which a rock formation is named or the type specimen of a fossil species comes.

type specimen. Individual fossil chosen as the most authentic representative of a species, primarily for the purpose of stabilizing nomenclature.

ultrabasic. Igneous rock containing less than 45 per cent silica (SiO_2), consisting essentially of ferromagnesian silicates.

unconformable. Having relation of an unconformity to underlying rocks separated from them by interruption of sedimentation, with or without accompanying erosion of older rocks.

unconformity. Contact between rocks that denotes more or less prolonged nondeposition, with or without accompanying erosion of older rocks; types of unconformity are angular unconformity, diastem, disconformity, nonconformity, and paraconformity.

underclay. Plastic clay bed underlying a coal bed.

uniformitarianism. Doctrine that the present is a key to the past; principle of uniformity in physical and biologic conditions and operations.

upthrown. Describes a rock mass pushed relatively upward on one side of a fault.

upwarp. Segment of the earth's crust broadly uplifted.

varve. Seasonal or annual layer of sediment.

vascular. Type of plant characterized by tissue adapted for transmission of fluids, many of them woody.

ventral. Side toward the stomach, opposite the back, commonly directed downward.

volcanic ash. Fine, unconsolidated pyroclastic material, commonly formed by explosive eruption of viscous (acidic) lavas.

zone. Bed or group of beds distinguished by paleontologic content or by other specified characters; as commonly employed in stratigraphy, comprises essentially time-defined rocks forming subdivision of a stage or larger time-stratigraphic unit.

INDEX

See also Glossary, pages 636 to 638

Acadian mountain building, 192, 194, 204, 233
Acanthoceras (ammonite), 385
acanthodians, Devonian, 207
Acanthodii (placoderms), 322
Acanthoscaphites (ammonite), 414
Acheulean culture, 563
Acidaspis (trilobite), 307
Actiniscus (dinoflagellate), 570
Actinomma (radiolarian), 573
actinopterygian fishes, 320, 322
Actinoptychus (diatom), 570
Actinostroma (stromatoporoid), 590
adaptive convergence, 42
adaptive divergence, 42
Adirondack region, 68
   Cambrian, 113
Africa, dinosaurs, 421
   Jurassic pterosaurs, 400
   Pennsylvanian orogeny, 242
   Permian, 278, 282
   Precambrian uranium, 104
African ape men, 559
African Shield (Precam.), 66
Aftonian Stage (Pleist.), 463, 505, 513
Aganides (ammonoid), 225, 306
Age, of Ammonites, 395
   of Cycadeoids, 395
   of Dinosaurs, 417
   of Fishes, 319
   of Invertebrates, 284
   of Mammals, 528
   of Reptiles, 327, 395
age (time unit), 29
   measurement methods, 30
agglomerate, significance, 3
Aglaspida (chelicerates), 308
Agnew, A. F., 161
Alabama, Appalachian folding, 269
   Cambrian, 109
   Cretaceous, 371, 375
   Eocene, coal, 454
      coral reefs, 530
   Mississippian, 213, 218
   Ordovician, 137
   Pennsylvanian, 234
      fern, 13
   Silurian, 164, 168, 173, 183
Alaska, Cretaceous, 382
   angiosperms, 404
   conifers, 404
   Jurassic, 349
      cycadeoids, 401
      ginkgos, 403
   Laramian revolution, 384
   Mississippian, 213
   Paleogene, 435, 451
   Permian, 258, 267
   Silurian orogeny, 182
Alberta, ceratopsian dinosaurs, 424
   Cretaceous, coal, 390
      oil, 389
   Devonian, 193, 195, 202

Alberta, dinosaur quarry, 10
   Mississippian, 213, 220, 229
   Paleogene, 445, 451
   Precambrian, 64, 93
Albertan, 114, 120
Albian Stage (Cret.), 374
Alcyonidium (bryozoan), 594
Alethopteris (fern), 578
algae, blue-green, description, 569
   brown, 571
   Cambrian, 129
   Cryptozoic, 98
   Eocene, 529
   grass-green, 569
   Jurassic, 358
   Ordovician, 157
   Paleozoic, 285
   Pennsylvanian, 247
   Permian, 266, 281
   red, 571
Algoman Granite, 80
Algonkian Era, 62, 70
   duration, 32
Algonkian rocks in Grand Canyon, 62
allantois, 324
Allegheny Front in relation to structure, 275
Allegheny Series (Penn.), 241
Alps Mountains, Neogene deformation, 492
   Paleogene orogeny, 452
   Pleistocene glaciation, 518
   Triassic, 328, 333
   zinc, 345
Alsace-Lorraine, Jurassic iron ores, 364
Altyn Limestone (Precam.), 93
amblypods (mammals), 537, 621
Amebelodon (elephant), 622
Ameura (trilobite), 252
ammonites, Cretaceous, 382, 387, 410
   Jurassic, 360
   Mesozoic, 395
   straight-shelled, 387
   Triassic, 341
ammonoids, description, 602
   Devonian, 306
   Mesozoic, 412
   Mississippian, 306
   Paleozoic, 303
   Pennsylvanian, 252, 305
   Permian, 259, 305
amnion, 324
amphibians, Cenozoic, 534
   description, 615
   Devonian, 200
   Jurassic, 357
   Mesozoic, 417
   Mississippian, 227
   Paleozoic, 322
   Pennsylvanian, 40
   Permian, 275, 277

amphibians, Triassic, 342
Amphineura (chitons), 596
Amphiroa (red alga), 571
Amplexus (horn coral), 293
Ampyx (trilobite), 307
Amsden, T. W., 185
amygdaloids, Keweenawan, 104
anapsid reptiles, 616
Andes Mountains, Cenozoic orogeny, 453
   Laramian revolution, 384
Andrews, H. N., Jr., 430
Andrichuk, J. M., 209
angiosperms, Cretaceous, 367, 379, 404
   description, 578
   Jurassic, 403
   Mesozoic, 399
   Neogene, 529
angular unconformity, 19
   base of Cambrian, 116
   of Cretaceous, 251
   of Neogene, 447
   of Paleogene, 390, 441, 490
   of Pennsylvanian, 233
   of Pleistocene, 450, 476
   of Silurian, 165
anhydrite, Jurassic, 349, 356
   Permian, 266
   Silurian, 178
Animalia, 568
animals, characters, 579
   main divisions, 580
Animikie Sub-sequence (Precam.), 81
Anisian Stage (Trias.), 333
Ankareh Formation, 336
ankylosaurs (dinosaurs), 422
annelids, description, 603
Annularia (horsetail rush), 251
Anodonta (pelecypod), 599
Antarctica, Cambrian archaeocyathans, 290
   Jurassic, 357
      cycadeoids, 401
   Pleistocene "interglacial" icecap, 502
Antevs, Ernst, 525
Anthozoa (corals), 591
anthracite, Pennsylvanian, 238, 252
antimony, Cretaceous, 388
   Silurian, China, 185
Apatosaurus (dinosaur), 419
ape men, Africa, 559
   China, 558
   eastern Asia, 556
   Java, 558
Apennine Mountains, Paleogene orogeny, 452
   Pleistocene glaciation, 519
Appalachia, 124, 219
Appalachian geosyncline, 124, 267
Appalachian mountain building, 242, 269

Appalachian Mountains, 275
former Cretaceous cover, 485
Neogene, erosion, 480
history, 484
surface features, 275
Appalachian Piedmont, 24, 370
rock structure, 275
Appalachian Plateau, Pennsylvanian, 238
rock structure, 275
Appalachian region, Cambrian, 109, 115
Cambro-Ordovician, 29
Devonian glass sand, 208
Ordovician, 142, 147
Pennsylvanian, 232, 249
Precambrian, 88
(*See also* specific states)
Appekunny Formation (Precambrian), 93
Aptian Stage (Cret.), 374
aquatic carnivores (mammals), 547
aquatic reptiles, 397, 399
Cenozoic, 534
Cretaceous, 384
(*See also* marine reptiles)
Aquitanian Stage (Mio.), 463
Arachnida (chelicerates), 308
arachnids (chelicerates), 309
description, 605
Paleozoic, 309
Araneida (true spiders), 309
Arbuckle Mountains, 250
Cambrian, 117
Ordovician, 144, 148
Precambrian, 89
Arca (pelecypod), 600
Archaeoconularia (conulate), 588
archaeocyathans, Cambrian, 290
description, 584
Archaeocyathus, 584
Archaeopteris (fern), 286
Archaeopteryx (bird), 359, 429, 619
Archaeornis (bird), 429, 619
archaic hoofed mammals, Cenozoic, 536
Archaic Stage (post-Folsom man), 564
archaic ungulates, description, 621
Archean, 62, 72
in Grand Canyon, 61
pillow lava, 72
Archean Era, duration, 32
Archidiskodon (elephant), 546
Archimedes (bryozoan), 225, 269, 298
Arctic, Devonian, 195, 203
Jurassic, 354, 357
Neogene warmth, 491
Pleistocene, 508
Arctinurus (trilobite), 180, 184, 295
Arenigian (Ord.), 142
Arizona, Cambrian, 118, 121
Cretaceous, 378, 390
Grand Canyon, 1, 18
Jurassic, 349, 352
meteor crater, 56
Mississippian, 213
Neogene, 462
erosion, 489
lava, 459
Pennsylvanian, 234, 242

Arizona, Permian, 257, 262, 267, 271
reptile tracks, 15
Pleistocene glaciation, 518
Triassic, 333, 341
badlands, 327
conifers, 403
Arkansas, Cretaceous, 371, 375
diamonds, 391
Jurassic, 349, 355
manganese, 161
Mississippian, 213
Ordovician, 144, 161
Paleogene, 440
bauxite, 454
Pennsylvanian, 238
Arkansas River, Neogene history, 489
Arkell, W. J., 430
armored dinosaurs, 396, 422
Arpadites (ammonite), 341
arthrodires (placoderms), 322
Arthrophycus (?worm trail), 314
arthropods, Cambrian, 130
Cenozoic, 533
description, 604
Silurian, 179, 183
Artinskia (ammonoid), 305
Artinskian Stage (Perm.), 263
artiodactyls (mammals), 543
description, 622
asbestos, Cambrian, 132
Ashgillian (Ordovician), 142
Asia, ape men (Pleist.), 556
distribution of Pleistocene ice, 496
Laramian revolution, 384
migrations of man from, 562
Paleogene coal, 454
Pennsylvanian orogeny, 242
Permian, 259, 267
Silurian orogeny, 182
Asia Minor, Permian, 259
Astartella (pelecypod), 302
Asteroidea (starfishes), 611
asteroids, Devonian, 612
Ordovician, 612
Asteroxylon (psilopsid), 575
asterozoans, description, 611
Mesozoic, 406
Astian Stage (Plio.), 463
Astraeospongia (sponge), 291
Astylospongia (sponge), 291
Athabaska district, age of rocks, 32
Archean (Precam.), 74
Atlantic Border, Cretaceous, 370, 373, 375
Neogene, 462
Paleogene, 434, 438
Triassic, 337
Atlantic Coastal Plain, Pleistocene, 503
structure, 275
Triassic, 329
"Atlantic Province," Cambrian, 109, 123
Atopochara (chlorophyte), 570
Atrypa (brachiopod), 204, 296
Augusta (Ga.), Fall Line, 370
Aulacophyllum (horn coral), 293
Aulacopleura (trilobite), 183
Aurignacian culture, 564
Austinaster (starfish), 408

Australia, archaeocyathan reefs, 290
Cretaceous, crinoids, 406
glaciation, 382
Devonian mountain building, 204
gold in Ordovician, 161
graptolite beds, 319
Jurassic, coal, 364
cycadeoids, 401
Pennsylvanian glaciation, 247, 253
Permian, coal, 275, 282
glaciation, 278
Precambrian gold, 104
Silurian land plants, 182, 285
Australian Shield, Precambrian, 66
Australopithecus (manlike ape), 599
Austria, Pleistocene glaciation, 518
Autunian Series (Perm.), 263
Auversian Stage (Eoc.), 434
Avery Island (La.), salt, 442
Aviculopecten (pelecypod), 302

bacteria, description, 568
Paleozoic, 285
Baculites (ammonite), 387, 414
Badlands National Monument, 446
Baiera (ginkgo), 578
Bajocian Stage (Jur.), 352
Baku district (U.S.S.R.), Neogene oil, 492
Balanus (barnacle), 607
Baltic Shield, Precambrian, 65
Baltimore (Md.), Fall Line, 370
baluchitheres (rhinoceroses), 541
Baluchitherium (rhinoceros), 542
Banff Formation (Miss.), 220
Baragwanathia (lycopsid), 574
barite, Cambrian, 132
barnacles, description, 608
Paleozoic, 310
Barnes, V. E., 161
Barremian Stage (Cret.), 374
Barton, D. C., 454
Bartonian Stage (Eoc.), 434
Barycrinus (crinoid), 227, 317
basal conglomerate, Old Red Sandstone (Dev.), 209
Pennsylvanian, 233
Timiskaming (Precam.), 77
basin deposits, Permian, 264
Bathonian Stage (Jur.), 352
Bathyurisicus (trilobite), 306
Batocrinus (crinoid), 316
bats, Cenozoic, 549
description, 619
wing structure, 37
bauxite, Cretaceous, 388
Jurassic, 364
Paleogene, 454
Baylea (gastropod), 252
Bear, T. L., 493
Beatricea (stromatoporoid), 292
Beaver, Harold, 325
bedding planes, 6
"Bedford" limestone, 229
Beekmantown dolostone (Ord.), 144
Belcher Mountains, Canada, 59, 82
Belemnitella (belemnite), 387, 410
belemnites, Jurassic, 361
belemnoids, Cretaceous, 382, 387
description, 603
Jurassic, 413, 416
Mesozoic, 415

belemnoids, Mississippian, 415
Belgian Congo, age of rocks, 32
  copper, 132
  uranium, 104
Belgium, Cretaceous, 366
  crinoids, 318
  Devonian, 188
  Oligocene, 433
  Paleocene, 433
Bellerophon (gastropod), 302
Beloceras (ammonoid), 306
Belt Sequence (Precam.), 93
  fossils, 99
  Waterton Lakes region, 93
Bendian Stage (Penn.), 240, 244
Bennettitales (cycadeoids), 399,
  577
bentonite, 3
  Cretaceous, 22
  Ordovician, 154
Berriasian Stage (Cret.), 374
Berry, E. W., 255, 364
Bicrisina (bryozoan), 409
Big Horn Mountains, Triassic, 328
birds, Cenozoic, 534
  Cretaceous, 42, 381, 619
  description, 618
  Jurassic, 358, 619
  Mesozoic, 428
  skeletal structures, 619
  wing structure, 37
bituminous coal, Pennsylvanian, 255
Black Hills, Cretaceous, 22
  Jurassic, 348
    belemnoids, 413
  Mississippian, 213, 219
  Precambrian, 94
    gold, 104
  Triassic, 328
black shale, Devonian, 195, 201
  Mississippian, 215
Blackriveran (Ordovician), 142
blastoids, description, 609
  Devonian, 196
  Mississippian, 225, 610
  Paleozoic, 314
Blattoidea (cockroaches), 311
blue-green algae, description, 569
Blue Ridge, Appalachians, 275
Bolivina (foraminifer), 530
bone bed, Neogene, 39
bony fishes, Paleozoic, 322
borax, Neogene, 492
borderlands, 123
boron, Neogene, 492
Bothriocidaris (echinoid), 318
boulders, glacial, Pleistocene, 497,
  499
Bowmanville low-water stage
  (Pleist., Great Lakes), 516
brachiopods, Cenozoic, 531
  description, 595
  Devonian, 196, 204, 206, 595
  Jurassic, 361
  Mesozoic, 407
  Ordovician, 154, 595
  Paleozoic, 295–301
  Pennsylvanian, 252
  Permian, 12, 276, 279, 281
  Silurian, 183
Brachiosaurus (dinosaur), 420
Brachycythere (ostracode), 533
Bradyan Stage (Pleist.), 463, 505,
  514

branchiopods, description, 606
Brazil, Cretaceous diamonds, 391
  Permian reptiles, 275
  Precambrian iron ores, 103
Brazilian Shield, Precambrian, 66
Bretonian mountain building, 204
Bretz, J. H., 525
Bridge, Josiah, 133
Bridger Mountains, 220
Bright Angel Shale, 28
British Columbia, Burgess Shale
    fauna, 294
  Cambrian fossils, 128
  Cretaceous, 372
  Jurassic, ammonite, 361
    mountain building, 362
  mountain glaciation, 518
  Permian, 258, 267
  Precambrian ores, 104
  Triassic, 329, 334
British Isles, ostracoderms, 320
  Pleistocene glaciation, 518
  Triassic salt, 345
brittle stars, Mississippian, 227, 317
  (*See also* ophiuroids)
bromine, Neogene, 492
brontosaurs (dinosaurs), 419
Brontotherium (titanothere), 622
Bronze Age (man), 564
Brooksella (jellyfish), 99
Brooksella (protomedusa), 587
Bruce Sub-sequence, 80
Bryce Canyon National Park, 447
Bryophyta, 574
bryozoans, Cenozoic, 531
  description, 592
  Devonian, 196
  Mesozoic, 406
  Mississippian, 225
  Ordovician, 154
  Paleogene, 593
  Paleozoic, 295
  Permian, 279
Buena Vista oil field (Calif.), 479
Bugula (bryozoan), 593
building stone (*see* stone)
Bulman, O. M. B., 325
Bumastus (trilobite), 307
Bunter Series (Trias.), 333
Burdigalian Stage (Mio.), 463
Burgess Shale fossils (Cam.), 128,
  294
Burlington (Iowa), crinoids, 318
Burlington Limestone (Miss.), 212
Burnett, R. W., 44

Cacops (stegocephalian), 322
Calamophyton (horsetail rush), 208
calcareous algae, Eocene, 529, 569
  Jurassic, 358
calcareous sponges, Paleozoic, 291,
  293
Calceola (horn coral), 294
calcification, 13
calcium chloride, Neogene, 492
Caledonian mountain building, 182,
  203, 209
caliche, Pleistocene, 504
California, Cambrian, 114
  Cretaceous, 372, 374, 379
  Jurassic, 348, 352, 362, 364
  Neogene, 463, 470
    alluvial deposits, 459, 468
    gold, 492

California, oil fields, Neogene, 476
  Paleogene, 434
  Permian, 258, 262, 267, 272
  petroleum, 492
  Pleistocene glaciation, 503, 518
  San Andreas fault, 479
  Triassic, 329, 333
  (*See also* Great Valley; Los An-
    geles Basin; San Joaquin Val-
    ley; Sierra Nevada; Ventura
    Basin)
Callixylon (early conifer), 289
Callovian Stage (Jur.), 352
Caloceras (ammonite), 360
Calymena (trilobite), 181
Cambrian, Appalachian region, 29
  Arizona, 28
  chelicerates, 308
  climate, 129
  cystoids, 314
  distribution, 108, 110
  graptolites, 319
  guide fossils, 119
  life, 126
  Ozark region, 153
  Tennessee, 29
  time-rock divisions, 114
  Virginia, 29
  Wales, 107
  worm borings, 314
Cambrian Period, duration, 32
camels, Cenozoic, 544, 622
Camerata (crinoids), 317
camerate crinoids, 227, 295, 316
Cameroceras (nautiloid), 305
Camp, C. L., 566
Campanian Stage (Cret.), 374
Campbell, M. R., 255
Canada, Cambrian, 109, 114, 118
  Cretaceous, 368, 377
  Devonian, 190, 192
  Jurassic, 350
  land surface, 67
  Mississippian, 216
  mountain glaciation, 518
  Neogene, 460
  oil and gas, 208
  Ordovician, 138, 142, 151
  Paleogene, 436, 454
  Pennsylvanian, 236
  Permian, 259
  petroleum, 389
  Precambrian, 64
    uranium, 104
  Silurian, 166, 172, 178
  Triassic, 330
  (*See also* specific provinces)
Canadian Rockies, Precambrian, 93
  (*See also* Alberta; British
    Columbia)
Canadian Series (Ord.), 137, 140
Canadian Shield, 68
  Pleistocene, 508
Canadocystis (paracrinoid), 609
Cancellaria (gastropod), 533
cap rock of salt domes, 442
Capitan Limestone (Perm.), 264
Caradocian Series (Ord.), 142
carbon-14, age determinations, 459,
  465, 522
  age measurement, 31
carbonate rocks, origin, 5
Carboniferous rocks, 211
carbonization, 13

Carcharodon (shark), 534
Cardioceras (ammonite), 360
Cardioecia (bryozoan), 409
Carnian Stage (Trias.), 333
carnivores (mammals), Cenozoic, 547
  description, 620
Carpathian Mountains, Neogene deformation, 492
  Paleogene orogeny, 452
  Pleistocene glaciation, 519
Carsey, J. B., 454
Carthage gas field, Texas, 390
Cary Till (Pleist.), 514
Caryan Substage (Pleist.), 514
Cascade Mountains, 456
  Neogene, deformation, 492
  history, 471
  peneplain, 471
Cascadia, 125, 215
Case, E. C., 283
Casea (reptile), 35
cast, fossil, 13
Castile Formation (Perm.), 266
Catenularia (chain coral), 293
cats, saber-toothed, 41
Catskill Mountains, 197–199
cattle, Cenozoic, 545
Caucasus Mountains, Neogene deformation, 492
causes of Pleistocene glaciation, 523
Cayugan Series (Sil.), 171
Cedaria (trilobite), 126
cement rock, Devonian, 208
  Ordovician, 161
  Silurian, 185
Cenomanian Stage (Cret.), 374
Cenozoic Era, duration, 32
Cenozoic fish, 15
Cenozoic life, 527
centipedes, 608
Central America, Eocene coral reefs, 530
Central States, pre-Wisconsinan drainage, 517
cephalopods, Cambrian, 304
  Cenozoic, 533
  Cretaceous, 381, 385, 387, 410
  description, 601
  Devonian, 196, 206
  Jurassic, 360
  Mesozoic, 412
  Mississippian, 227
  Ordovician, 151
  Paleozoic, 295, 303
  Pennsylvanian, 252
  Permian, 259, 281
  Silurian, 180, 183
  Triassic, 341
  types, 600
  (*See also* ammonoids; belemnoids; nautiloids)
Ceratites (ammonite), 341, 414
Ceratocephala (trilobite), 307
Ceratocorys (dinoflagellate), 570
ceratopsian dinosaurs, 381, 422
Cerithium (gastropod), 533
Cetaceans (whales, porpoises), 547
cetaceans, description, 620
Chaetetes (tabulate coral), 295
chain corals, Paleozoic, 292
chalicotheres (mammals), 537, 543
chalk, Cretaceous, 366, 381
  of Kansas, 379

Chamberlin, T. C., 47
Champlainian, 140
Chancelloria (siliceous sponge), 294
Chara (grass-green alga), 569
"chat," Mississippian, 229
Chattian Stage (Oligo.), 434
Chazyan Series (Ord.), 141
Cheirolepis (fish), 321
Cheirurus (trilobite), 183
chelicerates, description, 605
  Paleozoic, 308
Chellean culture, 563
Chelonia (turtles), 617
Cheney, M. G., 230
chenier plain (Pleist.), Louisiana, 466
chert, Mississippian, 215
Chesteran Stage (Miss.), 214
chimpanzee, 555, 560
China, ape men, 558
  Jurassic coal, 364
  Silurian antimony, 185
  Triassic coal, 345
Chinle Formation (Trias.), 334
Chiroptera (bats), 619
chitons, description, 596
Chlamys (pelecypod), 532
Chlorophyta (grass-green algae), 569
Chondrilla (sponge), 584
chromium, Precambrian, 105
Chrysophyta, 570
Chugwater Formation (Trias.), 332
Churchill district, age of rocks, 32
Cibicides (foraminifer), 530
Cidaris (echinoid), 613
Cincinnati region, Ordovician, 135
Cincinnatian Series (Ord.), 140
Cirripedia (barnacles), 310
cirripeds (barnacles), description, 608
  Mesozoic, 416
Cladoselache (shark), 207
clams (*see* pelecypods)
Clarno Formation (Eoc.), 447
clastic rocks, 3
Clathrodictyon (stromatoporoid), 292
Clathrospira (gastropod), 303
clay (commercial), Jurassic, 364
  Neogene, 493
  Pennsylvanian, 255
clay, Cretaceous, 391
cliff dwellers (early men), 563, 565
Cliftonian Stage (Sil.), 171
Climacograptus, graptolite, 157, 614
climate, Cretaceous, 382
  Cryptozoic, 97
  Devonian, 202
  Jurassic, 362
  Mississippian, 228
  Neogene, 491
  Paleogene, 451
  Pennsylvanian, 247
  Permian, 272, 276
  Silurian, 182
Cline, L. M., 325
Clintonian Stage (Sil.), 171
Clionites (ammonite), 341
Cloud, P. E., Jr., 161
Clymenia (ammonoid), 306
coal, Cretaceous, 390
  Devonian, 208
  Jurassic, 364

coal, Mississippian, 219
  Paleogene, 454
  Pennsylvanian, 235, 249, 254
  Permian, 275, 282
  Triassic, 345
coal swamp, Pennsylvanian, 43
Coast Ranges (Calif.), 362
  Cenozoic orogeny, 453
Coastal Plain, Atlantic, structure, 275
cobalt, Precambrian, 105
Cobalt Sub-sequence (Precam.), 80
Cobban, W. A., 391
coccoliths, description, 570
Coccosteus (placoderm fish), 207
Cockerellites (fish), 534
cockroaches, Pennsylvanian, 245, 253, 289, 311, 609
Coconino Sandstone (Perm.), 15, 272
Codiacrinus (crinoid), 611
coelenterates, description, 586
  Mesozoic, 405
  Paleozoic, 291
Coelodonta (rhinoceros), 543
Cohee, G. V., 133
Colbert, E. H., 44, 283, 345, 364, 430, 551
Coleman, A. P., 105
Colombia, Laramian revolution, 384, 387
Colorado, Cambrian, 114
  Cretaceous, 372, 375, 377
  clay, 391
  coal, 390
  oil, 389
  dinosaurs, 421, 426
  Eocene oil shale, 454
  Jurassic, 353
  Mississippian, 229
  Neogene, 468, 486
  gold, 492
  Ordovician, 143
  fishes, 319
  Paleogene, 434, 444, 451
  Pennsylvanian, 234, 240, 242, 248
  Permian, 274
  Pleistocene, glaciation, 518
  loess, 503
  Precambrian, 92, 95
  Triassic, 333
Colorado Plateau, Jurassic, 349, 353
  Paleogene, 446
  Permian, 258, 273
  superposed drainage, 491
Colorado River, Neogene history, 489
Columbella (gastropod), 533
Columbia (S.C.), Fall Line, 370
Columbia Plateau, Neogene, 469
Columbia River diversion (Pleist.), 517
Comanchean Series (Cret.), 373
Cometodinium (dinoflagellate), 570
Comstock lode (Nev.), Neogene silver, 492
Conchidium (brachiopod), 180, 183, 299
condylarths (mammals), 537, 621
Conemaugh Series (Penn.), 241
conglomerates, copper-bearing, 104
Coniacian Stage (Cret.), 374
Coniferales (conifers), 578

conifers, Cretaceous, 379
  description, 578
  Mesozoic, 399, 401
  Paleozoic, 285, 289
  Pennsylvanian, 251, 253
  Triassic, 401, 403
Connecticut, Triassic, 328, 333, 339
Connecticut River Valley, 23
  Triassic, 344
Conocoryphe (trilobite), 126
conocoryphid trilobites, 307
conodonts, Paleozoic, 312
Constellaria (bryozoan), 297
continental shelf, Gulf region, 466
continents, average specific gravity, 57
  origin, 55
continuity of rocks in correlation, 25
conulariids, 587
conulates, description, 587
Cooke, H. C., 105
Cooper, B. N., 325
Cooper, G. A., 209, 325
Cooperoceras (nautiloid), 281
copper, Cambrian, 132
  Cretaceous, 387
  Neogene, 492
  Paleogene, 453
  Permian, 282
  Precambrian, 103
coral reefs, Eocene, 530
  Silurian, 174
corals, Cenozoic, 530
  description, 591
  Devonian, 196, 199, 204, 206
  Jurassic, 361
  Mesozoic, 405
  Mississippian, 227, 316
  Paleozoic, 292
  Pennsylvanian, 252
  Permian, 279
  Silurian, 181, 183
Cordaitales (early conifers), 577, 579
  Paleozoic, 288
Cordilleran geosyncline, Cambrian, 119, 125, 215
  Pennsylvanian, 239
Cordilleran ice sheet, 508
Cordilleran region, Cambrian, 117
  Devonian, 189, 193
  Mississippian, 218
  Neogene, 462, 469
  Ordovician, 143
  Silurian, 171, 173
correlation, 21
  criteria for, 25
  glacial and nonglacial deposits, Pleistocene, 499
  methods, 25
Coscinodiscus (diatom), 570
cosmoid fish scales, 322
cosmopolitan faunas, 244
Costula (bryozoan), 409
cotylosaurs (reptiles), 324
  description, 617
Coutchiching rocks (Precam.), 73
Crandall Mountain thrust fault, 93
Crassatellites (pelecypod), 410
Crater Lake (Ore.), 473
Craterolophus (jellyfish), 588
Craters of the Moon (Idaho), 471
Crawfordsville (Ind.), crinoids, 318

creodonts (mammals), Paleogene, 547
Cretaceous, ammonites, 410, 414
  angiosperms, 404
  armored dinosaurs, 396
  belemnoids, 416
  birds, 429, 619
  bryozoans, 407, 409
  calcareous algae, 570
  climate, 382
  corals, 405
  crinoids, 406
  dinosaurs, 10, 419
  distribution, 368
  echinoids, 406, 410
  economic resources, 387
  fishes, 417
  gastropods, 410
  glaciation, 382
  guide fossils, 367
  ichthyosaurs, 424
  life, 379
  mammals, 430, 620
  mosasaurs, 424
  overthrust by Precambrian, 93
  pelecypods, 409
  plesiosaurs, 427
  sponges, 405
  Texas, 23, 251
  thickness in West, 378
  time-rock divisions, 374
  turtles, 427
Cretaceous Period, 366
  duration, 32
crinoidal limestone, 315
crinoids, Cenozoic, 531
  Cretaceous, 382, 406
  description, 610
  Devonian, 196, 611
  Jurassic, 361, 406
  Mesozoic, 406
  Mississippian, 225, 227, 316
  Neogene, 610
  Ordovician, 316
  Silurian, 182, 183, 317
  Triassic, 342
Cripple Creek district (Colo.), Neogene gold, 492
crocodiles, description, 617
  Jurassic, 359
Croixian Series (Cam.), 114
Cro-Magnon men (Pleist.), 560
cross-bedded limestone, 222
  Cretaceous, 380
  Jurassic, 356
  Permian, 8, 272
crossopterygian fishes, Paleozoic, 322, 616
Crotalocrinites (crinoid), 317
crustaceans (anthropods), 310
  description, 606
  Mesozoic, 416
  Pennsylvanian, 313
Cryptolithus (trilobite), 307
Cryptozoic Eon, 59
  classification, 69
  duration, 32
cryptozoön (calcareous alga), 569
Ctenocrinus (crinoid), 611
Ctenophyllum (cycadeoid), 401
Ctenopterus (eurypterid), 606
Cuba, Jurassic, 349
Cuisian Stage (Eoc.), 434
Cyathocrinites (crinoid), 227, 317

Cyathophyllum (coral), 293, 295
Cyathoseris (coral), 531
Cycadales (cycads), 577
Cycadeoidea (cycadeoid), 402
cycadeoids, Cretaceous, 379, 401
  description, 577
  Jurassic, 356, 401
  Mesozoic, 399
  Triassic, 341
cycads, 399, 401
  description, 577
cyclic sedimentation, boundaries of cycles, 246
  Pennsylvanian, 239, 246, 248
  Permian, 267
Cyclolobus (ammonoid), 306
Cyclopora (bryozoan), 297
Cyclopyge (trilobite), 307
Cyclotropis (gastropod), 183
Cymbella (diatom), 570
Cynodesmus (dog), 621
Cyrtoceras (nautiloid), 183, 304
Cyrtograptus (graptolite), 614
Cystiphyllum (horn coral), 293
cystoids, description, 609
  Devonian, 196
  Ordovician, 609
  Paleozoic, 314
Cythereis (ostracode), 608

Dake, C. L., 133
Dakota Sandstone (Cret.), 378, 380
Dalmanella (brachiopod), 204
Dalmanites (trilobite), 184, 306
Dana, E. S., 345
Danian Stage (Paleoc.), 434
Darwin, Charles, 36
Daugherty, L. H., 345
Dawsonoceras (nautiloid), 184
Death Valley, 449
decapods (crustaceans), Cretaceous, 416
deer, Cenozoic, 545
Deinotherium (elephant), 546, 548
Deiss, Charles, 133
Delaware Mountains, Permian, 263
Deltatheridium (insectivore), 620
Deltocyathus (coral), 531
Demorest, Max, 525
Dendraster (echinoid), 613
Denmark, Cretaceous, 366
  Pleistocene glaciation, 518
Dentalium (scaphopod), 597
Derbyia (brachiopod), 252
Desmoinesian Stage (Penn.), 240, 244
Devonian, amphibians, 322
  asteroids, 612
  blastoids, 314
  brachiopods, 595
  chelicerates, 309
  climate, 202
  corals, 316
  crinoid localities, 318
  crinoids, 318, 611
  cystoids, 316
  distribution, 188, 190
  echinoids, 318
  eurypterids, 309
  fishes, 319, 321
  life, 195, 284
  ostracoderms, 614
  Ozark region, 153
  placoderms, 320

Devonian, time-rock divisions, 193
  type region, 187
Devonian Period, duration, 32
diamonds, Cretaceous, 391
diapsid reptiles, 616
diastems, 18
diatomaceous earth, Neogene, 492
diatomaceous shale, Neogene, 475
diatoms, description, 570
dibranchiates (cephalopods), 601
Dicellograptus (graptolite), 614
Diceratherium (rhinoceros), 622
Dichocrinus (crinoid), 317
Dichophyllum (ginkgo), 578
Dicotyledonales (angiosperms), 579
dicotyledons (angiosperms), 403
Didymograptus (graptolite), 614
Diluvarca (pelecypod), 532
Dimorphocellaria (bryozoan), 409
Dimorphodon (pterosaur), 428
Dinichthys (placoderm), 320
dinoflagellates, description, 570
dinosaur eggs, 425
Dinosaur National Park, 355
dinosaur tracks, Triassic, 342
dinosaurs, carnivorous, 394, 618
  Cretaceous, 381
  description, 618
  disappearance, 423
  duck-billed, 11
  herbivorous, 397, 419
  Jurassic, 358
  pelvic structures, 618
  Triassic, 342
Diphyphyllum (coral), 294
dipleurozoans, description, 587
Diplodocus (dinosaur), 397
Diplograptus (graptolite), 614
Diplovertebron (amphibian), 323
direction of ice movement, Pleistocene, 498
disconformity, 18
discordant rock structure, 17
Discoscaphites (ammonite), 414
dogs, Cenozoic, 547
Dolichopterus (eurypterid), 606
dolphins, Cenozoic, 549
Donau Stage (Pleist.), 521
Downtonian (ostracoderms), 320
dragonflies, Pennsylvanian, 253, 311
drainage changes, Pleistocene, 515
Dresbachian (Cambrian), 114
drift, Pleistocene, 496
driftless area, Pleistocene, 502
drumlins, Pleistocene, 498, 502
duck-billed dinosaurs, 420
Dunbar, C. O., 33, 391, 493, 566
Duncan, Helen, 325
Dunkard beds (Perm.), 231, 270, 282
duration, Pleistocene time, 521
Durham, J. W., 525
Dyas (Perm.), 259

Eardley, A. J., 391
early conifers, description, 577
early men, North America, 562
  Patagonia, 562
  South America, 562
Earth, age of beginning, 32
  formation of crust, 32
  main features, 46
East Indies, Permian, 259
East Texas oil field, 388

echinoderms, Cenozoic, 531
  description, 609
  Jurassic, 361
  Mesozoic, 406
  Mississippian, 227
  Paleozoic, 314
echinoids, Cretaceous, 367, 382, 410
  description, 612
  Jurassic, 361, 613
  Mesozoic, 406
  Neogene, 613
  Paleozoic, 318
  Triassic, 613
echinozoans, description, 612
Echioceras (ammonite), 360
economic resources, Cambrian, 132
  Devonian, 205
  Jurassic, 364
  Mississippian, 229
  Ordovician, 159
  Pennsylvanian, 249
  Permian, 280
  Precambrian, 100
Ectoconus (mammal), 451
Edaphosaurus (reptile), 278
Edenian (Ordovician), 142
edentates (mammals), Cenozoic, 549
  description, 620
egg, reptilian, 617
Elburz Mountains (Iran), Neogene deformation, 492
elephants, Cenozoic, 545
  description, 621
  evolution, 546
Elephas (elephant), 550
Ellenburger Group (Ord.), 141
Ellison, S. P., Jr., 325
Encope (echinoid), 613
Endoceras (cephalopod), 304
Endopachys (coral), 531
England, Caledonian orogeny, 182
  Cambrian, 115
  Cretaceous crinoids, 406
  crinoid localities, 318
  Devonian, 188
  Dover chalk cliffs, 366
  graptolite beds, 319
  Jurassic, 348, 357, 364
    cycadeoids, 401
  Ordovician, 142
  Paleocene, 433
  Precambrian, 65
  Silurian, 164
  supposed "dawn man," 560
entelodonts (hogs), 544
Eoanthropus (false "dawn man"), 560
Eoasianites (ammonoid), 305
Eocambrian, 113
Eocene, Colorado, 387
  glaciation, 451
  meaning of name, 438
  time-rock divisions, 434
  type sections, 433
  Wyoming, 390
  (*See also* Paleogene)
Eocene Epoch (Paleog.), 432
Eoconularia (conulate), 588
Eodiscus (trilobite), 306
Eohippus (horse), 541, 622
eoliths, 556
Eophrynus (spider), 607

Eospermatopteris (tree fern), 208, 286
Eothalassoceras (ammonoid), 305
Eparchean peneplain, 63
epoch, 29
Equus (horse), 539, 622
era, 29
erratics, dispersal patterns, 499
  Pleistocene, 497
Eryon (crustacean), 416
Estonia, Pleistocene glaciation, 518
Eucaenus (insect), 609
Eucalyptocrinites (crinoid), 184, 317
Eumorphocystis (cystoid), 609
Eumycophyta, 571
Euomphalus (gastropod), 225
Euplectella (sponge), 584
Euritina (bryozoan), 409
Europe, Cambrian, 115
  volcanism, 132
  Cretaceous, 367, 374
  Devonian mountain building, 204
  Jurassic, 348, 352, 362
    ichthyosaurs, 424
  Laramian revolution, 384
  Neogene, 456
  Ordovician, 142
  Paleogene stages, 434
  Pennsylvanian, 241
    orogeny, 242
  Permian, 259, 278
  Pleistocene, glaciation, 518, 520
    ice distribution, 496, 520
    stages, 505
  Precambrian, 64
  prehistoric men, 559
  Silurian, crinoids, 317
    land plants, 182
    orogeny, 182
  Triassic, 328
    reptiles, 395
    salt, 345
euryapsid reptiles, 616
Eurypterida (chelicerates), 308
eurypterids, Cambrian, 309
  description, 605
  Ordovician, 309
  Paleozoic, 308
  Silurian, 178, 182, 309, 311
Eusarcus (eurypterid), 311
Eutrochocrinus (crinoid), 225
evaporites, Cretaceous, 382
  Permian, 259, 281
  Silurian, 177
  (*See also* anhydrite; gypsum; salt)
even-toed hoofed mammals, 543
Evitt, W. R., II, 326
evolution, evidence, 36
  trends, 43
Exoconularia (conulate), 588
Exogyra (pelecypod), 386, 409

facies, 5
Fall Line, 370
  relation to rock structure, 275
Falls of the Ohio, Devonian corals, 294
Farmdale Loess (Pleist.), Illinois, 512
faults, age significance, 17
faunas, 10
Favia (coral), 531

Favosites (honeycomb coral), 183, 204, 294
Fenestrellina (lacy bryozoan), 225, 297
Fenneman, N. M., 454, 493
Fenton, C. L., 105
Fenton, M. A., 105
ferns, Cretaceous, 379, 402
  description, 575
  Devonian, 208
  Jurassic, 402
  Mesozoic, 399, 402
  Paleozoic, 285
  Pennsylvanian, 253, 287, 289
  Triassic, 402
fertilizers (*see* glauconite; phosphate)
Filicea (bryozoan), 409
Filicineae (ferns), 575
Filisparsa (bryozoan), 409
Finland, Pleistocene glaciation, 518
Fischer, A. G., 431
fishes, Cenozoic, 533
  Cretaceous, 417
  description, 614
  Devonian, 40, 197, 207
  Eocene, 39, 534
  Jurassic, 357
  Mesozoic, 416
  ostracoderms, 320
  Paleozoic, 319
  Permian, 275
  placoderms, 320
  Silurian, 182
  Triassic, 417
Fisk, H. N., 493
Flattop peneplain, Rockies, 487
Flexibilia (crinoids), 317
flexible crinoids, 227
Flexicalymene (trilobite), 306
Flint, R. F., 525
flints, Old Stone Age, 563
floras, 10
Florida, Cretaceous, 371
  Devonian, 189
  Eocene coral reefs, 530
  Neogene, 463
  Ordovician, 137
  Paleogene, 438
  Pleistocene, 503
Florissant (Oligo.) fossils, 11
Flower, R. H., 325
fluviatile deposits, Pleistocene, 504, 509
fluvioglacial deposits, Pleistocene, 498, 503
flying reptiles (*see* pterosaurs)
folds, age significance, 17
Folsom points, 561
foraminifers, Cambrian, 290
  Cretaceous, 367, 381, 404
  description, 571
  Jurassic, 361, 404
  Miocene, 530
  Paleogene, 449
Forbesiocrinus (crinoid), 227, 317
formation, 27
Fort Union Formation (Paleoc.), 445, 454
fossil forest, Devonian, 286
fossil zones, 27
fossils, features, 9
foundry sand, Ordovician, 161

Fountain Formation (Penn.), 242, 248
France, Cambrian iron, 132
  Cretaceous, 366, 386
    crinoids, 406
  Devonian, 188
  Jurassic, 347, 364
  Paleogene, 433, 452
Franconian stage (Cam.), 114
Fredericksburg Group (Cret.), 23
Front Range (Rockies), 387
  Neogene erosion, 488
fungi, description, 571
  Precambrian, 99
Fusulina (foraminifer), 290
fusulinids, Paleozoic, 290
  Pennsylvanian, 233, 245
  Permian, 267, 276, 573

Gamow, George, 57
"gangplank" (Wyo.), Neogene, 487
ganoid fish scales, 322
Garnettius (scorpion), 253
gastropods, Cenozoic, 533
  Cretaceous, 385, 387, 410
  description, 597
  Devonian, 196
  Jurassic, 361
  Mesozoic, 412
  Ordovician, 154
  Paleogene, 449
  Paleozoic, 296, 302
  Pennsylvanian, 252
  Permian, 279
  Silurian, 183
geanticline, 124
Geikie, Archibald, 185
Gennaeocrinus (crinoid), 611
genus (genera), 567
geologic column, 26
geologic formation, 27
geologic time, divisions, 32
  measurement, 30
  perspective diagram, 31
  scale, 26
Georgia, Cambrian, 109
  Cretaceous, 370, 377
  Eocene coral reefs, 530
  Neogene, 464
  Ordovician, 137
  Paleogene, 438, 454
Gephyroceras (ammonoid), 306
Germany, Cambrian iron, 132
  Cretaceous, crinoids, 406
    subdivisions, 366
  Devonian, 188
    crinoids, 318
  Jurassic, 347, 362
    bird, 429
    pterosaurs, 400, 427
  Oligocene, 433
  Permian, 259, 282
  Pleistocene glaciation, 518
  Triassic, 328, 333, 342
    zinc, 341
giant primates, 559
gibbon, 555
Gigantella (brachiopod), 300
Gigantopithecus (manlike ape), 559
Gilbertsocrinus (crinoid), 227, 317
Gilluly, James, 493
Ginkgoales (ginkgos), 577
ginkgos, description, 577
  Mesozoic, 402

gizzard stones, 13
glacial deposits, Huronian, 81
  Neogene, 480
glacial erratics, Pleistocene, 497
glacial lake deposits, Pleistocene, 499
glacial till, Pleistocene, 497
glaciation, Cretaceous, 382
  Cryptozoic, 97
  Eocene, 451
  Pennsylvanian, 247, 253
  Permian, 278
  Pleistocene, 508
Glacier National Park, 93
Glass Mountains, 251, 263, 279
glass sand, Cretaceous, 388
  Devonian, 208
  Ordovician, 161
  Silurian, 185
glass sponges, Paleozoic, 291
glauconite, Cretaceous, 388
Glen Dean Limestone (Miss.), 224
Glossopleura (trilobite), 121
Glycimeris (pelecypod), 532
Glyptocrinus (crinoid), 155, 316
Glyptodon (edentate), 620
glyptodonts (mammals), Cenozoic, 549
gold, Cretaceous, 388
  Jurassic, 364
  Mississippian, 229
  Neogene, 492
  Ordovician, 161
  Paleogene, 453
  Permian, 281
  Precambrian, 103
Gomphonema (diatom), 570
Gondwanaland, 278
Goniasma (gastropod), 252
goniatite (ammonoid), 603
Gonioloboceras (ammonoid), 305
Goniograptus (graptolite), 614
Goniophyllum (horn coral), 181, 293
gorilla, 554, 556
Grammysia (pelecypod), 302
Grand Canyon (Ariz.), 18, 28, 61
  Cambrian, 118
  Neogene, erosion, 485
  lava, 459
  Permian, 271
Grand Canyon Sequence, 28, 61
Grand Coulee (Wash.), 517
Graneros Shale (Cret.), 373
granites, Cretaceous, 362
  ?Jurassic, 362
Grantia (sponge), 586
graphite, Precambrian, 105
graphitic coal, Pennsylvanian, 238
graptolites, description, 613
  Devonian, 197
  Ordovician, 136, 154, 157, 614
  Paleozoic, 318
  Silurian, 614
grass-green algae, description, 569
Great Basin, Cambrian, 114
  Cretaceous, 371
  Neogene, 463, 468, 473
  Paleogene, 447
  Pleistocene, 507
Great Bear Lake district, age of rocks, 32
Great Britain, Cambrian iron, 132
  (*See also* England)

Great Carolina Ridge, 440
Great Lakes region, Neogene erosion, 485
  Niagaran reefs, 177
  Pleistocene history, 514
  Silurian salt, 178
Great Plains, Neogene, 462, 468
Great Salt Lake (Utah), 473
Great Slave Range, 82
Great Smokies (N.C.), Neogene erosion, 483
Great Valley, Appalachians, 275
Great Valley (Calif.), 447
  Neogene, 468
Green River, Neogene history, 489
Green River Basin (Wyo.), Paleogene, 442
Green River beds (Eoc.), fossils, 11
Greenhorn Limestone (Cret.), 373, 380
Greenland, Cretaceous, 382
  angrosperms, 404
  conifers, 404
  Devonian amphibians, 322
  ice sheet, 508
  Jurassic, coal, 364
    cycadeoids, 401
    ginkgos, 403
  ostracoderms, 320
  Paleogene, 451
  Pleistocene, 588
    "interglacial" icecap, 502
  Silurian orogeny, 182
Gregory, H. E., 391
Gregory, W. K., 209
Grenville district, 68
  age of rocks, 32
Grenville Sub-sequence (Precam.), 86
ground moraine, Pleistocene, 500
ground sloths, Neogene, 550
ground water, in Cambrian, 132
  in Cretaceous, 378
  in Neogene, 493
  in Ordovician, 161
  group, 28
Gryphaea (pelecypod), 409, 410
Guadalupe Mountains, Permian, 263, 265
Guadalupian Stage (Perm.), 258, 260
Guianan Shield, Precambrian, 66
guide fossils, 14
  Cambrian, 119
  Cretaceous, 367
  Devonian, 196
  Jurassic, 360
  Mississippian, 212
  Neogene, 457
  Ordovician, 154
  Paleogene, 435
  Pennsylvanian, 233
  Permian, 257
  Silurian, 180
  Triassic, 341
Gulf of Maine, Triassic, 329
Gulf Coastal Plains, Triassic, 329
Gulf geosyncline, 441, 465
gulf region, Cretaceous, 367, 371, 376
  Jurassic, 352, 355, 364
  Neogene, 464
    petroleum, 492
  Paleogene, 434, 440, 454

gulf region, Pleistocene, 504
Gulfian Series (Cret.), 373
gumbotil, 512
Günz-Mindelian Stage (Pleist. interglacial), 505
Günzian Stage (glacial), Pleistocene, 505
Gymnospermae, 576
Gypidula (brachiopod), 299
gypsum, Mississippian, 229
  Pennsylvanian, 242
  Permian, 259, 267, 270, 282
  Silurian, 178, 185
Gyroceras (nautiloid), 206
Gyrodendron (coral), 405
Gyroma (gastropod), 303

Hage, C. O., 133
Haliclona (sponge), 584
Hallopora (bryozoan), 297
Halysites (chain coral), 292
Haplocytheridea (ostracode), 533
Harding Sandstone (Ord.), fishes, 319
Harrisburg erosion surface (Pa.), Neogene erosion, 483
Harrodsburg Limestone (Miss.), 223
Hastings Sub-sequence (Precam.), 86
Hauterivian Stage (Cret.), 374
Hebertella (brachiopod), 155
Heidelberg man (Pleist.), 559
Helderberg escarpment, 192, 195
Helicoceras (ammonite), 387
Heliophyllum (coral), 293, 296
Helvetian Stage (Mio.), 463
Hemiaster (echinoid), 410
Hemicyclaspis (ostracoderm), 614
Hesperornis (bird), 42, 429, 619
Hettangian Stage (Jur.), 352
hexactinellid sponges, 291
Hexagonaria (colonial coral), 295
Hickey, Maude, 454
High Plains, Cretaceous, 371
Hill, M. L., 493
Hill, W. C. O., 566
Himalaya Mountains, Cenozoic orogeny, 453
  Neogene deformation, 492
Himalayan region, Eocene, 449
Hippurites (pelecypod), 386
Holland, Cretaceous, 366
holothuroids, Cambrian, 130
  description, 613
Holston Limestone (Ord.), 152
Holzmaden beds (Jurassic), 362
honeycomb coral, 204, 294
hoofed mammals, 537
  Paleogene, 451
Hoots, H. W., 493
Hoplolichas (trilobite), 307
Hoplophoneus (cat), 41, 621
Hormotoma (gastropod), 155, 302
horn corals, Devonian, 316
  structure, 592
horses, 537, 622
  evolution, 539
horsetail rushes, description, 575
  Devonian, 208
  Mesozoic, 399, 402
  Paleozoic, 288
  Pennsylvanian, 251

House Range (Utah), Cambrian, 121
Hoyle, Fred, 57
Hudson Bay region, Precambrian, 64
Hudsonaster (starfish), 612
Hull Limestone (Ord.), 150
human cultures, successive, 563
human migrations from eastern Asia, 562
Huronian district, 68
  age of rocks, 32
Huronian Sequence (Precam.), 80
Hustedia (brachiopod), 252, 299
hyalosponges, Paleozoic, 294
Hydnoceras (glass sponge), 291
hydrozoans, description, 588
  Mesozoic, 405
Hynek, J. A., 57
hyolithids, Cambrian, 120
Hypothyridina (brachiopod), 595
Hyracodon (rhinoceros), 622
Hyracotherium (horse), 539, 622

ice sheets, growth stages, 510
  origin, 508
Ichthyornis (bird), 429
ichthyosaurs, adaptive convergence, 42
  description, 617
  Jurassic, 399
  Mesozoic, 424
Idaho, Cambrian, 117
  Jurassic, 348, 352
  Neogene, 470
  Pennsylvanian, 240
  Permian, 258, 267, 272, 282
  Pleistocene loess, 503
  Precambrian ores, 104
  Silurian, 170
  Triassic, 329, 333, 336
Idaho Springs Formation (Precam.), 95
Idoceras (ammonite), 360
igneous rocks, age determination, 2
  features, 3
  Neogene, 462
  Pleistocene, 508
  relations, 2
Illaenus (trilobite), 295, 307
Illinois, Archaic man, 564
  blastoids, 316
  Cretaceous, 371
  Devonian, 189, 193
  Mississippian, 211, 213, 221, 229
  Ordovician, 160
  Paleogene, 441
  Pennsylvanian, 233, 241, 244, 248
  Pleistocene, limit of glaciation, 502
    stratigraphic sequence, 512
    units, 505
  Silurian, 164, 168, 171, 174
Illinoisan glaciation, maximum, 506
Illinoisan Stage (Pleist.), 463, 505, 513
Ilyanassa (gastropod), 533
Imlay, R. W., 365
Inadunata (crinoids), 317
inadunate crinoids, 227
index fossil, 14
India, Cretaceous diamonds, 391
  Permian, 278, 282
  reptiles, 275

India, Precambrian gold, 104
Indian Shield, Precambrian, 66
Indiana, Devonian, 189, 193, 196, 201
  corals, 295
  Mississippian, 223
    crinoids, 318
  Ordovician, 142
  Pennsylvanian, 239, 245, 254
  Pleistocene, moraines, 501
    units, 505
  Silurian, 164, 168, 170, 174
"Indiana" limestone, 229
Inoceramus (pelecypod), 386, 409, 411
insectivores (mammals), Cenozoic, 549
  description, 619
insects, Cenozoic, 533
  description, 608
  Jurassic, 357
  Mesozoic, 416
  Paleogene, 620
  Paleozoic, 310
  Pennsylvanian, 245, 253, 289, 609
  Permian, 275
interfingering of sediments, 6
interglacial ages, Pleistocene, 504
interglacial deposits (Pleist.), 512
interior platform (continental), 125
intrenched meanders, Neogene, 489
invertebrates, Cenozoic, 529
  Cretaceous, 381
  Mesozoic, 404
  Paleogene, 435
  Paleozoic, 289
  Triassic, 341
  (*See also* life, under specific periods, e.g., Cambrian, etc.)
Inyo Mountains, 117
Iowa, Devonian, 193, 196, 200
  glacial boulders, 499
  Mississippian, 212
    crinoids, 318
  Ordovician, 147, 160
  Pennsylvanian, 239
  Pleistocene, glacial and nonglacial deposits, 499
    stratigraphic sequence, 511
    units, 505
  Silurian, 164, 171, 174
Iowan glaciation, maximum, 506
Iowan Stage (Pleist.), 463, 505, 513
Ireland, Caledonian structures, 182
  Silurian orogeny, 182
Iron Age (man), 564
iron ores, Jurassic, 364
  Ordovician, 160
  Pennsylvanian, 255
  Precambrian, 100
  Silurian, 170, 173
Ischadites (?sponge), 291
island universes, 46
Isophyllia (coral), 531
Isotelus (trilobite), 157, 307
Italy, Triassic manganese, 345

Jackson Formation (Eoc.), 434, 441
Jackson Uplift (Miss.), 441
Japan, Jurassic coal, 364
  Paleogene coal, 454
  Triassic coal, 345

Jasper Park, Alberta, 93
Java ape men, 558
Jeans, Sir James, 47, 57
Jeffersonville Limestone (Dev.), 201
Jeffreys, Harold, 47
jellyfishes, Cambrian, 131
  description, 587
  Mesozoic, 405
  Paleozoic, 291, 294
  Precambrian, 99
John Day Basin (Ore.), 13
John Day Formation (Mio.), 458
Johnson, D. W., 485
Jones, T. S., 283
Judson, Sheldon, 57
Jura Mountains, 347
Jurassic, angiosperms, 403
  belemnites, 410, 415
  birds, 429, 619
  climate, 362
  corals, 405
  crinoids, 406
  cross-bedded sandstones, 8
  crustaceans, 416
  dinosaurs, 397, 419
  distribution, 348
  echinoids, 406, 613
  economic resources, 364
  guide fossils, 360
  ichthyosaurs, 424, 426
  insects, 416
  life, 356
  mammals, 430
  mountain building, 362
  pelecypods, 409
  plants, 356
  pterosaurs, 427
  sponges, 405
  time-rock divisions, 352
  vertebrates, 357
Jurassic Period, 347
  duration, 32

Kaibab Limestone (Perm.), 28
Kanawha Group (Penn.), 241
Kansan glaciation, maximum, 506
Kansan Stage (Pleist.), 463, 505, 513
Kansas, Cambrian petroleum, 132
  Cretaceous, 375, 377
    birds, 429
    clay, 391
    crinoids, 406
    mosasaurs, 424
    pelecypods, 411
    pterosaurs, 427
  Mississippian, 213, 229
  Neogene, 463, 468
  Ordovician, 137, 147, 153
  Paleogene absent, 445
  Pennsylvanian, 26, 233, 241, 246
  Permian, 262, 269, 275, 281
    insects, 312
  Pleistocene, fluviatile deposits, 509
    glacial and nonglacial deposits, 499
    glaciation, 502
    loess, 503
    units, 505
  Silurian, 168, 172
Kansas Till (Pleist.), Iowa, 511
Kant, Immanuel, 49
Kay, Marshall, 133, 161

Kazanian Stage (Perm.), 263
Keewatin center, Pleistocene glaciation, 510
Keewatin district, 68
  age of rocks, 32
Keewatin Sequence (Precam.), 72
Kentucky, blastoids, 316
  Devonian, 193, 199
    corals, 294
    crinoids, 318
  Mississippian, 213, 221, 226, 229
  Ordovician, 141, 153
  Paleogene, 441
  Silurian, 164, 168, 171, 185
Keokuk Limestone (Miss.), Iowa, 212
kerogen, Paleogene, 453
Kettleman Hills oil field (Calif.), 478
Keuper Series (Trias.), 333
Keweenaw district, 68
  age of rocks, 32
  copper ores, 103
Keweenawan Sequence (Precam.), 82
Keyseran Stage (Sil.), 171
Killarney Granite (Precam.), 82
Killarneyan Range (Precam.), 82
Kimberley district (South Africa), 391
Kimmeridgian Stage (Jur.), 352
Kinderhookian Stage (Miss.), 214
Kindle, E. M., 185
King, P. B., 133, 454
king crabs, description, 605
Kionoceras (nautiloid), 206, 305
Kirkland Lake district, Canada, 104
Klamath Mountains (Calif.), 362
Kleinpell, W. D., 493
Korea, Precambrian ores, 105
Kummel, Bernhard, 345
Kungurian Stage (Perm.), 263

Labechia (stromatoporoid), 292
Labrador, Cambrian, 122
  archaeocyathans, 290
  Pleistocene ice, 508
Labrador center, Pleistocene glaciation, 510
Labrador Range, 82
Labrador Trough, 68
  age of rocks, 32
labyrinthodonts (stegocephalians), 323, 417
lacy bryozoans, Paleozoic, 296
Ladinian Stage (Trias.), 333
lagoonal deposits, Permian, 266
Lake Agassiz (Pleist.), 515
Lake Algonquin (Pleist.), 516
Lake Bonneville (Pleist.), 473
Lake Champlain region (Ord.), 141
Lake Chippewa (Pleist.), 516
lake deposits, glacial, 499
Lake Lahontan (Nev.), Pleistocene, 474
Lake Maumee (Pleist.), 516
Lake Superior region (Precam.), 83
Lake Warren (Pleist.), 516
Lake Whittlesey (Pleist.), 516
Lalicker, C. G., 431
land plants, Cenozoic, 528
  Cretaceous, 379
  Devonian, 202, 208

land plants, Jurassic, 356
  Mesozoic, 397
  Paleogene, 435, 449
  Paleozoic, 285
  Permian, 272
  Silurian, 182, 285
  Triassic, 341
La Place, Pierre de, 49
Laramian revolution, 384
Laramie Range (Wyo.), 384
Laramie River, Neogene history, 489
Latvia, Pleistocene glaciation, 518
Laudon, L. R., 325
Laurentian Granite (Precam.), 73, 76
Laurentide ice sheet, Pleistocene, 508
lead method of age measurement, 30
lead ores, Cambrian, 132
  Mississippian, 229
  Ordovician, 160
  Precambrian, 104
leafless plants, Devonian, 208
  Paleozoic, 285
Lebachia (conifer), 289
Lecanospira (gastropod), 302
Leda (pelecypod), 302, 532
Leet, L. D., 57
Le Grand (Iowa), crinoids, 318
Leighton, M. M., 525
Leith, A., 105
Leith, C. K., 80, 105
lentil, 27
Leonardian Stage (Perm.), 258, 260
Lepidodendron (lycopsid), 287, 575
Leptaena (brachiopod), 206, 296, 298
Leptodus (brachiopod), 279, 300
Leptophyllaraea (coral), 405
Leptopterygius (ichthyosaur), 424
Le Vene, C. M., 365
Lewis thrust fault, 93
limestone (commercial), Devonian, 208
  Jurassic, 364
  Mississippian, 228
  Ordovician, 161
Limulus (chelicerate), 308
Lingula (brachiopod), 595
Linoproductus (brachiopod), 252
Lirosoma (gastropod), 410
lithistid sponges, 291
lithologic similarity in correlation, 25
lithologic symbols, 623
Lithophyllum (red alga), 571
lithosphere, configuration, 56
  relief of surface, 56
Lithuania, Pleistocene glaciation, 518
liverworts, description, 574
lizards, description, 617
Llandeilian Stage (Ord.), 142
Llandoverian Stage (Sil.), 171
Llano Estacado, Neogene, 468
Llano region (Precam.), 89
Llanvirnian Stage (Ord.), 142
lobe-finned fishes, Paleozoic, 322
lobes of continental ice sheet, 502
Lockport Dolostone (Sil.), 173
Lockportian Stage (Sil.), 171
loess, Pleistocene, 498, 507
  thickness, 503
  relation to glacial outwash, 503

Logan, Sir William, 80
Long Island (N.Y.), glacial moraine, 497
Longwell, C. R., 345
Lophophyllidium (horn coral), 252, 279, 295
Lord, C. S., 133
Los Angeles Basin, marine terraces, 476
  Neogene deposits, 475
  oil fields, 475, 477
  Pleistocene, deformation, 476
  tar pits, 527
Louisiana, Cretaceous, foraminifers, 404
  oil, 388
  Jurassic, 349, 355, 364
  Neogene, 463, 466
    petroleum, 492
  Paleogene, 434, 440
  Pleistocene, 504
Louisiana Limestone (Miss.), Missouri, 212
Louisville (Ky.), crinoids, 318
Louisville Limestone (Sil.), 201
Lowenstam, H. A., 185
Lower Carboniferous (*see* Mississippian)
Lowman, S. W., 454
Lowville Limestone (Ord.), 151
Lucas, F. A., 44
Ludian Stage (Eoc.), 434
Ludlovian, 171
Lull, R. S., 44
Lund, R. J., 105
Lutetian Stage (Eoc.), 434
Lycopodium (club moss), 574
lycopsid plants, description, 574
  Devonian, 208
  Paleozoic, 287
Lytton Springs oil field, 388

Maastrichtian Stage (Cret.), 374
MacCurdy, G. G., 566
McKee, E. D., 133, 346
Maclurites (gastropod), 302
Macrotaeniopteris (cycadeoid), 341, 401
Maine, Cambrian, 109
  Devonian land plants, 285
  Silurian volcanics, 177
malacostracans, description, 608
mammal adaptations, Cenozoic, 535
mammal-like reptiles, description, 617
mammals, Cenozoic, 535
  Cretaceous, 381, 620
  description, 618
  fossilization, 536
  Jurassic, 357
  limb structure, 37
  Mesozoic, 430
  Neogene, 620
  oldest known, 325
  Paleogene, 449, 620
  Triassic, 325
mammoth (elephant), 547
Mammuthus (elephant), 622
man, arm structure, 37
  fossil remains, 556
  origin, 554
  structural relationships, 554
Mancos Shale (Cret.), 372, 381
  origin, 6

manganese, Ordovician, 161
  Precambrian, 105
  Triassic, 345
Manhattan geanticline, 378
Manitoba, Archean rocks, 73, 75
  oil and gas, 208
  Precambrian ores, 103
  Silurian, 168
Mankato Till (Pleist.), 514
Mankatoan Substage (Pleist.), 514
Maple Mill Shale (Miss.), Missouri, 212
Marathonites (ammonoid), 306
marble, Ordovician, 161
Marble Gorge (Grand Canyon), 220
Margarosmilia (coral), 405
Marginifera (brachiopod), 252
marine reptiles, Jurassic, 359
  Mesozoic, 424
marine terraces, Neogene, 476
  Pleistocene, 503
Marquette range (Precambrian iron), 101
marsupials (mammals), description, 619
  Neogene, 620
Martha's Vineyard Island, 464
Martinsburg Shale (Ord.), 165
Maryland, Cretaceous cycadeoids, 402
  Devonian, 193
  Neogene, 464
  Silurian, 171
  Triassic, 328
Massachusetts, Cambrian, 109
  Neogene, 464
  Triassic, 328, 339
mastodon (elephant), 547
Mastodonsaurus (amphibian), 343
Maysvillian Stage (Ord.), 142
Mazon Creek, Pennsylvanian fossils, 313
Meandrina (coral), 531
measurement of geologic time, 30
Medinan Series (Sil.), 165, 171
Mediterranean region, Eocene, 449
  Triassic, 328
Medlicottia (ammonoid), 306
Meekella (brachiopod), 279
Megalaspis (trilobite), 307
Meganthropus (manlike ape), 559
Megarietites (ammonite), 360
Megatherium (ground sloth), 551
Megistocrinus (crinoid), 611
Melocrinites (crinoid), 611
Melonechinus (echinoid), 318
member, 27
Meramecian Stage (Miss.), 214
mercury, Silurian, Spain, 185
Merostomata (chelicerates), 308
merostomes, Cambrian, 308
  description, 605
Merychippus (horse), 539
Mesa Verde National Park, 383, 564
Mesa Verde Plateau, 382
Mesabi range (Precambrian iron), 101
Mesaverde Sandstone (Cret.), 372
  origin, 6
Mesohippus (horse), 539
Mesolobus (brachiopod), 252
Mesozoic Era, 327
  duration, 32

Mesozoic life, 394
  contrast with Paleozoic, 395
Metacrinus (crinoid), 610
metamorphic rocks, correlation, 24
  features, 19
Meteor crater, Arizona, 56
meteorite, 47
  Texas, 55
Mexico, Cambrian, 110
  Cretaceous, 368, 371, 377
    foraminifers, 404
    oil, 389
  Devonian, 189
  Eocene coral reefs, 530
  Jurassic, 349, 355
  Laramian revolution, 384
  Mississippian, 216
  Neogene, 460
  Ordovician, 138
  Paleogene, 436, 440
  Pennsylvanian, 236
  Permian, 259
  Silurian, 166
  Triassic, 330
mica, Precambrian, 105
Michelinoceras (nautiloid), 155, 183
Michigan, Devonian, 189, 193, 196,
    208
  corals, 294, 296
  crinoids, 318
  iron ores, 100
  Mississippian, 228
  Pennsylvanian, 234
  Pleistocene, moraines, 501
    units, 505
  Precambrian copper, 103
  salt deposits, 185
  Silurian, 168, 171, 175, 178
midcontinent region, Silurian
    petroleum, 185
middens (waste mounds), 565
Middle East, Jurassic oil, 364
  Neogene petroleum, 492
Midway Group (Paleoc.), 446
Miller, A. K., 325
millipedes, Silurian, 182, 608
milleporid colony (hydrozoan),
    590
Mindel-Rissian Stage (interglacial
    Pleist.), 505
Mindelian Stage (Pleist. glacial),
    505
Minnesota, Cambrian, 116
  iron ores, 100
  Pleistocene units, 505
Minnesota man, 561
Miocene, lavas, Columbia Plateau,
    470
  marine fossils, 9
  meaning of name, 438
Miocene Series (Neog.), 463
Mississippi, Cretaceous oil, 388
  Paleogene, 440
  Pleistocene, 504
  Silurian, 168
Mississippi Embayment, Cretaceous,
    371
  drainage, 465, 467
  Paleogene, 440
Mississippi River deltas, Neogene
    history, 465, 467
  Pleistocene, 504, 508
Mississippi Valley, Cambrian, 113
  Devonian, 189

Mississippi Valley, Mississippian,
    212, 218
  Neogene erosion, 480
  Ordovician, 143
  Pleistocene terraces, 466
  Pleistocene units, 505
  Silurian, 164
Mississippian, amphibians, 323
  Arizona, 28
  blastoids, 314, 610
  brittle stars, 317
  calcareous algae, 570
  chelicerates, 309
  crinoid localities, 318
  crinoids, 316
  distribution, 212, 216
  echinoids, 318
  economic resources, 229
  eurypterids, 309
  graptolites, 319
  guide fossils, 212
  life, 222
  mountain building, 222
  Ozark region, 153
  rocks, 211
  time-rock divisions, 218
Mississippian Period, duration, 32
Missouri, blastoids, 316
  Cambrian, 115, 132
  Devonian, 192, 204
  Mississippian, 212
  Ordovician, 137, 141, 143, 160
    lead, 160
  Paleogene, 441
  Pennsylvanian, 244
  Pleistocene units, 505
  Silurian, 168
Missourian Stage (Penn.), 240, 244
Mistassini fault, 68
Modoc Rock Shelter, 564
Moeritherium (elephant), 546
Mohawkian Series (Ord.), 142
mold, fossil, 13
mollusks, Cenozoic, 532
  Cretaceous, 382
  description, 596
  Mississippian, 227
  (*See also* cephalopods; gastro-
    pods; pelecypods)
Mongolia, ceratopsian dinosaurs,
    422, 425
Monocotyledonales (angiosperms),
    579
monocotyledons (angiosperms), 403
Monongahela Series (Penn.), 241,
    255
Montana, Cambrian, 114
  Cretaceous, 22, 374
    oil, 389
  Devonian, 189, 193
  Jurassic, 349, 352, 354
  Mississippian, 215, 218, 220
  Ordovician, 143
  Paleogene, 445, 454
  Pennsylvanian, 234, 240
  Permian, 258
  Pleistocene, 504, 518
  Precambrian, 96
  Silurian, 168
  Triassic, 334
Montana Group (Cret.), 390
Monterey Shale (Mio.), 475
Montian Stage (Paleoc.), 434
Monticuloporella (bryozoan), 297

Moody, C. L., 454
moon, 53
Moore, R. C., 44, 230, 391, 431, 493
Mooreoceras (nautiloid), 305
moraines, glacial, Pleistocene, 497,
    501
Morenci district (Ariz.), Neogene
    copper, 492
Morocco, Precambrian, 65
Morrison Formation (Jur.), 355, 357
Morrowan Stage (Penn.), 240
Mortoniceras (ammonite), 385
mosasaurs, Cretaceous, 384
  description, 617
  Jurassic, 359
  Mesozoic, 424
Moscow (U.S.S.R.), crinoids, 318
mosses, description, 574
Mother Lode, Jurassic gold, 364
Moulton, F. R., 47
mound builders (early men), 565
mounds, possible offshore salt plugs,
    466
Mt. Lassen (Calif.), 473
Mt. Rainier (Wash.), 456, 471
Mt. Shasta (Calif.), 473
mountain building, Appalachian, 269
  Cambrian, 131
  Devonian, 192
  Jurassic, 362
  Laramian, 384
  Mississippian, 222
  Neogene, 492
  Ordovician, 158
  Paleogene, 452
  Pennsylvanian, 242, 250
  Permian, 269
  Precambrian, 82
  Silurian, 182
  Taconian, 158
  Triassic, 345
mountain glaciation, Pleistocene,
    495, 502, 507, 518
Mousterian culture, 563
Moy-Thomas, J. A., 44
Muav Limestone, 28
Mucrospirifer (brachiopod), 595
mud-cracked limestone, Precam-
    brian, 96
mud cracks, 7
Muller, S. W., 346, 391
multituberculates (mammals), 430
  description, 619
mummies, natural, 11
Murchisonia (Silurian gastropod),
    183
Murray, G. E., 493
Muschalkalk Series (Trias.), 333
mussels (*see* pelecypods)
myriapods, description, 608
  Pennsylvanian, 313
Myxophyta (blue-green algae), 569

Namurian Stage (Carb.), 241
nappes, Alps Mountains, Neogene,
    492
natural gas, Cretaceous, 388
  Ordovician, 159
nautiloids, coiled, 304
  description, 601
  Devonian, 206
  "giants," 304
  Mesozoic, 412
  Mississippian, 304

nautiloids, Ordovician, 304
  Paleozoic, 295, 303
  Pennsylvanian, 304
  Permian, 281
  Silurian, 304
  straight-shelled, 304
Nautilus (cephalopod), 602
Navajo Sandstone (Jur.), 356
Neanderthal men, 553, 560
near-shore sedimentation, 6
Nebraska, Cretaceous, 380
  Miocene mammals, 544
  Mississippian, 213
  Neogene, 463, 468
    mammal beds, 39
  Ordovician, 137
  Pennsylvanian, 241
  Permian, 258, 262
  Pleistocene, glacial and nonglacial
    deposits, 499
    glaciation, 502
    loess, 503
    units, 505
  Silurian, 168
Nebraska Till (Pleis.), 500
Nebraskan glaciation, maximum, 506
Nebraskan Stage (Pleist.), 463, 500,
  505, 513
nebula, spiral, 46
negative region, 67
Nelson, C. A., 117
Nelson, S. J., 325
Neocomian Stage (Cret.), 374
Neogene, 366
  calvareous algae, 571
  climate, 491
  crinoids, 610
  definition, 456
  distribution, 460
  echinoids, 613
  economic resources, 492
  faulting, 479, 482, 492
  guide fossils, 457
  mammal beds, Nebraska, 39
  mammals, 620
  marine fossils, 9
  mountain building, 492
  subsidence in Gulf region, 441
  thickness, 465
  time-rock divisions, 463
  types of deposits, 462
  volcanism, 459, 469, 492
  volcanoes, 471
Neogene Period, duration, 32, 456
Neolithic culture, 564
Neospirifer (brachiopod), 279, 301
Neuropteris (fern), 287, 578
Nevada, Cambrian, 117
  Cretaceous land area, 378
  Devonian, 193
  Jurassic, 349, 353, 362
  Mississippian, 213
  Neogene, 468, 474
    alluvial deposits, 459
    silver, 492
  Ordovician, 143
  Pennsylvanian, 239
  Permian, 258, 267, 282
  Silurian, 170
  Triassic, 329, 333, 339
Nevadan orogeny, 362, 373
New Brunswick, Cambrian, 109
  Pennsylvanian, 233
  Silurian volcanics, 177

New England, glacial erratics, dis-
  persal, 499
  metamorphic rocks, 24
  Neogene monadnocks, 483
New Hampshire, White Mountains,
  483
New Jersey, Cretaceous clay, 391
  Neogene, 463
  Paleogene, 438
  Pleistocene, 503
  Precambrian ores, 104
  Triassic, 328, 333, 338
New Mexico, Cretaceous coal, 390
  Jurassic, 352
  Neogene, 462
  Pennsylvanian, 234, 240, 242
  Permian, 258, 267, 274, 281
  Silurian, 168
  Triassic, 334
New River Group (Penn.), 241
New South Wales, Pennsylvanian
  glaciation, 253
  Precambrian ores, 104
New Stone Age, 564
New York, Cambrian, 113, 129
  Cretaceous, 370
  Devonian, 188, 192, 194, 196
    crinoids, 318
    fossil forest, 285
    sponges, 292
  Mississippian, 214
  Ordovician, 141, 145, 147, 150
  Pleistocene glacial till, 497
  Silurian, 164, 168, 171, 178
    salt, 178, 185
  Triassic, 328, 338
Newark deposits (Trias.), 344
Newell, N. D., 283
Newfoundland, Cambrian, 109, 122
  Ordovician, 151, 161
    iron, 161
  Silurian, 164
Niagara Falls, Pleistocene recession,
  521
  Silurian beds, 174
Niagara gorge, Silurian, 163, 173
Niagaran reefs, 177
Niagaran Series (Sil.), 171
nickel, Precambrian, 103
Nipissing Great Lakes (Pleist.), 516
nonconformity, 18
  base of Ordovician, 140
nonglacial deposits, Pleistocene, 499
Norian Stage (Trias.), 333
North America, early men, 561
  Pleistocene ice distribution, 496
North Carolina, Cretaceous, 371
  Jurassic, 356
  Neogene, 464
  Paleogene, 438, 440
  Triassic, 328, 337, 345
    ferns, 402
North Dakota, Cretaceous, 379
  Devonian, 189
  Paleogene, 435, 454
  Pennsylvanian, 234
  Silurian, 168
  Triassic, 334
Norway, ostracoderms, 320
  Silurian orogeny, 182
Notharctus (primate), 557
Nova Scotia, Mississippian, 228
  Pennsylvanian, 234
  Permian, 258, 267

Nova Scotia, Triassic, 328, 337
Nucleocrinus (blastoid), 314
Nummulites (foraminifer), 433
Nummulitic System, 432

Obelia (hydrozoan), 589
Obolella (branchiopod), 126
ocean basins, average specific grav-
  ity, 57
  origin, 55
Ochoan Stage (Perm.), 259, 262
odd-toed hoofed mammals, 537
Odontochile (trilobite), 310
Oesterling, W. A., 230
offlap, 17
offshore oil well, Gulf region, 465
offshore sedimentation, 6
Ohio, ancient Pleistocene drift, 513
  Devonian, 193, 201
    corals, 294
  Mississippian, 218, 229
  Ordovician, 142
  Pennsylvanian, 232, 241, 245, 255
  Pleistocene, moraines, 501
    units, 505
  Silurian, 164, 170, 185
    salt, 178
Ohio River, Neogene history, 465,
  467
Ohio Valley, Devonian, 189
  Ordovician, 142
oil shale, Paleogene, 453
Oklahoma, Cambrian, 115, 117
  Cretaceous, 371
  Devonian, 192
  Mississippian, 213, 229
  Ordovician, 27, 137, 143, 147
  Pennsylvanian, 233, 240, 242, 244
  Permian, 262, 281
  Silurian, 168, 172
Okulitch, V. J., 325
Old Red Sandstone (Dev.), 182, 209
Old Stone Age (Neog.), 563
oldest known rocks, 73
olenellid trilobites, 307
Olenellus (trilobite), 117, 122
Olenoides (trilobite), 128, 294
Oligocene, 432
  meaning of name, 438
  Nebraska, 469
  saber-toothed cat, 41
  time-rock divisions, 434
  type sections, 433
  (*See also* Paleogene)
Olympic Peninsula, Miocene, 475
Omphyma (coral), 183
Onondaga Limestone (Dev.), in-
  vertebrates, 206
Ontario, Archean rocks, 74
  Cambrian, 116
  Cryptozoic algae, 98
  Devonian, 189, 193, 196
  Keweenawan rocks, 84
  Ordovician, 140
  Pleistocene, 503
  Precambrian ores, 103
  Silurian, 171, 173
    salt, 178
Ophiacodon (reptile), 324
Ophileta (gastropod), 302
Ophioderma (ophiuroid), 612
ophiuroids, description, 611
  Mississippian, 317
orangutan, 555

Ordovician, Appalachian region, 29
 barnacles, 310
 calcareous algae, 569
 chelicerates, 309
 climates, 158
 crinoids, 316
 cystoids, 314, 609
 distribution, 138
 economic resources, 159
 fishes, 319
 graptolites, 318, 614
 guide fossils, 154
 life, 152
 mud cracks, 7
 Oklahoma, 27
 ostracodes, 310
 ripple marks, 7
 starfishes, 318, 612
 Tennessee, 29
 time-rock divisions, 143
 Virginia, 29
 volcanic activity, 150
 Wales, 135
 worms, 312
Ordovician Period, duration, 32
Oregon, Cretaceous, 372
 Eocene coal, 454
 Jurassic, 348, 352, 362
  cycadeoids, 401
  ginkgos, 403
 Neogene, 458, 470, 474
 Paleogene, 434, 447, 450
 Permian, 258, 267, 272
 Pleistocene loess, 503
 Triassic, 329
oreodonts (mammals), 544
organic remains, in correlation, 25
 in sedimentary rocks, 9
organisms, classification, 567
Oriskany Sandstone (Dev.), 208
ornithischian dinosaurs, 420
 description, 618
Orria (trilobite), 306
orthid brachiopods, Paleozoic, 298
Orthoceras (nautiloid), 304
Orthorhynchula (brachiopod), 299
Osagian Stage (Miss.), 214
Osteichthyes (bony fishes), 322
Ostracoda (crustaceans), 310
ostracoderms (fishes), 319
 Devonian, 614
ostracodes, Cenozoic, 533
 description, 606
 Mesozoic, 416
 Paleogene, 608
 Paleozoic, 310, 314
 Silurian, 182
Ostrea (pelecypod), 408
Ouachita geosyncline, 238
Ouachita Mountains, Cambrian, 117
 Ordovician, 144
outwash plains, Pleistocene, 498
overlap, 16
Oxfordian Stage (Jur.), 352
oysters, Cretaceous, 381, 386
 Mesozoic, 408
Ozark region, Mississippian, 213
 Ordovician, 147, 153
 Precambrian, 89

Pachycephalosaurus (dinosaur), 422

Pacific Border, Cretaceous, 372, 378
 Neogene, 463
 orogeny, 492
 Paleogene, 434, 447
Pacific Northwest, Pleistocene loess, 503
"Pacific Province," Cambrian, 109, 123
Painted Desert, Triassic, 327
Palaeochiropteryx (bat), 620
Palaeodictyoptera (insects), 311
Palaeomastodon (elephant), 546
Palaeoscincus (dinosaur), 396, 422
Palaeosuchus (reptile), 343
Paleocene, meaning of name, 438
 time-rock divisions, 434
 type sections, 433
 (*See also* Paleogene)
Paleocene Epoch, 432
Paleogene, 366
 bryozoans, 593
 climate, 451
 coal swamps, 445
 Colorado, 387
 distribution, 436
 economic resources, 453
 guide fossils, 435
 life, 449
 mammals, 630
 marine oscillations, 438
 mountain building, 452
 ostracodes, 608
 time-rock divisions, 434
 volcanism, 447
 (*See also* Eocene; Oligocene; Paleocene)
Paleogene Period, 432
 duration, 32
paleogeography, Cambrian, 123
Paleolithic culture, 563
Paleozoic, amphibians, 322
 blastoids, 314
 bony fishes, 322
 chelicerates, 308
 conodonts, 312
 crustaceans, 310
 echinoderms, 314
 echinoids, 318
 fishes, 319
 graptolites, 318
 insects, 310
 placoderms, 320
 reptiles, 323
 sharklike fishes, 322
 starfishes, 318
 therapsids, 325
 vertebrates, 319
 worms, 312
Paleozoic Alps, 242
Paleozoic Era, duration, 32
Palisade Mountains, 344
Palisades disturbance, 345
Pannulirus (malocostracan), 607
Pantolambda (amblypod), 621
Parabrodia (dragonfly), 253
paraconformity, 18
 Black Hills, 219
 Cambrian-Mississippian, 219
 above Cretaceous, 367
 Devonian, 195, 201
 Pennsylvanian, 232
 Silurian-Devonian, 201
paracrinoids, 609
Paradox Basin, 242

Paradoxides (trilobite), 307
paradoxidid trilobites, 307
parapsid reptiles, 616
Parasmilia (coral), 405
Paris Basin, Paleogene, 433
Pasadenan orogeny, 492
Patagonian early man, 562
peccaries (mammals), 544, 622
Pecopteris (fern), 253
Pecten (pelecypod), 410
Pelagia (jellyfish), 589
pelecypods, Cenozoic, 532
 coral-like, 386
 Cretaceous, 367, 381, 386, 410
 description, 598
 Devonian, 196
 Jurassic, 361
 Mesozoic, 408
 Ordovician, 154
 Paleogene, 449
 Paleozoic, 300, 302
 Permian, 279, 281
Pelmatozoa, description, 609
pelvic structures, dinosaurs, 618
pelycosaurs, description, 617
 Paleozoic, 325
peneplain, Canadian Shield, 70
 Precambrian, 79
peneplanation, Neogene, 483
Pennsylvania, Appalachian folding, 269, 276
 Cambrian, 113, 132
 Devonian, 188, 193, 196
  amphibians, 322
 Mississippian, 213, 218, 222, 229
 Neogene erosion, 483
 Ordovician, 144, 147, 161
 Pennsylvanian, 232, 238, 241, 245
 Permian, 270
 Silurian, 165, 169, 171
  salt, 178
 Triassic, 328, 341
  ferns, 402
Pennsylvanian, amphibians, 43, 323
 arachnids, 309, 313
 blastoids, 314
 chelicerates, 309
 climate, 247
 coal swamp, 43
 cockroaches, 609
 crustaceans, 313
 distribution, 234, 236
 echinoids, 318
 economic resources, 249
 eurypterids, 309
 evenly bedded sandstone, 6
 ferns, 13, 578
 glaciation, 247, 253
 guide fossils, 233
 insects, 311
 Kansas, 26
 life, 242
 mountain building, 242, 250
 myriapods, 313
 Ozark region, 153
 pelycosaurs, 325
 persistent thin rock units, 244
 plants, 579
 reptiles, 324
 rocks, 231
 spiders, 309, 313, 607
 time-rock divisions, 240
Pennsylvanian Period, duration, 32
Penokeean Range, 82

Pentacrinus (crinoid), 406
pentamerid branchiopods, Paleozoic, 300
Pentamerus (brachiopod), 295, 299
Pentremites (blastoid), 225, 314, 610
Peoria Formation (Pleist.), Iowa, 511
period, 29
perissodactyls (mammals), 537
  description, 622
perlite, Neogene, 492
Permian, amphibians, 323
  Arizona, 28
  blastoids, 314
  chelicerates, 309
  climate, 272, 276
  distribution, 258, 260
  echinoids, 318
  economic resources, 280
  eurypterids, 309
  glaciation, 278
  guide fossils, 257, 259
  insects, 311
  life, 272
  ostracodes, 310
  pelycosaurs, 325
  persistent thin rock units, 269
  reptile tracks, 15
  reptiles, 35, 324
  rocks, 257
  time-rock divisions, 262
  volcanism, 272
Permian Period, duration, 32
Perrinites (ammonoid), 259
persistent thin rock units, Pennsylvanian, 244
  Permian, 269
Pervinquieria (ammonite), 410
Petalocrinus (crinoid), 317
Peterson, J. A., 365
Peterson, J. J., 455
Petrified Forest, Triassic, 341
Petrified Forest National Monument, 401
Petrolacosaurus (reptile), 252
petroleum, Cambrian, 132
  Cretaceous, 388
  in igneous rocks, 389
  Jurassic, 364
  Mississippian, 229
  Neogene, 388, 492
  Ordovician, 160
  Paleogene, 453
  Pennsylvanian, 242, 255
  Permian, 281
  Silurian, 185
Pettijohn, F. J., 105
Peytoia (jellyfish), 294
Phacops (trilobite), 205, 306
Phaeophyta, 571
Phanerozoic Eon, 59
  duration, 32
Phenacodus (condylarth), 621
Philadelphia (Pa.), Fall Line, 370
Phillipsastrea (colonial coral), 294
Phororhacos (bird), 535, 536
phosphate, Mississippian, 229
  Neogene, 492
  Permian, 267, 282
Phosphoria Formation (Perm.), 282
Phragmoceras (nautiloid), 180, 295, 304
Phragmolites (gastropod), 303

Phthonia (pelecypod), 302
Phyllograptus (graptolite), 157
Phyloblatta (cockroach), 253
phylum, 568
phytosaurs, description, 617
  Triassic, 342
Piacenzan Stage (Plio.), 463
Piedmont, Appalachians, rock structure, 275
Pike, W. S., Jr., 391
pillow lava, Archean, 72
Piltdown man, 560
Pinnularia (diatom), 570
Pisocrinus (crinoid), 317
pisolitic limestone, Permian, 266
Pithecanthropus (ape man), 558
Pittsburgh coal bed (Penn.), 242
Placenticeras (ammonite), 385, 387, 414
placoderms, Devonian, 207, 320
Plaesiomys (brachiopod), 299, 595
planetary system, 51
planetesimals, 48
planetoids, 46
Plantae, 568
plants, Cenozoic, 528
  Cretaceous, 379
  description, 572
  Jurassic, 356
  main divisions, 573
  Mesozoic, 397
  Paleozoic, 284
plated dinosaurs, 420
platinum, Precambrian, 104
Platybelodon, 549
Platycrinites (crinoid), 316
Platyrachella (brachiopod), 204, 299
Platystrophia (brachiopod), 155
Pleistocene, definition, 457
  deformation, California, 476, 478
    Cascade Mountains, 471
  deposits, distribution, 502
  direction of ice movement, 498
  drainage changes, 515
  duration, 459, 521
  fluvioglacial deposits, 498
  glaciation, 558
    causes, 523
    limit, 502, 506
    mountain, 495
  maximum distribution of ice, 496
  meaning of name, 438
  pack ice, 496
  saber-toothed cat, 41
  soils, 505, 509
  terrace deposits, Mississippi Embayment, 467
  time-rock divisions, 505
  volcanics, 472
  volcanism, 508
Pleistocene Epoch, 495
Pleistocene Series (Neog.), 463
plesiosaurs, description, 617
  Jurassic, 359, 399
  limb structure, 37
  Mesozoic, 424
Pleurophorus (pelecypod), 302
Pliensbachian Stage (Jur.), 352
Pliocene, meaning of name, 438
  Nebraska, 469
Pliocene Series (Neog.), 463
Poland, Pleistocene glaciation, 518
  Triassic zinc. 345

Polydiexodina (fusulinid), 573
Polypora (bryozoan), 279
Polypterus (ganoid fish), 320, 322
Pontiac rocks (Precam.), 73
Pontian Stage (Mio.), 463
Porcupine district, Canada, 104
porpoises, Cenozoic, 547
Portheus (fish), 417
Portlandian Stage (Jur.), 352
Portugal, Ordovician trilobite, 154
positive region, 67
potash salt, Permian, 281
potassium method of age measurement, 31
Potomac Marble, 340
Pottsville Series (Penn.), 241
Pratt, W. E., 493
Precambrian, economic resources, 100
  glaciation, 97
prehistoric cave-wall carvings, 563
prehistoric stone carvings, 565, 623
Primary System, 433
primates (mammals), 554, 620
  Cenozoic, 550
Prince Edward Island, 267
Prismopora (bryozoan), 296
productid brachiopods, Paleozoic, 226, 298
Prolecanites (ammonoid), 306
Prorichtofenia (brachiopod), 279, 300
Proterozoic Era, 68, 70
Protista, 568
  Cenozoic, 529
  Mesozoic, 404
Protoceratops (dinosaur), 425
Protolepidodendron (lycopsid), 208, 287, 575
Protomedusae, description, 587
Protozoa, description, 571
protozoans, Cenozoic, 529
  Mesozoic, 404
  Paleozoic, 289
Prouddenites (ammonoid), 252
Prozeuglodon (whale), 621
Pseudocrinites (cystoid), 316
Pseudoschloenbachia (ammonite), 410
Psilophyton (leafless plant), 208, 285
psilopsid plants, description, 574
  Devonian, 285
Pteranodon (pterosaur), 384, 427
Pteraspis (ostracoderm), 614
Pteridospermales (seed ferns), 576
Pterodactylus (pterosaur), 427
Pteropsida (ferns), 575
pterosaurs, 397, 400
  Cretaceous, 384
  description, 617
  Jurassic, 359
  largest, 384
  limb structure, 37
  Mesozoic, 427
Ptilodus (insectivore), 620
Puget Valley (Wash.), 449
pumice, Neogene, 492
  significance, 3
Purbeck beds (Jur.), 352
Pycnogonida (sea spiders), 308
Pyrenees Mountains, Paleogene orogeny, 452
  Pleistocene glaciation, 519

pyritization, 13
Pyrrhophyta, 570

Quaternary Period, 497
Quaternary System, 433, 457
Quebec, Cambrian asbestos, 132
  Devonian, 194
  glacial varves, 523
  Ordovician, 141
  Pleistocene ice, 508
  Precambrian, 77
    conglomerate, 4
    iron ores, 103
  Silurian volcanics, 177
Queensland, Permian, 282
Queenston redbeds (Ord.), 150

rabbits, description, 620
radioactive age measurement, 30
radiocarbon dating, Pleistocene, 522
radiolarians, description, 572
  Precambrian, 290
Rafinesquina (brachiopod), 155, 298
Rancho La Brea tar pools, 527, 536
ray-finned fishes, 321
Raymond, P. E., 105
Recent, definition, 457, 496
Recent deposits (Pleist.), Gulf region, 466
Recent Stage (Pleist.), 463, 505, 514
Receptaculites (?sponge), 291
recession of falls, Pleistocene, 521
red algae, description, 571
redbeds, Jurassic, 349
  Pennsylvanian, 248
  Permian, 259, 267, 269
Redlichia (trilobite), 126
Redwall Limestone (Miss.), 208, 220
reef flank rock, structure, 176
reef limestone, Permian, 264, 266
reef structure, Niagaran, 175
Reeside, J. B., Jr., 346, 391
refractories (silica brick), 161
regressing sea, Pennsylvanian, 246
Reptescharipora (bryozoan), 409
reptiles, aquatic (*see* aquatic reptiles)
  Cenozoic, 534
  Cretaceous, 367, 381, 384
  description, 615
  Jurassic, 357
  limb structure, 37
  Mesozoic, 417
  Paleozoic, 323
  Pennsylvanian, 245, 253
  Permian, 35, 275, 277
  structure of eggs, 617
Retrorisirostra (brachiopod), 299
Rhaetian Stage (Trias.), 333
Rhamphorhynchus (pterosaur), 400
rhinoceroses, 622
  Cenozoic, 540
Rhipidozyra (coral), 405
rhizome, 574
Rhizostomites (jellyfish), 406
Rhode Island, Pennsylvanian, 238
Rhodophyta, 571
Rhombopora (bryozoan), 297
Rhymia (psilopsid), 575
rhynchonellid brachiopods, Paleozoic, 300

Rhynchotrema (brachiopod), 300
Rhynie Chert (Dev.), 575
Richards, H. G., 455
Richmond (Va.), Fall Line, 370
Richmondian Stage (Ord.), 142
Ridge and Valley Belt of Appalachians, 275
Rio Grande Valley (N.M.), Neogene, 469
ripple marks, 7
Riss-Würmian Stage (Pleist. interglacial), 505
Rissian Stage (Pleist. glacial), 505
Ritz, C. H., 454
rock characters, historical significance, 2
Rocky Mountain National Park, 92, 487
Rocky Mountains, Cambrian, 114
  Cretaceous, 371
  front in Colorado, 366
  geosyncline, 377
  Neogene, 469
  history, 486
  Paleogene, 442
  Pennsylvanian, 234
  Pleistocene, 507
  Precambrian, 89
  Triassic, 328
Rocky Mountains peneplain, Neogene, 487
rodents, Cenozoic, 599
  description, 620
Rodgers, John, 33, 133
Romer, A. S., 551
Rotliegend (Perm.), 259, 263
Royal Gorge (Colo.), Neogene erosion, 489
Rubey, W. W., 391
rubidium method of age measurement, 31
rudistid pelecypods, Cretaceous, 386
  Mesozoic, 411
Ruedemann, Rudolf, 325
Rugosa (tetrameral corals), 592
Rundle Formation (Miss.), 220
Rupelian Stage (Oligo.), 434
Russia, Neogene oil, 492
  Permian reptiles, 275
  Pleistocene glaciation, 518
  (*See also* U.S.S.R.)

saber-toothed cats, 41
St. Anthony Falls, Pleistocene recession, 521
St. Louis Limestone (Miss.), 214, 221
St. Peter Sandstone (Ord.), 3, 146, 161
Ste. Genevieve Limestone (Miss.), 214, 221
Sakmarian Stage (Perm.), 263
Salem Limestone (Miss.), 223, 229
Salinan Series (Sil.), 171
salt, Jurassic, 349, 356, 364
  Mississippian, 229
  Pennsylvanian, 242
  Permian, 259, 267, 281
  Silurian, 178, 185
  Triassic, 345
salt domes, 442
  Neogene, in Gulf region, 467
  possible offshore, 466
Salterella (?cephalopod), 304

San Andreas fault (Calif.), 479, 482
San Francisco earthquake, 479
San Joaquin Valley (Calif.), Neogene, 475, 477
San Luis Valley (Colo.), Neogene, 469
sand (commercial), Ordovician, 161
Sangamonian Stage (Pleist.), 463, 505, 513
Santonian Stage (Cret.), 374
Sarmatian Stage (Mio.), 463
Saskatchewan, Paleogene, 451
  Pleistocene ground moraine, 500
  Precambrian copper, 103
  Silurian, 168
saurischian dinosaurs, 419
  description, 618
Saxonian Series (Perm.), 263
Scandinavia, Pleistocene glaciation, 518
scaphopods, description, 596
Scheele, G. G., 44
Schenck, H. G., 391
Schizophyta (bacteria), 568
Schoelhamer, J. E., 493
Schooley peneplain, Appalachians, 483
Schroederoceras (nautiloid), 155
Schuchert, Charles, 125, 230, 365
Scleractinia (hexameral corals), 592
scolecodonts (worm jaw parts), 312, 603
scorpions, Paleozoic, 308
  Pennsylvanian, 253
  Silurian, 182
  structure, 607
Scotland, Devonian psilopsids, 575
  Jurassic angiosperms, 403
  Silurian, orogeny, 182
  scorpions, 182
Scyphomedusae, description, 588
Scyphocrinites (crinoid), 183
Scyphozoa, description, 588
Scythian Stage (Trias.), 333
sea anemone, 587
sea cucumbers, Paleozoic, 294
  (*See also* holothuroids)
sea lilies (*see* crinoids)
sea spiders, Paleozoic, 308
sea urchins (*see* echinoids)
seaweeds, Cretaceous, 387
Secondary System, 433
Sedalia Limestone (Miss.), 212
sedimentary facies, 5
sedimentary rocks, features, 3
  lateral variation, 6
  significance, 3
sedimentation cycles, boundaries, 246
seed ferns, description, 576
  Paleozoic, 287, 289
Sellards, E. H., 566
Senonian Stage (Cret.), 374
sequence, 61
Sequoia (conifer), 578
series, 29
Seven Rivers Formation (Perm.), 266
Seymouria (reptile), 277, 324
sharklike fishes, Paleozoic, 322
sharks, Cenozoic, 534
  Devonian, 207
  Jurassic, 322

Shawangunk Conglomerate (Sil.), 173
shelf-basin margin deposits, Permian, 265
shelf deposits, Permian, 265
shields, 66
Siberia, Cambrian archaeocyathans, 290
    Jurassic, coal, 364
        ginkgos, 403
    Paleogene, 451
    Permian coal, 275, 282
    Precambrian ores, 105
    woolly mammoth, 11
Siberian Shield, Precambrian, 66
Sicidium (chlorophyte), 570
Sierra Nevada, 362, 364, 449
    Pleistocene glaciation, 502, 518
Siever, Raymond, 255
Sigillaria (lycopod), 288
Signal Hill oil field (Calif.), 477
silica bricks, Ordovician, 161
siliceous sponges, Paleozoic, 291, 293
silicification, 13
silicified fossils, Permian, 276
silicoflagellates, description, 570
Silurian, chelicerates, 309
    climate, 182
    coral reefs, 174
    crinoids, 317
    cystoids, 314
    distribution, 164, 166
    echinoids, 318
    economic resources, 183
    eurypterids, 311
    evaporites, 177
    fishes, 319
    graptolites, 318, 614
    life, 180
    Ozark region, 153
    time-rock divisions, 171
    type region, 163
    volcanism, 177
    worm trails, 314
    worms, 312
Silurian Period, duration, 32
silver, Cretaceous, 388
    Mississippian, 229
    Neogene, 492
    Paleogene, 453
    Precambrian, 104
Simpson, G. G., 44, 365
Sinanthropus (Pleist. ape man), 558
Sinemurian Stage (Jur.), 352
Sinian Sequence (Precam.), 65
Siphonophrentis (coral), 206, 296
siphuncle (cephalopods), 304
Siych Limestone (Precam.), 93
Skolithos (worm boring), 314
skull structure, amphibians, 616
    fishes, 616
    reptiles, 616
slate (commercial), Cambrian, 132
    Ordovician, 161
sloths, Cenozoic, 549
Smilodon (cat), 41, 547
Smith, William, 347
snails (*see* gastropods)
sodium carbonate, Neogene, 493
sodium sulfate, Neogene, 493
soils, Pleistocene, 505, 509
solar system, main features, 47
    origin, 47

Solenopora (red alga), 571
Solnhofen, Jurassic fossils, 406
Solnhofen Limestone (Jur.), 362
    crustaceans of, 416
Solutrean culture, 564
South Africa, age of rocks, 32
    Cretaceous diamonds, 391
    Precambrian ores, 105
    Triassic, coal, 345
        reptiles, 395
South America, early men, 561
    Laramian revolution, 384
    Permian, 259, 278
South Carolina, Neogene, 464
    Paleogene, 438, 440
South Dakota, Cambrian, 117
    Cretaceous, 373, 375
    Devonian, 189
    Jurassic, 346, 354
        belemnoids, 413
    Mississippian, 219
    Neogene, 462, 486
    Paleogene, 445
    Pennsylvanian, 234, 240
    Pleistocene, 505
    Precambrian, 94
    Silurian, 168
    Triassic, 333
South Platte River, Neogene history, 489
Southern Hemisphere, Permian floras, 275
Sowerbyella (brachiopod), 165, 298
Spain, Cambrian iron, 132
    Paleogene orogeny, 452
Spangler, W. B., 455
species, 567
Sphenophyllum (lycopsid), 576
sphenopsid plants, description, 575
Sphenopsida, Mesozoic, 399
Sphenopteris (fern), 253
Sphenozamites (cycadeoid), 401
Spicker, E. M., 391
spiders, Cenozoic, 533
    Paleozoic, 308
    Pennsylvanian, 245, 313, 607
Spindletop salt dome, 443
spiral nebula, 46
spire-bearing brachiopods, Paleozoic, 300
Spirifer (brachiopod), 300
Spitsbergen, Devonian coal, 208
    Jurassic coal, 364
    ostracoderms, 320
sponge spicules, 586
sponges, Cambrian, 130
    Cenozoic, 530
    Cretaceous, 405
    description, 585
    Devonian, 207
    Jurassic, 361, 405
    Mesozoic, 404
    Paleozoic, 291, 293
    Permian, 279, 281
    Triassic, 405
sporangia, 574
sporangiophores, 575
sporophylls, 575
Springeran Stage (Penn.), 240
Squamularia (brachiopod), 252
stage, 28
starfishes, Cretaceous, 408
    description, 611
    Paleozoic, 318

Stassfurt, Permian salt, 282
Staurocalyptus (sponge), 584
Steep Rock Lake district, iron ore, 103
Steep Rock Limestone (Precam.), 74
stegocephalians (amphibians), 322
    Triassic, 342
Stegosaurus (dinosaur), 358, 420
Stenodictya (insect), 609
Stephanian Stage (Carb.), 241
Stephanophyllia (coral), 531
Stephenson, L. W., 391, 455
Stereocrinus (crinoid), 611
Stewart, J. S., 133
Stokes, W. L., 365
stone (commercial), Cambrian, 132
    Cretaceous, 388
    Mississippian, 229
    Neogene, 493
    Pennsylvanian, 255
stony bryozoans, Paleozoic, 295
Stose, G. W., 161
stratification, 6
Stromatocerium (stromatoporoid), 292
stromatolites, 60, 569
Stromatopora (stromatoporoid), 590
stromatoporoids, description, 591
    Devonian, 196
    Paleozoic, 292
Strombodes (colonial coral), 293
Stropheodonta (brachiopod), 296
Strophomena (brachiopod), 595
strophomenid brachiopods, Paleozoic, 298
structure, discordant, 17
Struthiomimus (dinosaur), 418
Stumm, E. C., 325
stylolite in Ordovician limestone, 152
Stylosmilia (coral), 405
submarine canyons, Neogene, 466
sub-sequence, 80
Sudbury district, Precambrian ores, 103
sulfur, Neogene, 493
sun, main features, 47
Supai Formation (Perm.), 28
superposed Pleistocene deposits, 511
superposition law, 15
Sutton, A. H., 230
Sweden, Precambrian iron ores, 103
    Silurian orogeny, 182
Switzerland, glacial erratics, 497
    Jurassic, 347
    Pleistocene glaciation, 518
synapsid reptiles, 616
Synaptophyllum (colonial coral), 295
synchronogenic rock equivalents, 21
syntopogenic rock equivalents, 21
system, 29

tabulate corals, Paleozoic, 294
Taconian mountain building, 147, 158, 165, 172
    Vermont, 112
Taeniopteris (fern), 253
talc, Precambrian, 105
Tampico district, Cretaceous oil, 389
Tapirus (tapir), 622
Tarphyceras (nautiloid), 305
Tartarian Stage (Perm.-Trias.), 263
Tasmania, Jurassic coal, 364

Taylor, F. B., 185
Tazewell Loess (Pleist.), 512
Tazewell Till (Pleist.), 512, 514
Tazewellian Substage (Pleist.), 514
Teays River (Pleist.), Ohio-Ind., 517
Teleiocrinus (crinoid), 316
Teleoceras (rhinoceros), 541
telson (arthropod tail), 308
Tennessee, Cambrian copper, 132
    Cambro-Ordovician strata, 29
    Devonian, 189, 192
    Mississippian, 221
    Ordovician, 141, 143, 146
        marble, 161
    Paleogene, 441, 454
    Pennsylvanian, 239
    siliceous sponges, 291
    Silurian, 168
Tennesseean Series (Miss.), 214
Terataspis (trilobite), 206, 296, 309
terebratulid brachiopods, Paleozoic, 301
terrace deposits (Pleist.), Mississippi Embayment, 467
terraces, marine, Pleistocene, 503
Tertiary System, 366, 433, 457
tetrabranchiates (cephalopods), 601
Tetragraptus (graptolite), 614
Texas, Cambrian, 117, 129, 132
    Cretaceous, 375, 388
        foraminifers, 404
    Devonian, 189, 192
    Jurassic, 349, 355, 364
    Lower Cretaceous, 23
    meteorite, 55
    Mississippian, 213, 229
    Neogene, 462, 468
    Ordovician, 137, 141, 143
    Paleogene, 434, 440, 453
    Pennsylvanian, 233, 240, 242, 251
    Permian, 258, 262, 267, 275
        oil, 281
    Pleistocene, 504
    silicified Permian brachiopods, 12
    Silurian, 168, 171
    Triassic, 328, 334
Thamnasteria (coral), 405
Thamniscus (bryozoan), 279
Thanetian Stage (Paleoc.), 434
thecodonts (reptiles), Triassic, 419
Therapsida (mammal-like reptiles), 617
therapsids (mammal-like reptiles), 325
Thiessen, Reinhardt, 255
Thomas, E. P., 455
Thuringian Series (Perm.), 263
Thylacosmilus (marsupial), 620
tillite, Precambrian, 81
time-rock divisions, Cambrian, 114
    Cretaceous, 374
    Devonian, 193
    Eocene, 434
    Jurassic, 352
    Mississippian, 218
    Neogene, 463
    Oligocene, 434
    Ordovician, 143
    Paleocene, 434
    Paleogene, 434
    Pennsylvanian, 240
    Permian, 262
    Pleistocene, 505
    Silurian, 171

time-rock divisions, Triassic, 333
time-rock units, 28
Timiskaming conglomerate, 4
Timiskaming district, age of rocks, 32
Timiskaming Sequence (Precam.), 73
Timorites (ammonoid), 259
tin, Paleogene, 453
tintinnines, description, 572
Titanites (ammonite), 361
titanotheres (mammals), 453, 537, 541, 622
Toarcian Stage (Jur.), 352
Tongrian Stage (Oligo.), 434
tongue, 28
Tonolowayan Stage (Sil.), 171
Tonopah district (Nev.), Neogene silver, 492
Toroweap Formation (Perm.), 28
Tortonian Stage (Mio.), 463
Tournaisian Series (Carb.), 215
Trachodon (dinosaur), 418, 420
tracks, dinosaur, 398
transgressing sea, Pennsylvanian, 246
trap ridges, Triassic, 344
tree ferns, Devonian, 208, 286
Tremadocian Stage (Ord.), 108, 142
Trempealeauan Stage (Cam.), 114
Trenton (N.J.), Fall Line, 370
Trentonian Stage (Ord.), 142, 145
Trepospira (gastropod), 252
Triadocidaris (echinoid), 613
Triarthrus (trilobite), 307, 605
Triassic, ammonites, 414
    amphibians, 417
    Canada, 330
    corals, 405
    distribution, 328
    echinoids, 613
    economic resources, 345
    facies, 336
    fishes, 418
    guide fossils, 341
    ichthyosaurs, 424
    invertebrates, 341
    life, 341
    mammals, 325, 430
    Mexico, 330
    mountain building, 345
    reptiles, 419
    sponges, 405
    stegocephalians, 323
    time-rock divisions, 333
    type region, 328
    United States, 330
    vertebrates, 342
Triassic Period, 327
    duration, 32
Triceratops (dinosaur), 383, 422, 426
Tricrepicephalus (trilobite), 126
Trigonia (pelecypod), 409, 410
trilobites, appendages preserved, 128
    Cambrian, 120, 126, 306
    description, 604
    Devonian, 196, 205, 206, 306
    evolutionary features, 306
    largest known, 307
    Mississippian, 227
    obsolete trilobation, 308
    Ordovician, 154, 306
    Paleozoic, 294, 296, 306

trilobites, Pennsylvanian, 252
    Silurian, 180, 183, 306
trilobitoids, description, 604
Trimeroceras (nautiloid), 304
Trinity Group (Cret.), 23
Triticites (foraminifer), 290
Triton (gastropod), 597
trituberculates, Mesozoic, 430
Trochiliscus (chlorophyte), 570
Trochocyathus (coral), 531
tuff, significance, 3
Turonian Stage (Cret.), 374
Turritella (gastropod), 385
turtles, description, 617
    Mesozoic, 427
Tylosaurus (mosasaur), 384
Tyrannosaurus (dinosaur), 394, 418

Uinta Mountains (Utah), Pleistocene glaciation, 520
Uintacrinus (crinoid), 406
uintatheres (mammals), 452, 537, 621
Uintatherium (ungulate), 621
Ulrich, E. O., 125
unconformity, 18
    base, of Cretaceous, 251
    of Timiskaming, 77
underclay, 235
uniformitarianism, 2
U.S.S.R., Jurassic coal, 364
    Neogene oil, 492
    Permian, 259
    Precambrian iron ores, 103
    (*See also* Russia)
United States, Cambrian, 110
    Cretaceous, 368
    Devonian, 190
    graptolite beds, 319
    Jurassic, 350
    Mississippian, 216
    Neogene distribution, 460
    Ordovician, 138
    Paleogene, 436
    Pennsylvanian, 236
    Permian, 260
    Silurian, 166
    Triassic, 330
    (*See also* specific states)
Uperocrinus (crinoid), 227, 317
Upper Carboniferous, 233
Uralichas (trilobite), 307
Urals mountain building, 242
uranium, Precambrian, 104
Urey, H. C., 57
Urosalpinx (gastropod), 533
Utah, Cambrian, 114, 121
    Cretaceous, 374, 377
    Devonian, 193
    Jurassic, 347, 352, 356
        cross-bedded sandstone, 8
    Mississippian, 218
    Neogene, deposits, 469, 473, 486
        erosion, 489
        volcanics, 459, 473
    Ordovician, 143
    Paleogene, 432, 444, 454
    Pennsylvanian, 239, 242, 247, 250
    Permian, 258, 262, 282
    Pleistocene glaciation, 520
    Silurian, 170
    Triassic, 333
Utica Shale (Ord.), 145

Valanginian Stage (Cret.), 374
vanadium, Cretaceous, 388
Van Hise, C. R., 80
Variscan mountain building, 242
varves, Pleistocene, 522
Vauxia (siliceous sponge), 294
Vedder, J. G., 493
Venericardia (pelecypod), 532
Venezuela, Cretaceous oil, 390
   Neogene oil, 492
   Precambrian iron ores, 103
Ventura Basin (Calif.), Neogene, 475, 477
Venus (pelecypod), 599
Vermont, Cambrian, 112
   mountain building (Cambrian), 132
   Ordovician marble, 161
vertebrates, Cenozoic, 533
   Jurassic, 357
   Mesozoic, 416
   Mississippian, 227
   oldest known, 157
   Paleogene, 435
   Paleozoic, 319
   Triassic, 342
   (*See also* life, under specific periods)
Vicksburg Formation (Oligo.), 434, 441
Viola Limestone (Ord.), 145
Virgilian Stage (Penn.), 240, 244
Virginia, Cambrian, 112, 132
   Cambro-Ordovician strata, 29
   Cretaceous, 371
   Devonian, 193
   manganese, 161
   Mississippian, 219, 228
   Neogene, 464
   Ordovician, 142, 146, 154, 161
      mud-cracked limestone, 7
      ripple-marked sandstone, 7
   Paleogene, 438, 454
   Silurian, 171
   Triassic, 328, 341, 345
      coal, 401
      ferns, 402
Visean Series (Carb.), 215
Vishnu Schist (Precam.), 61
Volborthella (?cephalopod), 304
volcanic ash, significance, 3
volcanic rocks, age relations, 2
volcanics, Triassic, 329, 340
volcanism, Cambrian, 132
   Cretaceous, 379
   Jurassic, 349
   Neogene, 459, 469, 492
   Paleogene, 447
   Permian, 272
   Pleistocene, 508
   Silurian, 177
   Triassic, 329
volcanoes, Neogene, 471
Volutoderma (gastropod), 387

Waagenoceras (ammonoid), 259, 306

Walchia (conifer), 251, 253
Walcott, C. D., 133
Wales, Cambrian, 115, 132
   Devonian, 188
   Ordovician, 142
   Precambrian, 64
   Silurian, 164
Wancoban Series (Cam.), 114, 117
Wang, Y., 326
Wanless, H. R., 255
Wanneria (trilobite), 127, 307
Warsaw Formation (Miss.), 212
Wasatch Formation (Paleog.), 432
Washington, Cascade Mountains, 471
   Cretaceous, 372
   Jurassic mountain building, 362, 364
   Miocene lavas, 470
   Paleogene, 434, 454
   Permian, 258, 267
   Pleistocene loess, 503
   Triassic, 329
Washington (D.C.), Fall Line, 370
Washita Group (Cret.), 23
Water lime, Silurian, 178
Waterton Lakes National Park, 93
Waterton Quartzite (Precam.), 93
Waverlyan Series (Miss.), 214
weathering of drift, Pleistocene, 521
Weller, J. M., 230, 255
Wells, J. W., 326
Wenlockian Series (Sil.), 171
West Indies, Eocene coral reefs, 530
   Jurassic, 349
West Virginia, Mississippian, 213, 218, 229
   Pennsylvanian, 232, 238, 241, 245
   Permian, 258, 282
   Silurian petroleum, 185
Western Interior, Paleogene, 434
Westphalian Stage (Carb.), 241
whales, Cenozoic, 547
Wheeler, H. E., 133
Whipple, F. L., 57
White, David, 255
White Mountains (N.H.), Neogene erosion, 483
White River Group (Oligo.), 445
Whitewater Sub-sequence (Precam.), 82
Whittington, H. B., 326
Wichita Mountains, Cambrian, 117
   Precambrian, 89
Wilcox group (Eoc.), 434, 441
Willamette Valley (Ore.), 449
Williams, Alwyn, 326
Williams, J. S., 230
Williana terrace, Pleistocene, 466, 504
Williston Basin, Devonian, 189
   petroleum, 229
Willman, H. B., 525
Wilmington (Del.), Fall Line, 370
wind-laid deposits, Pleistocene, 507, 509
Wind River Mountains, Triassic, 328

Wisconsin, Cambrian, 115, 117, 132
   Devonian corals, 294
   driftless area, 502
   Ordovician, 160
      lead-zinc, 160
   Pleistocene, drumlins, 502
      units, 505
   Silurian, 164, 171, 174
Wisconsin River, Dalles, 117
Wisconsin Till (Pleist.), Iowa, 511
Wisconsinan glaciation maximum, 506
Wisconsinan Stage (Pleist.), 463, 505, 514
Wolfcampian Stage (Perm.), 262
Woodbine Formation (Cret.), 388
Woodford, A. O., 493
Woodward, H. P., 161, 209, 283
Wormington, H. M., 566
worms, Cambrian, 130
   Jurassic, 361
   Paleozoic, 294, 312
   Precambrian, 99
Worthenia (gastropod), 303
Worthenopora (bryozoan), 297
Würmian Stage (Pleist. glacial), 505
Wyoming, Cretaceous, 22, 374, 377, 388
   oil, 389
   Jurassic, 352, 364
   Laramian revolution, 384, 388
   Neogene, 469, 486
   Ordovician, 143
      fishes, 319
   Paleogene, 434, 444, 454
   Pennsylvanian, 240, 250
   Permian, 258, 262, 267, 282
   Pleistocene glaciation, 502, 518
   Triassic, 332, 336

Xenaster (starfish), 612
Xiphosura (king crabs), 605
Xiphosurida (chelicerates), 308
Xylodes (Silurian coral), 183

Yarmouthian Stage (Pleist.), 463, 505, 513
Yellowknife district, age of rocks, 32
Yerkes, R. F., 493
Yosemite National Park, 363, 519
Ypresian Stage (Eoc.), 434

Zaphrentis (horn coral), 293, 316
Zechstein Series (Perm.), 259, 263
Zetoceras (ammonite), 360
zinc, Cretaceous, 388
   Mississippian, 229
   Ordovician, 160
   Paleogene, 453
   Precambrian, 104
   Triassic, 345
Zion National Park, Jurassic, 347, 355
Zygospira (brachiopod), 156

Hr Test	100
Quiz	100
Lab Ex	150
Term Paper	100
Final	150
	600

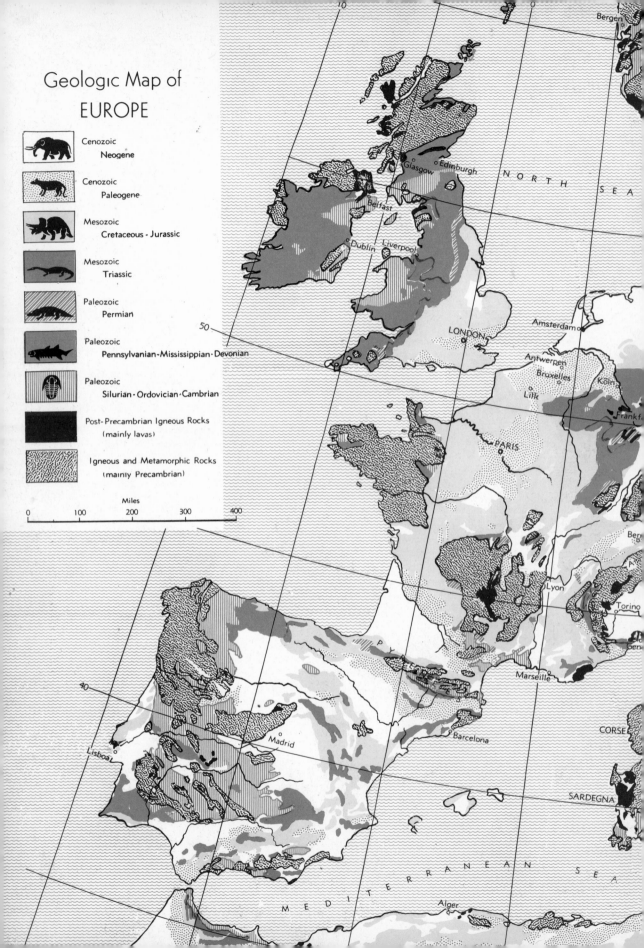

Geologic Map of
EUROPE

	Cenozoic
	Neogene
	Cenozoic
	Paleogene
	Mesozoic
	Cretaceous · Jurassic
	Mesozoic
	Triassic
	Paleozoic
	Permian
	Paleozoic
	Pennsylvanian·Mississippian·Devonian
	Paleozoic
	Silurian · Ordovician · Cambrian
	Post-Precambrian Igneous Rocks
	(mainly lavas)
	Igneous and Metamorphic Rocks
	(mainly Precambrian)

Miles

0   100   200   300   400

NORTH SEA

Bergen

Glasgow   Edinburgh

Belfast

Dublin   Liverpool

LONDON   Amsterdam

Antwerpen
Bruxelles   Köln

Lille   Frankfa

PARIS

Ber

Lyon

Torino

Marseille   Gen

CORSE

Barcelona

Madrid

Lisboa

SARDEGNA

MEDITERRANEAN SEA

Alger

50

40

Introduction to

Introduction to HISTORICAL GEOLOGY

5-11, 13-15, 17,18.

Robert G. Wiese, Jr.

VERTEBRATES

Neogene

Paleogene

Cattle-Swine (86)

Camels (85)

Titanotheres (84)

Rhinoceroses (83)

Horses (82)

(81) Condylarth

(80) Elephants

(79) Sea cows

(78) Amblypods-
Uintatheres

(77) Whales-Dolphins

(76) Carnivores

(75) Rodents-Rabbits

(74) Primates (apes, man)

(73) Edentates

(72) Bats

(71) Insectivores

(70) Marsupials

(69) Multituberculates

(68) Birds

(67) Ankylosaurs

(66) Ceratopsians

(65) Stegosaurs

(64) Ornithopods (trachodonts)

(63) Sauropods (brontosaurs)

(62) Theropods (tyrannosaurs)

(61) Pterosaurs

(60) Crocodiles

(59) Phytosaurs

(58) Lizards-Snakes

(57) Plesiosaurs

(56) Ichthyosaurs

(55) Pelycosaurs-Therapsids

(54) Turtles

(53) Cotylosaurs

(52) Amphibians

(51) Ray-finned bony fishes

(50) Lobe-finned bony fishes

(49) Sharks

(48) Placoderms

(47) Jawless fishes

Cretaceous

Fishes

Jurassic

Dinosaurs

Triassic

Permian

(69-86) Mammals

Pennsylvanian

(64)

Mississippian

(63)

Devonian

(62)

(66)

(57)

(56)

Silurian

(85)

(86)

Ostracoderms

(84)

(83)

(82)

(75)

Ordovician

(76)

(81)

(73)

(72)

(74)

(78)

(80)

Cambrian

(61)

(68)

(77)

(78)

(79)